THE 1992
PRICE GUIDE TO
CRESTED CHINA

Best Wishes

Nicholas Pine

THE 1992
PRICE GUIDE
TO CRESTED CHINA

Nicholas Pine

MILESTONE
PUBLICATIONS

Original listings taken from
Crested China by Sandy Andrews

Published by Milestone Publications
Goss & Crested China Ltd,
62 Murray Road,
Horndean, Waterlooville, Hants. PO8 9JL.

Edited by Lynda Pine, Vanessa Amis and Pat Withey

Photography Michael Edwards Studio, Images

Typeset by Barbara James Typesetting, Rowlands Castle, Hants

Printed and bound in Great Britain by
The Bath Press, Avon

British Library Cataloguing in Publication Data

The price guide to crested china.
  1992
  1. Crested porcelain. Prices - Lists
  338.437382

ISBN 1-85265-118-0

Contents

Acknowledgements

I would like to thank all those who have informed the author and the Goss & Crested China Club of previously unrecorded pieces. The result has been this latest edition, which has been further improved by the addition of factory marks and factory histories taken from *Crested China* by Sandy Andrews.

The original compilation of these listings was undertaken by Sandy Andrews in 1980 and I am very grateful for her permission to include extracts from *Crested China* in this book and for her providing original research into Crested China.

I am also grateful to my wife Lynda, Pat Withey, Vanessa Amis, Christine Hogben and the staff of Goss & Crested China Ltd who carefully check through all stock which passes through their hands, and continually update values, dimensions, variations and new models.

In particular, I would like to thank Len Harris for his work on Locke & Co, Worcester, and for tirelessly and methodically checking every item he buys and sells.

Special thanks also go to Stephen Godley, Norman Pratten, Michael Shears, Tony Munday and Robin and Philip Riley.

Our thanks also go to P.D. Williams who has collected examples of every different crested china factory mark and variations, which are listed and sketched in this Guide.

When the heraldic souvenir ware industry faded in the 1930's, no-one could have foreseen that its popularity would return a second time. No records were kept by the potteries as they either closed down or were taken over, or switched to different lines of production in order to survive. It is to the credit of collectors today that we have amassed such a listing of shapes made, but there are certainly many more. So please, if you have come across any pieces not listed in this book, write to me and the Goss & Crested China Club at the address at the front of this book with the relevant details.

Nicholas Pine

The following collectors have all forwarded lists, new information, photographs, and details to be included in this edition, and we are extremely grateful to them.

J. Akehurst, S. Allen, R. Anderson, Miss M. Auborn, M.J. Banthorpe, Mrs C. Barnes, J. Barnes D. Bates, G. Berryman, D.E. Beveny, P. Bolton. J.R. Boyle, D. Brook, C. Brown, Mrs P. Bullock, B.D. Burgess, E.A. Burns, J.J. Cheney, P. Coleman, I. Cooper, Mrs S. Courtier, C. Cropley, P. Crowther, Miss L. Davies, J.S. Davey, G. Davis, Mr & Mrs R.E. Doubleday, L. Dunn, E.J. Elliott, A.J. Elston, G. Fenlon, R.F.W. Finch, G. Flett, N. Foddering, S.D. Fullylove, P. Gabriel, N. George, A. Glover, S. Godly, R. Gough, Mrs D.G. Griffiths, P. Hacker, Mrs J.J. Hall, Mrs M. Hall, L. Harris, R. Harris, Miss J.A. Haskey, Mr & Mrs Hibberd, T. Hood, B. Holmes, J. Howarth, G. Karon, J. Kelly, T. Kirby, E. Knol, G. Langley, Mrs M. Latham, D. Leach, R.C. Leng, Miss Logan, R.C. Leng, G.J. Long, N.M. Long, Mr McIntosh, R. Mathers, N. Meakins, D. Mills, W. Moors, A. McVeigh, A.M. Munday, Mr & Mrs M. Munday, R. Nichols, C. Parker, Mrs S. Paye, B.J. Pearce, T. Pepper, E. Pote, E. Poucher, V.N. Prentice, B. Prindiville, S. Reece, Mrs S. Rigby, Mr & Mrs P. Riley, Mrs R. Shaw, Mrs K. O'Shaughnessy, Mrs J. Smith, Mr & Mrs W.G. Smith, R. Southall, K. Stevenson, L. Stoughair, Mr & Mrs W.M. Temple, Mrs P.M. Thornley, A.E. Trout, Miss J.A. Turnbull, Miss J.E. Vanderfield, B.J. Waller, M. Wallington, Mrs V.A. Waterman, J. Wesson, Mrs S. Westbrook, Mr & Mrs J. Whipp, Mrs M. White, E.J. Wilkins, F. Will, Miss J. Wilson, Mr & Mrs K. Wilson, G. Witts, Mrs A.M. Younger.

Please continue to send details of any new models to Milestone Publications for inclusion in future editions of *The Price Guide to Crested China.*

Preface

This volume is essentially a listing of all pieces produced, with the exception of mundane jugs, pots, vases and similar shapes, with sizes thereof, with full descriptions of each factory where known, and an example of each variation of factory mark. The total number of recorded pieces is now in excess of 8000. If you have accurate information on any piece or factory mark that cannot be located in this Guide, please inform the publishers in order that it may be included in a future edition.

To find the value of any piece first look up the correct manufacturer; this will be found by reference to the mark on the base of the piece in question. All items are listed in the order of the headings given on Page 22.

This guide is designed to represent average prices that one would expect to pay from a dealer. The market has continued to rise strongly since publication of the 1989 edition. Both common and rare pieces have mainly risen by some 25%, and by as much as 50% in exceptional cases. As the years go by, it is becoming clearer which pieces are scarce and which are not, so we are able to set prices more accurately, or rather, the market sets the prices for we can only respond to supply and demand, reflecting the 'collectibility' of a piece. We constantly assess and discuss prices and alter our master listings every working day.

In order to assist the reader, we have included a section where over 1000 pieces are illustrated and valued including items in every theme and price range. This section should allow one to quickly obtain the approximate value of any item and will be of use to market traders and dealers who do not specialize but need to value pieces rapidly when buying or selling. This, when used in conjunction with the illustrations in the previous (1989) edition will assist the reader to build up a comprehensive record of illustrated price information.

Values quoted in this guide represent the prices charged by Goss and Crested China Ltd in 1991 and are, in our opinion, fair and true values of the current retail selling price, net of any Value Added Tax.

Goss & Crested China Ltd are the leading dealers in heraldic porcelain and whilst we do not have every piece we do have a constantly changing stock of several thousand pieces to interest the collector. We produce *Goss & Crested China* an illustrated monthly catalogue containing 32 pages of items for sale. This is available by subscription, please enquire for details of this and our range of publications on the subject of heraldic china, a full list of which will be found at the back of this book. Visitors are welcome to view our stock at the Goss & Crested China Centre, our Hampshire showroom.

We run the Goss & Crested China Club, the leading collectors club, membership of which is free to subscribers to *Goss & Crested China* or to regular customers. Please ask for details.

Any notable decorations will add value to a piece, i.e. transfer printed scenes, views, birds, animals or floral decorations or indeed some pieces may be found solely coloured in blue, red or yellow. A premium of between £5 and £15 should be added for any piece having an unusual or attractive decoration or verse. Inscriptions have been omitted from the guide unless they are essential in determining the nature of the piece. Some models have military inscriptions, i.e. details of particular engagements during the Great War. For such pieces, usually produced by Savoy, £10-£15 should be added. Matching crests are very few and far between on models produced by factories other than W.H. Goss and may be disregarded in most instances. In the case of buildings, monuments and the like a small premium should be paid for the correct arms although most items will be found to display local crests as they were usually sold in those areas.

Much domestic ware was produced, often carrying coats of arms as an afterthought as much as by design. Such pieces, including cups and saucers, plates, milk jugs, large pots and vases, are only worth around £3-£5 each but tend to be the most overpriced items at fairs, markets etc. Such ware is not very collectable. Ordinary small vases, jugs, pots, ewers, etc. from factories are worth £2-£3 and named models £3-£5. Those of German or Czechoslovakian descent are worth half these values.

Many similar pieces carry different factory marks on their bases, for example Arcadian, Swan and Clifton were all made by Arkinstall & Son Ltd. Where the same piece could have been produced with several different marks the reader's attention is drawn in such cases to the names of the factories and chapters under which one should look if the piece cannot be found listed under the factory or mark shown on the base. To aid the reader a table of the principal manufacturers of crested china and their trademarks, subsidiaries and firms using their products will be found on page 19. Manufacturers were constantly merging, being taken over, ceasing production and selling their designs and moulds to other potters so pieces constantly appear with different marks.

Many items which are normally found coloured can also be found white, either with or without gilding and sometimes having no factory mark. All these variations are individually listed and priced, but in general, such items would normally be worth approximately ½ to ⅔ of the value of the coloured version. Similarly, a piece normally found white glazed only would be increased in value by ½ to ¾ should a coloured variety be found. Likewise, a piece bearing no inscription would require a price reduction of some 20% from that of one priced in this guide with an inscription, and vice-versa.

New items are constantly coming to light but after assuming that a piece is a new model as it is not listed under the appropriate heading in this guide, one must refer to *Crested China* or the table of principal manufacturers on page 19 and check under all other relevant factory headings. Many known models are now being seen with different factory marks, these are all worth the same as identical pieces listed elsewhere.

One point that needs to be clearly made is that pieces from one factory are not worth more than those from another. For example, Savoy is not worth any more than Swan or for that matter Carlton, Grafton or Shelley etc. Over the years one has often been told by amateur dealers and stallholders that Arcadian is worth more than other factories. This is not so. The only reasons for the constant uttering of this myth I would venture are that firstly Arkinstall & Son Ltd were more prolific than most and that there are hundreds of Arcadian pieces to be found, dealers therefore would usually have a number in stock and these would be preferred to items with no factory mark or a lesser known - in fact little-known marks are definitely rarer, but, alas they are not worth a premium either. Secondly, this fallacy has been passed on over the years and in this vacuum of knowledge, such gems as this have thrived. I am pleased to say that I have heard it little during recent years.

The value of crested china may be determined by three factors: theme, rarity and condition – in that order. The most popular themes are: Great War; Buildings; Animals (including birds); Transport; Memorials; Monuments; Statues; Cartoon/Comedy Characters; Comic/Novelty; Sport; Alcohol and Musical Instruments. This list is by no means exhaustive but it does cover the main spheres of interest among collectors. Rarity is self explanatory; a 'Bomb Thrower' is rarer than a 'Cenotaph' and therefore it is worth more. These two factors may be summed up as 'Collectability', for example a scarce animal would be worth far more than, say, a unique billiken because there is far more demand for the animal from theme collectors. Thus supply and demand play an important part. It should always be borne in mind that even the most attractive and rare crested cup and saucer will never be worth more than a few pounds whereas a rare military piece could command as much as £650.00.

Condition is another factor which affects price. Whilst not as important as with Goss china, it still affects the value of an item considerably and the following remarks should be noted. Crested china produced by other manufacturers was never as fine as that of the Goss factory. William Henry Goss conducted over one thousand experiments which took many years before he perfected the parian body which he used as his medium. The other producers were not interested in the high standards that Goss set himself, they were only concerned with jumping on the crested china bandwagon and producing wares as quickly and as cheaply as possible for the profitable souvenir trade which was rapidly developing. Some factories were better than others and Grafton and Alexandra in particular produced some very detailed and delicate models, all in porcelain. Most foreign ware (mainly German or Czechoslovakian) is of poor quality, tending to be rather crude and heavy, therefore worth less as a general rule than English china.

Having made the point that crested china factories were not that particular about the quality of their products it follows that many pieces were substandard even before leaving the factory. The producers were not usually too concerned about this and many pieces were sold having firing cracks, chips (under the glaze) or other flaws; rubbed, poorly applied or non-existent gilding, imperfect transfers, crooked coats of arms and inscriptions as well as having indifferent glazing. This was sometimes incomplete and often heavy and too liberally coated, leading to a green-grey tinge in grooves and internal corners where the glaze has built up. This latter occurrence often leads to minor glazing cracks appearing in such build ups of glaze. These do not affect value. In addition, pieces were often wrongly named on the base, or not named at all.

Minor defects such as those given above are commonplace and do not affect value although naturally a piece completely free of such manufacturers' imperfections would be preferable. Such items however number less than 10% of all crested china produced so to restrict a collection to these pristine items only would be frustrating if not impossible. If one seeks perfection then W.H. Goss is the only factory that can be considered by the serious collector, indeed, many if not most Goss collectors consider other crested china to be inferior and would not dream of collecting it themselves. It does however have charms other than those of complete perfection to commend it. Pieces with particularly bad factory defects were often sold off without factory mark, crest or inscription, such items are worth around ⅔ of the price of a normal item.

Damage occuring in the period subsequent to manufacture such as cracks or chips affect values and any sub-standard piece would be worth between 50%-75% of the perfect price. The same applies with restoration. In the past two years, as prices of perfect items have risen, those of sub-standard items have risen by a higher percentage due to such pieces being cheaper and more plentiful.

I urge you however, to be especially vigilant when buying from market stalls, antique fairs and shops where dealers seem to disregard damage when endeavouring to sell their wares. Damaged items are usually overpriced, if indeed the damage has even been noticed by the dealer concerned; it must be fully allowed for in the price when buying. It is only when one comes to sell that the wisdom of this advice will become apparent.

No forecast can be made as to whether prices will rise or fall in the future, that will depend upon economic factors. During the last decade however, prices have multiplied approximately ten times with the rarer items increasing many times faster than the smaller pots and vases and the more common shapes. Over the years crested china has been a very good investment with all the fun of collecting thrown in. The publication of *Crested China* by Sandy Andrews has substantially increased interest in the subject and this price guide now in its fourth edition can only further that interest. Two major London auction houses now include crested china in with their sales of Goss and overseas interest is on the increase.

Goss & Crested China Ltd. would be pleased to hear of any pieces or unusual or notable crests or decorations (apart from non-models and domestic ware) that are not mentioned in the listings in this guide or in the main book for inclusion in future editions.

   Should you wish to sell please note that the prices in this guide are used as a basis for purchasing and that we will pay good, fair market prices for all items offered. Please send us a list of the pieces that are for sale or part-exchange stating in each case the factory, height, crest and condition in order to receive our individual offers.

Nicholas Pine

Introduction

Collecting heraldic porcelain miniatures became a national craze in late Victorian and Edwardian times when it is thought that some 90% of all homes contained some 'crested china' as it is now popularly known. Between 1890 and 1930 no holiday or trip to the seaside was complete without a porcelain memento, with the arms of the place in which it was purchased. For dedicated collectors, the trip away was merely a means of acquiring the next prized piece, for agencies were quite strict in only stocking local arms. To get a Llandudno crest one really did have to go to Llandudno!

Sales of souvenirs were boosted by the introduction of Bank holidays in 1871, paid holidays for workers and improved wages. These factors, combined with improved travel by train, paddlesteamer, charabanc and bicycle, saw the advent of a nation that was becoming more inquisitive and acquisitive.

In the 1880's the pottery firm of W.H. Goss of Stoke-on-Trent had begun a new line, miniature souvenir ware for Queen Victoria's jubilees and for pupils of public schools. The eldest son of William Henry Goss who had invented his own particular type of parian, Adolphus Goss, hit on the idea of reproducing miniatures of famous antiquities found in museums all over the country, and decorating them with the relevant coats of arms. These 'matching' crests as they were popularly termed soon gave way to agents (appointed originally by Adolphus who was also the firm's traveller), being able to order any of his shapes with their own respective local arms. These artefacts and models started off a whole national craze, with Goss producing miniature cottages after 1893 and increasing their range to teasets, early religious crosses, animals and fonts.

The 1880's and 1890's were hard for the British pottery industry, virtually all centred in the Staffordshire pottery towns, and hundreds of other manufacturers leapt to cash in on the Goss prosperity and fame. Whilst the Goss kept to the exact and sober representation of objects of historic importance, other potteries took a new lead in producing more light-hearted souvenirs, with comical, puzzling, exaggerated and amusing connotations of every conceivable theme, ranging from alcoholic souvenirs, hats, shoes, black cats, musical instruments, pillar boxes to modes of transport and even everyday domestic items. In short, they brought a sense of fun into collecting.

The Germans had always competed against the British china industry and souvenir ware was their speciality. It was mostly ornate domestic shapes including ribbon plates, baskets, jug and bowl sets and tankard mugs that were made, heavily decorated with gilded scrolls, bouquets of flowers, or even completely bright pink. Transfer scenes were used more than crests.

Whilst the German, Austrian and Czechoslovakian potteries were flooding the British market, even the inmates of the German prisons were producing their own souvenir ware. They were unwilling to compete with their own potteries at home, so they decorated their wares with British emblems and exported to the UK with determination.

Often the spelling of the crest was incorrect, which rather adds to the charm. They used greyish, hard paste porcelain or very white bisque which was less expensive to produce than porcelain, up to date kilns and cheap labour, so even with the added cost of exporting, they were able to supply wares more cheaply than British potters and so were successful commercially. In 1905 a German firm 'Mosanic' could take an order for a reproduction model of a building in Britain, send back a postcard photograph of it to their German pottery, and have the order in the British shops within a fortnight. Their British counterparts maintained that their own slow delivery was due to the care and skill in manufacture. An over-used advertising slogan in the Staffordshire pottery industry at the time was 'Best English China at foreign prices'. Stockists of crested china varied from newspaper stands at railway stations, lending libraries, tea rooms, fancy goods shops and chemists to specialist china shops, Boots and W.H. Smith.

The Goss arms were most accurate in their use of arms. Where there was none, or permission had not been obtained, the registration seal (No 77966) was used, together with some emblem within the seal to represent the particular place. Other potteries simply invented their own designs instead to fulfil orders. Some rather odd creations can be found masquerading as correct heraldic devices.

Most crested ware was decorated after it was glazed. For a full account of how crested china was made, fired and decorated, see *William Henry Goss – The Story of the Staffordshire Family of Potters who Invented Heraldic Porcelain* by Lynda and Nicholas Pine (Milestone Publications).

Coats of arms were decorated by means of a transfer of the black outline of the crest being affixed, then coloured in, each different colour needing time to dry before the next was applied. Some items were in themselves coloured partly or fully, and the Arcadian and Willow black boy series was typical of its time – it certainly could not be produced now. The sales of transfer printed view wares declined with the popularity of the picture postcard, and therefore transfers are less common that coats of arms.

By 1910 *The Pottery Gazette* was predicting that the craze would soon be over. Indeed, all through the regular weekly copies published over the decades during 'crest china' production, *very* little is mentioned apart from advertisements, possibly because many suspected its popularity would be short-lived.

The charm of heraldic china lays in its representing a bygone era. The transfer scenes show buildings long gone, deserted narrow lanes where by-passes now rule the day, ladies in long skirts and boaters, and gentlemen walking with canes. Captured in porcelain are the comedians of the day like Ally Sloper, Jackie Coogan, and cartoon characters such as Felix the Cat and Bonzo. Even those funny little seated billikens, sometimes found named 'God of Luck', invented by Florence Pretz in America in 1908, soon found their way over here. Who knows who 'Dr Beetle' and 'Teddytail' are now?

The First World War caught Britain at the height of its collecting craze, and although the nation's men were drafted to the Front, the potteries soldiered on and carried out a good trade in producing tanks, guns, military figures, shells and grenades. After the war, memorials were none too popular, apart from the Cenotaph, and the majority are scarce.

When a fresh mood swept the nation after peace had been signed in 1919, the craze for crests was on the decline. Out with the old, in with the new. The older amongst us will possibly remember their parents consigning collections to the dustbins. I have lost count of the number of times I have been told that 'Mother threw out a bathful after the war'. It is quite likely that only 10% of what was originally made now exists.

From the late sixties onwards, boxes of crested china were to be found unwanted in corners of second-hand shops, at a penny a piece, with few takers. By the seventies the Goss Collectors Club had been formed and John Magee's monthly auction and magazine were gaining in popularity. 1980 saw the publication of *Crested China* by Sandy Andrews and the first *Price Guide to Crested China* soon after. This book is now in its fourth edition and its popularity shows that collecting heraldic porcelain is indeed a craze again.

Nicholas Pine

Manufacturers and Trade Marks

The plethora of different manufacturers, wholesalers, retailers, marks and names found on the bases of crested china can be confusing to those not familiar with heraldic china. There are perhaps only eight major and a further two relatively important manufacturers who accounted for the bulk of crested china produced. These are followed by some eighty to one hundred very minor firms, which are usually only responsible for the production of a handful of pieces, and often only then as a sideline to their main areas of manufacture.

In order that the original manufacturer of a piece may be ascertained more easily, the following table should be referred to as an aid to identification. Under the name of the manufacturer that firm's main trade name has been given in bold in each case. Under this name will be found all known trade marks that can be attributed to that firm.

Therefore, if you have a piece that does not appear in the listings for that particular mark, try looking it up in the following table and check under firstly, the main and then under the subsidiary marks until it is located, you can then note the value of the item.

I have therefore included below, a table of manufacturers showing the various trademarks that they used. Often these are retailers, agents or wholesalers.

Every known example of factory mark has been drawn and illustrated in its relevant listing.

Table of the principal manufacturers of Crested China and their Trade Marks, Subsidiaries and other firms using their products

Arkinstall & Son
Arcadian China
Albion China
Aldwych China
Amber China
Avon China
Birks Crest China
Botolph
Boots
Bute China
Carmen China
Christop China
C.J.B. & Co
Clifton
Coronet Ware
Ford & Pointon
Fords China
FL
FP & S

The Griffin China
Grosvenor Series
Iceni Crest China
JW
Kensington China
Nelson China
One and All
Palatine China
Queens Crest China
R & L
Robinson & Beresford
Robinson & Leadbeater
Raphael China
Shamrock China
Snowdon China
Sporting Series
Sussex China S.P. Co.
Swan China
Tuskar Rock

Vectis
Victis
Warwick China
Waverley China
Wembley China

Belleek Pottery
Belleek Pottery
Shamrock China

Wiltshaw & Robinson Ltd.
Carlton Ware
Aldwych China
Alpha China
Caledonia Heraldic China
Cambrian China
Craven China
Crown China
Cyclone
Eclipse
Kahess China
Kangaroo Brand
Lion China
Mother Shipton
Queens Crest
Eugene Rimmel
Syren China

Sampson, Hancock & Sons
Corona
Alexandra
Anglo-Heraldic Co.
British Manufacture
C.J.B. & Co
Dolphin
The Duchess China
Exceller
F.L.
Granic China
Grosvenor Ware
Heraldic China
JBM
Mayfair Ware
Melba China
Raleigh China
Regency Ware
Sussex China
Talbot China
Triood
Tudor Arms China
Victoria China
Waterloo Ware
Willper Heraldic China

E. Hughes & Co.
Fenton
E. Hughes & Co.
Royal China

Taylor & Kent
Florentine
Albion China
Atlas Heraldic China

Bell China
Bute China
C & SC
Caledonia China
Cascade China
Challenge China
Civic
Coronet Ware
Crown Duchy English China
Cyclone
The Dainty Ware
Doric Herald
English Souvenir China
Filey China
Gladstone China
Griffin China
Hamilton China
Ionic Heraldic
Keltic
Kent Bone China
Poppyland China
Premier
Queen China
Royal Vale China
Taylor & Kent

Charles Schmidt & Co.
Gemma
Alexandre
Empire Gem
Empress China
Fairy Ware
Ness

Alfred B. Jones & Sons Ltd.
Grafton China
ABJ & Sons
Argosy
Best English Make
C.L. Reis & Co.
Diamond China
English China
English Herald China
Herald China
Herald Series
King China
Royal Grafton
Wil-Wat China

Wm. Kutzscher & Co.
Impero
Princess China
St. George China
W.H.H. and S.
Unmarked
Saxony
Made in Saxony

Edwin Leadbeater
H & L
Leadbeater Art China
Marine Art China

Nornesford China
Panorama
R & M

James MacIntyre
J. MacIntyre
Argonauta Porcelain
Caledonia China

Max Emanuel & Co.
Mosanic
Maxim China
Unity China
Austria
Czechoslovakia
Foreign
Germany

Nautilus Porcelain Co.
Nautilus Porcelain
Celtic Porcelain

Podmore China Co.
Podmore
Strand China

William Ritchie & Son Ltd.
Porcelle
Empire China
Ivora Ware
Mermaid
W.R. and S

Robinson & Leadbeater
R & L
Royal Ivory Porcelain
Victoria Porcelain

Birks, Rawlins & Co.
Savoy China
Aldwych China
Birks China
Birks Rawlins & Co.
Bow China
Caledonia Heraldic China
Diamond China
Empire China
Endor China
Mermaid
Niagara Art China
Patriotic China
Porcelle
Queens China

Wileman & Co
Shelley China
The Foley China

R.H. & S.L. Plant Ltd.
Tuscan China
Nornesford China
Rowena China
Shamrock Crest China

Charles Waine & Co.
Venetia China
CW & Co.

Etruscan China
Kyle Series

James Reeves
Victoria China
Botolph China
English Emporium China
Gothic China

Hewitt and Leadbeater
Willow Art China
Abbey China
Alexandra
Asbury China
Balmoral China
Cable China
Caledonia Heraldic China
Clays
Curzon Art
Devonia Art China
Diamond China
Disa Art China
Elite China Series
Esbeco
Famous Henley China
H & L
H & S
JBC
Kangaroo Art China
Kingsway Art China
Kingsway Crest China
Lochinvar
Marine Art China
The Milton China
Niagara Art
Norfolk Crest China
Oxford Art China
Palmer
Panorama
Pearl Arms China
Regis
Royal Ivory Porcelain
Roman Bath China
J. Shaw
Signal China
St. Pauls
Star Bazaar Art China
Success (Art) China
Sussex Ware
Thistle China
Tourist Art China
Towy China
Victoria Arms China
Viking China
Waterfall Heraldic
Wilco Series
Willow China
W and R
Wy Knot
Wy Not

Explanation of Entries

Entries have been arranged by trademark in alphabetical order, with manufacturer's name, if known, and recorded models after each mark.

The models have been grouped into types of souvenirs and have been arranged for the most part in the order in which they would have been made. Two themes are now listed under their own heading, namely hats and footwear, formerly included under Miscellaneous. The headings are as follows:

Ladies and Figures, Coloured

Unglazed/Parian
Parian busts are also found under this heading.

Ancient Artefacts
Models of historic interest.

Buildings - Coloured

Buildings - White
Including bridges

Monuments (including Crosses)

Historical/Folklore

Traditional/National Souvenirs
These have been listed in the following order: Britain, England, Ireland, Scotland, Wales, other countries.

Seaside Souvenirs
These have been listed in the following order: Bathing Machines, Crafts, Fishermen/Lifeboatmen, Lighthouses, Shells, People and Punches.

Bathing Belles/Twenties Flappers

Figures
These listings include only the figures which do not belong under any other heading.

Countryside

Animals
These listings include animals which are really regional symbols as the Sussex Pig. Most collectors would include these in an animal collection.

Birds (including Eggs)
These listings also include regional or national emblems such as the Kiwi.

Great War
These models have been grouped as follows:
Personnel, Aeroplanes/Airships/Zeppelins, Ships/Submarines, Armoured Cars/Red Cross Vans/Tanks, Guns/Mortars, Small arms, Shells, Bombs, Grenades, Mines, Torpedoes, Personal Equipment, Memorabilia and Memorials. (Florence Nightingale statues are always included in Great War collections although she died before 1914. Certainly the statue was offered for sale at the same time, so it is listed under this heading).

Home/Nostalgic

Comic/Novelty

Cartoon/Comedy Characters

Alcohol

Sport/Pastimes
This section includes card trump symbols and chess pieces. Sporting items have been listed first, then those used for pastimes.

Musical Instruments

Transport

'Modern' Equipment
'Modern', that is, at the time it was made.

Hats

Footwear
These listings also include regional or national symbols such as the Lancashire clog and Dutch sabot.

Miniature Domestic

Domestic

Miscellaneous

Under these headings models are listed alphabetically, if that is possible. All inscriptions and verses are printed in *italics*.

If a model is best described by its inscription this will be placed at the beginning of an entry in *italics*.

Sizes are height unless otherwise stated.

All values are given in £ and p in Sterling currency.

Crested China Manufacturers

Abbey China

Trademark used by J.A. Robinson Ltd. and Hewitt & Leadbeater for a fancy goods retailer or wholesaler in Tewkesbury. Usual trademarks Arcadian and Willow Art.

Stock numbers where known as Willow Art. For details of this china and manufacturers see Arcadian China, Willow Art and Willow China. C C of Tewkesbury must have been a wholesaler as crests from several places have been recorded; these include Cheddar, Devizes, Upton on Severn and Wincombe as well as Tewkesbury. Possibly the firm owned a chain of souvenir shops. No view ware or late transfers have been found on models with this mark.

Abbey Models
Seaside Souvenirs
Lighthouse pepper pot. 110mm.   6.00
(There is almost certainly a
   matching salt pot.)

Animals
Black Cat, operating radio. (Arcadian
   Registered Series No. 13). 68mm.   100.00
Cat, sitting, one ear down. 102mm.   10.50
Dog, sitting, red eyes. No details
   of size.   10.50

Birds
Peewit posy holder. 78mm long.   6.50

Home/Nostalgic
Grandfather Clock, inscribed: *Make
use of time let not advantage slip.
Shakespeare.* No. 149. 140mm.   10.50

Cartoon/Comedy Characters
Baby with arms outstretched,
   inscribed: *Cheerio.* Some
   colouring on face. 125mm.   30.00

Sport/Pastimes
Cricket Cap. 62mm long.   45.00

ABJ & Sons

Trademark used by Alfred B. Jones and Sons
Ltd., Grafton Works, Longton, Staffs.
For all details of manufacturer and china,
please see Grafton China entry.

Wm. Adams & Sons

JW Adams & Sons, Tunstall produced some
ornamental ware and domestic china with
crests for Langhams China Shop, Bury St
Edmunds.
The pieces produced are worth £2.50 or
more.

A 78mm vase in a matt black finish
with a yellow and orange pattern
around the neck has been recorded.   10.00

Adderleys

A.F. & S.

Used 1912-1926.

1887-1901.

Trademark used by Alfred Fenton & Sons, Brook Street, Hanley.
No details of this factory or its products are available.

Used 1912-1926.

Trademark used by Adderleys Ltd. Daisy Bank Pottery, Longton.
Adderleys Ltd., established in 1906 manufactured china and earthenware throughout the 'crested china' period. They did not as far as is known manufacture crested ware but they did produce a range of 'smalls' to commemorate the Great War, these are inscribed: 1914 EDITION, and are often found in Great War china collections.

Range of 'smalls' to commemorate
the Great War – inscribed: 1914
WAR EDITION.   from 6.50

Alba Pottery

Trademark used by a British pottery for exported goods. The only model found has an Honduras crest.

Monuments
Iona Cross. 110mm.   7.50

Albion China
(Robinson & Beresford)

1907-1910.

This mark originally thought to be a variation of the Albion China T.C. & P. mark now appears clearly to be a mark used by J.A. Robinson Ltd. (Usual mark Arcadian). As they took over Robinson & Beresford (see below) they presumably went on using the 'Albion China' trademark.

In 1901 Mr W.H. Robinson set up as a china manufacturer in Longton, specialising in Queens White Ware. In 1903 Mr Robinson had need to take into partnership a Mr Beresford and the firm was then known as Robinson and Beresford. The firm seems to have been under financed from the start and by 1907 Harold Taylor Robinson (see Arcadian China) had gained control and merged Robinson and Beresford with Charles Ford (see Swan China). In 1910 these firms were made branches of J.A. Robinson Ltd.

All known models with the Albion China mark are exactly the same as Arcadian and Swan pieces. It is unlikely that Robinson and Beresford made crest china before the merger, and as only early models and 'smalls' have been recorded it seems that the Albion mark was not used after 1910.

Numbering System. The stock numbers found on the base of Albion models are exactly the same numbers as found on Arcadian models. They are listed below. The dashes and other pointed symbols found near the trademark are paintresses' marks.

Albion (Robinson and Beresford)
Models
Ancient Artefacts

Ancient Tyg, Model of. 68mm.   4.00
Exeter Vase. 65mm.   3.00
Glastonbury Bowl, No. 55. 50mm.   3.00
Lincoln Jack, inscribed: *Model of the Lincoln Jack from original in museum.* No. 50. 63mm.   4.00
Loving Cup originated by Henry of Navarre King of France. 2 or 3 handled. No. 579. 40mm.   3.00
Newbury Leather Bottle. No. 83. 65mm.   4.00
Portland Vase. No. 52. 45mm.   3.00
Shrewsbury Salopian Ewer, inscribed: *Roman Salopian Ewer found at Uriconium now in Shrewsbury museum.* No. 613. 75mm   4.00
Silchester Vase. No. 54. 60mm.   3.00

Historical/Folklore
Ancient Coaching Hat, Model Of. No. 687. 65mm long.   7.50

Albion China
(T.C. & P)

Usual mark 1913-25.

Mark only rarely found and thought to be a variation used by the firm.

Mark only seen on a leatherbound 60mm book.

Trademark used on china made for a Scottish
wholesaler by Taylor and Kent (Ltd.),
Florence Works, Longton. (Usual
trademark Florentine.)

For details of this china and manufacturer
see Florentine China.

'Smalls' and models found with this mark
have Scottish crests or coloured transfer
printed views. Some useful crested
domestic ware has been recorded
including plates, beakers, bagware vases
and a money box with a handle 70mm
long. (Stock numbers were not used by
Taylor and Kent).

The initials T.C. and P. are probably those of
the wholesalers. They are remarkably
similar to the initials T.C. and P.G. which
appear on Thistle China, manufactured
for L.M. Mack, Ayr. However, we have no
further evidence to suggest any
connection between the two.

Albion (T.C. and P) Models

Ancient Artefacts

Aberdeen Bronze Pot. 57mm.	3.00
Canterbury Roman Vase. No. 289.	3.00
Glastonbury Bowl. 40mm.	3.00
Irish Bronze Pot. No. 62. 42mm.	3.00
Puzzle Jug. 67mm.	5.50

Buildings – White

Blackpool Tower. 120mm.	10.00

Historical/Folklore

Mother Shipton. 72mm.	8.00

Traditional/National Souvenirs

Welsh Hat with blue band. 62mm.	5.00

Seaside Souvenirs

Lighthouse on rocky base. 100mm.	5.50
Whelk Shell. 100mm long.	5.00
Yacht. 130mm.	10.50

Animals

Camel, kneeling. 100mm long.	13.00
Cat sitting, very furry coat. 90mm.	10.00
Cat, Manx. 90mm long.	19.50
Dogs, 2 Spaniel pups in top hat. 72mm.	15.00
Dolphin Jug. 100mm.	5.50
Elephant kneeling. 88mm long.	20.00
Frog Jug. 80mm long.	6.50
Hare. 95mm long.	12.50
Pig standing. Can be found with the inscription: *The Pig that won't go.* 90mm long.	10.50

Toad. 35mm.	13.00

Birds

(Giant) Hen, brooding. 91mm long.	10.00
Pelican Jug. 83mm long.	5.50
Swan posy holder. 80mm.	5.00

Great War

Bust of Sailor. 85mm.	34.50
Monoplane with roundels and 4-bladed movable propeller. 170mm long.	110.00
Tank, (wide Florentine mould with side guns standing proud. 125mm long.	20.00
Shell. 75mm.	5.00
Bury St. Edmunds Bomb. 75mm.	17.00

Home/Nostalgic

Book.	6.50
Firebucket. 65mm.	5.00
Old Armchair, The with verse. 85mm.	7.50
Lamp. 69mm.	5.00
Pillar Box. 76mm.	8.50
Portmanteau. 60mm long.	4.00
Shaving Mug. 56mm.	6.50

Comic/Novelty

Negro Minstrel, bust, some colouring. 100mm.	34.50

Modern Equipment

Box Gramophone. 58mm.	15.00

Musical Instruments

Grand Piano. 83mm long.	15.00
Harp. 92mm.	6.50

Alcohol

Carboy. 76mm.	4.00

Footwear

Boot with gold buckle. 95mm long.	5.00
Lancashire Clog. 88mm long.	5.00
Oriental Slipper. 100mm long.	5.00

Miniature Domestic

Coffee Pot with lid. 76mm.	7.50
Dish, circular with 3 handles. 80mm.	2.00
Jelly Mould. 53mm.	9.50
Tea Pot with lid. 60mm.	7.50
Tea Pot with lid, squat. 35mm.	7.50

Domestic
Candle Stick and holder with snake
  curled around stem. 105mm.   5.50

Aldwych China

Mark used on wares manufactured by
Arkinstall & Son Ltd.

Mark used on wares manufactured by Birks,
Rawlins & Co.

Mark used on wares manufactured by
Wiltshaw & Robinson Ltd.

Trade name used by the retailer, Samuels, The Strand, London on crested china manufactured by Arkinstall and Son Ltd. (usual trademark Arcadian), Birks, Rawlins and Co. (usual trademark Savoy) and Wiltshaw and Robinson Ltd. (usual trademark Carlton).

Stock numbers where known coincide with those used on other models made by above firms.

Samuels either changed their supplier often or all three companies produced crested wares for them at the same time. For details of the china and manufacturer see the appropriate entry in these lists. Many 'smalls' have also been recorded.

Aldwych (A and S) Models
Mark used on wares manufactured by Arcadian.

Parian/unglazed
Bust of George V. 130mm.	47.50
Bust of Queen Mary. 130mm.	47.50

Ancient Artefacts
Puzzle Jug. 67mm.	5.50

Buildings – White
St. Paul's Cathedral. 103mm.	20.00

Monument
Nelson's Column. 169mm.	47.50

Animals
Elephant. 75mm long.	30.00
Tortoise. 72mm long.	9.00

Birds
Cock, standing, inscribed: *Cock o' the South*.100mm.	20.00
Swan. 50mm long.	7.50

Great War
Tommy in Sentry Box, not named. 105mm.	82.50
Cannon Shell, inscribed: *Jack Johnson*. 90mm.	8.50
Steel Helmet with EP on side. 70mm long and only 24mm high.	39.50

Home/Nostalgic
Grandfather clock, inscribed. 108mm.	10.50

Miscellaneous
Horseshoe. 55mm long.	3.00

Aldwych (BR and Co) Models
Mark used on wares manufactured by Savoy.

Most pieces found with this mark are small vases etc. Only one model has been recorded.

Countryside
Acorn, model of. No. 110. 56mm.	7.50

Aldwych (W & R) Models
Mark used on wares manufactured by Carlton.

Monuments
Nelson's Column with four lions at base. 165mm.	75.00

Great War
Tank inscribed: *HMLS Creme de Menthe*. 150mm long.	30.50

Alexandra China

Mark found on some domestic ware.

Marks thought to be used by Sampson, Hancock & Sons.

Trademark used by a wholesaler, china manufactured by several leading producers of crested china, particularly Sampson Hancock (Corona Pottery).

CEB must have been a wholesaler for souvenir china with showrooms in London. Many such companies advertised in the *Pottery Gazette*, but so far I have been unable to place these initials. Alexandra China has presented an enormous problem for researchers, the china is of good quality and many of the buildings are not found in other ranges. All the buildings with the exception of the Bottle Oven are to be found in London, and many Alexandra models carry London crests. Once one had realised that the china was not made by one

Marks used on china made by Hewitt Bros.

manufacturer and that the buildings were probably (with the exception of the Bottle Oven) made by Hewitt Bros (see Willow China) this mark is not so problematic.

It would seem that before the war CEB probably sold cheaper German china wares as there are very few early 'crested' models in the range. Most of the models in the Great War, animals and home/nostalgic categories appear to have been made for the firm by Sampson Hancock and Sons (see Corona China) during the war years. Many of the Alexandra models listed below will also be found in the Corona range including that puzzling Bottle Oven. Hewitt Bros seem to have become the supplier after the Great War, working to a higher standard than usual. The buildings are not recognisably Willow but one finds that hardly any London buildings are found marked Willow, the exception being Nelson's Column. A Cenotaph has been found bearing a Willow mark as well as an Alexandra mark which goes some way to proving this theory correct. Later 'smalls' and models with 'Lucky Black Cat' transfers were very obviously made by Hewitt Bros, the paintresses' marks and the stock numbers being identical. Many of the models listed below will also be found in the Willow range.

It is quite probable that other manufacturers made china for this wholesale firm and hopefully other clues will indicate which these were.

No view ware or foreign crests have been found with these marks, but 'Lucky Black Cat' transfers have been found on some later wares. No 'Lucky White Heather' devices have been found. The only war badges are Aldershot Command – Blackdown Camp, Aldershot Command – Deepcut Camp, Longmoor Camp and Cranwell.

Numbering System. Unfortunately stock numbers have not been recorded with any regularity. This is a pity as they would help in identifying manufacturers. Numbers are given where known.

Alexandra Models
Ancient Artefacts
Aberdeen Bronze Pot.	3.00
Bronze Bowl. 50mm.	3.00

Buildings – White
Marble Arch. 75mm.	28.00
Bottle Oven. No. 233. 82mm.	19.50
St Pauls Cathedral.	
2 sizes: 90mm.	15.50
135mm.	30.00
Tower Bridge. 140mm long.	30.50
Westminster Abbey, West Front.	
3 sizes: 90mm.	16.00
114mm.	16.00
130mm.	27.50

Monuments
Cleopatra's Needle. 130mm high,	
130mm wide.	110.00
Monument, The. 159mm.	110.00
Nelson's Monument. Trafalgar Square.	
165mm.	75.00

Historical/Folklore
Ark. 85mm long.	5.00
Burns and Highland Mary (also	
impressed WILLOW). 117mm.	30.00
Man in the Moon. 35mm.	20.00
Peter Pan Statue. 144mm.	60.00

Traditional/National Souvenirs
Welsh Harp. No. 292. 95mm.	7.50
Welsh Hat. 50mm.	5.00

Seaside Souvenirs
Bathing Machine. 73mm.	8.00
Canoe. 106mm long.	7.50
Lighthouse. No. 192.	5.50
Shell. No. 56. 83mm long.	3.00

Animals
Black Cat in Boot. 93mm long.	26.00
Cat Candle Snuffer. 53mm.	13.00
Cat, sitting, with ruff of fur. 100mm.	17.50
Cat, sitting, very long neck. 68mm.	6.50
Cat, Manx, 75mm long.	16.00
Dog, Bulldog, standing. 63mm.	15.00
Can be found inscribed *'Duggie	
Haig'* with Union Jack on back.	
63mm.	145.00
Dog, Bulldog standing.	
120mm long.	15.00
Dog, Scottie with glengarry. 88mm.	13.50
Dog, Labrador Puppy, sitting.	
80mm.	10.00
Fish, 120mm long.	4.00
Fish Vase, 63mm.	5.00
Monkey holding coconut. 75mm.	22.00
Pig, standing, 80mm long.	10.00

Polar Bear. 185mm long.	47.50
Polar Bear, sitting up. 100mm.	40.00
Rabbit, crouching, ears back.	
67mm long.	5.50
Shetland Pony. 110mm long.	22.00
Teddy Bear sitting upright.	14.50

Birds
Swan, 51mm.	6.50
Swan posy holder. 78mm.	5.00
Wise Owl with verse. 110mm.	14.50

Great War
Monoplane, with movable prop.	
145mm long.	65.00
British Airship on stand.	
130mm long.	20.00
Battleship with 2 guns forward and	
1 aft. 120mm long.	20.00
Lusitania. 163mm long.	82.50
Submarine, inscribed: E4.	
110mm long.	19.50
Red Cross Van. 98mm long.	30.50
Tank with inset trailing wheels.	
100mm long.	20.00
Renault Tank. 115mm long.	74.00
Field Gun. 130mm long.	15.00
Howitzer. 120mm long.	16.00
Torpedo. 150mm long.	50.00
Bell Tent. 85mm.	16.00
Flash Light, flat. 90mm.	11.00
Gurkha Knife. 140mm long.	20.00
Ad Astra, RAF Memorial with	
inscription: *Unveiled by HRH*	
Prince of Wales July 16th 1923.	
170mm.	85.00
Cenotaph, inscribed: *The Glorious*	
Dead MCMXLV-MCMXLX, with	
green wreaths.	
3 sizes: 105mm.	4.00
145mm.	5.50
184mm.	7.50
Edith Cavell Memorial, London.	
2 sizes: 115mm.	16.00
155mm.	16.00
Florence Nightingale Statue.	
146mm.	16.00

Home/Nostalgic
Anvil. 48mm.	5.50
The Old Armchair, with inscription.	
95mm.	7.50
Baby in Bootee. 76mm.	11.00
Basket, 1 handle. 58mm.	4.00
Cigarette Case. 70mm.	15.00

Hip Bath. 95mm long.	10.50
Chair, high backed. 105mm.	6.50
Desk, with inkwells. 58mm wide.	7.50
Grandfather Clock. 138mm.	9.50
Jardiniere and stand, one piece.	
No. 214. 85mm.	5.00
Sundial with verse. 112mm.	7.50
Tobacco Pouch. 75mm long.	9.50
Watering Can. 70mm.	5.50

Comic/Novelty
Hand holding flower. 80mm.	5.00
Man's Head, Cream Jug. 78mm.	10.50

Alcohol
Barrel on Stand. 65mm.	5.50
Hand holding a beaker. 50mm.	6.50
Spirit Flask. 89mm.	13.00

Sport/Pastimes
Club Trump indicator. 66mm.	4.00
Castle, chess piece. 67mm.	11.00
King chess piece.	
2 sizes: 82mm.	26.50
110mm.	26.50
Queen chess piece. 84mm.	24.50

Musical Instruments
Harp. 96mm.	6.50
Upright Piano. 62mm.	16.00

Transport
Petrol Can. No. 249. 66mm.	13.00

Modern Equipment
Gas Cooker. 70mm.	10.00
Gramophone, box. 55mm.	15.00

Footwear
Boot with buckle. 75mm long.	7.50
Ladies' Button Boot. 65mm.	8.50
Lancashire Clog. 83mm long.	5.50
Ladies' Riding Shoe with square toe	
and blue laces and tie.	
No. 118. 114mm long.	13.00
Ladies' 18th Century Shoe. 2 sizes:	
70mm & 85mm long.	7.50
Ladies' lace-up Walking Shoe,	
scalloped edge, button up.	
114mm long.	14.50
Sabot. 102mm long.	5.00

Miniature Domestic
Bagware Jug. 48mm.	4.00

Cheese Dish, 1 piece.

2 sizes: 70mm long. No. 407.	5.50
82mm long.	5.50

Cheese Dish and cover.

2 sizes: 50mm.	5.50
60mm.	5.50
Coffee Pot with lid. 75mm.	7.50
Kettle with lid. 85mm.	8.50
Tea Pot with lid, bagware. 70mm.	7.50
Tea Pot with lid, bulbous. 56mm.	7.50

Domestic

Candlestick. 84mm.	3.00

Alexandra

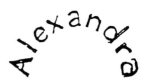

Trademark used by C. Schmidt and Co., Carlsbad (Bohemia).

A wide range of domestic shapes coloured beige with maroon or green trim and a heavy embossment of gold around the coat of arms is found with this mark, together with similar ware marked Durbar, Gemma, Rococco, Victoria and Empire. Some also have gold bows painted above the arms, and numbers painted on the bases in gold. An important feature of this ware is the sprays of pink roses and rosebuds found on a pastel-coloured background with a glazed area for the crest.

Domestic

Pepper Pot. 75mm.	8.00

Alpha China

Amber China

"ALPHA" CHINA
A.O. & Cº
B.

Trademark used by Wiltshaw and Robinson Ltd. (usual trademark Carlton). Presumably the initials, A.O. & Co. refer to a retailer.

Only a 75mm ewer has been recorded, this having the Yorkshireman's arms and verse.

Trademark used by a retailer or wholesaler probably in Manchester on pottery manufactured by Arkinstall & Son Ltd. (usual trademark Arcadian).

Great War
Tank with inset steering wheels.
110mm long.   19.50
Peaked Cap, amber coloured.
72mm long.   14.50

Anglo Heraldic Co

Trademark used by Sampson Hancock (&
Sons), Bridge Works, Stoke (usual
trademark Corona).
For details of this china and the manufacturer see Corona China.
Sampson Hancock appear to have used this
mark before the Great War, as most pieces
found with this mark are 'smalls', ancient
artefacts (unfortunately un-named and
therefore not often recorded as such) and
the usual animals, shoes, etc. made before
1914.
Some pictorials and views are found on
china with this mark but as yet only
monochrome (black) transfers have been
recorded. (Stock Numbers are the same as
Corona models, and are listed where
known).

Anglo Heraldic Models
Ancient Artefacts

Canterbury Leather Bottle. No. 156.	3.00
Chichester Roman Ewer. 65mm.	3.00
Glastonbury Bowl. 40mm.	3.00
Lincoln Jack. No. 123. 57mm.	3.00
Loving Cup, 3 handled. No. 135. 50mm.	3.50
Puzzle Jug with verse. No.148. 70mm.	5.50

Countryside

Milk Churn. No. 168. 70mm.	4.50

Animals

Teddy Bear, sitting. 85mm.	14.50
Bulldog, standing. 112mm long.	15.00

Cheshire Cat always smiling, The.

95mm.	6.50
Pig, standing. 84mm long.	10.00

Home/Nostalgic

Coal Scuttle. 64mm.	4.00
Shaving Mug. 58mm.	5.50
Watering Can. 70mm.	5.50

Footwear

Ladies' Button Boot. 65mm.	8.00
Ladies' 18th Century Shoe. No. 146. 90mm long.	7.50

Miniature Domestic

Cheese Dish and cover. 50mm.	5.50
Tea Pot with lid, frilled top. No. 122. 65mm.	7.50
Tea Pot with lid. 65mm.	7.50

Arcadian China

From 1903.

Probably introduced 1910.

Probably introduced 1912.

Arcadian
China

Mark used on models with small bases
1903-20's.

ARCADIAN CHINA

Mark used on models with small bases
1920's.

Mark found on late domestic wares.

Mark used on wares to be sold in non-English speaking countries.

Trademark used from 1904 by Arkinstall & Son Ltd., Arcadian Works, Stoke on Trent, subsequently a branch of J.A. Robinson & Sons, later Cauldon Ltd., and finally Coalport China Co. (John Rose & Co.) Ltd. and Aynsley.

Arkinstall & Sons were the largest British producers of crested china over the longest period, therefore, it follows that the history of the firm and its wares is of great importance to collectors and anyone interested in the development of popular china souvenirs from the early part of this century to just before the Second World War. The story of Arcadian China has to be the story of its owner Mr Harold Taylor Robinson, possibly the most interesting and important person in the Potteries during the period crested china was made. He was the central figure in the production and promotion of cheap china souvenirs for the lower end of the market. One cannot imagine that he did so with the integrity and enthusiasm for quality of some Potters, the Goss family for example. He was first and foremost the entrepreneur, a brilliant and daring business man (his critics would add almost reckless), interested in china only as a marketable commodity. During his amazing career he managed to draw many of the most important crested china manufacturers, including Goss, into his enormous empire; a study of his business dealings and eventual bankruptcy does much to explain why so many identical pieces of crested china can be found with different marks.

Harold Taylor Robinson began his career as a traveller for Wiltshaw & Robinson (the makers of Carlton China) in 1899 when he was twenty-two years old. He was paid £156 per annum plus commission, and one can only assume that he managed to earn a huge amount of commission because he was able, four years later, in 1903 to start out on his own as a china manufacturer. With capital of approximately £1,500, which he claimed represented his savings, he formed the company Arkinstall & Son. Using the tradename 'Arcadian', Arkinstall produced china novelties and souvenirs, and was probably the only company formed specifically to manufacture crested china. Mr Robinson continued some kind of association with Wiltshaw and Robinson Ltd and became a partner in that firm by 1906. (The early Arcadian and Carlton crested wares were very similar). Mr Wiltshaw seems to have been unwilling to be taken over and he managed to keep the ownership and control of the company in his own hands. From 1903 to 1920 however Harold Taylor Robinson was interested alone or jointly in the acquisition of a number of china and earthenware manufacturing concerns, either for resale or to form new companies to take them over and run them.

He was particularly active in 1910; having gained control of Robinson & Leadbeater

(R & L) he merged this firm with Arkinstall. This explains the number of R & L parian busts found with Arcadian marks. Later in August of that year having gained control of more firms he formed a new company, J.A. Robinson and Sons, Ltd. (J.A. Robinson was his father, the directors included Harold Taylor, his father and his brother, Hubert Alcock Robinson), to carry on the businesses of Robinson & Leadbeater, Charles Ford (Swan China) and Wardle's Art Pottery Ltd. Arkinstall became a branch of J.A. Robinson in 1912 and Ford & Pointon (Coronet), having been taken over by Mr Robinson, became yet another branch in 1919. From the dates of their amalgamation models marked Arcadian, Coronet and Swan are from the same moulds and were obviously produced in the same works.

At the 1920 British Industries Fair, J.A. Robinson presented a huge exhibit showing all types of ornamental and domestic china and earthenware, but this was just proof of the first stage of Harold Taylor Robinson's empire building. In April of that year he bought Cauldon (Brown, Westhead, Moore & Co) Ltd for £100,000 and promoted Cauldon Potteries Ltd to amalgamate most of the concerns he by then either owned or in which he had controlling interest. These included J.A. Robinson & Sons, Ltd. and branches, F.R. Pratt & Co. Ltd. (Greekware and sundries for chemists), Henry Alcock Pottery Co. (Fancy Goods), Grindley Hotel Ware (Hotel Vitrified Ware), Geo. L. Ashworth & Bros (Manufacturers of Masons ironstone), and Brown Westhead, Moore & Co. (Cauldon China, earthenware and fire proof ware).

Between 1920 and 1920, through a series of share deals, which although not dishonest were rather questionable morally, as he was often the Managing Director of the firms buying and selling the shares, he managed to gain control of some of the bigger names in the china industry. Ridgways (Bedford Works) Ltd., Wedgwood & Co. Ltd., Tunstall (not to be confused with Josiah Wedgwood & Sons), Bishops & Stonier Ltd., The Coalport China Co., Royal Crown Derby Porcelain Co. Ltd., and Royal Worcester Porcelain

were all in some way controlled by him. He moved into the sanitary ware side of the business too, gaining control of F. Winkle & Co. Ltd. and Baker & Co. Ltd.

On the way he picked up the almost bankrupt firms of W.H. Goss and Hewitt Bros. ((Willow), forming in 1925 Willow Potteries Ltd. as part of the Cauldon Group and in 1930 W.H. Goss Ltd. He continued to use the moulds and marks of both companies, but from this date the quality of Goss China was never what it had once been. Most of these late Goss pieces are marked Goss England now termed third period, but this is not always the case. Models from the Arcadian and Willow ranges are often found with the Goss mark. In recent years, prices of items marked Arcadian or Willow have almost peaked that of those marked W.G. GOSS ENGLAND. The production of late coloured crested Arcadian and Willow China was obviously combined at the Arcadian Works in Stoke, the only difference between late Arcadian or Willow Black Boys being the mark printed on the base. The Willow mark was not used after 1930, there being no demand for it as crested china was already out of fashion.

During this period, 1920-30, Harold Taylor Robinson had become the largest employer in North Staffordshire, his interest in the fine china trade being such that he dominated it. His turnover during these years was between £850,000 and £900,000 per annum and he was the director of thirty-two companies. His ultimate scheme was to form an amalgamation of all the companies of which he obtained control into one huge company (perhaps he was a little before his time; such companies exist in the china industry today). It is not surprising, given his speculative genius, that at this stage he started buying into the companies of his suppliers, Parkhouse Collieries Ltd. and Goldenhill & Clive's Marl Co. Ltd. in order to provide cheap fuel and clay for his works.

Mr Robinson told the court during his bankruptcy hearing that he had been assured by a very important and respectable accountant that if outside events had not overtaken him he would by 1932 have been a millionaire; who could doubt it? Unfortunately, like so many other large concerns at the time, this enormous monument to enterprise he had so cleverly built came crashing down in that year, unable to withstand the crippling effects of world depression. He had had to face a series of disasters, beginning with the coal strike in 1921; the loss of foreign markets, notably America, Australia, West Canada and Brazil, as trade internationally was unsettled; the loss of the 'West End' trade in London (for the Depression hit the rich as well as the poor), and Britain going off the gold standard in 1924. He is quoted in the *Pottery Gazette* at his Bankruptcy Proceedings in 1932:

'When I saw the depression was developing to the extent it was, I left my country house and came to live practically next door to the works and I have been working fifty weeks out of fifty-two to try and circumvent the terrible effects of that depression.

'When you get down to basic facts you will realise that as the largest potter in North Staffordshire I have been the largest victim.'

In his frantic efforts to save his empire, his financial dealings became more and more wild. He borrowed money from the banks that he had no hope of repaying, he distributed money and stocks from one of his firms to another in an enormous and over optimistic attempt to keep afloat. His efforts came to nothing and when he was declared bankrupt most of his firms were already in the hands of the Receiver.

Throughout his bankruptcy and discharge proceedings (for which he petitioned in 1934) no one had call to question his honesty, but his dealings could only be described as unorthodox and disturbed and often puzzled the judge, but not as much as his behaviour while still a bankrupt. The Secretary of the Cauldon Potteries had been buying up the debts on the debtors' behalf for very small sums. Fifty-three creditors had sold their debts amounting to £3,733 for £593. Rates varied alarmingly, ranging from 1s.5d. to 20s. in the £. Some of these people were creditors who would have received nothing out of the bankruptcy, whereas preferential creditors got nothing at all.

'Do you suggest that he is only acting for the debtor in this matter?' asked the judge. 'I say that he is the bankrupt's catspaw,' answered a very heated Official Receiver. Harold Taylor absolutely denied any knowledge of the transactions. The judge refused to discharge Mr Robinson for a further two years.

Proving once more that it had been impossible to keep a 'good' man down, Mr Robinson had already been appointed Sales Organiser of the newly formed company, George Jones and Sons Ltd. in 1933 when the old established firm of George Jones had been merged with Bishops & Stonier. The new company continued to use the Crescent Potteries that had always been the home of the George Jones firm. Mr Robinson must have been a fairly good Sales Organiser, for George Jones and Sons Ltd. soon bought up the old and well-known firm of Allertons. Later in 1933 Cauldon merged with Coalport China Co. (John Rose & Co.) Ltd.; the Arcadian trademark was still being used, as was Goss. One could almost guess what would happen next! In 1937 the Coalport China Co. was amalgamated with George Jones and Sons, Cauldon, Coalport, Allertons, Crescent and Goss china were all produced at the Crescent Pottery. Arcadian had disappeared without trace and the Goss trademark was not listed by the firm after the Second World War. It probably was not used after 1939. What happened to Harold Taylor Robinson after 1933 is not clear: an employee at the Crescent Potteries in the late thirties has no recollection of him, and he is certainly not listed as an officer of that firm. He was by then in his sixties and it may well be that he had retired. The two surviving companies from this last merger have both been sold, Cauldon Potteries Ltd. was acquired by Pountney & Co. Ltd. of Bristol in 1962 and Coalport became a division of the Wedgwood Group in 1977.

Having considered his career, it is not at all surprising to learn that Mr Robinson made a huge commercial success out of his first company, Arkinstall and Sons. W.H. Goss had agents in every reasonably sized town in Britain; Arkinstall's Arcadian was sold in just about every conceivable retail outlet; bazaars, lending libraries, cafés, pubs, seaside kiosks, stationers, fancy emporiums, pharmacies, sub-post offices as well as china shops. The wares of the company were not advertised in trade journals, probably because Arcadian retailers were unlikely to read them, and Harold Taylor Robinson relied on a large team of travellers to bring back the orders. They obviously left no stone unturned!

Arcadian China is not particularly fine, it cannot be compared with Shelley or Grafton wares, but it is adequate and really quite well produced when one considers the selling price. ('Smalls' were usually sold for less than a shilling). Early wares for the most part were copies of the historic shapes sold by Goss on the one hand and the small animals and grotesques of the German souvenir. industry on the other. It is very difficult to assess which of these early models were original Arcadian moulds and which were brought to the firm as a result of all the mergers. It was during the war years that Mr Robinson showed his flair for innovation, when Akinstall's provided the war-minded public with an enormous range of crested military souvenirs. Often these models were designed from newspaper descriptions and are therefore very unlike the real thing, but as the public hadn't seen them either no one seemed to mind. As each new weapon was brought into the war Mr Robinson showed great speed in making a china model of it. The day after the *Daily Mail* ran a photograph of the first tank, Mr Robinson registered his model (Rd. No. 658588). The tank had seen some action and had lost one of its steering wheels. Unfortunately this was not explained, and the first china tanks also had only one wheel, and looked very odd! Mr Robinson had the copyright on models of British tanks, so I doubt if he lost much sleep over it as he collected the dues from all the other manufacturers. (Nearly all the early tanks carry the same registration number).

It was during the war years and immediately afterwards that Arcadian became the brand leader in the china souvenir field. (They were particularly busy after the war making the Memorials which were sold for many years). In 1921 Arkinstalls were described to trade as 'Manufacturers of Arms China Miniatures and Coats of Arms Tea Ware' and apart from Goss they were the only firm who made little else. By the mid-1920s they were offering models with a great deal of colouring and introduced their popular Black Cat series. A catalogue from this period has been discovered; although undated it must have been produced around 1925. It is particularly short on words but visually it provides us with an enormous amount of information. The Black Cats were obviously a new and important line as they were the only items illustrated in colour. The cheapest Black Cats sold for 12/- per dozen to the retailer, the most expensive for 18/-. 'Smalls' were only 4/6 per dozen and small animals 6/-, whereas models of St. Paul's were as much as 36/- per dozen. Certain items were sold to retailers as singles, these being large domestic pieces such as fern pots and tobacco jars; one of these, a delightful Art Deco 'Ballet Girl Puff Box' priced at 5/- has not as yet been found by collectors, presumably few were made as they were so expensive. At this time the catalogue offers any of the models in 'Arms China, Black Cat, 'Good Luck From', Lucky White Heather or Coloured Views'.

After 1925, for the most part, only coloured models were added to the range. These include Black Boys, cute children and novelty, joke items, all unique to this firm and particularly appealing. The crests found on these models are purely incidental and one suspects they would have sold just as well with a simple 'Souvenir from' message. The craze for crests was nearly over so it is surprising to find a large advertisement in the *Daily Mail* 22nd May 1928 for 'Arcadian Arms China'. It reads:

'Arcadian Arms China can be obtained from over 10,000 Retail Fancy Goods Stores in practically every town and village in Great Britain, decorated in correct colours with local Coat-of-Arms.

If not already collecting Arcadian Arms China, START AT ONCE! It is a fascinating hobby.

The collection of Arcadian Arms China creates an added interest and preserves pleasant recollections of a holiday. Friends will appreciate nothing better than a gift of Arcadian Arms China on your return.

No other souvenir is so conveniently carried home.'

Arcadian China can be found decorated with a great number of other devices and designs. View ware, both monochrome (black only) and polychrome, was produced throughout the life of the company. A huge number of views and pictorials of reasonable quality can be found, usually on small vases and named artefacts but occasionally on animals, Great War and other unlikely models. Transfer prints of a regional nature are very desirable; these include: 'Devonshire Dumplings', 'Hampshire Hog', 'Somerset Cuckoo', 'Trusty Servant', 'York-shireman's Advice', Royal Stewart Tartan and 'Welsh Teaparty'.

Later, other transfer prints were introduced, the most popular being the Lucky Black Cats which can be found in great quantity on small pieces and domestic ware. Less easily found transfers are the range of tropical looking birds on branches; these can be coloured yellow, yellow and brown, pink and brown and pink and blue; they are usually found inscribed: 'A Gift from . . . ' or more unusually 'A Souvenir from . . . '.

Other transfer prints have some hand colouring added, the same technique as used on crests. These include 'Lucky White Heather', 'Raphael Tuck Cartoons' and an early range of beautifully and brightly coloured cocks and hens. The Lucky White Heather device is found on many small models and domestic ware, either of which can have a lustre finish or be made in cream ware. The Raphael Tuck cartoons, usually of a small Dutch boy and girl, or Derby & Joan figures in Dutch costumes are found on small and domestic china including nursery ware. 'By Special Permission of Raphael Tuck & Sons Ltd', is usually found printed on domestic ware. Various mottoes accompany these cartoons, including such gems as:

'He that is satisfied is rich.'
'None but the brave deserve the fair.'
'No life can be dreary when work is a delight.'
'Deeds are fruits, words are but leaves.'
'A good life and health are a man's best wealth.'

'Tis deeds alone must win the prize.'
'He loves me! He loves me not! He loves me!'

Cockerel or Hen transfers have only been found on small vases and jugs of various sizes and they are quite rare. These too are found with rather trite mottoes and sayings, but oddly not the same as the ones above. They are:

'Joy, temperance and repose slam the door on the Doctor's nose.'
'If you can't be aisy, be as aisy as you can.'
'All the world's a stage and man in his time plays many parts.'
'Little and often fills the purse.'
'To err is human to forgive divine.'
'A handsome shoe often pinches the foot.'

How many relatives were irrevocably offended by receiving one of these offerings is not recorded.

Floral transfer decorations are also rarely found, red poppies being the most common, but forget-me-nots and much later floral designs of sprays of mixed flowers were also used, although they are difficult to find, as are the transfer prints of butterflies, but they do exist.

In 1921 Arkinstalls advertised 'Nursery Rhyme Ware', but very little of this has survived. One example is a child's plate with a charming hand coloured transfer print of 'Ride a Cock Horse'.

Pieces with transfer prints other than Views can be found edged in colour rather than gilt, orange (Black Cats and Lucky White Heather); green (Black Cats, Flowers, Nursery Ware, Cockerels and Cartoons) and black (tropical birds).

Arcadian was exported and many foreign crests have been recorded; models for non-English speaking countries were marked Porcelaine Arcadienne. Crests of the Allies are often found on models made during the Great War, as are Military Crests. These are much collected by Great War enthusiasts, the following have so far been recorded:

Army Ordnance Corps
Army Service Corps
Berkshire Regiment
Black Watch
Canadian General Services
Cheshire Regiment
Coldstream Guards
Denbighshire Regiment
Denbighshire Hussars

Derbyshire Regiment
Devonshire Regiment
Devonshire Regiment 11th Foot
Duke of Cornwall's Light Infantry
2nd Dragoon Guards (Royal Scots Greys)
3rd Dragoon Guards
5th Dragoon Guards
Durham Light Infantry
East Kent Regiment 'The Buffs'
East Surrey Regiment
East Yorkshire Regiment
Essex Regiment
Gloucestershire Regiment
Gordon Highlanders
Hampshire Regiment
11th Hussars
18th Hussars
Inns of Court OTC
Kings Own Liverpool Scottish
Kings Own Scottish Borderers
Kings Own Yorkshire Light Infantry
Lancashire Fusiliers (20th Foot)
Lancaster Regiment
1st Life Guards
Light Infantry
Lincolnshire Regiment
Liverpool Regiment (8th Foot)
Liverpool Regiment (11th Foot)
Liverpool Scottish, The King's
London Scottish
Machine Gun Corps
Manchester Regiment
Middlesex Regiment
5th Norfolk Regiment
Northumberland Fusiliers
North Staffs Regiment; 64th & 98th Foot
Notts & Derby
Oxfordshire & Buckinghamshire Light
    Infantry
Prince Albert's Own Hussars
Prince Albert's Somerset Light Infantry
Prince Consort's Own Rifle Brigade (Swan)
Prince of Wales North Staffordshire
    Regiment
Queens Bays
Queens Own Cameron Highlanders
Queens Own Royal West Surrey Regiment
Queens Own Royal West Kent Regiment
Royal Artillery
Royal Aircraft Establishment
RAE Ewshott
Rifle Brigade – The Prince Consort's Own
Royal Air Force (2 versions)
Royal Army Medical Corps
Royal Bucks Hussars

Royal East Kent Mounted Rifles – Imperial
    Yeomanry
Royal West Kent (The Queen's Own)
Royal Engineers
Royal Field Artillery
Royal Flying Corps
Royal Garrison Artillery
Royal Gloucestershire Hussars
Royal Irish; 5th Lancers
Royal Irish Regiment 18th Foot
Royal Irish Dragoon Guards
Royal Horse Artillery
Royal Marines
Royal Military College Camberley
Royal Naval Air Service
Royal Navy
Royal Shropshire Light Infantry
Royal Tank Corps
Royal Warwickshire Regiment
Royal Welsh Fusiliers
Royal West Surrey Regiment
Staff College Camberley
Royal Sussex Regiment
Shropshire Light Infantry
South Staffordshire Regiment
South Wales Borderers
Staffs Regimental Insignia (Staffordshire
    Knot)
Staffordshire Imperial Yeomanry
Suffolk Regiment
Walmer Camp
West Riding Regiment
Wiltshire Regiment (62nd & 69th Foot)
York & Lancaster Regiment
H.M.S. Barham
H.M.S. Hercules
H.M.S. Queen Mary
H.M.S. Thunderer
H.M.S. Achilles (Transfer view of ship)
Apart from Great War flags of the allies
    transfer 'United we stand', very few
    commemoratives seem to have been
    produced, the only ones known being:
    South Africa 1900-1901 and British Empire
    Exhibition 1924 and 1925.
It is not surprising that the very late products
    of the firm are eagerly sought and have
    risen in price over the last few years.
    Unlike other firms Arkinstall did not
    make a range of uncrested coloured
    models in the early 1930s, except for
    female figures. These are of particular
    interest as they are very like the Goss
    England ladies and were made at the same
    time. The Arcadian ladies are more

detailed and rather more delicate than the Goss England versions. The range was wide, and includes male figures, as well as seated and other less traditional forms.

Late lustre ware marked Arcadian is suspiciously like that marked Goss, and one wonders if they were produced by the same hands. Vases, bowls and domestic ware can be found, but not all that often, with mother-of-pearl, orange, green, mauve, purple and yellow lustre finishes.

Numbering System. Printed stock numbers are found on early models and these have been given where known in the following lists. It must be emphasised that registration numbers printed on later Arcadian models are notoriously unreliable and are often found not to be the number that the piece was actually registered under. Mr Robinson registered up to twenty models at a time and given that more moulds became available with each new merger presumably no one could be bothered to check that the correct number was being used on each model. (Printing any number or 'Registration applied for' was an indication that the model was registered and therefore copyright). The Registration Number most often found on a model, whether it is the correct one or not, has been given in the lists – hopefully this will help with identifying an un-named item. The tiny numbers, initials and marks often found painted on the base of Arcadian china are paintresses' marks.

Arcadian Models
Coloured Ladies/Figures

Antoinette.	85.00
Aristocrat, taking pinch of snuff. 150mm.	100.00
Miss Ascot, wearing large Ascot hat. 150mm.	115.00
Ballet Girl, seated on three-legged stool, wearing a crimson dress. 164mm.	95.00
Balloon Lady, old lady in pink dress, mauve apron and green shawl, holding balloons. No. 43. 145mm.	100.00
Breeze. No. 15.	95.00
Bridesmaid, wearing pink dress and holding flowers. No. 15. 135mm.	85.00
Cavalier, with Van Dyke style beard. 150mm.	65.00

Laughing Cavalier. No. further details known.	65.00
Cherry Ripe, wearing yellow dress and holding basket of flowers. 175mm	145.00
Cherry Ripe, with feather in hat, holding skirts and a basket of cherries, wearing blue and red dress. 163mm.	145.00
Clarissa, tying her bonnet. No. 142. 200mm.	145.00
Doris, curtseying, wearing green dress and bonnet. No. 66. 118mm.	95.00
Fair Huntress, holding hat and lurcher dog. 175mm.	115.00
Grace. 84mm.	90.00
Miss Holland, dressed in mauve, wearing a cap, long plaits and hands on hips. 127mm.	145.00
Joan, young girl wearing mob cap, holding hands together. 113mm.	110.00
Jester, seated figure. No. 222. 150mm.	65.00
June, wearing bonnet and wide crinoline, holding a single rose. No. 70. 115mm.	120.00
Lady Bountiful, carrying basket of fruit on her right arm. 170mm.	135.00
Lady Maria, 105mm.	95.00
Lady Marie, wearing yellow dress, sitting on rock. 125mm.	145.00
Lady Marie, wearing green dress. No. 21. 145mm.	125.00
Her Ladyship, large seated figure. No. 182. 150mm.	150.00
Lucy. There are no details of dress or size available.	85.00
Market Woman, old lady in blue dress and red shawl, holding a basket of fruit. No. 43. 155mm.	125.00
Monk, from Lilleshall Abbey wearing black robe, with tankard. 96mm.	95.00
Pauline, wearing black and yellow tight dress with fur stole and cuffs. 100mm.	175.00
Peggy, curtseying to side, holding flower. 100mm.	90.00
Miss Prudence, sitting on settee, holding fan and book. 108mm.	150.00
Miss Prudence, wearing a green dress and pink hat, holding a spray of flowers. 175mm.	140.00
Tinker, wearing green jacket and yellow trousers, carrying bag in	

left hand. No. 210. Two sizes have
been recorded,
150mm and 182mm.   145.00
Tulip Boy, in Dutch costume. 150mm.   85.00
Tulip Girl, in Dutch costume, with
basket of tulips at her feet. No.
133. 150mm.   85.00
Victorian Belle, wearing yellow and
green dress with blue shawl and
frilled crinoline, holding fan,
with flowers in hair, which is in
ringlets. 193mm.   160.00
Wendy, Mediaeval Lady.   135.00
Boy/Girl, sitting figure on stool.
150mm.   90.00

Parian/unglazed
Bust of King Edward VII in military
uniform, later models found with
inscriptions. On circular glazed
base. Add £5 for matching arms.
2 sizes: 130mm.   45.00
        140mm.   45.00
Bust of King Edward VII wearing
trilby, overcoat and suit, on
circular glazed base. With
inscription. 125mm.   57.50
Bust of Queen Alexandra, on
circular glazed base.
2 sizes: 120mm.   45.00
        140mm.   45.00
Smaller size can be found named
in blue lettering.
Bust of King George V, can be found
with circular glazed or keyhole
base. With inscription. 135mm.   45.00
Bust of King George V, robed,
holding orb, on O-shaped base.
140mm.   50.00
Bust of Queen Mary, can be found
with a glazed circular or keyhole
base, with inscription. 135mm.   45.00
Bust of Prince of Wales (later
Edward VIII) in midshipman's
uniform, can be found inscribed
in red and blue. On glazed
circular base. 135mm.   75.00
(Any of the above can be found with
matching crests on their glazed
bases, for which £5.00 may be
added).
Bust of *Burns*, found with poem by
Wordsworth. On circular glazed
base. 120mm.   35.00
Bust of *Napoleon*, on square glazed
base. 125mm.   75.00

Bust of *Nelson*, on square glazed base.
2 sizes: 120mm.   75.00
        140mm.   75.00
Bust of *John Peel*, with verse. 120mm.   75.00
Bust of *Scott*, on circular glazed
base. 120mm.   40.00
Bust of Duke of Wellington on
glazed base. 130mm.   75.00
Bust of *King of the Belgians* on square
glazed base, sculpted by W.C.
Lawton.
2 sizes: 155mm.   60.00
        175mm.   65.00
Bust of *Sir Douglas Haig* on square
glazed base, sculpted by S.R.
Sanders. 150mm.   75.00
Bust of *Sir John French* on square
glazed base, sculpted by W.C.
Lawton. 155mm.   75.00
Bust of *Sir John Jellicoe* on square
glazed base, sculpted by W.C.
Lawton. 170mm.   75.00
Bust of *General Joffre* on square
glazed base, sculpted by W.C.
Lawton.
2 sizes: 155mm.   75.00
        175mm.   75.00
Bust of *Lord Kitchener* on circular
glazed base. 119mm.   40.00
Bust of *Lord Kitchener* on square
glazed base, sculpted by W.C.
Lawton.
3 sizes: 155mm.   70.00
        162mm.   75.00
        175mm.   75.00
Bust of Chamberlain on circular
glazed base. 115mm.   40.00
Bust of David Lloyd George on
circular glazed base. 135mm.   40.00
Bust of *Lord Roberts* on square
glazed base, in uniform. Sculpted
by W.C. Lawton. 155mm.   100.00
Bust of Rt. Hon. W.S. Churchill on
square glazed base, sculpted by
W.C. Lawton. 160mm.   110.00

Ancient Artefacts
Most inscriptions begin *model of*, so
this will not be repeated
throughout the listing. These
models are sometimes found not
named and numbered.
Aberdeen Bronze Pot. 74mm.   4.00
Ancient Bronze British Pot. No. 618.
68mm.   4.00

*Ancient Roman Vase now in
Wedgwood Museum, Burslem.*
No. 202. 65mm.   4.00
Ancient Tyg, 1 or 2 handles. No. 58.
70mm.   4.00
Ancient Urn. No. 85. 35mm.   4.00
Ashbourne Bushel, with inscription.
No. 99. 67mm dia.   10.00
Bath Roman Ewer, inscribed: *Roman
Ewer in Dorset Museum found at
Bath*. No. 69. 70mm.   4.00
Butterpot, old, of 17th Century. 45mm.   4.00
Cadogan teapot, working model of.
45mm.   12.00
Cambridge Roman Jug. No. 67.
2 sizes: 60mm.   4.00
75mm.   4.00
Canterbury Roman Ewer. 2 shapes:
No. 23. 60mm.   4.00
No. 25. 75mm.   4.00
Canterbury Roman Vase, inscribed:
*Roman Vase found near Canterbury
original in Canterbury museum.*
9 different shapes:
No. 21. 65mm.   3.00
No. 22. 60mm.   3.00
No. 24. 66mm.   3.00
No. 27. 66mm.   3.00
No. 28. 70mm.   3.00
No. 29. 60mm.   3.00
No. 30. 60mm.   3.00
No. 31. 80mm.   3.00
No. 32. 63mm.   3.00
Canterbury Leather Bottle. 40mm.   3.00
Celtic Water Bottle. No. 625. 63mm.   4.00
Chester Roman Jug. No. 133. 80mm.   4.00
Chester Roman Vase, inscribed:
*Roman vase now in Chester
Museum.* 2 different shapes:
No. 131. 56mm.   4.00
No. 136. 60mm.   4.00
Chester Roman Vase, inscribed:
*Roman vase found at Chester from
original in Museum.* No. 263.
58mm.   4.00
*Chinese vase, original in Hanley
Museum.* No. 127. 38mm.   4.00
Colchester Vase.   3.00
Derby Roman Vase. No. 26. 63mm.   3.00
Devon Oak Pitcher. No. 165. 60mm.   3.00
Dogger Bank Bottle. No. 206.
2 sizes: 50mm.   3.00
70mm.   3.00
Dorchester Jug. No. 66. 55mm.   4.00
Eddystone Spanish Jug. No. 585.
60mm.   4.00

Egyptian Urn. No. 130.   4.00
Egyptian Vase, ancient, about 230 BC.
No. 155. 45mm.   4.00
Egyptian Water Bottle, 60mm.   4.00
Exeter Vase from original in Museum.
No. 70. 68mm.   4.00
Fountains Abbey Cup. No. 64. 50mm.   4.00
Glastonbury Bowl. No. 55. 40mm.   4.00
Glastonbury Bronze Bowl. No. 74.
40mm.   4.00
Glastonbury Vase. No. 642. 55mm.   4.00
Grecian Bronze Pot found at Pompeii.
No. 138. 50mm.   4.00
Greek Cauldron, Ancient. No. 288.
44mm.   4.00
Hastings Kettle. No. 237. 62mm.   3.00
Hereford Terracotta Kettle with lid.   10.50
Highland Whisky Jar. No. 679. 72mm.   4.00
Highland Quaich or Whisky Bowl. can
be inscribed: *Scaub Asi.*
134mm wide.   7.50
Horsham Vase, inscribed: *13th
century vase found at Horsham.*
No. 201.
2 sizes: 45mm.   4.00
75mm.   4.00
Ipstones Jug. No. 73. 60mm.   4.00
Irish Bronze Pot, Ancient. No. 62.
50mm.   4.00
Irish Kettle. No. 95. 70mm.   4.00
Jersey Milk Can, Ancient, with lid.
No. 523. 72mm.   6.00
Kendal Jug. No. 9. 75mm.   3.00
Lichfield Jug. No. 60. 70mm.   3.00
Lincoln Jack from original in museum.
No. 50. 62mm.   4.00
*Lincoln Vase from original in the
museum.* No. 80. 66mm.   4.00
*Loving Cup originated by Henry of
Navarre King of France.* 2 or 3
handled. No. 579. 40mm.   4.00
Newbury Leather Bottle, inscribed:
*Leather bottle found on battlefield of
Newbury 1044 now in museum.*
No. 83.
2 sizes: 50mm.   4.00
65mm.   4.00
Norwich Cinerary Urn. 50mm.   4.00
Peterborough Tripod, unnamed. 40mm.   3.00
*Phoenician Vase original in Stoke-on-
Trent museum.* No. 25. 60mm.   4.00
Pompeian Vessel. No. 208. 55mm.   5.00
Pompeii Lamp. No. 603. 90mm long.   5.00
Portland Vase now in British Museum.
No. 52. 60mm.   4.00

*Puzzle Jug original in South
Kensington Museum*. No. 147. 70mm. 5.50
Puzzle Teapot. 50mm. 10.50
Roman Urn. No. 305. 63mm. 3.00
Salisbury Jack. 4.00
Salisbury Kettle. No. 90. 107mm. 4.00
Salt Maller. 3.00
Scarborough Jug. No. 82. 52mm. 4.00
Scotch Coggie, inscribed: *Model of
Scotch Coggie used by the Highlands
before the introduction of
earthenware*. No. 149. 80mm. 6.00
Shakespeare's Jug, 60mm. 3.00
Shrewsbury Salopian Ewer. No. 613.
75mm. 4.00
Silchester Vase. No. 54. 55mm. 3.00
Southwold Jar. No. 627. 95mm. 3.00
Suffolk Palace Jug, inscribed: *Model
of antique jug found on site of
Suffolk Palace Hull now in museum*.
No. 122. 60mm. 4.00
Toby Jug, inscribed: *This is an exact
copy in miniature of the old toby jug*.
No. 253. 75mm. 10.00
Tutankhamun's Cup, inscribed:
*Kings wishing cup found in King
Tutankhamuns tomb at Luxor*.
55mm. 27.50
West Malling Elizabethan Jug or stoup.
No. 152. 75mm. 10.50
Winchelsea Roman Cup. No. 137.
50mm. 3.00
Winchelsea Vase, inscribed: *Model of
Roman Cup found near Winchelsea*.
2 sizes: No. 68. 55mm. 4.00
No. 87. 75mm. 4.00
Winchester Bushel, blue feet and
handle. 83mm dia. 30.50
Winchester Vase. 4.00
Windsor Roman Urn. No. 123.
50mm. 3.00
Wokingham Tankard. No. 88. 78mm. 4.00
York Roman Ewer. No. 57. 60mm. 3.00

Buildings – Coloured
These buildings are not normally
found crested.
Alton Round House, inscribed: *The
Ancient Lock Up*. Light brown
colour. 86mm. 82.50
Ann Hathaway's Cottage.
50mm long. 17.50
Bridlington Priory Church, model of.
Light brown colour. 68mm long. 82.50
Burns Cottage. 68mm long. 22.00

Dean Goodman's Birthplace.
85mm long. 110.00
First and Last House with annexe.
2 sizes: 100mm long: 65.00
136mm long: 75.00
Guildhall, Thaxted, 88mm. 200.00
Jean Mac Alpines Inn, Famous Inn in
'Rob Roy' where the scene of a
fray between Bailie Nicol Jarrie
and the Highlanders took place.
Unglazed. 104mm long. 125.00
*Old Blacksmith's Shop and Marriage
Room, Gretna Green*, 85mm long
(late Willow mould). 40.00
Old Star Inn, Alfriston. 80mm. 150.00
Shakespeare's House.
2 sizes: 63mm long. 20.00
127mm long. 30.00
Wells Cathedral. Stone coloured
with some colouring on doors
and windows. 110mm long. 70.00

Buildings – White
Aberystwyth University. 110mm long. 110.00
Alton, The Round House. 83mm. 60.00
Ann Hathaway's Cottage.
2 sizes: 83mm long: 11.00
100mm long. 16.00
Bath Abbey, front. 107mm. 37.50
Big Ben, also found inscribed:
City of London.
3 sizes: 92mm. 16.00
135mm. 17.50
150mm. 19.50
Blackpool Tower. 144mm. 13.00
Blackpool Tower with Buildings.
107mm. 10.50
Blackpool Tower with Buildings on
heavy base.
2 sizes: 135mm. 10.50
165mm. 12.50
Boston Stump.
2 sizes: 89mm long. 45.00
110mm long. 65.00
Bridge on grassy banks.
136mm long. 20.00
Bunyan's Cottage.
2 sizes: 83mm. 19.50
95mm. 20.00
Canterbury Cathedral. West front.
126mm. 40.00
Canterbury, Westgate. 93mm. 26.00
Chester Cathedral. 120mm long. 45.00
*Chesterfield Parish Church AD 1037.
Model of*. 125mm and 90mm. 55.00

Clifton Suspension Bridge.		Margate Clock Tower, sometimes	
175mm long.	75.00	inscribed: *Clock Tower.*	
Cottage, very detailed.		2 sizes: 140mm.	17.00
2 sizes: 50mm:	8.50	152mm.	17.00
100mm:	13.00	*Martello Tower,* with inscription:	
Cottage on rectangular base usually		'Erected for Coast Defence 1804'.	
found with no inscription.		73mm dia.	39.00
80mm long.	14.00	Morpeth Clock Tower, not found	
Can be found inscribed: *Model of*		named. 122mm.	16.00
Highland cottage, Welsh cottage or		Mundesley-on-Sea Castle Ruins.	
Irish Cottage. 60mm.	21.00	105mm.	55.00
Douglas Jubilee Clock Tower.		Norwich Cathedral. 105mm long.	47.50
125mm.	40.00	*Old Curiosity Shop. Immortalized by*	
Ely Cathedral. 140mm long.	75.00	*Charles Dickens. No. 14 Portsmouth*	
Fair Maid's House, Perth. 84mm.	50.00	*Street.*	
Farringtons Girl School Chapel,		2 sizes: 70mm long.	30.00
Chislehurst Kent. 125mm long.		95mm long.	30.00
(Very rare). Unglazed.	200.00	*Old Pete's Cottage* (near Ramsey).	
First and Last Refreshment House in		2 sizes: 75mm long.	40.00
England. Often found without		100mm long.	40.00
'refreshment' inscription.		*Pegwell Bay, Clock Tower,* 135mm.	25.00
75mm long.	12.00	*Plymouth, Clock Tower.*	
Also found with annexe.		2 sizes: 150mm.	17.50
2 sizes: 100mm long.	40.00	180mm.	18.50
138mm long.	40.00	*Portsmouth, Guildhall.* 60mm long.	40.00
Forth Bridge. 158mm long.	32.50	*Queen Mary's Dolls House.*	
Gloucester Cathedral. 128mm long.	47.50	3 sizes: 75mm.	30.00
God's Providence House. 82mm.	40.00	95mm.	40.00
Grimsby Hydraulic Tower. 170mm.	27.50	118mm.	47.50
Hastings Castle Ruins. 96mm.	30.00	Two smaller sizes are often found	
Hastings, Clock Tower.		as boxes with loose roof lids.	
2 sizes: 135mm.	12.00	(These models can be found with	
152mm.	14.00	the 'Cauldon' mark as well as	
Hop Kiln. 86mm.	27.50	'Arcadian': Same price.)	
Houses of Parliament. 73mm long.	35.00	*Rochester Castle, dating from 1126.*	
Irish Round Tower. 106mm.	13.00	70mm.	47.50
King Alfred's Tower. 92mm.	35.00	Rowton Tower, with inscription:	
Lantern Hill Church. *Ilfracombe.*		*King Charles 1st stood on this tower,*	
98mm long.	24.50	*Sept. 24th 1645 and saw his army*	
Launceston Castle. 112mm long.	80.00	*defeated on Rowton Moor.* 88mm.	35.00
Lincoln Cathedral, West Front.		*St Albans. The Clock Tower.* 125mm.	40.00
2 sizes: 98mm.	40.00	*St. Nicholas Chapel, Ilfracombe.*	
115mm.	40.00	100mm long.	30.00
Lincoln Stonebow. 88mm long.	22.50	*St. Pauls Cathedral.* No. 114.	
Lloyd George's Early Home,		3 sizes: 72mm.	17.00
Llanstymdwy, Criccieth.		95mm.	20.00
120mm long.	47.50	130mm.	25.50
London Bridge. Ye olde.		St. Tudno's Church, Llandudno.	
2 sizes: 88mm long.	18.00	73mm.	65.00
170mm long.	22.00	Can sometimes be found as a	
Marble Arch.		money box.	
4 sizes: 45mm.	25.00	*St. Winifred's Bath,* Holywell. 75mm.	65.00
65mm.	28.00	Salisbury Cathedral. 120mm long.	65.00
76mm.	29.50	Salisbury Clock Tower, not found	
80mm.	30.50	named. 130mm.	15.00

Shakespeare's House.

3 sizes: 50mm long.	10.50
83mm long.	13.00
100mm long.	16.00

Skegness, Clock Tower, 125mm.   16.00

Smallest House in Great Britain. (at 10 Lower Gate Street, Conway)

3 sizes: 88mm.	22.00
97mm.	25.00
115mm.	30.00

Southampton, the Bargate. 66mm.   24.50

Temple Bar.

2 sizes: 60mm.	25.00
95mm.	34.50

Tom Tower, Christchurch, Oxford.
88mm.   25.00

Tower Bridge. 135mm long.   34.50

Tower of Refuge, Douglas I.O.M.
68mm.   30.00

Tudor House, L shaped. 80mm.   40.00

Tynwald Hill, Model of, with lengthy inscription. 110mm dia.   110.00

Wembley Sports Stadium, with capacity details. 136mm long.   95.00

Westminster Abbey, West Front.

2 sizes: 72mm.	20.00
118mm.	28.00

Weymouth Jubilee, Clock Tower on octagonal base. 128mm.   39.00

Wimborne Minster. 127mm long.   65.00

Windmill with movable sails.
85mm.   30.00

Very rarely found inscribed:
Windmill, Woodhouse.   40.00

Windsor Castle.

2 sizes: 55mm.	25.00
80mm.	28.00

Windsor Round Tower.

2 sizes: 58mm.	28.50
90mm.	40.00

Worcester Cathedral.

2 sizes: 127mm long.	35.00
140mm long.	40.00

York Minster. 105mm.   57.50

Monuments (including Crosses)

Banbury Cross, with nursery rhyme: *Ride a cock horse.* 160mm.   40.00

Bloody Corner, Ilfracombe with very lengthy inscription of slaying of King Hubba on all 3 sides. Same mould as Rufus Stone. 100mm.   60.00

Bunnyan Statue. 140mm.   20.00

Burns, Monument with dog. 70mm   20.00

Caister on Sea Lifeboat Memorial.
150mm.   25.50

Castleton Village Cross. 140mm.   30.00

Celtic Cross. 125mm.   12.00

Conway *Seven are we* Grave, with inscription: 'The Grave immortalized by Wordsworth's Poem' and 'Two of us in the churchyard lie'. This is a triangular tube shaped tomb with seven small towers. 110mm long. (Rare).   65.00

Drake Statue. 160mm.   19.50

Ethelfreda Memorial. 150mm.   75.00

'Fisherman's Memorial', appears with crest of Fleetwood. 155mm.   19.50

Gibbets Cross, Hindhead with inscriptions. 136mm.   10.50

(The) Globe, Swanage, Model of.
80mm.   20.00

Hull Fisherman's Memorial, with inscription. 155mm.   19.50

Iona Cross. 142mm.   12.00

Irish Monument, not named but appears with Irish Crests. Circular base with man standing on top. 138mm. This is the metal man at Tramore.   56.50

King *Alfred the Great,* Statue. Winchester. Rd. No. 521701. 170mm.   30.00

Maiwand Memorial, Forbury Gardens, Reading. (Lion on base). Can be found with black lion, add £8.00.
100mm.   20.00

Margate Surf Boat Memorial.

2 sizes: 118mm.	20.00
125mm.	20.00

Nelson's Column. 102mm.   45.00

Nelson Monument, Great Yarmouth. 206mm.   65.00

Newton Monument. 165mm.   38.50

Plymouth Armada Memorial.
181mm.   30.00

Richmond, Yorks, Market Cross.
125mm.   20.00

(The Great) Rock of Ages, Burrington Coombe, near Cheddar, Som. with three verses of hymn. 83mm.   13.00

Rufus Stone. 100mm.   9.00

St. Anne's on Sea Fisherman's Memorial. 155mm.   30.00

Sailor's Stone, Hindhead. 100mm.   12.50

Saxon Lady and Child, both with swords, on glazed base. 153mm.   55.00

Series of at least three figures standing on a square plinth. (These are not easily identifiable and could be statesmen, industrialists or literary figures. It is thought that one is Joseph Chamberlain and another is Charles Dickens); inscribed: *Industry is the parent of success.* Edged in green. 135mm.   Each 65.00

Toad Rock. 85mm.   17.00

Tom Hughes Monument, Rugby School. 142mm.   30.00

Victorian Lady and Gentleman figure group on base, inscribed: *He that is satisfied is rich.* Found with colour transfer of children. 115mm.   65.00

Statue found with York Crest, Lion and three Imps or Satyrs on a square pedestal. 115mm.   34.50

Wallace Statue Aberdeen. 117m.   40.00

Historical/Folklore

Archbishop of Canterbury's Chair now in cathedral AD5541. 95mm.   19.00

Bell, squashed appearance. Inscription in red relief: *CAMPAN Athome.* 58mm.   39.00

Burns with Plough on rectangular base. 120mm.   75.00

Coaching Hat, can be found inscribed: *Model of ancient coaching hat.* No. 687. 65mm long.   7.50

Coronation Chair, inscribed: *Model of Chair on which King George V was crowned Westminster Abbey June 22nd 1911* and on the back: *All the world's a stage and man in his time plays many parts.* 107mm.   10.50

Devil looking over Lincoln. 108mm.   12.00

Ducking Stool, 2 pieces, hinged together. With long details of its last employment in Leominster in 1809 and 1817. 120mm long.   85.00

English Folksong Bride beside chest. 93mm.   55.00

Execution Block with Axe. 50mm.   30.00

Henry V Cradle, Monmouth. 78mm.   40.00

Jenny Geddes Stool 1637, 3 legged. 40mm. More often found unnamed.   5.50
Named.   10.50

Judge Bust.
2 sizes: 55mm.   14.00
75mm.   20.00
Can be found inscribed: *Defend the children of the poor and punish the wrong doer.* Add £10.00.

Lady Godiva, Coventry, on horseback, circular base.
3 sizes: 76mm.   26.00
85mm.   26.00
115mm.   30.00

Lady Godiva on horseback, on heart shaped base. 80mm.   26.00

Miner's Lamp, inscribed: '1836'. 85mm.   16.00

Mother Shipton, can be found with verse.
2 sizes: 76mm.   8.00
115mm.   13.00

Peeping Tom, bust. 110mm.   16.00

Man in the Sun. 94mm.   47.50

Man standing in Pillory, can be found inscribed: *Time for reflection. AD1600.* 190mm.   17.00

Man sitting in Stocks, can be found inscribed: *Time for reflection* and   20.00
very rarely: *Berkswell stocks* or *The stocks, Dartmouth.* 88mm.   25.75

Ripon Hornblower. 130mm.   20.00

Shakespeare's Desk from the original in the museum, model of. Can be found in lustre. 62mm long.   65.00

Trusty Servant on ornate rectangular base, with verse. Fully coloured and without crest. 137mm.   110.00

Trusty Servant on small square base, can be found with verse. Fully coloured with crest and unglazed. 130mm.   110.00

Wishing Chair, Giants Causeway. 75mm dia.   56.50

Witches Cauldron with inscription. 47mm.   5.50

Yorick's Skull, inscribed: *Alas poor Yorick.* 57mm.   12.00

Traditional/National Souvenirs

John Bull, bust.
3 sizes: 65mm.   14.50
85mm.   25.50
96mm.   25.50
Largest 2 sizes found with a black hat.

ARRY, bust of Pearly King. 86mm.   40.00

ARRIET, bust of Pearly Queen.   80.00

Blackpool Big Wheel.
3 sizes: 60mm.   14.00
78mm.   16.00
110mm.   19.00

Bolton Trotter, hand holding.
110mm long. 5.50
Cheddar Cheese, Prime, with slice out.
35mm high, 65mm diameter. 9.00
Cornish Pasty, with verse.
98mm long. 11.00
Devonshire Dumpling. 45mm. 17.50
Isle of Wight, relief map standing
upright on pintray. Coloured.
106mm long.˙ 55.00
Lancashireman's Jug with verse.
75mm. 10.00
Lincoln Imp. 110m. 6.50
Lincoln Imp, on square stand.
125mm. 8.50
Manx Legs, flat. 85mm dia. 13.00
Manx Legs on stand, can be found
in lustre. 101m. 16.00
Manx Legs on rock. 51mm. 30.00
Melton Mowbray Pie, with verse.
54mm. 19.50
Mill Lass, bust, shawl draped round
head and shoulders. 60mm. 26.00
Sometimes inscribed:
Lancashire Lass. 30.00
Ripon Hornblower, with verse.
130mm. 16.00
The Winton Imp on pedestal. (Thin
budah with hand in mouth).
135mm. 55.00
Yorkshireman's Jug with verse.
83mm. 10.00
Irish Colleen, fully coloured on
ashtray base. 105mm. (One of a
series of ashtrays, *see* **Comic**
section). 56.50
Irishman and pig on shamrock
ashtray base. 100mm long. (One
of a series of ashtrays, *see* **Comic**
section). 56.50
Irish Harp with green shamrocks.
108mm. 10.50
Irish Jaunting Car, Model of. With
horse and driver. 120mm long. 110.00
Irish Lady, bust, inscribed: *My
simple graceful Nora Criena.* 85mm. 30.00
Pat the Irishman, bust. 80mm. 20.00
Shamrock shaped dish. 80mm long. 4.00
Bagpipes. 110mm long. 19.00
Gretna Green, Anvil from, with verse.
66mm. 7.50
Scotsman, bust of. 65mm. 20.00
If named *Harry Lauder.* 30.00
Scotsman, coloured, holding
Matches container. (Late). 90mm. 30.00

Souter Johnny, sitting figure on chair
with verse. Some colouring.
130mm. 30.00
Tam o'Shanter (bonnet) inscribed:
Tha can sit on the thistle noo.
Coloured feather and pompom.
95mm dia. 30.00
Thistle candlestick. 50mm. 5.00
Thistle on stalk base (Candlestick or
Vase) inscribed: *Tha can sit on the
thistle noo.*
2 sizes: 85mm. 5.50
113mm. 7.50
Thistle vase, wide necked.
4 sizes: 45mm. 3.00
55mm. 3.00
70mm. 3.00
85mm. 5.00
Thistle Vase on ornamental base.
55mm. 5.00
Ladies of Llangollen, the. Standing
figures on base. 100mm. 30.00
Welsh Harp. 80mm. 8.50
Welsh Hat, Model of. Often unnamed.
Can be found with longest Welsh
place name round brim, for
which add £3.00
2 sizes: 52mm. 5.50
72mm. 8.00
Welsh Hat, much wider brim.
Reg. No. 450915. 49mm. 9.00
Welsh Lady Bust, can be found fully
coloured, inscribed: *Wales! Wales!
My Mother's Sweet Home.*
3 sizes: 65mm. 14.00
85mm. 20.00
100mm. 26.00
Welsh Lady with stick sitting on
bench on oval ashtray base.
Coloured. 114mm. 85.00
Welsh Leek, can be found with
inscription: *King Henry V. The
Welshmen did goot servace (at
Crecy) in a garden where Leeks did
grow.* Shakespeare.
2 sizes: 76mm. 4.00
98mm. 5.50
Welsh Tea Party, 3 Welsh ladies
taking tea, can be found with hats
and cloaks coloured.
2 sizes: 50mm. 35.00
95mm. 40.00
Welsh Tea Party, as above, on oval
base. 100mm. 40.00
Welsh Tea Party, as above, on ashtray
base. 42mm. 50.00

Welsh Lady Tea Pot & Lid.
Coloured. 152mm. 30.00
Japanese Girl, with fan and parasol,
No 250. 64mm. 35.00

Seaside Souvenirs
Bathing Machine. *Morning Dip 7am.*
4 sizes: 50mm. 10.00
55mm. 10.00
65mm. 10.00
85mm. 20.00
Lifebelt. 80mm dia. 10.50
Lifeboat with yellow and blue rope.
110mm long. 12.50
Can be found inscribed with any
of the following names: *Brother &*
Sister; Bob Newson; Charles Arkcoll;
Charles Medland; Charles Susanna
Stephens; The Charlie and Adrian;
Co-operator No 2 also Co-operative
No 2; Eliza Aveus; Elizabeth
Simpson; James Stevens No 5; James
Stevens No 10; Kentwell; Mark Lane;
Nancy Lucy; Richard Coleman; The
William Earle. Add £7.
Liner, 4 funnels. 180mm long. 55.00
Paddlesteamer. 160mm long. 95.00
Rowing Boat. 83mm long. 9.50
Trawler. 125mm long. 19.50
Yacht. 125mm long. 12.50
Lifeboatman, bust.
3 sizes: 65mm. 15.50
70mm. 19.00
85mm. 30.00
Fishing Basket, found inscribed:
A good catch. 50mm. 5.50
Fisherman's Creel, with separate
lid. No. 18. 60mm. 5.50
Fisherman's Creel with fixed lid.
50mm. 5.50
Lighthouse.
2 sizes: 106mm. 7.50
145mm. 9.00
Beachy Head Lighthouse,
with black band.
2 sizes: 102mm. 7.50
140mm. 12.50
Bell Rock. Lighthouse. No. 14.
108mm. 25.50
Cove Sea Lighthouse. 136mm. 34.50
Eddystone Lighthouse, smaller sizes
unnamed.
3 sizes: 70mm. 5.00
105mm. 7.50
140mm. No. 10, named. 17.00

Flamborough Head Lighthouse
2 sizes: 130mm. 25.00
145mm. 30.00
Kinnaird Lighthouse. 145mm. 30.00
Longships Lighthouse, Lands End.
142mm. 24.00
Manghold Head Lighthouse. 60.00
Pharos Lighthouse, Fleetwood, Model
of. No. 255.
2 sizes: 100mm. 5.50
140mm. 10.50
If named, with matching crest. 14.00
Smaller size (fully inscribed) has
been found as pepper pot.
Scurdyness Lighthouse, Montrose.
Pepper pot 104mm. 30.00
Spurn Head Lighthouse. 110mm. 17.50
Winterton Lighthouse, Model of.
100mm. 30.00
Withernsea Lighthouse. 105mm. 16.00
Wolf Lighthouse. 105mm. 30.00
Crab, very detailed. No. 6 or 9.
85mm long. 13.00
Crab Ashtray. 90mm long. 7.50
Oyster Shell dish. 72mm dia. 3.50
Oyster Shell dish on 3 tiny feet.
90mm long. 6.50
Nautilus shell on three 3 legs.
80mm long. 16.00
Scallop Shell.
2 sizes: 70mm. 3.00
92mm dia. 3.00
Scallop Shell dish, very ornate.
83mm dia. 4.00
Scallop Shell on rock, *Menu holder.*
58mm. 10.50
Shell Ink Well, one open shell
inverted on another, usually
inscribed: *We are always glad to*
hear from you. Can also be found
inscribed: *We're aye prood to hear*
fae ye or *pins.* 105mm. 10.50
Whelk Shell, can be found
inscribed: *Listen to the sea* or *We*
are always glad to hear from you.
Size varies from
80mm-100mm long. 5.00
Punch and Judy Show. Rd. No. 37083.
90mm. 55.00
Judy, bust, some colouring. 90mm. 30.50
Punch, bust, some colouring.
2 sizes: 65mm. 25.50
80mm. 30.00

Bathing Beauties/Twenties
Flappers

Bathing Belle on trinket box. 122mm long.	120.00
Can also be found in coloured lustre finish.	
Bathing Belle on ashtray. Some colouring inscribed: *cum fra dip*. 57mm.	85.00
Bathing Belle dipping feet in pool, with inscription: *Cumfradip*. 98mm long.	50.00
Flapper, sitting on bench – on oval or heart-shaped tray, yellow hat and dress. 105mm.	65.00
Flapper in yellow dress and headscarf reclining on rectangular box and lid. 122mm long.	115.00

Countryside

Acorn. 55m.	7.50
Beehive on table. 78mm.	11.00
Hay Stack, circular. 58mm.	6.50
Hay Stack, rectangular. 50mm.	8.50
Milk Churn. 60mm.	5.00
Pinecone, curved. 88mm long.	4.00
Tree Trunk vase. 70mm.	4.50
Tree Trunk Hatpin Holder. 105mm.	10.50

Animals

Small models of 'pets' were obviously made in great numbers for many years so the moulds do vary. Large, more exotic animals were much more expensive at the time and so are consequently rare.

Bear and Ragged Staff. 80mm.	30.00
Bear sitting. No. 2. 85mm.	30.00
Bull, Highland. 130mm long.	56.50
Calf, inscribed: *Why the Natives are called Isle of Wight calves*. 100mm long.	20.00
Camel, 2 humps – Bactrian. 70mm.	25.50
Cat, angry, standing with arched back and green eyes, sometimes inscribed: *My word if you're not off*. 63mm long, white.	10.50
With colouring.	16.00
Inscribed.	19.50
Cat, climbing into boot, which has a mouse peeping out of its toe. 100mm long.	40.00
Cat, Cheshire. No bow round neck, inscribed: *Keep smiling*.	

2 sizes: 70mm.	6.50
90mm.	7.50
Cat, The Cheshire. With orange or red bow round neck, inscribed: *The smile that won't come off*. 95mm.	12.50
Cat, long necked and sitting. 108mm. Inscribed: *My word if you're not off*.	8.50
	16.00
Cat, Manx.	
2 sizes: 70mm long.	20.00
80mm long.	23.00
Can be found with coloured face. Add £7.00	
Cat with bow, sitting on plinth. Bow sometimes coloured blue. 123mm.	30.00
Cat sitting with tail curled round feet, red bow and green eyes. No. 77. 67mm.	17.00
Cat sitting and smiling (grotesque, rather similar to Cheshire Cat), bow round neck, sometimes coloured orange. 75mm.	7.50
Cat sitting with bow round neck. 56mm.	11.00

Arcadian Black Cat
Registered Series

No. 1 Black Cat on Jug. 60mm.	55.00
No. 2. Black Cat on vertical horseshoe 76mm.	75.00
No. 3. Black Cat on pillar box posting letter. 56mm.	65.00
This cat has also been found in cobalt blue instead of black.	75.00
No. 4. Black Cat on telephone. 65mm.	82.50
No. 5. Black Cat in canoe. 80mm long.	95.00
No. 6. Black Cat on wall. 70mm.	75.00
No. 6. Black Manx Cat on wall, cat without tail. The model has a matching Douglas Crest. (A different mould to the above).	95.00
No. 7. Black Cat in boot. 61mm.	55.00
No. 8. Black Cat with bottle, bottle can have solid or cork top, can be inscribed: *Cheerio from...* (can be found in lustre). 70mm.	75.00
No. 9. Black Cat on milk churn. *New Milk* moulded on churn. (Can be found in lustre). 70mm.	55.00
No. 10. Three Black Cats in bed.	82.50
No. 11. Black Cat on swing. 63mm.	75.00
No. 12. Black Cat in well. (Can be found in lustre). 63mm.	47.50

No. 13. Black Cat operating radio.
63mm.   100.00
No. 14. Black Cat in Pram. (Can be
found in lustre). 70mm.   160.00
No. 15. Three Black Cats in basket,
and one on top. 70mm.   115.00
No. 16. Black Cat on scooter. (Can be
found in lustre.). 70mm.   110.00
No. 17. Black Cat with umbrella.
65mm.   125.00
No. 18. Black Cat on bicycle.
80mm long.   150.00
No. 19. Black Cat in yacht.
96mm long.   125.00
No. 20. Black Cat playing double
bass. 70mm.   160.00
No. 21. Two Black Cats on seesaw.
85mm long.   135.00
No. 22. Five Black Cats on a house,
their tails spell: *Good luck*. 65mm.   150.00
No. 23. Three Black Cats on sledge
(very rare).   135.00
No. 24. Black Cat playing piano.
52mm (very rare).   160.00
There are also very similar black
cats which are not part of the
Registered Series:
Black Cat, wearing kilt and
glengarry, playing golf standing
on golf ball. 70mm.   82.50
(This is from a Willow mould.)
Black Cat, standing alongside Welsh
leek wearing Welsh hat. 60mm.   82.50

Sitting Black Cats
Can be found on the following
bases:
Armchair
2 sizes: 55mm.   25.50
          90mm.   28.00
Ashtray, horseshoe shaped.
93mm long.   39.00
Ashtray, octagonal shaped. 100mm.   23.00
Pouffe, inscribed: *Good luck*.
2 sizes: 80mm.   24.00
          95mm.   25.50
Trinket box, horseshoe shaped.
70mm.   27.50
(All of these cats have blue/green
eyes and usually red bows, but
yellow bows are sometimes
found.)

Chimpanzee, sitting. 70mm .   22.00

Cougar (or Panther).
102mm long (rare).   82.50
Cow, Jersey. 125mm long.   65.00
Cow, some colour, sitting on lid of
butter dish, inscribed: *Butter.*
115mm dia.   30.00
Crocodile (or alligator).
125mm long.   75.00
(Can be found with blue lustre
finish.)
Bill Sykes Dog, Model of, sitting.
No. 300. 103mm.   12.50
Sometimes inscribed: *My word if
you're not off.*   add £7.00.
Bill Sykes Dog. Model of, standing.
Sometimes inscribed: *My word if
you're not off.*
3 sizes: 88mm.   16.00
          102mm.   17.50
          118mm long.   20.00
Bulldog, black, emerging from
kennel inscribed: *The Black Watch.*
2 sizes: 56mm.   15.00
          96mm.   18.50
Bulldog, sitting, very thin face.
52mm.   25.50
Bulldog, standing. No. 301.
Sometimes inscribed: *Who said
Germans.*   add £12.50.
2 sizes: 120mm.   17.50
          130mm long.   18.50
Dog, Collie, lying down.
78mm long.   19.50
Dog, Collie, standing. Sometimes
inscribed: *Shetland collie*   add 4.00
and larger size *Sheep Dog*   add 8.00
2 sizes: 60mm.   16.00
          95mm long.   17.50
Dog, Dachshund. 90mm long.   35.00
Dog, King Charles Spaniel, begging
on cushion.
2 sizes: 68mm.   11.00
          95mm.   12.50
Dog, Labrador Puppy, sitting,
sometimes inscribed: *Daddy
wouldn't buy me a bow wow* or *My
word, if you're not off.*   add 7.50
2 sizes: 65mm.   10.00
          75mm.   10.00
Dog, Puppy, head on one side.
115mm.   10.50
Dog (Pup), sitting with one ear
raised. 68mm.   9.00
Dog, Scottie, standing. 60mm.   13.00

Dog, Scottie, sitting wearing blue
   Glengarry. 60mm.   10.50
Dog, Scottie sitting wearing Tam
   o'Shanter. Hat can be found
   coloured blue. 85mm.   10.50
   If with coloured hat.   16.00
Dog, Scottish Terrier, can be found
   inscribed: *Scotch Terrier.*   add 6.50
   As old Mrs Terrier said to her pup, in
   all life's adventures keep your tail
   *up.*add 4.00
   2 sizes: 66mm long.   13.00
           85mm long.   13.00
Dog, standing, facing sideways,
   curly tail and blue collar.
   80mm long.   19.50
Dog, Staffordshire Bull Terrier.
   2 sizes: 70mm   10.50
           80mm.   12.00
Dog, Staffordshire Bull Terrier,
   sitting, looking left. Inscribed:
   Model of Bill Sykes Dog on base
   and *My word if you're not off* on
   rear. Brown eyes.   30.00
Dog, walking, blue collar. with *Old*
   Mrs Terrier inscription.
   90mm long.   19.50
Dog, Terrier looking out of kennel.
   Inscribed: *Beware of the Dog.*   20.00
Dog posy holder, some colouring.
   103mm long.   12.50
Donkey.
   3 sizes: 80mm long.   34.50
           96mm long.   36.00
           120mm long.   39.00
   Smaller size has saddle. Large
   size can have inscription:
   Hee-haw.   add 4.00
Elephant, Indian, trunk attached to
   body. 55mm.   30.00
Elephant, Indian, trunk modelled
   free from body, sometimes
   inscribed: *Baby Jumbo.*   add 5.00
   55mm.   30.00
Fawn, sitting. 50mm high, 80mm long. 34.50
Fawn, standing on oval base. 88mm.   34.50
Fish, fat. 98mm long.   5.50
Fish, open mouthed.
   2 sizes: 80mm.   5.00
           108mm.   5.50
Fish, lying on its right side.
   122mm long.   7.50
Fish, curved body. 110mm long.   6.50
Fish ashtray in shape of plaice,
   usually inscribed: *A pla(i)ce for*

ashes, but can be inscribed:
   Caught at... 125mm long.   7.50
Fox. 102mm long.   40.00
Fox on square plinth. 114mm.   40.00
Frog, closed mouth. 45mm.   30.00
Frog, open mouthed and green eyes,
   larger sizes inscribed: *Always*
   croaking.
   3 sizes: 60mm – no inscription.   16.00
           80mm.   20.00
           100mm long.   24.00
Goat. 82mm long.   40.00
Hare.
   2 sizes: 73mm long.   15.00
           80mm long.   17.00
Kangaroo. 75mm.   75.00
Hippopotamus. 88mm long.   56.50
Lion, roaring. 85mm long.   22.00
Lion, walking.
   3 sizes: 85mm long.   16.00
           116mm long.   16.00
           140mm long.   17.00
   Smallest sizes can be found
   inscribed: *King of the forest,* for
   which   add 2.00
Monkey, sitting hand to mouth.
   65mm.   13.00
Monkey, sitting holding coconut.
   No. 34. 85mm.   22.00
Monkey, wearing coat. 75mm.   13.00
Mouse, holding acorn. 60mm.   23.00
Otter, holding fish in mouth.
   120mm long.   47.50
Pig, smiling and sitting. 63mm long.   20.00
Pig, short and standing, inscribed: *I*
   won't be druv. 63mm long.   10.00
Pig, tall and standing, inscribed:
   You can push or you can shuv but
   I'm hanged if I'll be druv. 78mm.
   63mm long.   10.50
Hampshire Hog. Model of, sitting.
   No. 148C. 70mm long.   12.50
Hampshire Hog. Model of, standing
   inscribed: *Wunt be draw* and verse
   No. 145. 105mm long.   14.00
Sussex Pig, Model of, short, standing
   pig inscribed: *Wunt be druv.*
   No. 148.
   2 sizes: 70mm long.   14.50
           80mm long.   16.00
Sussex Pig, Model of, sitting,
   inscribed: *Wunt be druv.* No. 148.
   88mm long.   17.00
Sussex Pig, Model of. standing fat   12.50

Pig, can be found inscribed:
Mochyn bad with Welsh crest.
No. 148. 80mm long, if named   19.50
Sussex Pig, Model of, standing thin
pig, inscribed: *You can push or you*
can shuv but I'm hanged if I'll be
druv or *Won't be druv*. No. 148.
2 sizes: 78mm long.   12.50
        85mm long.   14.50
Wiltshire Pig, Model of, sitting up on
haunches, alert ears. No. 148.
60mm.   21.50
Wiltshire Pig, Model of, standing fat
pig with double chin, inscribed:
Wunt be druv. No. 148. 85mm.   14.50
Piglet, kneeling. 70mm long.   11.00
Polar Bear.
3 sizes: 93mm long.   52.50
        100mm long.   55.00
        135mm long. Inscribed:
        Polar Bear.   65.00
Pony, New Forest, can be found
unnamed. 100mm long.   24.00
Pony, Shetland, often found
unnamed.
3 sizes: 93mm long.   25.00
        110mm long.   25.00
        120mm long.   30.00
Rabbit, ears lying along back. Found
numbered 22 and 23. sizes vary
between 65-80mm long.   8.00
Rabbit sitting, ears apart. No. 13.
Sizes vary between 50-68mm.   7.50
Rhinoceros. 90mm long.   75.00
Russian Bear, inscribed: *War Edition*
and carries Russian Imperial
crest. 70mm.   85.00
Seal. 102mm long.   19.50
Squirrel, holding nut, on base.
65mm.   31.50
Squirrel Jug. 80mm.   17.00
Teddy Bear, sitting.
2 sizes: 60mm.   19.50
        90mm.   30.00
Smaller size is not found
inscribed.
Tortoise. 72mm long.   9.00
Tortoise, standing upright, wearing
blue or orange policeman's
helmet. 65mm.   55.00
Welsh Goat, Model of, inscribed: *Yr*
Afr Cymreig. 100mm long.   47.50
Wembley Lion. 100m long. (stylised
symbol of the B.E.E.).   24.00
3 Wise Monkeys on wall inscribed: *I*
see no evil, I speak no evil, I hear no
evil. 76mm.   13.00

Isn't this Rabbit a Duck. On its base a
rabbit, turned on its side a duck.
(Can be found in lustre.) 75mm.   25.50

Birds (including Eggs)
Chick, breaking out of egg. Can be
found inscribed: *Just out.*   add 3.00
2 sizes: 63mm long.   9.00
        86mm long.   9.00
Larger size can be found
inscribed: *Easter egg*   12.50
Chick in Egg pepper or salt pot.
58mm.   5.50
Can have yellow head.   add 4.00
Chick, very tiny and completely
yellow, sitting on a white egg,
inscribed: *Every little helps mother*
will be pleased. 50mm long.   20.00
Egg salt and pepper pots. 58mm.
                                            Each 2.50
Eggshell, broken open. 39mm.   3.00
Egg with flat base, can be found   4.00
inscribed: *Sparrows egg.* 44mm.   5.50
Cock, standing, legs modelled
separately, usually inscribed:
Cock o' th' North or *Cock o' th'*
South. Some colouring to head.
100mm.   16.00
If named.   20.00
Can be found inscribed: *Chantelle.*   23.00
Cock, standing, legs modelled
together. Some colouring to head.
85mm.   20.00
Hen, standing, some colouring.
62mm (matches above).   20.00
Hen, roosting. 54mm.   7.50
Heron, on circular base. 83mm.   28.00
Bird perched on circular base.
(Reputedly a blackbird). 68mm.   16.00
Bird, perched on tree trunk, wings
extended. (Very impressive).
2 sizes: 125mm.   37.00
        162mm (lustre).   40.00
Bird salt and pepper pots. 70mm.
                                            Each 5.50
Dove, Fantail on square base. 70mm.   20.00
Goose. 86mm.   19.00
Norwich Canary. 100mm.   7.50
If coloured yellow.   13.00
Norwich Warbler. Canary on rock,
with whistle and bubble blower
base, Often found unnamed.
126mm.   25.50
Can be found on tree stump base
without blower. 125mm.   17.00

Owl, baby. 40mm.	12.50
Owl, Barn. 63mm.	12.50
Owl, Horned (long eared).	
2 sizes: 74mm.	14.50
95mm.	15.50
Owl (wise), one eye closed, with	
verse. 98mm.	20.50
Parakeet.	
2 sizes: 60mm.	12.50
83mm.	12.50
If inscribed: *Pretty Polly.*	14.50
Parrot, sometimes inscribed: *Pretty*	
Polly. No. 751. 70mm.	13.00
Peacock, yellow beak and coloured	
plume. Rd.	
2 sizes: 115mm.	31.50
125mm.	34.50
Peacock on ashtray. (Can be found	
in lustre.) 80mm long.	20.00
Pelican, giant beak with verse.	
80mm long, 50mm high.	55.00
Pelican. 70mm.	40.00
Penguin. No details of size.	40.00
Roysten Crow, perched on tree	
trunk. 123mm.	40.00
Seagull. 76mm (rare).	35.00
Seagull, colouring to tip of wings	
and yellow beak. 100mm.	25.50
Seagull, brooding, yellow beak, blue	
head and tail. 50mm high,	
110mm long.	75.00
Stork. 80mm.	33.50
Swan, detailed plumage.	
3 sizes: 50mm long.	7.50
70mm long.	7.50
90mm.	9.00
Swan posy bowl. 88mm.	7.50
Turkey, on round base. 60mm.	24.50
Turkey, on round lustre base. 78mm.	30.00

Great War

Many of these models are found with the inscription *War Edition AD 1914* and a crest of 'one of the allied countries', (add £8.00 for this).

Some of the soldiers, although sold separately, were based on the same design idea and form a set. They are therefore grouped together in the listings.

British Soldier, Model of, more often than not unnamed. 135mm.	95.00

Two versions exist. The later mould has the rifle touching the hat, and rifle butt turned sideways.

Colonial Soldier, Model of. 135mm.	170.00
French Soldier, Model of. 135mm.	170.00
Scots Soldier, Model of. 135mm.	170.00
Bugler Boy, Model of. 135mm.	170.00
Drummer Boy, Model of. 135mm.	170.00
Sailor, standing with hands on hips 132mm.	65.00

(All the above figures are standing to attention on an oval domed base.)

British Cavalry Soldier, Model of. on horseback. 122mm.	185.00
Russian Cossack, Model of, on horseback. 122mm.	185.00
Despatch Rider, Model of, on motorbike. (Can be found in lustre). 120mm long.	75.00
Nurse and Wounded Tommy, Model of. 108mm long.	125.00
Nurse, inscribed: *Soldier's friend.* Red cross on chest. 132mm.	75.00
Sailor, bust, found with hatband impressed: *HMS Queen Elizabeth* or with plain hatband. Inscribed: *The Handyman, HMS Dreadnought.* 92mm.	34.50
There are 2 moulds, one with hat tilted to left and one tilted to right. Add £3.00 if with verse.	43.50
Can be found with hat coloured blue but this is rare.	65.00
Sailor Winding Capstan, Model of. 105mm.	110.00
Soldier, bust, inscribed: *Tommy Atkins,* or *Territorial,* either found with verse 'Its the Soldiers of the King my lads'. Some colouring. 90mm.	43.00
with verse	47.50
Soldier with Respirator, bust, inscribed: *Model of new gas mask.* 95mm. (rare)	215.00
Tommy driving a Steam Roller over the Kaiser, inscribed: *To Berlin.* 120mm. (very rare).	480.00
Tommy in Bayonet Attack, Model of. 130mm.	135.00
Tommy and his Machine Gun, Model of. 72mm.	39.00
Tommy on Sentry Duty. Model of, in sentry box. 110mm.	82.50
Tommy throwing Hand Grenade, Model of. 130mm.	150.00

New Aeroplane, Model of. Biplane
with fixed prop, and roundels in
relief. 120mm long.   115.00
New Aeroplane, Model of. Monoplane
with revolving propeller.
135mm long.   65.00
New Aeroplane, Model of. Monoplane
with fixed propeller. 147mm long.   65.00
Monoplane, movable prop.
149mm long.   65.00
Monoplane, V winged, with fixed
prop. Propeller can be found with
2 or 3 blades.
2 sizes: 118mm long. 2-bladed.   75.00
        118mm long. 3-bladed.   82.50
        140mm long. 2-bladed.   85.00
        140mm long. 3-bladed.   110.00
(This model has a circular portion
added for no other reason than to
carry the crest.)
Aeroplane Propeller. 150mm long.   26.00
RAF/RFC crest.   30.00
Rarely factory marked.
British Airship, Model of, with
suspended engine. 120mm long.   82.50
British Airship on stand.
128mm long.   34.50
Observer or Sausage Balloon, Model of.
84mm.   75.00
Super Zeppelin, Model of. 127mm long.   30.00
Battleship: *HMS Queen Elizabeth.*
160mm long.   30.00
Battleship. 160mm long. *HMS Queen
Mary* (inscribed on deck). Rare.   100.00
Battleship, 3 funnels and tiny gun
fore and aft. 120mm long.   17.50
Minesweeper, not found named.
126mm long.   30.00
RMS Lusitania, not found named.
180mm long.   75.00
Torpedo Boat Destroyer, Model of.
115mm long. (Can be found in
lustre).   25.00
Submarine, inscribed: *E4.*
95mm long.   19.50
New submarine, Model of, inscribed:
E5. 126mm long.   23.00
Armoured Car, Model of. 95mm long.   40.00
Red Cross Van, red cross on each
side and rear. 'EH 139' printed on
radiator.
3 sizes: 78mm long.   30.00
         85mm long.   30.00
        160mm long.   435.00
(The large size is extremely rare).

Tank, Model of; (without wheels).
4 sizes: 100mm long.   50.00
        115mm long.   13.00
        160mm long.   30.00
        325mm long.   525.00
115mm size can be found inscribed:
Original made in Lincoln.   30.00
Also found inscribed *285.*
The two largest sizes also exist with
green/brown camouflage markings.
The smallest size is quite rare and
the largest size is very rare, being
so enormous that it must have
been made for shop display. It
has also been seen in lustre.
Tank, Model of, with inset wheels.
115mm long.   19.50
Can be found inscribed: *Original
made in Lincoln.*   30.00
Tank, Model of, with trailing steering
wheels. 144mm long.   30.00
Tank, Model of, exactly as above but
with one trailing wheel. 144mm
long. (Rare).   350.00
Tank, Model of, exactly as above but
with a second wheel attached to
the one-wheeled tank.   56.00
Whippet Tank, large hexagonal gun
turret at rear. 172mm long. (Rare).   350.00
Field Gun.
4 sizes: 120mm long.   17.50
        140mm long.   19.50
        150mm long.   23.00
        175mm long.   25.00
*New Field Gun with Screen and Sight
Hole, Model of.* 105mm long.   23.00
German Howitzer, Model of.
3 sizes: 115mm long.   19.50
        140mm long.   20.00
        150mm long.   23.00
Trench Mortar, Model of. Can be
rarely found inscribed: *Roaring
Meg.* 75mm long.   17.50
If inscribed   35.00
Mortar on square base. (Krupp).
70mm.   17.50
Revolver, Model of. 83mm long.   47.50
Anti-aircraft Shell, Model of. 98mm.   20.00
Cannon Shell, sometimes named.
3 sizes: 70mm.   4.50
         70mm named.   6.50
         90mm.   3.50
         90mm named.   8.00
        135mm.   8.00
        135mm named.   12.50

The 90mm and 135mm sizes are
often inscribed: *Jack Johnson.*

       add 5.00

or sometimes: *Hartlepool's
Bombardment Dec 16th 1914.*

Cannon Shell Salt and Pepper pots.
70mm. Each   5.50

Shell Case. 56mm.   7.50

Clip of Bullets, Model of. 57mm.   17.50

Trench Flying Pig, Model of. (Flying
pig is a nickname for a type of
Stokes bomb.) 95mm long. (Very
rare).   150.00

There are two different versions.
One has a tail at the back and the
factory mark is on the side which
is used as a stand. A later version
has no tail and a factory mark on
base which is its stand.

Bomb dropped from Zeppelin, Model of.
Inscription sometimes reads:
German Zeppelin or *on Bury St.
Edmunds.* 75mm.   11.00

If inscribed and with matching
crest.   17.00

*Bomb dropped from Zeppelin upon
Sheringham during first raid on
England 8.30 Jany, 18th 1915, Model
of.* With movable three bladed
propeller. 115mm.   82.50

Also found with the following
inscription: *First bomb dropped
from Zeppelin at Loftus Sept 8th
1915 at 9.30* or *Model of first bomb
dropped from Zeppelin on
Skinningrove Ironworks Sept. 8th
1915 at 9.30p.m.*   100.00

British Aerial Bomb, Model of. 75mm.   40.00

Canister Bomb, Model of. 60mm.   17.50

Plum Pudding Bomb, Model of. Often
found unnamed. 72mm. (Rare).   80.00

German Hand Grenade, Model of.
78mm. (Rare).   85.00

Hairbrush Grenade, Model of.
104mm long. (Rare).   130.00

Mills Hand Grenade, Model of. 62mm.   19.50

British Aerial Torpedo, Model of.
102mm long.   30.00

German Aerial Torpedo, Model of.
88mm long.   30.00

Bandsman's Drum. No. 226. 53mm.   10.50

Bell Tent. 64mm dia.   10.50

If inscribed: *Camping out.*   16.00

Capstan. 56mm.   11.50

Gurkha Knife, Model of.
110mm long.   20.00

Pair of Field Glasses, Model of. Often
found not named. 78mm long.   16.00

Sandbag, Model of. 73mm long.   22.50

Tommy's Hut, Model of. 105mm long.   47.50

Trench Dagger, Model of. 102mm long.   47.50

Trench Lamp, Model of. 70mm.   13.00

Water Bottle, Model of. 65mm.   17.50

Colonial Hat, Model of, (rarely found
inscribed: *Anzacs*). 88mm wide.   16.00

Inscribed.   20.00

Glengarry. 90mm long.   19.50

New Zealand Hat. 71mm dia.   25.50

Officer's Peaked Cap, white or more
usually with coloured badge and
hatband. 65mm dia. Can be
found inscribed: *Territorials cap.*   add 5.50

White hatband.   10.50

Coloured hatband.   15.50

Solar Topee (Pith helmet). 60mm.   25.50

Steel Helmet, sometimes inscribed:
Tommy's Steel Helmet. 65mm dia.

Named   30.00

Unnamed   25.00

Anti-Zeppelin Candle Holder.
65mm.   17.50

Fireplace inscribed: *We've kept the
home fires burning.*

4 sizes: 60mm.   12.50

         90mm.   14.50

        110mm.   17.00

        115mm.   19.50

Angel with raised arms, found with
R.A.F. crest (not named) but must
be R.A.F. Memorial. No details of
size.   95.00

Bishop's Stortford *War Memorial.*
132mm.   125.00

Brora War Memorial. 155mm. (Rare).   145.00

Burford War Memorial, with
inscription. 128mm. (Rare).   170.00

Burnham on Crouch *War Memorial.*
146mm. (Rare).   95.00

*Carillon Tower, Loughborough. War
Memorial.*

2 sizes: 155mm.   60.00

        162mm.   60.00

*Cavell Statue, inscribed: Nurse
Cavell.*

3 sizes: 110mm.   12.50

        147mm.   14.50

        160mm.   19.00

Cavell *Memorial Statue, Norwich,*
inscribed: *Edith Cavell – Nurse,*
Patriot and Martyr. 175mm.   25.50
Cenotaph, Model of, with green
wreaths.
4 sizes: 80mm.   4.00
             100mm.   5.00
             140mm.   5.50
             180mm.   7.50
Three larger sizes with inscription.
Cheltenham War Memorial.
2 sizes: 150mm.   95.00
           185mm.   95.00
Chesham *War Memorial.* 159mm.   95.00
Coventry War Memorial. 140mm.   95.00
Dingwall *War Memorial,* soldier on
wide plinth. 125mm.   95.00
Dover Patrol Memorial. 130mm.   39.00
Dover *War Memorial.* 140mm.   75.00
Dovercourt War Memorial.
2 sizes: 120mm.   110.00
           137mm.   110.00
East Dereham War Memorial, with
inscription (rare). 132mm.   160.00
Florence Nightingale Statue,
inscribed: *The Lady of the Lamp.*
2 sizes: 147mm.   20.00
           170mm.   24.00
(Different moulds)
Folkestone War Memorial inscribed:
May their deeds be held in reverence.
2 sizes: 97mm long at base.   65.00
           156mm long at base,
           95mm wide.   65.00
Fryatt Memorial, with inscription
(rare).   110.00
Great Yarmouth *War Memorial,* with
inscription. 146mm.   30.00
Invergordon *War Memorial.* 148mm.
(Rare).   125.00
Killin War Memorial. 150mm.   145.00
Earl Kitchener Memorial, drowned off
Marwick Head, Orkney, 5th June
1916. 110mm.   115.00
Lewisham War Memorial. 155mm.   62.50
Loughborough War Memorial.
155mm.   75.00
Margate *War Memorial.* 160mm.   95.00
March War Memorial. 160mm.   145.00
Moffat War Memorial with ram on a
rock. (Rare). 108mm.   125.00
Newhaven Mercantile Memorial,
with inscription. 155mm.   125.00
Norwich *War Memorial.*
134mm long, 60mm high.   115.00

Plymouth War Memorial, with female
figure. 120mm.   125.00
Plymouth *Naval War Memorial,* with
inscription.
3 sizes: 125mm.   56.50
           156mm.   60.00
           178mm.   65.00
Plymouth Royal Naval Memorial,
on octagonal stepped base. 144mm.   65.00
Portsmouth *Naval War Memorial.*
2 sizes: 140mm.   50.00
           162mm.   75.00
Sheringham War Memorial, with
inscription. 165mm.   125.00
Stowmarket Memorial Gates.
110mm long.   115.00
Walsall War Memorial.   165.00
Warminster War Memorial. 150mm.   125.00
Woodhouse Eaves, War Memorial with
inscription. 130mm.   160.00

Most war memorials are relatively
rare, possibly because they were
ordered in small numbers by
local shops, and were only made
for a relatively short period.

Home/Nostalgic
Anvil on tree trunk base, horseshoe,
tongs etc. against base. 70mm.   6.50
Armchair. 65mm.   9.00
Armchair, inscribed: *The old*
armchair, with verse. 90mm.   7.50
Ball of String, match holder and
striker. 55mm.   20.00
Ball of String. 55mm.   20.00
Basket with twisted handle.
73mm long.   4.00
If inscribed: *Fruit Basket*   6.50
Basket of Milk, six bottles, tops gold
or brown. 65mm.   19.50
Bell, no clapper. 54mm.   7.50
Bellows. 95mm long.   11.50
Chair, highbacked. 90mm.   6.50
Coal Scuttle. 65mm.   4.00
Coal Scuttle, sometimes found
inscribed: *Coal scuttle.* 80mm.   5.50
Cradle. 48mm.   10.00
Dressing Table Swing Mirror, with
drawer. 50mm.   14.50
Dust pan.
3 sizes: 95mm.   7.50
             105mm long.   8.00
             143mm long.   11.00
Firebucket. 55mm.   4.00

Fireplace, with teapot, cat etc. in
bold relief. Inscribed: *There's no
place like home.* Some colouring.

2 sizes: 90mm. — 12.50
112mm. — 14.50

Fireplace, with cauldron, teapot, etc.
moulded in slight relief.
Inscribed: *There's no place like
home.* Some colouring.

2 sizes: 65mm. — 15.00
110mm. — 15.00

Flat Iron. 77mm long. — 14.50

Frying Pan.

2 sizes: 114mm long. — 17.00
120mm long. — 17.00

Gladstone Bag. 82mm long. — 12.50

Grandfather Clock, narrow,
inscribed: *1:30.*

2 sizes: 105mm. — 10.50
145mm. — 16.00

Grandfather Clock, Model of. Usually
inscribed: *Make use of time let not
advantage slip. Shakespeare.* Can be
found inscribed: *Top o' the morn.*
No. 209. 108mm. (Two moulds,
one with ornate moulding at top). — 12.00

Invalid Cup. 50mm. — 5.50

Jardiniere on fixed base. 95mm. — 5.00

Kennel, can be found inscribed:
Beware of the dog. 50mm. — 12.50

Lantern.

2 sizes: 70mm. — 5.50
90mm. — 6.50

Lantern, horn, not found named but
sometimes inscribed: *Watchman
what of the night.* 85mm. — 6.50

Lantern, with open sides. 125mm. — 20.00

Oil Lamp, flat. 92mm long. — 5.00

Pillar Box, with inscription: *If you
haven't time to post a line here's the
pillar box.* 63mm. — 12.00
Found marked *G.R.V.*
70mm. *E.R. VII* — 16.00
— 17.00

Potty. 36mm. — 5.00

Saucepan with handle and separate
lid. 45mm, 80mm long. — 9.00

Shaving Mug. 60mm. — 5.50

Spinning Wheel. 84mm. — 20.00

Stool, 3 legs. 40mm. — 7.50

Sundial, inscribed: *Life's but a
walking shadow.* Add £2 for
inscription.

2 sizes: No. 41. 86mm. — 5.50
115mm. — 8.50

Sundial on square base. 115m. — 7.50

Table, square with four legs. 40mm. — 5.50

Thimble. *Tak a Thimble Full.* 41mm. — 20.00

Umbrella, open. 50mm dia. (Usually
not marked.) — 14.50

Village Pump with trough. 90mm. — 7.50
Can be found inscribed. — add 4.00

Old Warming Pan, Model of,
inscribed: *Polly warm the bed.*
No. 254. 125mm long. — 17.00

Old Warming Pan, Model of, with
ornate handle. No. 251. 120mm long. — 15.50

Watering Can. No. 126. 74mm. — 12.00

Water Pitcher, inscribed: *Tak Hod
An' sup lad.* 60mm. — 8.50

Wheelbarrow. 100mm long. — 11.00

Comic/Novelty

Alarm Clock, inscribed: *Many are
called but few get up!*

2 sizes: 40mm. — 19.50
60mm. — 20.00

Billiken, often found not named.
63mm. — 6.50

Boy Scout, inscribed: *Be prepared.*
105mm. — 55.00

Clown, bust. No inscription or
colouring. 65mm. — 14.50

Clown, bust, inscribed: *Put me
amongst the girls.* Some colouring.
Reg. No. 522477. 80mm. — 25.50

Clown, candlesnuffer, standing,
hands on hips, wearing baggy
suit. 104mm. — 47.50

Couple in Bed, inscribed: *John is
everything shut up for the night - All
but you darling.* Some colouring.
70mm long. — 75.00

Couple in Bed, man sitting up,
woman with all the blankets,
inscribed: *They don't need many
clothes in the daytime but they want
'em all at night.* 70mm long. — 75.00

Fat Lady on weighing scales, scale
registers 20 stone. Inscribed:
Adding weight. Blue bonnet. 90mm. — 72.50

Jester, doubled faced bust, happy
with eyes open and sad with eyes
closed. Can be found inscribed:
Ye Jester awake. Ye Jester asleep.
Some colouring on larger size.

2 sizes: 70mm. — 11.50
90mm. — 14.50
inscribed — 16.00

Judge in his box reading a book.
82mm. — 55.00

Lavatory Pan with brown seat, inscribed: *Ashes*. Not found crested. 69mm.   10.50

Mister Gollywog, Now children when I've tucked you safely in, just say Mr Gollywog good-night. Full figure, standing. 118mm.   125.00

Negro Minstrel, bust, verse by Eugene Stratton. Some colouring. 100mm.   30.00

Negro, standing with hands in pockets as vase. 105mm.   30.00

Petrol Pump Attendant, body is pump. Inscribed: *Petrol Sir*. Can be found with some colouring. 95mm. White   47.50
Coloured   55.00

Policeman, smiling, with arms behind back. 100mm.   28.50

Policeman, fat and jovial, with raised hand. Inscribed (on hand): *Stop*. 94mm.   34.50

Policeman on duty, with verse. 148mm.   34.50

Policeman, jovial holding large truncheon. Uniform and helmet blue. 106mm. (Rare).   65.00

Robinson Crusoe standing figure with gun. 122mm.   110.00

Pierrot candle snuffer, standing. 100mm.   24.50

Sailor, standing, cap can be found impressed: *Lion*. Blue cap and coloured face. 95mm.   55.00

Sailor Toby Jug, blue hat and coat. 60mm.   40.00
65mm. (fatter).   47.50
108mm.   55.00

Sailor Vase, pink face and some colouring. 103mm.   47.50

Sailor, negro features, Vase. 100mm.   30.00
(Late also found marked Goss England)

Suffragette double sided bust, front sour old lady, inscribed: *Votes for women*, back pretty young girl, inscribed: *This one shall have the vote*. Coloured features. 98mm.   55.00
A smaller version exists with no colouring or inscriptions. 72mm.   20.00

Suffragette candle snuffer, double faced as above. 72mm.   30.00

Suffragette hand bell, double faced as above, with same inscription and colouring. Also found inscribed: *Nature has endowed woman with so much power that the law gives them very little. Dr Johnson.* 110mm.   47.50
(All the suffragette items must be considered scarce).

Teapot with eyes, mouth and nose as spout. Reputedly Lady Cadogan's Puzzle Tea Pot. Some colouring.   39.00

A Truck of Coal from . . . Wagon of black coal. 80mm. long.   25.00

Comic Ashtrays: Coloured figures on white trays. (All are quite rare).

Bird, possibly a crow, fully coloured, dressed in top hat, frock-coat, waistcoat and trousers, carrying a black cane; standing on pentagonal brown base with a circular brown dish in centre. 85mm.   65.00

Bookmaker, with greyhound and hare on octagonal ashtray base. Some colouring. 90mm. long.   34.50

For Irish Colleen, Irishman and Welsh Lady see: National Souvenirs.

Jester, sitting on heart or spade shaped tray, other card symbols are on tray. 65mm.   65.00

Puppy with monacle, coloured with hat, bow, cigar and beer! on ashtray. (Can be found in brown lustre). 90mm.   60.00

Scotsman, really grotesque, sitting on bench on round tray. 95mm.   47.50
plain white   30.00

Comic Cruet Sets: Rarely found as a set. They are coloured.

Policeman salt pot. 80mm.   43.50

Regimental Sergeant Major pepper pot. 80mm.   55.00

Naval Petty Officer pepper pot. 80mm.   47.50

Sailor, comic figure in blue with green parrot on shoulder with white mustard barrel with lid. 63mm.   40.00

Sailor pepper pot, standing, cap can be found impressed *Lion*. Blue cap and coloured face. 85mm.   43.50

Little birds: these are fully coloured heads popping out of white eggs. They do not seem to match any other series of models, the black boy's face is much more carefully detailed than the black boys listed below.

Flapper's head hatching from egg, inscribed: *A little bird from* .... 50mm long. 30.00
white head 20.00
Black Boy's head hatching from Egg, inscribed: *A blackbird from* .... 50mm long. 40.00

Black Boys – often found marked Rd. No. applied for. All the boys are fully coloured but sit on white boxes, baths and so on. Later models are very brightly and carefully coloured and lightly glazed. These are marked as late in the listing below. All these models, with the exception of *A little study in black and fright*, are uncommon.

Black Boy standing with hands in pocket, also found as salt pot. 94mm. (Late). 115.00
Black Girl, standing with hands on hips, also found as pepper pot. (Pair with above). 94mm. 115.00
Black Boy playing banjo, boy can be wearing red, yellow or blue striped pyjamas. 85mm. 115.00
Black Boy in bath of ink, towel hanging at side, inscribed: *How ink is made* 110mm long. (Probably Willow Art mould). 105.00
Black Boy in hip bath holding yellow soap. 90mm (late). 82.50
Black Boy in bed with spider, inscribed: *A little study in black and fright*. Boy can have red or blue striped pyjamas. 70mm long. 112.50
Black Boy in bed, face only peeping out from bedclothes, inscribed: *Just a little study in black and fright*. 70mm long. 60.00
No colouring. 40.00
Black Couple in bed, inscribed: *They don't need many...* 71mm long. 82.50
Black Boy being chased up a tree by a crocodile. 80mm. 145.00
Black Boy eating slice of melon, sitting on a soapbox. 80mm. (late). 95.00

Black Boy eating melon slice, standing on corner of diamond shaped ashtray, inscribed: *I'se not melon-choly!* (Rare) 88mm. 115.00
Black Boy sitting at table eating a boiled egg which has a yellow chick popping out. 70mm. 95.00
Two Black Boys heads popping out of box, inscribed: *Box of chocolates*. 60mm. 75.00
Also found in white only. 30.00
Two Black Children, boy and girl sitting on a tree trunk. 80mm. 82.50
Black Boy holding giant pumpkin with lid. 72mm. 115.00
Black Boy holding container for cigarettes. 100mm (late). 115.00
Black Boy holding container for matches. Inscribed: *Matches*. 100mm. (Late). 115.00
Black Boy peering out of shower, coloured trousers hanging from top (rare) 67mm. 170.00
Black Boy Toby Jug. 66mm. 47.50

Children: very late models, beautifully coloured and detailed children on white armchairs, baths etc.. Usually found marked Rd. No. applied for. They are particularly appealing and unfortunately rare.

Girl and Boy sitting in armchair. Girl is wearing a frilly dress and has a large bow on her head; boy is dressed in top hat and tails. 60mm. 95.00
Girl and Boy sitting in armchair. Boy wears black jacket and hat. 75mm. 95.00
Girl and Boy as above sitting on tree trunk. 87mm long. 82.50
plain white 40.00
Boy in nightgown, yawning and stretching. Candle snuffer. 100mm. 24.00
Boy riding a Pig. Boy wearing a coloured coat. 94mm long. 115.00
Girl standing by hip bath, wearing towel. 75mm. 85.00
Girl, naked, blonde hair with red bow, standing in circular bath, draped in white and blue towel and holding yellow sponge. Registration applied for. 90mm. 190.00

Baby in Bath with a coloured transfer of an insect (variously described as a wasp or a fly). 80mm long.   52.50

Cartoon/Comedy Characters
Ally Sloper, bust, with inscription. 85mm.   40.00
Baby, with arms outstretched, inscribed: *Cheerio.* Some colouring on face. 120mm. (from Willow mould)   30.00
Bonzo dog sitting, hind legs outstretched in front, name impressed on collar. 68mm.   40.00
Bonzo, sitting on feeding bowl. 65mm.   35.00
Bonzo and Felix sitting on bench, coloured and not named. 76mm.   75.00
Harry Lauder, bust. Inscribed: *Stop ye're tickling Jock.* Often found not named. Some colouring   17.00
83mm, named   30.00
98mm.   50.00
Mrs. Gummidge, standing figure with inscription: *A lone lorn creetur & everything goes contrairy with her.* 112mm (rare).   47.50
Winkie the glad-eyed bird, not named but can be found inscribed: *Glad eyes.* 60mm.   19.00

Alcohol
Series of late models of a fully coloured comic man (looks rather like Mr. Pickwick, bald with spectacles, wearing a green suit, but probably was a comedian or comic character associated with heavy drinking) on white models.
Man, as above, drinking beer from tankard. 92mm. Can be white, with silver tankard and coloured face   65.00
or fully coloured.   82.50
Man, as above, holding tankard on horseshoe ashtray, with inscription: *The more we are together the merrier we'll be.* 70mm.   35.00
White   25.00
Man, as above, clinging to neck of bottle. Fully coloured, white bottle.

2 sizes: 76mm.   40.00
95mm.   40.00
Man, as above, climbing into large beaker. 75mm.   47.50
Beaker, fluted, with inscription: *They speak o' my drinking, but they dinna consider my drouth, or Ye never ken the worth o' water till the well not is dry.* 78mm.   7.50
Beer Barrel on stand, inscribed: *XXX* on each end of barrel. 55mm.   5.50
Beer Bottle and tankard on horseshoe ashtray, with inscription: *The more we are together the merrier we'll be.*   12.50
Beer Bottle and tankard on square ashtray with inscription above. 90mm.   12.50
Bottle, syphon and glass on round tray inscribed: *Irish and Soda.* 58mm.   12.50
Bottle, stout. No. 44. 63mm.   5.00
Bottle with cork. 76mm.   5.50
can be found inscribed: *Special Scotch.*   7.50
or more rarely *Lacon's fine ale.*   10.50
Carboy.
2 sizes: 55mm.   6.50
85mm.   8.50
Drunk leaning against a statue on an ashtray. Inscribed: *How cold you are tonight dear.* Coloured figure on white tray. 100mm.   125.00
Monk, jovial, and holding glass with verse: *A jovial monk am I contented with my lot. The world without this gate. I flout nor care for it one jot.* Add £4.00 for black hat.
4 sizes: 70mm.   12.50
80mm.   12.50
112mm.   16.00
120mm.   19.50
A Nap Hand, hand holding coloured beer labels on heart shaped dish. 62mm long.   55.00
Silver Tankard. 85mm.   14.50
Soda Syphon. Can be found inscribed: *Soda Water Syphon.* No. 6. 100mm.   11.50
Tankard, foaming, with verse: 'The more we are together'. 50mm.   8.50
Tankard, shaped. No. 41. 47mm.   4.00
Thistle Vase, with verse: 'Just a wee deoch-an doris'. 70mm.   4.00

Toby Jug, sometimes found with verse: *No tongue can tell, No heart can think, Oh how I love a drop of drink*. 4 sizes:

45mm. Smallest size	8.50
can be found coloured	14.50
65mm. Middle size, is exactly the same as Old Toby Jug.	8.00
75mm.	12.50
85mm.	11.00

Whiskey Bottle, can have solid or cork top, inscribed: *One Special Scotch*. 100mm.   7.50

Whiskey Bottle and Soda Syphon on tray, inscribed: *Scotch and Soda*. 88mm dia.   12.50

Sport/Pastimes

Billiard Table, cue and three balls. 100mm long.	125.00
Cricket Bag.	
2 sizes: 80mm long.	12.50
100mm long.	12.50
Cricket Bat. 115mm long.	75.00
Curling Stone. 63mm dia.	16.00
Football. 50mm dia.	6.50
The F.A. Cup. 100mm.	16.00
named.	30.00

Golf Ball, often inscribed: *The game of golf was first played in the year 1448*. 42mm.   7.50
if inscribed   12.50

Golf Club Head. 94mm long.	17.00
Golf Bag and Clubs. 105mm.	75.00
Golfer, with clubs standing on golf ball. 76mm.	40.00
Golfer standing on small golf ball in centre of six-sided ashtray. 72mm.	47.50
Golfer's Caddie holding golf bag. Figure coloured. 116mm.	125.00
Golfer's Caddie, very tiny, holding huge bag of clubs. 88mm.	75.00
Jockey on Racehorse, oval base, some colouring, unglazed. 115mm.	55.00

Racehorse and jockey, some colouring, on horseshoe ashtray. Can be found inscribed: *Humorist Winner of the Derby 1921 Donoghue Cup*.   Add 20.00
100mm.   55.00

Tennis Racquet. 95mm long.   10.50

Chess Set. Complete sets can be found but these are very rare. It is extremely difficult to collect a set with the same crests. Individual pieces are often found however, the rook being the most common, the pawn, strangely, is quite rare.

King. 88mm.	25.00
Queen. 84mm.	25.00
also found in smaller size. 72mm.	25.00
Knight. 63mm.	14.50
Bishop.	
2 sizes: 60mm.	16.00
70mm.	16.00
Rook. 55mm.	6.50
Pawn. 52mm.	26.00

Musical Instruments

Banjo.	
2 sizes: 125mm long.	9.50
150mm long.	10.50
Double Bass. 153mm long.	30.00
Guitar. 153mm long.	14.50
Harp with green shamrocks. 104mm.	10.50
Piano, upright. 70mm long.	16.00
Tambourine. 50mm dia.	10.00
Violin with bow. 125mm long.	75.00

Transport

Car, open, Vauxhall. (Identical to Shelley No. 361). 135mm long.   40.00

Car, open tourer (2 seater) inscribed: *EH 139*; can be found also inscribed: *HELL*. 110mm long.   40.00

Car, saloon, inscribed: *EH 139*. 76mm long.   30.00

Car, open 2 seater showing exhaust pipes, curved boot, etc. 105mm long.   47.50

Car, taxi, inscribed: *EH 139*. Front two seats open, hood over back two. 85mm long.   65.00

Charabanc, 18 seater, inscribed: *7734 which upside down reads HELL*. 138mm long.   40.00

Can of Petrol, impressed: *Motor Spirit*. 55mm.   16.00

Omnibus, Double decker bus with stairs outside. 130mm long (rare).   170.00

Modern Equipment

Camera, folding. 60mm.	40.00
Gramophone in Cabinet, open top, black disc. 76mm long.	125.00
Horn Gramophone.	
2 sizes: 80mm.	20.00
112mm.	25.00

Hats

Boy Scout's Hat. 73mm dia.	16.00
Luton Boater with coloured band.	
100mm long.	17.50
Bishop's Mitre. 53mm.	6.50
Bishop's Mitre. No. 19. 50mm long.	6.50
Mortar Board with moulded tassel.	
64mm wide.	35.00
Straw Hat. 75mm long.	12.00
Top Hat. 40mm.	5.50
Top Hat, match striker and holder.	
45mm.	6.50

Shoes

Highboot. (Can be found in lustre).	
3 sizes: 73mm.	17.50
85mm.	12.00
104mm.	16.00
High backed narrow Shoe.	
2 sizes: 90mm.	7.50
130mm long.	10.50
Hobnail Boot.	
2 sizes: 65mm long.	5.00
80mm long.	5.50
Ladies Ankle Boot. 70mm long.	5.00
Lancashire Clog. 94mm long.	5.50
Lancashire Clog, high narrow type.	
2 sizes: 95mm long.	5.50
135mm long.	11.00
Dutch Clog. 102mm long.	4.50
Sabot, pointed toe. 60mm long.	5.00
Oriental Shoe.	
2 sizes: 85mm long.	5.00
105mm long.	6.50
Riding Boot.	
2 sizes: 73mm.	16.00
105mm.	28.00
Shoe posy holder. 100mm long.	7.50
Slipper. 100mm long.	7.50
Slipper wall pocket. 109mm long.	7.50

Miniature Domestic

These models can be found with crests, views, black cats and other transfer decorations.

Amphora Vase on three red balls.	
90mm.	6.50
Bagware Cream Jug.	4.00
Beaker. 40mm.	2.50
Beaker, fluted with inscription: *Ye never ken the worth of water till the well gangs dry.* 50mm.	5.50
Chamberpot. 98mm.	5.00
Cheese Dish, one piece. 50mm.	7.50

Cheese Dish and cover. 50mm.	7.50
with *Stilton Cheese* inscription.	25.00
Cream Jug. 52mm.	2.50
Milk Jug with crinkle top. 38mm.	2.50
Tea Cup and saucer. 40mm.	5.50
Tea Pot with lid.	
2 sizes: 50mm.	7.50
60mm.	7.50
Tea Pot with lid, bulbous. 52mm.	7.50
Tea Pot with lid. 45mm.	7.50
Tea Pot, one piece. 48mm.	7.50
Vase with ram's head in relief.	
55mm.	2.50

Domestic

This is listed as it was made specifically to carry crests. Pieces can also be found with 'Lucky Black Cat', 'Lucky White Heather' and other transfer decorations, but not usually views. Late pieces are found with the black cat *Arcadian* mark. Lettering is usually in blue.

Ashtrays, can be found inscribed: *Ashtray.* Various shapes: Club, diamond, heart and spade shaped with crinkle edges.	4.00
Club shaped tray with match box stand. 105mm wide.	14.00
Heart shaped bowl.	3.00
Horseshoe.	3.00
Octagonal.	3.00
Trefoil.	3.00
Round tray with match holder.	11.00
Bulb bowl, hexagonal.	3.00
Candle Snuffer, cone. No. 29. 63mm.	3.50
Candlesticks, various shapes:	
Column with ornate moulding.	3.00
Octagonal, fluted.	3.00
Short on fluted oblong base with handle. 156mm long.	10.50
Short on fluted leaf shaped base with handle.	3.00
Cup with the Wembley Lion moulded as the handle. 40mm dia.	15.00
Fern pots, fluted. 3 sizes:	3.50
Hexagonal. 3 sizes.	3.50
Flower bowl, octagonal.	3.50
Flower vase.	4.00
Hair pin box and lid, can be found inscribed: *Hairpins.* Fluted oblong or round.	5.50
Hair Tidy with lid, can be found inscribed: *Hair Tidy.*	

Various shapes:
Curved sided. 60mm.6.50
Hexagonal. 6.50
Octagonal with ornate moulding
and blue bow. 8.50
Square, fluted. 65mm. 7.50
Hat Pin Holder, can be found
inscribed: *Hat pins*. Various
shapes:
Octagonal. 12.50
Square fluted. 121mm. 12.50
Square with ornate moulding. 12.50
Fluted. 128mm. 12.50
Inkstand, with pen holder base.
150mm long. 7.50
Inkwell with lid. 68mm dia. 10.50
Match Holder, can be found
outpressed: *Matches*. Various
shapes:
Hexagonal. 5.50
Round. 5.50
Pill Box and lid.
2 sizes: 45mm dia. 4.00
50mm dia. 5.00
Pin Tray, can be found inscribed:
Pins. Fluted round, diamond or
oblong. 4.00
Pot Pourri, 2 shapes: Round vase
shaped, lid with knob. 4.00
Round with domed lid (rather
like a ginger jar). 4.00
Powder bowl, round. 3.50
Preserve jar with lid, round or tub
shaped. 90mm. 4.50
Puff Box, can be found inscribed:
Puff box, hexagonal or round. 6.00
Ring Stand, octagonal base. 55mm. 8.00
Rose Bowl, fluted with brass fittings. 12.00
Tableware: Cups and saucers, coffee
cans and saucers, and plates are
all found in classic and simple
shapes.
Also the following:
Beakers, plain and fluted. 3.00
Butter Tub. 5.50
Cream jugs and sugar bowls
(matching) in various shapes:
Hexagonal 2.50
Octagonal 2.50
Round, plain 2.50
Round, fluted 2.50
These can occasionally be found
inscribed: *Elp yurzel to the craim* or
Be aisy wid the crame/sugar. Add
£6.00 with these inscriptions.

Egg Cup. 6.50
Jugs, in a variety of sizes, also
bagware. 2.50
Mugs. 2 sizes. 2.50
Mustard Pots. Various shapes:
Round with pointed lid. 3.00
Round, fluted and ornate. 3.00
Round with silver lid. 10.00
Round, tall, with silver lid. 10.00
Napkin Ring inscribed *2* in blue.
45mm. 5.50
Pepper & Salt Pots, various shapes:
Cone shaped, small. 4.00
Cone shaped, tall with silver lids. 10.00
Egg shaped with screw base. *P*
55mm. 7.50
Hexagonal. 3.50
Round, with silver lids. 10.00
Plate, with thistles and leeks
moulded in relief. 5.00
Sugar Basin on stand. 3.50
Sugar Castor. 5.00
Sugar Castor with EPNS top.
Inscribed: *Sugar*. 110mm. 8.50
Sweet Dishes, various shapes:
Octagonal. 2.50
Round, crinkle edges. 2 sizes. 2.50
Round, fluted, 2 sizes. 2.50
Teapots. 1, 2 & 3 cup sizes. 7.50
Toast Rack. 120mm long. 13.00
Tobacco Jar with lid, inscribed:
Tobacco, with crossed pipes
transfer. 17.00
Trinket Boxes, can be found
inscribed: *Trinkets*. Various
shapes:
Heart shaped. 4 sizes. 5.50
Heart shaped with moulded ribbon. 7.50
Hexagonal. 4.00
Horseshoe shaped. 4.00
Oblong. 4.00
Oval. 4.00
Round. 2 sizes. 4.00
Square. 4.00
Square with bevelled corners. 4.50
Square, fluted. 4.00
Thistle shaped. 75mm long. 7.50
Vases in a variety of sizes and
shapes. 2.50

Miscellaneous
Flower Bud Vase. 40mm. 3.00
Flower (Pansy?) shaped pin tray.
80mm dia. 4.00

Horse's Hoof as inkwell. Inscribed:
We're aye prood tae hear frae ye.
90mm.   11.00
Horse's Hoof on base No. 151.
30mm.   4.00
Horseshoe. 55mm long.   3.00
Horseshoe on stand.   3.50

Argonauta Porcelain

Trademark used by James Macintyre & Co Ltd, Washington China Works, Burslem.

This small firm were earthenware manufacturers and in the Pottery Gazette in 1913, advertised their firm as specialising in 'Arms Ware, School, College or Town Arms on Tobacco Jars, match pots and ashtrays'. This mark has so far only been found on 'smalls'. J. Macintyre and Co. pieces found tend to be rather heavy.

Argonauta Models
Ancient Artefacts
Mug, 1 handled. No. 17. 35mm.   3.00
Salisbury Jack. 50mm. (With Trusty
    Servant motif and verse).   18.50

Miniature Domestic
Tea Pot and lid. 60mm.   12.50

Miscellaneous
Club shaped Dish. 75mm long.   3.00

Argosy China

Asbury China

ASBURY
LONGTON

D.W.KEE
PEEL
Asbury China

Trademark used by Alfred B. Jones & Sons Ltd., Grafton China Works, Longton, Staffs, for a wholesaler or retailer in Southend-on-Sea. (Usual trademark Grafton). See Grafton China for further details.

Most pieces found have been 'smalls' and many of them have carried Southend crests, so it is probable that the initials SEOS stand for Southend-on-Sea, and KB was a retailer. No device other than crests has been found on china with this mark. (A stock number has been recorded on one model and it is possible that many models carry such numbers).

Argosy Models
Seaside Souvenirs

Bathing Machine with large wooden wheels, and panelled body. 55mm.	11.00
Whelk Shell. 85mm.	5.00

Animals

Elephant, comic, standing with sandwich boards. 115mm.	100.00

Great War

Colonial Hat. 89mm long.	19.00

Footwear

Boot with laces. No. 234. 80mm long.	7.50
Shoe with turned up toe. 80mm long.	5.00

Miniature Domestic

Tea Pot with lid. 90mm long.	7.50

Trademark thought to have been used by Hewitt and Leadbeater, Willow Potteries, Longton. (Usual trademark Willow Art). Pieces were probably bought in for re-sale by Edward Asbury & Co., Prince of Wales Works, Sutherland Road, Longton, and marked with an Asbury trademark.

Edward Asbury and Co. manufactured china and earthenwares from 1875 to 1925. In the early 1900's the firm was making transfer printed wares for the fancy goods trade including 'Charles Dickens' Ware – drawings by 'Phiz' on mugs, plates jugs and beakers. The company probably bought in its small range of crested items during the Great War. A Great War Commemorative is often found on 'smalls' and models, consisting of a transfer print of '5 Flags of the Allies' and inscribed: 1914. (No numbering system seems to have been used).

Asbury Models
Buildings – White
Cottage. 55mm long.   6.50

Historical/Folklore
Man in the Moon. 60mm.   20.00

Traditional/National Souvenirs
Welsh Hat. 57mm.   5.00

Countryside
Tree Trunk Flower Holder. 80mm.   6.50

Animals
Bulldog, French, sitting. 110mm.   17.00
Pugdog, long neck, sitting. 115mm.   17.00
Dog, Scottie, wearing glengarry.
   88mm.   13.50
Elephant, walking, trunk free from
   body. 75mm long.   17.00
Lion walking. 110mm long.   12.50

Birds
Duck posy bowl. 70mm long.   7.50
Swan. 65mm long.   6.50

Great War
Monoplane, Bleriot type with
   movable prop. 147mm long.   65.00
HMS Lion. 142mm long.   30.00
Tank. 85mm long.   30.00
Kitchen Range, *Keep The Home Fires
   Burning*, with pot on red fire.
   65mm high, 78mm long.   14.50

Home/Nostalgic
Anvil. 56mm.   7.50

Comic/Novelty
Billiken, flat grotesque type. 68mm.   7.50

Alcohol
Toby Jug. 75mm.   12.50

Footwear
Sabot.
   2 sizes: 60mm long.   4.00
             80mm long.   4.50

Hats
Top Hat. 40mm.   5.50

Miscellaneous
Hammer Head. 82mm long.   13.00

Atlas China

Trademark used by Atlas China Co. Ltd.,
Atlas Works, Wolfe Street, Stoke.
1906-1910.

Mark used c. 1934-9.

This company formerly Chapman & Sons
Ltd was not thought to manufacture
heraldic china. Obviously they did so
during the early years when Goss
historical models were so popular. The
company was later taken over by
Grimwades Ltd.

Ancient Artefacts
Newbury Leather Bottle, not
   named. 67mm.   3.00

Domestic
Cup and Saucer. 80mm.   4.00
Sugar Bowl, late. 80mm.   3.00

Atlas Heraldic China

Trademark thought to have been used by Taylor and Kent, Florence Works, Longton, for a wholesaler in Scotland. (Usual trademark Florentine).

CR and Co. are not known to be china manufacturers (there was an Atlas china works in Stoke on Trent from 1889 to 1906 owned by Chapman and Sons, but they did not use this mark. From 1906 to 1919 the company was known as The Star China Co., and used a different mark together with the initials 'SCC').

All known models, except the thimble, are identical to Florentine models made by Taylor and Kent. (See Florentine China for details.) Taylor and Kent are known to have sold a great deal of china in Scotland so it is quite reasonable to suppose that they used this mark for a Scottish wholesaler.

All known models carry Scottish crests or Scottish colour transfer views, with the exception of a three-handled loving cup which has been found with a Blackpool crest. (Taylor and Kent did not use stock numbers).

Atlas Models
Ancient/Artefacts
Puzzle Jug. 68mm.	5.50
Salisbury Kettle, not named 100mm.	3.00
Three-handled loving cup. 40mm.	3.00

Monuments
Iona Cross. 108mm.	10.50
Statue: standing unglazed figure of possibly a Saxon or Viking	

Warrior with small oval shield in left hand. Square glazed base. 130mm. (The one model recorded has a Lanark Crest).   65.00

Traditional/National Souvenirs
Welsh Hat with blue cord and embossed tassels. 56mm.	5.00

Seaside Souvenirs
Whelk Shell. 100mm.	5.00

Animals
Elephant, kneeling. 67mm.	20.00
Fish, open mouth. 120mm long.	3.00
Toad. 70mm long.	19.50

Birds
Kingfisher. 80mm.	30.00
Pelican cream jug. 83mm long.	5.50
Swan posy holder. 80mm long.	5.00

Home/Nostalgic
Baby in Hip Bath. 100mm long.	12.50
Iron. 75mm long.	12.50
Napkin Ring. 38mm.	5.50
The Old Armchair, with verse. 85mm.	7.50
Sofa. 82mm long.	10.50
Portmanteau. 80mm long.	4.00

Alcohol
Carboy. 76mm.	4.00

Sport/Pastimes
Cricket Bag. 110mm long.	12.50

Musical Instruments
Harp. 92mm.	5.50

Footwear
Oriental Shoe with turned up toe. 95mm long.	4.50
Shoe, Ladies' 18th century. 95mm long.	7.50

Miniature Domestic
Cheese Dish and cover. 55mm.	7.50
Coffee Pot with lid. 63mm.	7.50
Cup and Saucer.	
2 sizes: 40mm.	5.00
55mm.	5.00
Tea Pot with lid. 70mm.	7.50

Miscellaneous
Thimble. 40mm.	10.50

Aurelian China

Avon China

Trademark used by an unknown English
manufacturer.
Only two models have been recorded so far.

Mark used 1903-1906

Vase. 40mm.	3.00
Small Jug (Cheltenham crest).	3.00

Trademark used by Arkinstall & Son Ltd,
Arcadian Works, Stoke-on-Trent.
Arkinstall more usually used the trademark
Arcadian China. (See under that heading
for details of china and manufacturer).
This mark is very like the earliest known
Arcadian mark used by the firm. It is
probable that Arkinstall tried out this
trademark for a time when the firm was
first established. (It is unlikely to be a
retailer's mark as crests are found from
places as far apart as Scotland and Wales.)
A range of coloured transfers were made,
identical to some with the Arcadian
trademark.

Avon Models
Ancient Artefacts
Model of Loving Cup originated by
Henry of Navarre, King of
France, 3 handled. 39mm.   4.00
Roman Vase, Model of, No. 285.   4.00

Traditional/National Souvenirs
John Bull, bust of. 85mm.   25.00

Animals
Hare. 80mm long.   12.50

Comic/Novelty
Suffragette Bust, double faced.
    89mm.   40.00

Sport/Pastimes
Golf Ball. 43mm.   7.50

Aynsley

AYNSLEY

AYNSLEY & SONS

Trademark used on china with military crests by John Aynsley and Sons, Portland Works, Longton. Aynsley models therefore almost always appear bearing military badges. Deduct £15 if no military badge.

John Aynsley and Sons are the well known firm that produce fine china today. The firm was established in 1864 to manufacture porcelain. In 1903 they advertised a 'number of fancy pieces, plain and white and enamelled in colours'. In 1904 they registered a number of designs of miniature military models as souvenirs of the South African war. These military items and 'smalls' are found with a series of military crests which pre-date the Great War. In 1908 with the introduction of the Haldane Act many of these Regiments disappeared. Obviously these models are of great interest to military model collectors and they are often found in Great War collections where unfortunately they have no business to be. Military crests found on Aynsley models are:

Argyll & Sutherland Highlanders
Army Service Corps
Black Watch (RH)
Berkshire Regiment
The Cameronians
City of London V.A.D.
Coldstream Guards
Connaught Rangers 88th & 94th Foot
2nd Dragoon Guards (Royal Scots Greys)
3rd Dragoon Guards

4th Dragoon Guards
154th Dragoon Guards
East Surrey Regiment
East Surrey Regiment Sutton Detachment
East Surrey Regiment Wimbledon
    Detachment
Essex Regiment 3rd Volunteer Battalion
1st Essex Volunteer Artillery Eastern
    Division R.A.
Essex Regiment
Gordon Highlanders
Grenadier Guards
Highland Light Infantry 71st & 74th Foot
13th Hussars
King's Dragoon Guards
King's Own Scottish Borderers
5th Lancers, Royal Irish
17th Lancers
21st Lancers
Leeds Company; RAMC Volunteers
1st Life Guards
2nd Life Guards
Lincolnshire Regiment
Liverpool Regiment
3rd (City of) London Rifles
The Lothians & Berwickshire Yeomanry
    Cavalry
Manchester Artillery
2nd V.B. Manchester Regiment
1st Middlesex Victoria & St. George's Rifles
1st Middlesex Regiment (Victoria and
    Albert's Rifles)
4th Middlesex Regiment
13th Middlesex RV: (Queen's Westminsters)
18th Middlesex Regiment
20th Middlesex (Artists) Rifles Volunteers
Northumberland Hussars
Notts & Derby Regiment
Queen's Own Cameron Highlanders 79th
    Foot
The Queen's Surrey 4th Battalion
Queen's Westminsters
Royal Army Medical Corps
Royal Artillery
Royal Garrison Artillery – Southern Division
Royal Horse Artillery
10th Royal Hussars
Royal Irish Rifles 83rd & 86th Foot
Royal Irish Fusiliers
Royal Marine Artillery
Royal Scots; 1st Foot
Royal Scots Fusiliers; 21st Foot
Royal Scots Greys
Royal Sussex Regiment
Royal Welsh Fusiliers; 23rd Foot

1st V.B. Queen's Royal West Surrey
2nd V.B. Queen's Royal West Surrey
Royal West Surrey Regiment (The Queen's)
Scottish Rifles 26th & 90th Foot
Scots Guards
Seaforth Highlanders (72nd & 78th Foot)
South Notts Hussars
South Wales Borderers 24th Foot
Staffs Imperial Yeomanry
Suffolk Regiment
Surrey Imperial Yeomanry
Sutton Detachment
Victoria & St. George's Rifles
West Yorkshire Regiment 14th Foot
Wiltshire Regiment
Aynsley produced only a few crests of towns
    and a range of Oxford and Cambridge
    colleges and do not appear to have made
    crested ware during the Great War. Some
    black monochrome transfer views can be
    found on domestic ware but as this firm
    made such a vast range of china this
    cannot be considered 'crested china' in the
    terms of this book.

Aynsley Models
South African War

Hand Grenade, with flames coming from the top. 88mm.	40.00
Cannon Shell. 104mm.	30.00
Empty Shell Case.	40.00
Bandsman's Drum. 55mm.	30.00
High Boot. 118mm.	30.00
Tent, with open flaps. 75mm.	25.00
Waterbottle.	
2 sizes: 80mm.	20.00
95mm.	20.00
Cap. 94mm long.	40.00
Colonial Soldier's Hat.	
2 sizes: 80mm long.	35.00
115mm long.	35.00
Forage Cap. 85mm long.	25.00
French Soldier's Cap. 75mm long.	
45mm high.	45.00
Glengarry. 90mm long.	25.00
Pickelhaube. 69mm long.	30.00
Pith Helmet. 68mm long.	30.00

Footwear

Boot. 60mm.	30.00
Ladies Shoe. 92mm long.	17.50

Domestic

Jug. No. 26. 94mm.	17.50

Miscellaneous

Button, oval. 40mm.	15.00
Horse's Hoof. No. 21. 84mm long.	20.00
Circular Plaque.	
2 sizes: 58mm.	25.00
75mm dia.	19.50
Circular Plaque with silver rim.	
75m dia.	19.50
Loving Cup, 2 handles. 53mm.	17.50
Square Porcelain Plaque inset in lid	
of pewter box. 85mm sq.,	
40mm high.	19.00
Shield, with upright.	
2 sizes: 63mm. No. 38	20.00
100mm.	25.00
Shield, no upright. 124mm long.	25.00
Trinket Box, heart shaped, with lid.	17.50
Vase. 58mm.	17.50

B

Trademark used by Blairs and Beaconsfield Pottery, Longton.

Blairs advertised 'Arms Ware' in 1902 but seem to have made very little. Only two models have been recorded so one can only assume that they sold other models unmarked or used another trademark. Certainly crested ware was only a side line and the firm produced other decorative china, much of it at this time being very Art Nouveau in style. The firm was established in 1880 and was subsequently known as Blairs Ltd in 1911. This firm produced Great War Commemoratives. (See Blairs China.)

B Models
Animals

Pig, standing. 80mm long.	10.00

Miniature Domestic

Cheese Dish, one piece. 50mm.	6.50

Balmoral China

Marks used 1909-1933.

Trademark used by Redfern and Drakeford (Ltd), Balmoral Works, Longton.

All china found with this mark, apart from the tankard below which has a Banff crest, has the British Empire Exhibition badge or an inscription *'Wembley 1925'* and was obviously made especially for this event. As some pieces are also seen with 'Willow Art' trademarks they could have been supplied for decoration by Hewitt & Leadbeater which had by then been purchased by Harold Taylor Robinson and was part of the J.A. Robinson Co.

Balmoral Models
Buildings – White
The Marble Arch, unglazed top.
    72mm.   25.00
Tower Bridge. 144mm long.   34.50

Birds
Goose, standing and very fat, with
    long slender neck. 155mm.   47.50

Home/Nostalgic
Pillar Box. *GVR* in red and blue,
    open slit and verse to rear. 77mm.   19.50

Domestic
Tankard. 85mm.   4.50

Bell China

This mark has been found on pieces of domestic ware with EPNS tops. Taylor and Kent specialised in producing china for manufacturers to add metal lids etc. as did many other potteries.

Domestic

Sugar Sifter with EPNS top. (Llandudno crest). 160mm.	8.50
Bottle for ink or perfume, screw top made from an early version of plastic. 80mm. (Birmingham crest)	7.50
Salt Pot with EPNS top. 100mm.	5.50

Belleek

Mark used from 1891. The name of a retailer can replace 'Co Fermanagh Ireland'.

Trademark used by Belleek Pottery (David McBirney and Co.), Belleek, Co. Fermanagh, N. Ireland.

This well known Irish firm employed the noted Goss modeller William W. Gallimore for a short period, during which he imported to Belleek Ivory Porcelain production invented by W.H. Goss. The firm produced a range of crested domestic ware, 'smalls' and probably a few simple models although only two have been recorded. These were produced in 1900-1910, during the 2nd period of the factory.

Belleek Models
Ancient Artefacts

Chester Roman Vase.	55.00
Hastings Kettle. 53mm.	55.00
Irish Bronze Pot, not named, with yellow interior, handles and feet. (Ayr crest). 45mm.	55.00

Traditional/National Souvenirs

Shamrock shaped loving cup, 3 handles. 50mm.	55.00

Animals

Pig, sitting, decorated with green shamrocks. 55mm.	82.50
Terrier, standing. 88mm.	82.50
Tortoise. 70mm long.	82.50

Countryside
Milk Churn, with 2 handles. 60mm.   55.00

Alcohol
Barrel. 57mm.   55.00

Many very fine 'smalls' were
   produced by this Pottery often
   with the characteristic Belleek
   lustre finish. These are valued at
   £55.00 each.

Best English Make

Trademark used by A.B. Jones and Sons Ltd.,
   Grafton China Works, Longton. (Usual
   trademark Grafton).

A 38mm bagware vase and several
   smalls have been recorded with
   this mark.   £3.00 each

Birks Crest China

Birks China

Trademark used by Arkinstall & Son Ltd., Arcadian Works, Stoke-on-Trent. (Usual trademark Arcadian).

Animals
Crocodile (or Alligator).
127mm long.   75.00

Trademark used by Birks, Rawlins & Co. (Ltd.), Vine Pottery, Stoke, previously L.A. Birks & Co., established in 1885.
Birks Rawlins and Co. used the Trademark SAVOY CHINA. (See that entry for details of china and manufacturer.)
This trademark was obviously used in 1928 to trade on the old and respected name of Birks. We know the new company was already in financial trouble by this date. 1928 was rather late to introduce a range of crested ware and this venture did nothing to help the firm's sales. One colour transfer view of Hampton Court Palace has been recorded on a teaplate but known crests are from all over England. (Savoy china always carry stock numbers but these have not been recorded on Birks china.)

Birks Models
Traditional/National Souvenirs
Thistle vase. 52mm.   3.00

Animals
Three Wise Monkeys on diamond
     ashtray. 65mm.   13.00

Great War
Battleship with 3 funnels,
     inscribed: *HMS Tiger*.
     116mm long.   75.00
Cenotaph. 180mm.   7.50

Home/Nostalgic
Basket. 48mm.   3.00

Handbag. 88mm.   11.00

Comic/Novelty
Biscuit, impressed: *Huntley &
    Palmers*. On stand.
    Impressed: 399. 85mm.   26.00
    With holes for hatpins.

Domestic
Tea Pot with lid. 110mm.   7.50

Birks, Rawlins & Co.

Trademark used by Birks, Rawlins and Co.
    (Ltd.), Vine Pottery, Stoke. (Usual
    trademark Savoy china).
All models will be found under the Savoy
    entry.

Blairs China

Boots

BLAIRS
CHINA
ENGLAND

1914

Trademark used by Blairs Ltd, Beaconsfield
Pottery, Longton.

This firm used the trademark B
until 1911 and then used the
trademark 'Blairs China'. Using
the latter trademark they
produced a range of 'smalls' in
1914 with Great War inscriptions
or commemorative prints. (See B
China.)   from £5.50

Trademark used for Boots The Chemist by
Arkinstall & Son Ltd, Arcadian Works,
Stoke-on-Trent. (Usual trademark
Arcadian).

Boots sold a range of crested 'smalls' in their
fancy goods departments. A transfer print
of Six Flags of the Allies is also found
inscribed: *In freedoms cause*. This
commemorative often occurs on
unmarked wares; it was probably used by
one of the known crested china
manufacturers who do not appear to have
marked their wares. (See Unmarked
Crested China.)

Boots Models
Ancient Artefacts
Glastonbury Abbot's Cup, not
named. No. 238. 48mm.   3.00

3-handled Loving Cup. 38mm.
  Bears the unusual combination of
  arms of City of London, Arms of
  Weymouth and Melcombe Regis
  and Dorchester.   4.00

Animal
Pig, standing, inscribed: *Wunt be
  druv*. 85mm long.   16.00

Home/Nostalgic
Frying Pan. 108mm long.   17.00

Many 'smalls' were also produced
  not of very good quality. These
  often have Great War
  inscriptions.
                                £2 – £10

Botolph China

BOTOLPH
J. W. & Co

Marks used c1914-1926.

Trademark used by an unknown wholesaler.
  Originally, it was thought that J. W. & Co.
  referred to J. Wilson and Son, Park Works,
  Fenton, but I now believe Botolph to be the
  trademark applied to bought in pieces by
  an unknown wholesalers, possibly
  London based.

J. W. & Co. were supplied with Great War
  and Buildings by J.A. Robinson Ltd.
  (Usual mark Arcadian and later Willow)
  and Home/Nostalgic and Comic/
  Novelty by Taylor & Kent (usual
  trademark Florentine). Pieces in other
  headings listed are all from one of these
  two factories.

Botolph was made mostly for the London
  retail trade, many crests of the City of
  London are found and all known
  buildings, with the exception of Blackpool
  Tower, are found in London.

No other forms of decoration other than
  crests are found on Botolph models and no
  military or commemorative crests have
  been found. (No numbering system was
  used on models.)

Botolph Models
Buildings – White
Big Ben.

2 sizes: 92mm.	17.50	
130mm.	19.50	
Blackpool Tower. 117mm.	13.00	
Houses of Parliament. 53mm.	30.00	

Marble Arch, Model of.

3 sizes: 48mm.	25.00
66mm.	28.50
80mm.	30.00
Nelson's Column. 124mm.	45.00

The Old Curiosity Shop, with
inscription. 95mm long. — 30.00
Old London Bridge, Ye. 86mm. — 25.00
St. Pauls Cathedral.

3 sizes: 76mm.	17.00
90mm.	20.00
127mm.	25.50
Temple Bar. 96mm.	34.50

Tower Bridge.

3 sizes: 76mm long.	29.00
118mm long.	29.00
133mm long.	35.00

Wembley Sports Stadium.
134mm long. — 95.00
Westminster Abbey, West Front.

2 sizes: 80mm.	20.00
116mm.	28.50

Historical/Folklore

Man standing in Pillory. 105mm.	17.00
Mother Shipton. 73mm.	8.00

Traditional/National Souvenirs

John Bull, bust. 68mm.	14.50
Yarmouth Bloater. 100mm long.	6.50
Irish Harp with green shamrocks. 106mm.	10.50

Seaside Souvenirs

Bathing Machine. 70mm.	10.00
Bathing Machine with bather wearing towel in doorway. 75mm.	14.50
Houseboat, square. 90mm long.	9.00
Yacht. 125mm long.	12.50
Lifebelt. 85mm dia.	9.00
Fisherman's Creel, fixed lid. 60mm.	4.00
Lighthouse. 95mm.	5.00
'The Glad Sea Waves'. 48mm.	18.50
Whelk Shell. 98mm long.	4.50

Countryside

Haystack, circular. 55mm.	5.00
Haystack, rectangular. 56mm.	5.50

Animals

Camel. 90mm long.	13.00
Angry Cat, arched back, coloured features. 82mm.	12.50
Cat, long neck. 106mm.	10.00
Cheshire Cat. 90mm.	6.50
Dog, Bulldog. 57mm.	13.00
Dog, Labrador puppy with curly tail, sitting. 90mm.	12.50
Dog, King Charles Spaniel, begging on a cushion. 70mm.	8.50
Dog, lying in cradle. 90mm long.	12.50
Dogs, King Charles Spaniels, two in Top Hat. 78mm.	15.00
Dolphin vase. 110mm.	5.50
Elephant, standing. 70mm.	20.00
Fish. 102mm long.	3.00
Hare. 93mm long.	9.00
Monkey, sitting, hands to mouth. 65mm.	13.00
Pig, lying. 68mm long.	8.50
Pig, standing, can be found with inscription: *The Pig that won't go.* 55mm.	10.50
Rabbit. 70mm long.	6.50
Rabbit, very fluffy. 100m long.	12.50
Seal with ball on nose. 75mm.	17.50
Tortoise. 70mm long.	9.00

Birds

Budgerigar. 100mm.	9.00
Canary on rock. 92mm.	14.50
Chicken in Egg. 63mm long.	9.00
Duck, comical, outstretched wings. 66mm.	35.00
Hen, roosting. 52mm.	7.50
Kingfisher. 76mm.	30.00
Kingfisher Jug. 60mm.	5.50
Owl, baby. 70mm.	12.50
Swan. 63mm.	6.50
Swan posy holder. 90mm long.	5.50

Great War

Nurse, inscribed: *A Soldier's Friend.* 125mm.	75.00
Sailor, bust of. 90mm.	35.00
Monoplane, with movable four-bladed prop. 175mm long.	82.50
Observer Sausage Balloon. 80mm.	75.00
Zeppelin on stand. 130mm.	30.00

Battleship.

2 sizes: 115mm.	15.50
165mm long.	30.00

Larger size found with inscription: *Great War 1914-18. The German Fleet surrendered 74 warships Nov 21st 1918.*

Torpedo Boat Destroyer. 110mm long.	24.50
Submarine, inscribed: *E4.* 95mm long.	19.50
Submarine, inscribed: *E5.* 127mm long.	23.00
Red Cross Van. *EH139,* with 3 red crosses. 88mm long.	30.00
Ambulance. 100mm long.	30.00
Tank, Model of, (without wheels) 2 sizes: 100mm long.	45.00
155mm long.	20.00
Tank with small integral steering wheels. 115mm long.	19.50

Tank, Model of (without wheels), wide version. There are at least two different moulds, possibly three. One has the side guns moulded flat to walls of tank, and the other has forward facing guns protruding from side turrets standing proud of sides.

125mm long.	21.00
Field Gun. 120mm long.	17.50
Howitzer. 135mm long.	20.00
Trench Mortar. 70mm.	17.50
Cannon Shell, inscribed: *Jack Johnson.* 94mm.	8.50
Shell, anti-aircraft. 96mm.	20.00
Clip of Bullets. 85mm.	17.50
Revolver. 83mm long.	35.00
Bandsman's Drum. 58mm dia.	5.00
Glengarry. 90mm long.	19.50
New Zealand Hat. 73mm long.	25.00
Fireplace, inscribed: *We've kept the home fires burning.* 110mm long.	19.50
Cavell Memorial, London, inscribed: *Nurse Cavell.* 2 sizes: 115mm.	12.50
160mm.	17.00

Cenotaph, Whitehall London, Model of. With green wreaths and inscription.

5 sizes: 80mm.	4.00
100mm.	4.50
120mm.	5.50
145mm.	5.50
180mm.	15.00

Home/Nostalgic

Armchair, inscribed: *The Old Armchair* and verse. 90mm.	7.50
Baby's Cradle. 45mm.	8.50
Baby in Hip Bath. 103mm long.	12.50
Coal Scuttle. 60mm.	4.50
Edwardian Boy and Girl cruet set. 90mm.	Each 16.00
Flat Iron. 78mm long.	12.50
Garden Roller. 85mm long.	12.50
Grandfather Clock. 130mm.	10.50
Keys, on ring. 46mm.	20.00
Lantern. 70mm.	5.50
Pillar Box. 78mm.	12.50
Sofa. 80mm long.	10.50
Suitcase. 58mm.	4.00
Watering Can. 70mm.	6.50

Comic/Novelty

Boy on Scooter. 103mm.	20.00
Bust of smiling Boy, spill holder. 71mm.	7.50
Jack in the Box. 95mm.	16.00
Screw, inscribed: *A big fat screw.* This refers to a wage rise. 75mm.	20.00
Pierrot, sitting, playing banjo. Some colouring on hands and face. 120mm.	35.00

Alcohol

Toby Jug. 65mm.	8.50

Sport/Pastimes

Cricket Bag, 2 sizes: 80mm long.	12.50
110mm long.	12.50
Golf Club Head. 2 sizes: 75mm.	17.00
95mm.	17.00
Snooker Table on 6 legs. With 3 balls and cue resting on top. 100mm long.	95.00
Tennis Racquet. 97mm long.	10.50
Rook chess piece. 55mm.	6.50

Musical Instruments

Grand Piano. 85mm long.	15.00

Transport

Car Horn, inscribed: *Pip Pip.* 90mm long.	22.50
Charabanc, with driver. 115mm long.	33.50
Omnibus, double decker bus with stairs outside. 130mm long.	170.00

Saloon Car, always found gilded on
    one side only. 86mm long.   40.00

Modern Equipment
Gramophone, square. 60mm long.   15.00
Radio Horn. 96mm.   25.00

Hats
Bishop's Mitre. 55mm.   6.50
Boater, hat. 75mm long.   9.00

Footwear
Oriental Shoe with pointed turned
    up toe. 98mm long.   4.50
Shoe, Ladies, 18th century.
    93mm long.   7.50
Thigh Boot, with scalloped rim.
    100mm.   16.00

Miniature Domestic
Cheese Dish and sloped cover.
    60mm.   7.50
Teapot with lid. 52mm.   7.50

Domestic
Flower Vase.
    2 sizes: 95mm.   4.00
           125mm.   4.50
Candlestick with snake around it.
    100mm.   7.50

Miscellaneous
Horses Hoof vase. 64mm long.   4.00

Bow China

Trademark used by Birks, Rawlins & Co
    (Ltd.), Vine Pottery, Stoke (Usual
    trademark Savoy).
This firm usually used the trademark
    SAVOY CHINA (see under this heading
    for details of the firm's history and the
    china).
A small range of models with this mark has
    been recorded. They are mostly Great War
    miniatures but a few domestic items have
    also been found. Four military badges
    have been recorded, these being Army
    Service Corps, Gordon Highlanders,
    Royal Army Medical Corps and Seaforth
    Highlanders.
Numbering System. Stock numbers coincide
    with those listed on the same models with
    the Savoy trademark.

Bow Models
Ancient Artefacts
Carlisle Salt Pot (not named).
    60mm.   3.00
Celtic Vase in British Museum,
    Model of. No. 25. 45mm.   4.00
Greek Vase, inscribed: *Model of Greek*
    Vase from the collection of Sir Henry
    Englefield. No. 66. 72mm.   4.00
Lincoln Jack from original in museum.
    Model of. No. 39. 60mm.   4.00
Persian Vase. No. 144. 75mm.   4.00

Animals
Elephant and Howdah. 70mm.
    (Rare).   30.00

Great War
Battleship found inscribed with one
  of the following: *HMS Lion*   75.00
  or *HMS Ramilies*.   85.00
  No. 524. 168mm long.
Submarine, inscribed: *E1*, usually
  found with inscription.
  150mm long.   40.00
Howitzer. 170mm long.   30.00
Cannon Shell, inscribed: *Iron rations
  for Fritz*. 115mm.   14.00

Hats
Top Hat. No. 339. 44mm.   5.50

Bramwell China

Trademark used by an unknown manufacturer for a retailer probably in
Sheffield.

Bramwell Models
Ancient Artefacts
Leather Jack, not named. No. 751.
  62mm.   3.00
(This number does not occur for a
  model like this in other ranges –
  possibly the Stock No. should be
  75 or 51. The other numeral being
  a paintresses mark).

Seaside Souvenirs
Lighthouse Pepper Pot. 97mm.   6.00

British Manufacture

Some models are found with a simple British Manufacture stamp, rather than marked. These include arks, anvils, cottages, footballs, grandfather clocks, lighthouses, petrol cans, parian straw boaters, pillar boxes, propellers, puzzle jugs and top hats. These often have tranfer views rather than crests. They are remarkably similar to the products of the Corona factory which they probably are.

Unglazed/Parian

Bust of *Burns*, beige. 162mm.	15.00

Ancient Artefacts

Puzzle Jug. 70mm.	5.00
Salisbury Kettle, unnamed. 100mm.	4.00

Buildings – White

Blackpool Tower. 122mm.	7.50
Brick Cottage, gilded features. 70mm long.	9.00
Gateway. 170mm.	19.50

Historical/Folklore

Mary Queen of Scots' chair. 74mm.	6.50
Noah's Ark. (sometimes listed as a houseboat) 90mm long.	5.00
Ye Olde Chertsey Bell, with coloured wooden base. 88mm.	26.00
without base	14.50

Traditional/National Souvenirs

Cheddar Cheese, inscribed *Prime Cheddar Cheese*, coloured yellow. 52mm.	12.00
Cheddar Cheese, model of, with verse and flowers. 60mm dia.	10.00
Laxey Wheel. 84mm.	34.50
Welsh Hat, blue band. 58mm.	5.00

Seaside Souvenirs

Canoe. 110mm long.	10.50
Yacht. 128mm.	10.50
Lighthouse. 100mm.	5.50
Whelk Shell. 84mm long.	5.00

Countryside

Milk Churn. 75mm.	5.00

Animals

Bull's head cream jug. 78mm.	5.50
Bulldog. 110mm long.	17.50
Camel. 96mm long.	13.00
Cat, angry with arched back, coloured face. 70mm.	12.50
Cat with long neck. 112mm.	7.50
Cat sitting, bow on neck. 96mm.	14.00
Manx cat. 90mm long.	16.00
Cat sitting, coloured face. 100mm.	10.50
Cat in Boot. 85mm long.	14.50
Dog, Labrador, sitting. 85mm.	10.50
Elephant, standing, tiny. 44mm.	16.00
Fish, gilded tail. 112mm long.	4.00
Fish vase. 90mm long.	3.00
Fox. 80mm.	30.00
Frog jug. 48mm.	6.50
Pig, hairy, standing with holes in nostrils. Inscribed: *The pig that won't go*. 85mm long.	10.00
Pig, standing. 90mm long.	10.00
Rabbit, crouching. 65mm.	7.50
Rabbit, fluffy. 110mm long.	12.50
Seal with ball on nose. 73mm.	19.50
Tortoise. 70mm long.	9.00

Birds (including Eggs)

Egg. 65mm upright.	4.00
Fledgling cream jug. 64mm.	5.50
Brooding Hen. 65mm long.	5.50
Crested tit posy holder. 80mm long.	5.50
Owl. 2 sizes: 62mm.	12.50
70mm.	14.50
Parrot. 95mm.	14.50

Great War

Tank, wide, large gun turrets. 126mm long.	24.00
Cannon Shell. 100mm.	6.00
Propeller. 140mm long.	30.00
Water Bottle. 88mm.	13.00

Home/Nostalgic

Anvil. 58mm.	6.50
Armchair with padded arms. 62mm.	14.50
Basket with coloured fruit. 85mm.	13.00
Hip Bath. 96mm long	10.50
Desk. 35mm long.	9.00
Grandfather clock. 129mm.	11.00
Pillar Box. Can be found inscribed: *I cant get...* 70mm.	9.50
Policeman's Lamp. 70mm.	5.50
Shaving Mug. 37mm.	5.50
Shaving Mug, angular handle. 44mm.	6.50
Shaving Mug. 55mm.	5.50
Suitcase, gilded straps. 57mm.	4.00
Suitecase, closed. 80mm long.	4.00

Comic/Novelty

Baby in Bootee. 80mm long.	11.00
Clown playing Banjo, some colour. 120mm.	30.00
Jack in the Box with open lid. 92mm.	20.00
Man's Head jug. 75mm.	12.00
Pierot, coloured face. 125mm. (Florentine).	35.00

Alcohol

Carboy. 74mm.	4.00

Sport/Pastimes

Football. 55mm.	6.50
Golfball on tee. 63mm.	12.50
Pawn Chess Piece. 60mm.	25.00

Musical Instruments

Harp. 92mm.	6.50

Transport

Petrol can impressed: *Motor Spirit*. 67mm.	17.50

Modern Equipment

Gramophone, square. No horn. 55mm.	15.00

Hats

Parian Straw Boater. 110mm long.	8.50
Top Hat. 45mm.	5.50

Footwear

Clog. 100mm long.	5.00
Lancashire Clog. 85mm long.	5.50
Sabot with turned up toe.	

93mm long.	5.00

Miniature Domestic

Candlestick, square. 80mm.	3.00
Kettle and lid. 80mm.	8.50
Cheese Dish and cover. 64mm long.	5.50
Cheese Dish and fixed cover. 64mm long.	5.50
Cheese Dish and fixed cover. 82mm long.	5.50
Cup and Saucer. 40mm.	5.00
Cup and Saucer. 45mm.	5.00
Jardiniere, one piece. 82mm.	5.00
Tea Pot and lid, ball-shaped. 2 sizes: 70mm.	7.50
85mm.	7.50

Domestic

Matchbox holder. 23mm.	3.00
Pin Tray, in shape of clover leaf. 70mm dia.	4.50

Bute China

Cable China

Trademark used by a retailer on pieces supplied by Taylor and Kent (Ltd), Florence Works, Longton. (Usual trademark Florentine).

Trademark used by a branch of J.A. Robinson & Sons, probably Willow Potteries ltd. (Usual trademark Willow).

Bute Model
Miniature Domestic
Coffee Pot with lid. 63mm.   7.50

Cable Models
Seaside Souvenirs
Lighthouse, not named. 135mm.   5.00

Home/Nostalgic
Anvil. 56mm.   7.50
Book, closed. 60mm.   6.50

Comic/Novelty
Minstrel bust, no colouring. 90mm.   9.00

Footwear
Shoe with blue bow. 113mm long.   13.00

Miscellaneous
Hand holding Tulip. 81mm.   4.50

Caledonia China

Can sometimes be found as Caledonia Heraldic China.

Trademark used by Taylor and Kent (Ltd), Florence Works, Longton for the Glasgow wholesaler CR and Co. (Usual trademark Florentine). (See also Atlas Heraldic China).

For details of this china and manufacturer see Florentine china.

Taylor and Kent used at least two different marks for this wholesaler, Atlas Heraldic China being the other known one. The Caledonia range mainly consists of small domestic ware and small pots and vases. All known crests are Scottish, and some transfer printed Scottish views can also be found on 'smalls'.

Caledonia (CR and Co.) China
Seaside Souvenirs
Yacht in full sail. 127mm long.   12.50

Animals
Dog, Bulldog, standing with verse:
   Be Briton still to Britain true,
   Among ourselves united. For never
   by but British hands, Maun wrongs
   be righted. Burns. 130mm long.   25.00
Camel, kneeling. 95mm long.   13.00
Fish Head Jug. 70mm.   8.50
Manx Cat, wiry. 53mm.   19.50
Pig, standing. 80mm long.   10.50
Rabbit. 105mm long.   7.50

Great War
Highland Infantryman with pack,
   rifle, on round plinth. 165mm.   110.00
Bust of Sailor, unglazed on glazed
   base, inscribed: *HMS Queen*
   Elizabeth on hat band. 140mm.   95.00
Monoplane. 127mm long.   55.00
Liner converted to troop ship,
   inscribed. *HMS Lion.* 140mm long.   95.00
Submarine, inscribed: *1.*
   150mm long.   30.00
Glengarry. 90mm long.   16.00

Home/Nostalgic
Kennel, inscribed: *Beware of the Dog.*
   62mm long.   6.50
Policeman's Lamp. 70mm.   10.00
Shaving Mug. 55mm.   6.50
Sofa. 82mm long.   10.50

Comic/Novelty
Policeman, standing, hands behind
   back, appears to be holding
   shears. 105mm.   24.50

Modern Equipment
Box Gramophone. 55mm.   15.50

Alcohol
Barrel inscribed: *Real Scotch.*
   No. 405. 55mm.   7.50
Bottle inscribed: *Real Scotch.* 90mm.   7.50

Sport/Pastimes
Cricket Bag. 120mm long.   12.50

Footwear
Sabot. 90mm long.   5.50

Miniature Domestic
Cheese Dish and cover. 2 pieces.   6.50

Caledonia China

Trademark used by James Macintyre and Co
  Ltd, Washington China Works, Burslem,
  for sale in Scotland.
For details of this china and manufacturer
  see Argonauta Porcelain.
Models, 'smalls' and domestic ware found
  with this mark, all carry crests of Scottish
  towns.

Caledonia (Macintyre) Models
Unglazed/Parian
Bust, *John Travers Cornwall, the boy
  hero aged 16, Hero of Jutland Battle.
  Faithful unto death.* On glazed
  base. *HMS Chester* impressed on
  hat band. 115mm.   325.00

Buildings – White
Burn's Cottage. 70mm long.   20.00

Traditional/National
Welsh Hat. 56mm.   5.00

Animals
King Charles Spaniel begging on
  cushion. 70mm.   9.00
Two King Charles Spaniels sitting in
  top hat. 75mm.   16.00
Elephant posy bowl. 75mm.   8.50
Polar Bear, inscribed: *Sam.*
  88mm long.   47.50

Birds
Hen, roosting. 51mm.   7.50
Parrot. 92mm.   10.00

Great War
Red Cross Van. 87mm long.   30.00
Cenotaph inscribed: *The blood of
  heroes is the seed of freedom.*
  140mm.   7.50

Home/Nostalgic
Policeman's lamp. 70mm.   10.00

Comic/Novelty
Screw inscribed *You could do with a
  big fat screw.* This means a wage
  rise. 75mm.   20.00

Transport
Motor Horn, outpressed *Pip Pip.*
  90mm long.   20.00

Footwear
Dutch Sabot. 70mm long.   5.00

Caledonia Heraldic China

Trademark used by a Scottish wholesaler on crested china manufactured by leading arms ware firms including Birks, Rawlins and Co. (Savoy), Hewitt and Leadbeater (Willow Art) and Wiltshaw and Robinson Ltd. (Carlton).

For details of china and manufacturers see Savoy China, Willow Art China and Carlton China.

Most models carrying this mark are recognisably Savoy or Willow Art pieces but only one Carlton model has been recorded. The domestic ware is unlike that of the two firms and may well have been made in Scotland. All known china has Scottish crests, no views or other transfer devices have been recorded.

Where models are known to be from Birks and Rawlins moulds they have, for the most part, the same stock numbers. However Birks and Rawlins use of stock numbers is at best perplexing (see Savoy China). Willow Art moulds always carry the same stock numbers when they are used.

Caledonia Heraldic Models
Parian/Unglazed

Bust of Admiral Sir David Beatty on circular plinth inscribed: *HMS Lion*. 150mm.	75.00
Burns at the Plough, standing on rectangular base with a red flower on ground. Inscribed: *Wee, modest, crimson tipped flower thou's met me in an evil hour*. Also inscribed: *Wee sleekit cowrin tim'rous Beastie...* 105mm.	75.00
Bust of Burns on square glazed base. 160mm.	30.00
Bust of Burns on round glazed base. 148mm.	30.00
Bust of Scott on square glazed base. 160mm.	17.50

Ancient Artefacts

Lincoln Jack. No. 34. 52mm.	3.00
Three handled Loving Cup. 48mm.	3.00

Buildings – Coloured

Model of House in Edinburgh where John Knox the Scottish Reformer died 24 Nov 1573. 93mm (Willow).	145.00

Buildings – White

Burns Cottage, Model of. 105mm long.	19.50
Carnegie's Birthplace. 70mm long.	65.00
Cottage, thatched. 60mm long.	6.50
Cottage, inscribed: *Tigh-na-gaat centre of Scotland*. 85mm.	30.00
First and Last House in England. 83mm long.	10.50
John Knox's House. 112mm.	40.00
Old Town House Dunbar, The. 135mm.	47.50
Windmill, movable sail. 86mm.	25.00

Historical/Folklore

James V Chair. Stirling Castle. 100mm.	7.50
Mary Queen of Scots Chair. 80mm.	6.50
Mons Meg, Edinburgh Castle. 130mm long.	12.50

Traditional/National Souvenirs

Welsh Hat. 54mm.	5.00

Seaside

Bathing Machine. 80mm.	10.00
Grace Darlings Boat, Model of. Fully coloured boat on brown rocks. 108mm long, unglazed.	30.00
Longship's Lighthouse, *Lands End.* 118mm.	28.50
Lighthouse on rocky base. 115mm.	4.50

Animals

Angry Cat Pincushion. 78mm.	12.50
Cheshire cat posy holder, 2 sizes: 80mm long.	16.00
90mm long.	16.00
Collie, standing. 110mm long.	19.50
Dog, Bulldog, sitting. 55mm.	17.00
Fish. 130mm long.	5.00
Lion, standing, with verse: *Be Briton Still...* 130mm long.	16.00
Pig, lying down. 80mm long.	10.00
Pig, sitting. 100mm long.	12.50
Pig, sitting, inscribed: *You may push me.* 75mm.	12.50
Pig, standing. 35mm.	16.00
Rabbit. 60mm long.	6.50

Birds

Clara Cluck candlesnuffer. (Savoy No. 324) 70mm.	30.00

Great War

Scottish Soldier on circular base. 160mm.	110.00
Monoplane with revolving prop. 178mm long.	55.00
Airship, (Observation Balloon) inscribed: *Beta.* 80mm long.	55.00
Liner converted to a troop carrier inscribed: *HMS Lion.* 140mm long.	115.00
Battleship impressed: *HMS Lion.* 140mm long.	30.00
HMS Tiger, 3 funnels. No. 525. 167mm long.	75.00
Torpedo Boat Destroyer, Model of 140mm long.	100.00
Red Cross Van. 87mm long.	30.00
Armoured Car (Reputedly a Talbot, but not named). 125mm long.	110.00
British Motor Searchlight, Model of. 103mm long.	145.00
Tank with inset steering wheels, inscribed: *HMS Donner Blitzen* and *515* on side. 140mm long.	30.00
Tank, no steering wheels. Inscription exactly the same as above. 135mm long.	30.00

British Trench Mortar Gun. 100mm long.	47.50
Field gun, Model of. 150mm long.	17.00
Shell, inscribed: *Iron rations for Fritz.* 160mm.	9.50
French Trench Helmet. 82mm long.	40.00
Glengarry. 87mm long.	19.50
The Black Watch Memorial, Edinburgh. 127mm.	65.00
R.F.C. Cap. 80mm long.	40.00

Home/Nostalgic

Book. 60mm.	6.50
Suitcase, closed. 80mm long.	4.00

Alcohol

Thistle with inscription: *A wee deoch an doris.* 44mm.	4.00
Toby Jug. 62mm.	8.50

Sport/Pastimes

Curling Stone. No. 429. 57mm.	23.00

Musical Instruments

Upright Piano. 83mm long.	14.50

Transport

Charabanc. 125mm long.	33.00
Open Tourer. 112mm long.	40.00

Hats

Top Hat. 44mm.	5.50

Miniature Domestic

Cheese Dish. 1 piece. 40mm.	9.00
Cheese Dish and cover. 50mm.	10.00

Cambrian China

Carlton China

Trademark used for a Welsh retailer by Wiltshaw and Robinson Ltd, Carlton Works, Stoke-on-Trent. (Usual trademark Carlton).

For details of this manufacturer and china see Carlton China. Only two models have been recorded so far.

Cambrian Models
Traditional/National Souvenir
Welsh Hat, Model of, with longest Welsh place name round brim.
No. 283. 56mm.   7.50

Animals
Pup with one ear raised. 79mm.   14.50

c1902-30.

Carlton Ware
MADE IN ENGLAND

From 1928 – 1988, can also be 'China'.

Trademark used by Wiltshaw and Robinson Ltd, Carlton Works, Stoke-on-Trent.

Only one Carlton model found with this mark, the usual Carlton mark has been sandpapered off and this applied on top. The mark is indicative of a Scottish thistle and the only piece known bears the Edinburgh arms.

Wiltshaw and Robinson started manufacturing in 1890 (a previous trademark used the same bird and initials W and R but did not use the name Carlton). A visitor to the works in 1902 reported that the firm specialised in making a large assortment of fancy goods and that they had been busy filling orders for the coronation. The firm was reported to make 'vases, teapots and waterjugs etc. Also pieces for silver mounting e.g. biscuit boxes'. It was also first in 1902 that Wiltshaw and Robinson 'the Manufacturers of Carlton Ware, Tinted Faience, etc.' advertised their 'latest speciality – Carlton Heraldic China' which could be seen at their Longon Agents, Messrs Green Bros, 47 Hatton Garden, E.C. This early advert would seem to indicate that Carlton was the first of the big Goss competitors to make heraldic china.

It is surprising that this company managed to remain independent of the Cauldon mergers that took place later on in Stoke, especially as Harold Taylor Robinson began his career as a traveller for the firm in 1899 when he was 22. By 1906 he had become a partner in Wiltshaw and Robinson, after having left this firm in 1903 to start his own company. (J.A. Robinson, the manufacturers of Arcadian). But somehow (not publicly disclosed) one of the original owners managed to buy him out, or at least break the partnership, and registered the firms as a private company in 1911. In an advert

for Carlton Ware in the same year Mr J.F. Wiltshaw proudly announced he was the sole proprietor of Wiltshaw and Robinson Ltd.

Mr Wiltshaw seems to have been determined to produce unique and novel designs, and his modellers (in fact the owners often designed their own models) were not influenced overmuch by the wares of the other potteries working in Stoke. They continued to produce very individual and (using a term much liked at the time) artistic models. The company seemed very concerned that only correct coats of arms should be used. I have been told that one customer designed a crest for his town and forwarded it to Carlton with an order for china. The order was filled but Carlton finding later that the crest was bogus asked for all the china to be destroyed (not all the models were destroyed however, and one lucky collector must have the only 'Ise Making Ink' with this Bawtry Crest).

By 1920 the Carlton speciality, lustre ware had been developed, the *Pottery Gazette* was full of praise for the lustre finishes the firm was using. After this date Wiltshaw and Robinson used lustre finishes on all their wares, including some heraldic china. This was obviously popular and although other firms later added lustre to their range it remained very much a hallmark of Carlton. A great number of heraldic models can be found in lustre, sometimes rather unsuitably on buildings and figures. By 1924 the firm had developed 'twelve very smart colours' in lustre (only five have been found used on crested pieces: mother of pearl, orange, tangerine, turquoise and black).

Throughout the period that Wiltshaw and Robinson produced heraldic china, they also made other decorative pottery. 'There are few factories in North Staffordshire that can claim to produce a bigger or more interesting range of earthenware fancies' (*Pottery Gazette*). They also produced useful tableware but always in novel shapes or in 'lustrine', and decorated very much in the popular style of the time.

The firm exhibited goods ofthis kind at the 1924 British Empire Exhibition and appeared to be flourishing, but by 1931 Wiltshaw and Robinson Ltd was put into the hands of the Receiver. Presumably this firm, like many others, had found it difficult to overcome the Depression. Details of the firm's financial state were not made public and quite possibly the liquidation was voluntary, so that a new company could be formed. F.W. Carder ceased to act as Receiver on March 7th 1932 and 'Wiltshaw and Robinson Ltd, Manufacturers of earthenware, etc' merged with 'Birks, Rawlins and Co Ltd', china manufacturers, previously of Vine Pottery, Stoke on Trent (makers of Savoy china). The merged company went on using the Savoy trademarks as well as Carlton for a few years.

Carlton Ware decorative and novelty items have continued to be produced. The ownership of the firm has changed and in 1957 the company became known as Carlton Ware Ltd. Representatives of the company claim that no records of the manufacture of heraldic china have been kept and that they know nothing of the early history of the firm. (In fact two of them did not know what crested or heraldic china was!) One can only hope that the growing interest in collecting Carlton Ware will prompt someone to search through whatever files remain and supply some information, trade catalogues, details of personal and other company trivia, which would be of enormous interest to collectors.

The firm must have survived all these years because of someone's ability to quickly change the style of its products to suit each new public whim and fancy. (The only plan for survival if one is in the fancy goods trade). This is most obvious when surveying their range of crested china. The style of the Carlton models quite noticeably changed to exactly catch the mood of each period over the twenty odd years of production. The early ancient artefacts and historical models are properly labelled and have the right sober Victorian feel about them. The light hearted Edwardian holiday souvenirs are beautifully detailed and touched with colour. The Great War models are heavy with patriotism and yet the post war animals and novelty items are jolly and rather naive. Finally no other company produced quite such vulgar lustre and coloured models to suit the taste of the late 1920's.

The quality of Carlton cannot be compared with the fine china made by Shelley and Grafton. They produced heavy models and the crests are not always painted carefully, although many examples of fine china and beautiful crests can be found. Carlton were competing for the same end of the market as Arcadian souvenir shops, bazaars and the cheaper china shops. However at its best Carlton can be very beautiful and the detail to be found on models throughout the range is quite extraordinary when one considers how cheaply they were sold.

Early decorations on small models normally found with crests include roses, green shamrocks and forget-me-nots (these can be found forming initials on beakers – a design also used by Goss). Wiltshaw and Robinson produced some view ware, but as they did not advertise this and there is relatively little around one can only assume that this was an unimportant line for them. (Possibly the production of view ware was only an early activity as these transfers are usually found on small domestic items and very rarely on named models.) This is a pity because the coloured transfer views used by this firm are excellent and compare well with Shelley (possibly the leader in the field). Other coloured transfers used are of a regional nature, such 'Biddenden Maids', 'Welsh Teaparty', 'Grace Darling' and 'The Trusty Servant'. These prints are found on all kinds of models, including buildings, sundials, hats and animals.

Carlton produced a good range of Military badges:

Alexandra Prince of Wales Own Yorks Regiment
Army Service Corps
Canadian Forestry Battalion (224)
Duke of Lancaster's Own (Blackpool Troops)
East Lancashire Regiment
Fearnought (2 versions of Tank Corps)
Machine Gun Corps
RAF
RFC
RNAS
Royal Army Medical Corps
Royal Engineers
Royal Field Artillery
Royal Scots Greys
The Royal Scots

South Notts Hussars
Shropshire Light Infantry
Whitley Camp
They also produced the following Naval crests:
HMS Agincourt
HMS Andes
HMS Australia
HMS Bellerophon
HMS Birmingham
HMS Campania
HMS Caradoc
HMS Colossus
HMS Collingwood
HMS Conqueror
HMS Emperor of India
HMS Furious
HMS Hercules
HMS Indominatable
HMS Inflexible
HMS Iron Duke
HMS Lion
HMS Marlborough
HMS New Zealand
HMS Queen Elizabeth
HMS Ramilles
HMS Renown
HMAS Sydney
HMS Temeraire
HMS Tyrant
HMS Thunderer
HMS Warspite
RMS Lusitania
RMS Duchess
Royal Naval Air Service
(They also made an unusually large range of named battleships – one wonders if the firm had naval connections or whether this interest in the war at sea was due to the number of retail outlets in ports!)

Some foreign crests have been found – Australian Towns, Tasmania, Bermuda and Hawaii – indicating some exporting, but it does not appear that Carlton ware was sold in allied countries during the Great War. There seem to be very few commemorative crests for the collector, only the BEE, Four Flags of the Allies, 'United we Stand' and The Gloucester Historical Pageant 1907 are known. There is however, a commemorative transfer print of the *Titanic* with details of its sinking.

Wiltshaw and Robinson did produce a great number of models with the lucky white heather device rather than a crest. These are nearly always used on lustre pieces, some models, but more often vases, jugs and bowls. To a much lesser extent they also used Lucky Black Cat transfers, but the cats are usually part of a larger design incorporating horseshoes and four-leaf clovers and these again are often found on lustre models.

As Carlton manufactured coloured and non-crested wares, Toby jugs and ladies from 1925 onwards which are difficult to date these have not been listed here, although as they are often of a similar style to crested china they are frequently found in collections. There is also a range of model cars, made after the Second World War, which appeal to collectors but cannot be considered crested china. Anyone becoming addicted to Carlton might well look out for examples of all their products from 1890 to the present day. Early Art Nouveau and the later Deco style wares are already very expensive.

The factory closed in 1988 so any Carlton ware, and the variety of the range is vast, is worth collecting. Even modern items, such as teapots on legs, are worth looking for. Such a collection of items would almost certainly tell the story of 20th century popular taste.

Numbering system. Printed stock numbers appear on early models and can be taken as an indication that a model was made before 1914 at least. (Models that were originally numbered were made after this date but are found with no printed number.) Some early vases, mugs and trays have painted numbers, and these too are probably stock numbers. (Paintresses marks are usually small painted initials and cannot be confused with stock numbers.) Stock numbers are given where known in the following lists.

NB. Domestic ware and later gift items have impressed numbers (usually four numbers). By the 40's these reach the 1900's, so it is possible to find very late pieces impressed 1910, 1912, etc. Some misinformed stall holders will try to explain that this is the date of manufacture – do not be deceived!

Carlton Models
Parian/Unglazed

Unglazed models are mostly busts which are on circular glazed bases, normally carrying crests.

Bust of King Edward VII, later models inscribed. 135mm.	47.50
Bust of King Edward VII in trilby.	55.00
Bust of Queen Alexandra. 135mm.	47.50
Bust of King George V. 135mm.	47.50
Bust of Queen Mary. 135mm.	47.50
Bust of Burns, with verse by Wordsworth. 120mm.	30.00
Bust of *Sir Edward Carson KC, MP* with inscription: *Ulster will fight and Ulster will be right. Edward Carson.* 130mm.	75.00
Bust of Joseph Chamberlain. 115mm.	56.50
Bust of Dr Johnson, square base, no crest.	60.00
Bust of Lord Kitchener. Can be found inscribed: *In Memoriam Lord Kitchener of Khartoum went down in HMS Hampshire June 5th 1916 off the Orkney Islands. He did his duty.* 135mm.	75.00
Bust of Ruskin. 135mm.	40.00
Bust of Scott, on glazed base. Impressed *Scott*. 126mm.	40.00
Bust of Shakespeare. 120mm.	17.50
Bust of Sydney, inscribed: *Sir Philip Sydney. Thy necessity is greater than mine.* 135mm.	40.00
Bust of *Wordsworth*, no base. 77mm.	17.50
Bust of Wordsworth, on glazed base, impressed: *Wordsworth*.	
3 sizes: 115mm.	23.00
125mm.	23.00
135mm.	25.00

Ancient Artefacts

These models are often found not named, named models usually have a printed number and this is given where known. Most inscriptions begin: *Model of* so this will not be repeated throughout the list.

Ancient Lampfeeder found at St Mary's in a marsh near Hythe.	
2 sizes: No. 330. 46mm.	4.00
No. 829. 67mm.	4.00
Ancient Tyg, 1 handle. No. 184. 66mm.	4.00
Ancient Tyg, 2 handles. No. 245. 66mm.	4.00
Ancient Vase 1st Century AD, original in Wedgwood Museum, Burslem. No. 375. 60mm.	4.00
Ancient Roman Vase now in Wedgwood Museum, Burslem 1st Century AD.	
No. 369. Rd. No. 489060. 62mm.	4.00
No. 378. 65mm.	4.00
Assyrian Vase, Model of old. No. 258. 86mm.	5.00
Brading Vase, inscribed: *Roman Vase found at Brading.* No. 1. 35mm.	4.00
Cambridge Jug. No. 332. 60mm.	4.00
Chester Ancient Vase.	4.00
Chester Roman Jug. No. 261. 70mm.	4.00
Chester Roman Vase. Found numbered 154, 286 and 288 (possibly different shapes). 60mm.	4.00
Christchurch Harvest Vase, inscribed: *Ancient Harvest Vase found at Christchurch, Hampshire.* No. 407. 44mm.	4.00
Cobham Bottle, inscribed; *Model of Leather Bottle at Cobham, immortalised by Charles Dickens.* 60mm.	5.00
Colchester Ancient Vase, 4 models: No. 349. 50mm.	4.00
No. 351. 66mm.	4.00
No. 352. 55mm.	4.00
No. 353. 68mm.	4.00
Colchester Famous Vase. No. 80. 50mm.	4.00
Dartford Ewer, inscribed: *Roman Ewer found in Dartford Museum.* No. 457. 76mm.	4.00
Dogger Bank Bottle. No. 251. 65mm.	3.00
Dorchester Jug, inscribed: *Old Jug found in North Square, Dorchester.* No. 177. 52mm.	4.00
Dorchester Roman Jug found in Bath. 70mm.	4.00
Durham Abbey Sanctuary Knocker, Wall Pocket. 84mm long.	10.00
Eddystone Jug. No. 180. 58mm.	3.00
Elizabeth Jug or Stoup, inscribed: *Model of the West Malling Elizabethan Jug or stoup hallmarked London 1581, sold for 1450 guineas.*	
2 sizes: No. 360. 74mm.	12.50
90mm.	12.50

Etruscan Vase, inscribed: *Model of*
4th Century Etruscan Vase.
2 models: No. 262. 89mm long.   4.00
No. 227. 42mm.   4.00
Fountains Abbey Cup. No. 238.
50mm.   3.00
Glastonbury Bowl. No. 172. 39mm.   3.00
Grecian Vase. N. 257. 78mm.   4.00
Grecian Water Vessel, Ancient
No. 264. 85mm.   4.00
Hampshire Roman Vase. Inscribed:
Model of Roman Vase found in the
New Forest, Hampshire. No. 247.
65mm.   4.00
Hanley Chinese Vase. No. 263. 62mm. 4.00
Hanley Cyprus Vase. No. 374. 45mm.   4.00
Hanley Egyptian Vase.
2 different models:
No. 367. Rd. No. 489059. 64mm (2
large handles from neck to body).   4.00
No. 368. 63mm. (2 tiny handles
on body only).   4.00
Hanley Roman Jug. No. 370. 55mm.   4.00
Hanley Roman Vase. 2 vases:
No. 372. 63mm.   4.00
No. 373. 50mm.   4.00
Hastings Kettle. No. 166. 60mm.   3.00
Heckmondwicke Saxon Jug.
No. 240. 80mm.   4.00
Hull Suffolk Palace Jug. No. 276.
62mm.   4.00
Hythe Ewer. No. 339. 70mm.   4.00
(Ancient) Irish Bronze Pot. No. 183.
45mm.   4.00
Irish Kettle. No. 346. 65mm.   4.00
Jersey Milk Can, with lid. No. 242.
70mm.   5.50
Lichfield Jug. No. 181. 60mm.   3.00
Lincoln Jack (from original in
museum). No. 156. 60mm.   4.00
Loving Cup. 2 handled. Not named.
No. 97. 38mm & 47mm.   3.00
Loving Cup. 3 handled. Not named.
53mm.   3.00
Merthyr Tydfil Roman Pottery.
Inscribed: *Model of Roman Pottery*
excavated at Merthyr Tydfil.
4 models: No. 288. 75mm.   4.00
No. 382. 50mm.   4.00
No. 383. 52mm.   4.00
No. 384. 42mm.   4.00
Newbury Leather Bottle. No. 229.
65mm.   4.00
New Forest Roman vase found in
Hampshire. No. 243. 76mm.

Old Bronze Porridge Pot. No. 221   4.00
Penmaenmawr Urn. No. 213. 50mm.   4.00
Phoenician Vase (originally in Hanley
Museum).
2 sizes: No. 174. 70mm.   4.00
No. 259. 80mm.   4.00
Plymouth Jug. No. 180. 58mm.   4.00
Pompeian Vessel, not named.
60mm.   3.00
Portland Vase (now in British
Museum), often found not named.
2 sizes: No. 89. 58mm.   4.00
No. 117. 80mm.   4.00
Puzzle Jug, can be found with verse.
2 sizes: 68mm.   5.50
90mm.   6.50
Larger size carries verse.
Puzzle Teapot with verse. *This teapot*
pours but not until you find out how
the way to fill. 60mm.   16.00
Roman Pottery, *1st century in*
Wedgewood Museum, Burslem.
3 models: No. 376. 65mm.   4.00
No. 377. 70mm.   4.00
No. 378. 68mm.   4.00
Roman Urn found at Milborne Port.
No. 265. 44mm and 50mm.   4.00
St. David's Vase. Inscribed: *Model of*
Ancient Vase found at St. David's.
No. 249. 62mm.   4.00
Salisbury Kettle,
2 models: No. 188. 100mm.   4.00
No. 281. 77mm.   4.00
Salopian Ewer. No. 75. 76mm.   3.00
Shakespeare's Jug. 70mm.   4.00
Silchester Urn. No. 193. 54mm.   4.00
Silchester Vase, inscribed: *Vase from*
Silchester in Reading Museum.
No. 171. 50mm.   4.00
Southampton Pipkin. No. 204.
54mm.   3.00
Spilsby Jug excavated 1887.
No. 299. 75mm.   4.00
Suffolk Jug. *Antique Jug found on site*
of Suffolk Palace Hill now in
museum. 62mm.   4.00
(Old) Swedish Kettle. No. 344.
Rd. No. 473069. 70mm.   4.00
Weston Super Mare Vase. No. 300.
80mm.   4.00
Winchelsea Vase. No. 87 also
No. 211. 77mm.   4.00
Winchester Bushel. No. 323.
80mm dia.   30.00
Windsor Urn. No. 284. 50mm.   3.00

Wokingham Tankard, inscribed:
Model of old tankard jug found near
Wokingham.
No. 217. 78mmm. 4.00
York Roman Ewer. No. 178. 57mm. ... 4.00

Buildings – Coloured
Dove Cottage, the early home of
Wordsworth, Model of. 50mm. 130.00
Grasmere Church, Model of. 90mm. ... 110.00
(The) Transport and General Workers
Union Convalescent Home,
Littleport. 112mm long. 175.00
Hop Kiln. 98mm. 85.00

Buildings – White
Arundel Castle, The Keep.
120mm long. 47.50
Bandstand, inscribed: *O listen to the*
band. 85mm. 32.50
Beach House, Canvey-on-Sea. 65mm. ... 110.00
Blackpool Tower. 125mm. 10.50
Blackpool Tower with base.
3 sizes: 100mm. 8.50
125mm. 10.50
164mm. 11.00
Blackpool Tower and Big Wheel on
ashtray, inscribed: *Good old*
Blackpool. (Can be found in
lustre).
2 sizes: 108mm. 30.00
130mm. 30.00
Burns Cottage, unnamed. 50mm.
(Very delicate). 10.50
Burns Cottage, Ayr. 70mm long. 14.00
Carnarvon Castle, Eagle Tower.
100mm. 75.00
Conway Castle. 130mm long. 125.00
Cottage with coloured doors,
hedges and windows with a
removable roof lid, and inscribed:
Ours is a nice house ours is, or with
verse *A little wife well willed, A*
little farm well tilled, A little mouse
well filled and I am satisfied. 70mm. ... 43.00
Deller's Cafe, Paignton. 62mm. 95.00
Douglas Jubilee Clock.
2 sizes: 127mm. 55.00
132mm. 60.00
Douglas Tower of Refuge.
2 sizes: 73mm. 37.50
88mm. 40.00
Downham Clock 'Presented to the
town by James Scott 1878'.
150mm. 82.50

Dutch Cottage, Canvey Island, dated
1621. 75mm (scarce). 130.00
Fair Maid's House, Perth. 92mm.
found with inscription: *Fair Maids*
House 1393 and verse *"loves darts*
cleaves hearts..." Scott. 50.00
Farnham Castle, pearl lustre. 98mm. ... 25.00
Fire Engine House, Leatherhead.
115mm (uncommon). 82.50
Forth Bridge, with inscription.
166mm long. Also found in lustre. ... 32.50
God's Providence House Chester,
inscribed: *Gods providence is mine*
inheritance. Some colouring.
108mm. 37.00
Grasmere Church. 65mm. 65.00
Grimsby Hydraulic Tower, with
details. 165mm. 27.00
Guildford Castle. Ruins, with
inscription. 75mm. 72.50
Harrogate *Pump House.* 75mm.
Inscribed: *A nip and a smell from*
the old sulphur well. 55.00
Hastings Castle Ruins. 88mm. 22.00
Hastings Clock Tower.
2 sizes: 127mm. 22.00
156mm. 25.00
Hop Kiln with coloured transfer of
hop. 96mm. 30.00
Irish Cabin found with coloured
shamrocks round base. Inscribed:
There's a cabin in dear old Ireland.
No. 516. 75mm long. Inscribed 26.00
No inscription. 16.00
Irish Cabin, with woman and
spinning wheel outside, some
colouring. 82mm. 30.00
Irish Round Tower, found with
coloured shamrocks round base.
No. 520. 126mm. Unnamed. 10.50
named .... add 6.50
with Irish crest 19.50
Keswick Town Hall and Clock
Tower. 52.00
King Charles Tower, Chester.
2 sizes: 85mm. 30.00
105mm. 42.50
Lincoln Cathedral. No. 156. 60mm. ... 40.00
Marble Arch.
2 sizes: 90mm long. 17.50
127mm long. 20.00
Margate *Clock Tower.* 138mm. 20.00
Martello Tower, inscribed: *The Wish*
Tower, Martello Tower erected in
1804, the date of Napoleons

threatened invasion and verse.
67mm dia. — 40.00

Martello Tower, as above as a trinket
box and lid. 67mm dia. — 30.00

Moot Hall, Keswick. 102mm. — 50.00

Morecombe Clock Tower. 127mm. — 65.00

Old (Bishops) Tower, Paignton.
82mm (rare). — 55.00

Oldest chemyste shop in England, Ye.
Knaresborough. Coloured roof
and door. 100mm long. — 65.00

Old Pete's Cottage, with detail of
origin of Old Pete. 72mm long. — 30.00

Old Town House, Dunbar. House with
central tower & spire. 130mm. — 65.00

Old Welsh Cottage, Model of. No. 400.
75mm long. — 20.00

Pithead, Model of. 110mm (rare). — 160.00

Rochester Castle Keep. 80mm. — 47.50

Scarton Church. 90mm long. — 55.00

St. Leonards Tower, Newtonabbey.
123mm. — 65.00

St. Nicholas Church, Lantern Hill,
Ilfracombe. 98mm. — 30.00
Also found with some colouring. — 47.50

St. Pauls Cathedral. 112mm. — 20.00

Scarborough Castle, Model of. 80mm. — 40.00

Skegness Clock Tower. 124mm. — 16.00

Smallest House in Wales at Conway.
115mm. — 30.00

Tain Tower, Model of. Rare. 115mm. — 85.00

Tintern Abbey, with green moss on
walls. 105mm long. — 65.00

Tom Tower, Christchurch, Oxford.
127mm. — 28.00

Torquay Clock Tower. Inscribed:
*Model of Mallock Memorial,
Torquay.* 168mm. — 30.00

Tower Bridge, Model of. 88mm. — 30.00

Trinity Castle Clock Gate. 90mm. — 75.00

*Upleatham Old Church, the smallest
church in England.* 80mm. — 55.00

Wallace Tower. 144mm. — 82.50

Wembley Exhibition, British Hall.
88mm long. — 95.00

Wembley Stadium, inscribed: *Model
of British Stadium Wembley* and
details of cost and size.
110mm long. — 95.00

Westminster Abbey, West Front. — 30.00

Wimborne Minster. — 65.00

Windmill with revolving sails, can

be found inscribed: *The Sussex
Windmill.* Add £5.00. 103mm. — 30.00

A Window in Thrums. 55mm. — 40.00

Windsor Castle. 135mm long. — 28.00

Windsor Round Tower. 95mm. — 30.00

York, Bootham Bar. 114mm. — 25.00

York, Cathedral, West Front. 112mm. — 28.00

York, Micklegate Bar. 112mm. — 30.00

York, Walmgate Bar. 95mm long. — 30.00

Youghal Clock Gate, inscribed: *This
Clock Gate occupies the site of the
Ancient Trinity Castle Built in 1777.* — 90.00

Monuments (including crosses)

Barrow Memorial, Ulverston,
inscribed: *Sailor Beware.* 135mm. — 20.00

The Beacon, Alderley Edge 1799, with
verse. 102mm. — 52.00

Burns Statue, Burns holding a
crimson tipped daisy, with verse.
160mm (not often found). — 35.00

Cairn on Culloden Battlefield 1746.
65mm. — 43.00

Caister-on-Sea, Lifeboat Memorial.
170mm. — 25.00

Captain Cook's Monument on square
glazed base. 145mm. — 110.00

Cavell Memorial Statue. 165mm. See
Great War.

Celtic Cross. 142mm. — 12.00

Colne Market Cross 1822-1902.
125mm. (Rare). — 65.00

Cross, thin, mounted on plinth.
144mm. Only known example has
a High Wycombe crest. — 75.00

Downham, The Clock. 155mm. — 95.00

Feltwell Cross. 142mm. — 19.50

Flora MacDonald. Statue. 160mm.
(not common). — 40.00

Florence Nightingale Memorial. See
Great War.

Garstang Market Cross, inscribed:
Model of Market Cross. 135mm. — 43.00

Globe, Swanage, (Model of the)
Unglazed globe on glazed base.
86mm. — 20.00

Tom Hughes, Monument. Rugby
School. Unglazed figure on
glazed base. 135mm. — 40.00

Hull, Fishermans Memorial, with
inscription. 170mm. — 20.00

Hull South African War Memorial.
170mm. — 23.00

Irish Cross. No. 519, 2 sizes:
115mm and 136mm. — 13.50

Locke Tower, inscribed: *This tower was erected in memory of the donor of Locke Park by P. Locke, Joseph Locke MP, AD 1877.* 135mm.   40.00

Mallock Memorial, Torquay. Torquay Clock Tower. 165mm.   30.00

Nelson's Column, not found named. 163mm.   45.00

Queen Eleanor's Memorial Cross, Northampton. 138mm.   56.50

Ripon Market Cross. 115mm.   16.00

Rufus Stone. 96mm.   5.50

Ruskin Cross, Model of, glazed or unglazed cross on glazed base. Rd No. 597960.
2 sizes: 122mm.   20.00
170mm.   23.00

(John) Ruskin Monument.
2 sizes: 120mm.   19.50
172mm.   22.50

St. Annes on the Sea Lifeboat Memorial. 150mm.   25.00

Selby Market Cross. 130mm.   110.00

Battle of Stannard Hill Memorial. 116mm.   100.00

Toad Rock, Tunbridge Wells. 78mm.   20.00

Toad Rock, Near Hathersage, Model of. 100mm long.   75.00

Sir William Wallace Statue, Stirling, with long inscription. 130mm.   40.00

Wilberforce Statue, Hull, with inscription on base. 155mm.   65.00

Historical/Folklore

Bardic Chair, in lustre. 105mm.   30.00

Biddenden Maids, inscribed: *The Biddenden Maids were born joined together at hips and shoulders in year 1100* and *a 34Y in 1100.* 105mm.   40.00

Bonnie Prince Charles Chair. 1745. 110mm.   30.00

Caveman, standing figure holding club. Brown hair and club. Can have inscription: *Billie Bus, the man who called for the empties BC umpteen.* 113mm.   110.00

Crown. 70mm.   25.00

Dropping Well, Knaresborough, sometimes found with coloured details and water. 75mm.
Coloured   27.50
White   19.50

Font, not named. 133mm.   8.00

Fox's chair, inscribed: *Model of chair of George Fox the Quaker, original at Swarthmoor Hall Ulverston.* 96mm.   47.50

Grace Darling's Boat, Model of, and description. Boat in blue, white on brown rocks. 108mm long.   40.00

Great Peter, Bell with clapper. 10 tons 15 cwts. 55mm.   20.00

John Waterson's Clog. 100mm long.   15.00

Judge, bust, can be found inscribed: *Defend the children of the poor, Punish the wrongdoer (inscription on New Bailey Courts London).* 70mm.   20.00
With inscription   add £10.00

Man in Pillory with some colouring, can have inscription: *Ample time for Reflection.* 100mm. If coloured, add £10.00.   20.00

Mary Queen of Scots Chair, Edinburgh Castle. 80mm.   6.50

Mary Queen of Scots Bed, inscribed: *The Bed of Mary Queen of Scots, Holyrood Palace, Edinburgh.* Can also be found inscribed: *Sure I was born to everlasting cares like hydra heads, one no sooner disappears than another rises in its room and drives me from repose, Mary Stuart.* 90mm long.   82.50

Miner's Lamp. 110mm.   25.00
can be found inscribed: *Davey Lamp.* 110mm.   35.00

Mother Shipton. 110mm. and 115mm.   13.00

Mother Shipton, coloured figure on lustre oval base. 90mm.   25.00

Nose of Brasenose College Oxford. 94mm long.   11.00

Old Cromwell Cannon, also named *Mons Meg.* 130mm long.   17.00

Sanctuary Knocker, Durham, on vase or wall pocket.   10.00

Scarborough Ducking Chair formerly fixed on the Old Pier for the purpose of ducking scolding women!! Last used in ducking Mrs Gamble. Now in Museum. Period 1795. Chair 95mm.   47.50

Sedan Chair, inscribed: *Model of 17th century Sedan Chair.* 70mm.   25.00

Thomas A'Becket Shoe. 105mm long.   14.00

Ulphus Horn. (York) on base. 115mm long (quite rare).   27.00

(The) Wallace Sword, inscribed: *The sword that seem'd fit for the Archangel to wield was light in his terrible hand.* 105mm long.   40.00

Watchman's Lamp, inscribed: *Model of 16th century Watchman's Lamp* and *Watchman what of the night.* 2 sizes: 80mm and 115mm. — 10.50

Witch's Cauldron with Macbeth verse *Double, double, toyle and trouble, fyer burns and cauldron bubble.* 45mm. — 5.50

Cauldron, unglazed. 72mm. — 3.00

Xit, The Historical Dwarf with inscription. Figure. 137mm. — 65.00

Traditional/National Souvenirs

John Bull, bust. 100mm. — 25.00

John Bull with Bulldog, standing figure on oval base. Union Jack waistcoat and black hat, dog has red, white and blue collar. 125mm. — 130.00

Blackpool Big Wheel. Can be found in pearl lustre. 2 sizes: 80mm. — 14.00
100mm. — 20.00

Bolton Trotter. 105mm long. — 10.50

Bolton Trotter, hand holding a trotter inscribed: *A good hold on a Bolton Trotter.* 110mm long. — 8.50

Pair of *Bowton Trotters.* 106mm long. — 12.50

Cheddar Cheese, inscribed: *Prime Cheddar Cheese.* Can be found in dark yellow, both whole and with slice out. 50mm. — 9.00
with colour. — 14.50

Cheshire Cheese, inscribed: *Prime Cheshire Cheese,* with slice cut out. 53mm. — 11.00

Cornish Pasty, inscribed: *This is a Pasty don't 'ee see. Will 'ee have a piece with me. There's more in the kitchen.* 100mm long. — 12.00

Cotton Shuttle, Model of. 93mm long. — 55.00

Davy Lamp. See Miner's Lamp.

Laxey Wheel. Some colouring. 92mm (not often found). — 55.00

Lincoln Imp moulded in relief on Lincoln Jack, inscribed: *The Imp, Lincoln Cathedral.* No. 156. 60mm. — 10.50

Kelly from the Isle of Man. 3 legged man, holding Manx Kipper in hand, fully coloured. 110mm. — 95.00

Manx Legs on base. 95mm. — 16.00

(The) *Ripon Horn* on rectangular base, inscribed. 3 sizes: 67mm. — 19.50
80mm. — 20.00

120mm. — 17.00

Ripon Hornblower, Model of with verse. 120mm. — 16.00

(The) Sheffield Grinding Stone. 80mm long (rare). — 65.00

York Minster, The Fiddler of. 132mm. — 75.00

Yorkshireman, standing figure holding tankard – often found not named. Found with inscription: *Take hod and sup lad* and verses. 126mm. — 30.00

Irish Cabin Trunk, more often found without this inscription. 58mm long. Inscribed add £8.00. — 10.50

Irish Colleen, on circular base with shamrocks. Can have some colouring. 127mm. — 82.50

Irishman, in black hat with yellow pig, standing on rectangular base, green edge, inscribed: *X miles to Belfast* and *Don't be radin milestones all the day Allana.* 90mm long. — 150.00

Irishman's Hat, green band, inscribed: *It's a long way to Tipperary.....* 45mm. — 20.00

Irish Harp, with green shamrocks. 90mm. — 10.00

Irish Harp, Model of surmounted by crown. Decorated with shamrocks. 105mm. — 12.50

Irish Jaunting Car, with horse and driver, some colouring. 130mm long (This is quite rare). — 110.00

Irish Spinning Wheel. Irish lady sitting by spinning wheel, partly coloured with shamrocks. Lustre. 95mm. — 56.50

Saint Patrick's Mitre. 70mm. — 27.00

Shamrock. 70mm. — 3.00

Bagpipes. 114mm long. — 19.50

Crown of Scotland, inscribed: *'The Crown of Scotland. Robert Bruce Crowned 1306, Buried Dunfermline 1329'.* 68mm. — 40.00

Gretna Green, Model of Blacksmiths Anvil. This anvil is often found without inscription or verse. 70mm. With verse add £3. — 7.50

Scotch Fisher Girl at Work, coloured fish in barrel. 118mm. — 43.50

Scotsman, standing figure, blue tam-o'-shanter with red bobble and brown walking stick. With verse *Just a wee deoch and doris.* 130mm. Harry Lauder. — 80.00

Tam-o'shanter (bonnet) with coloured sprig of heather. 80mm dia. 24.50

Thistle hat pin holder. 80mm. 9.00

Thistle moulded Teapot with lid and coloured thistle handle, can be found in lustre. 85mm. 16.00

Thistle Vase, can be found with verse.
2 sizes: 76mm and 115mm. 3.00

Prince of Wales Feathers. 95mm. 13.00

Pat's Hat and Dudeen, green ribbon and black dudeen. With *Tipperary* inscription on reverse. 45mm. 20.00

Welsh Hat, Model of, can be found with longest Welsh place name round brim. No. 283. for which add £2.50. 56mm. 5.00

Welsh Hat, with orange band. Can be found in lustre. 44mm. 5.00

Welsh Leek, Model of, can be found with coloured leaves. 93mm.
white leaves 3.50
green leaves 5.50
black leaves 7.50

Jenny Jones. Two varieties Welsh lady, standing figure with black hat and red and green shawl.
125mm no basket 75.00
147mm with brown basket 35.00

Welsh Spinning Wheel, two Welsh ladies with spinning wheel, coloured hats and shawls. 95mm. 50.00

Welsh Tea Party, three Welsh ladies taking tea, coloured hats and shawls, etc. 90mm. 40.00

Bermuda Sailing Ship, can be found with Bermuda crest. 127mm long. 25.00

Gondola. 127mm long. 19.50

Seaside Souvenirs

Bathing Machine, found inscribed: *Morning dip.*
3 sizes: 55mm. 7.50
65mm. 11.00
70mm. 11.00

Lifebelt. 105mm dia. 12.50

Lifeboat. Can be found inscribed: *Queensbury* for which £8.00 should be added. 113mm long. 12.50

Motor Boat on waves. 120mm long. 17.50

Motor Boat with Driver on waves. 120mm long. 22.50

Rowing Boat. 108mm long. 8.00

Trawler, inscribed on sail: *SM.* 115mm long. 22.50

Yacht with billowing sail.
120mm long, some colouring. 20.00
no colouring 15.50

Yacht, in full sail, found inscribed: *Saucy Sue.* 110mm long. 24.50

Fisherman on Rock, holding brown net, inscribed: *Son of the sea.* 117mm. 30.00

Fisherman's Creel. 70mm long. 5.50

Lifeboatman, bust with colouring on face. 80mm. 24.50

Lifeboatman in boat on sea, black clothing. (Lustre). 105mm. 29.50

Lighthouse inscribed: *Sailor Beware,* also found as hatpin holder. 140mm. 12.50

Barnsness Lighthouse, Dunbar 118mm. 75.00

Beachy Head Lighthouse, with inscription. 148mm. 9.00

Chapman Lighthouse. 103mm (rare). 47.50

Douglas Lighthouse. 128mm. 75.00

Eddystone Lighthouse, Model of. 138mm. 10.50

Flamborough Lighthouse, Model of. Can be found as a hatpin holder. 115mm. 25.00

Flamborough Head Fog Siren Building. 87mm long. 47.50

Lighthouse Hatpin Holder inscribed: *Girdleness.* 136mm. 20.00

Mumbles Lighthouse and Telegraph Office. 127mm. 47.50

Pharos Lighthouse Fleetwood, Model of. No. 409. 100mm (Identical model, so named and with same stock number can be found as a pepper pot). 10.00

Portland Lighthouse Pepper Pot, with orange band. 100mm. 19.50

Scarborough Lighthouse. 135mm. 65.00

Withernsea Lighthouse. 134mm. 12.00

Lighthouse Pepper Pot. 100mm. 7.00

Lighthouse Pepper Pot, with orange band. 8.00

Limpet Shell with 3 feet. 23mm. 5.00

Oyster Shell, found inscribed: *A Whitstable native.* add £3.00. 70mm. 3.50

Scallop Shell on 3 tiny feet. 80mm long. 3.00

Shell Inkwell, inscribed: *We are always glad to hear from you.* 95mm. 10.50

Whelk Shell, inscribed: *Listen to the sea.* 100mm long. 5.00

Shell pin tray. 3.00
Bathing Beauty, reclining figure
with green or blue cap, hand
shielding eyes. 110mm long. 150.00
Bathing Beauty, fully coloured
figure, lying on edge of lustre
shell dish, bathing costume in
several colours. Inscribed: *Washed
up by the tide.* 115mm.
white 40.00
coloured 100.00
Bathing Belle, yellow bow to cap,
sitting, hands together by face,
legs stretched out. 77mm. 160.00
Boy on Donkey, can be found
inscribed: *Gee up Neddy* or more
occasionally: *This beats going to
school.* Can be found without
base. Sometimes partly coloured.
98mm long.
if inscribed: *Gee up Neddy.* 100.00
if inscribed: *This beats going to
school.* 110.00
white 75.00
Mr. Punch, bust. 82mm. 35.00
Punch and Judy Booth, with
coloured Punch and Judy.
Inscribed: *Good Morning Mr
Punch.* 133mm. 110.00

Countryside
Bee Hive on square stand, with
coloured transfer of bee. 64mm. 15.50
Campfire, cauldron inside three
upright poles on triangular base.
122mm. 30.00
Campfire, (lustre). 115mm. 30.00
Milk Can with lid. 55mm. 3.00
Pinecone, upright, closed. 79mm. 5.50
Tree Trunk candleholder. 113mm. 6.00
Tree Trunk vase, the Great Oak in
Sherwood Forest, Nottingham.
115mm. 11.50

Animals
Ape (Orang-utan) holding orange,
brown face, 58mm. 23.00
Bear, looks like a Polar Bear,
inscribed: *Russian Bear.*
130mm long. 55.00
Bear and Ragged staff. 85mm. 38.50
Bear wearing glengarry with blue
and orange stripes, sitting on
base. 104mm. 47.50

Bull, inscribed: *King of the Herd,* or
much more rarely: *The Ox of
Oxford.* 103mm long. 82.50
Cat, angry, with back up, inscribed:
My word if you're not off or *The
Midnight Rambler.* add £10.00.
80mm. 12.50
Cat, Cheshire, inscribed: *The
Cheshire cat,* and *The smile that
won't come off.* 90mm. 12.50
Cat, crouching. 81mm. 16.00
Cat lying down, tail curled up
behind. 84mm long. 40.00
Cat, on piano. 95mm. 40.00
Cat (black), doing hand stand on
oblong base, back legs up in the
air. Inscribed: *Well what about it.*
115mm (rare). 85.00
Cat, Manx. 75mm. 20.00
Manx Cat, back up, coloured face.
Inscribed: *I am Rumpy* on
forehead. 60mm. 43.00
Cat, long necked, inscribed: *My
word* etc. 110mm. 12.50
Cat sitting, chubby and kittenish.
63mm. 12.50
Cat sitting on square cushion,
impressed: *Good Luck.* 80mm. 13.00
Cat sitting, with red bow, salt pot or
pepper pot. 70mm. 13.00
Cat sitting, wearing black topper
with shamrock, bow tie can be
found coloured red or green.
Also found in lustre. 88mm. 16.00
Cat sitting, with blue bow (bow
sometimes left uncoloured)
56mm. 12.00
Cat sitting, with Swastika round
neck. 59mm. 10.00
This cat can also be found on a
pouffe and inscribed: *Good Luck.*
85mm. 14.50

Black Cat, small.
Can be found with accompanying
model coloured red or yellow, for
which £20.00 should be added.
Found on the following:
Armchair (upholstered) with green
swastika and red horseshoe on
arms, (lustre), inscribed: *Jolly good
luck.* 75mm. 26.00
(Old) Armchair with solid arms.
90mm. 26.00
Ashtray, circular, can be found with
transfer of cigarette, inscribed:
Who burnt the cloth. 110mm dia. 47.50

Ashtray, club shaped, lustre. 90mm long.	26.00
Ashtray, diamond shaped, lustre. 95mm long (It seems very likely that small black cats will be found on heart and spade shaped ashtrays as well and that all four were made in white and lustre.	26.00
Ashtray, horseshoe-shaped. 105mm long.	27.50
Chair. 90mm.	26.00
Dish, crinkle edge. 83mm dia.	26.00
Horseshoe ashtray, inscribed: *Jolly good luck*. 105mm long.	26.00
with Siamese black cat	25.50
with black kitten with red bow	20.00
Piano. 95mm.	75.00
Pillar Box. Inscribed: *Good luck*. 110mm.	65.00
Rectangular Box, inscribed: *Good Luck*. 90mm long.	26.00
Rocking Chair, lustre. 100mm.	35.00
Sofa. Inscribed: *Jolly good luck*. 80mm.	30.00
Trinket box, inscribed: *Trinkets*. 93mm long.	26.00
Trinket Box, inscribed: *Hairpins*. 57mm long.	26.00

Black Cat, large:

Found on the following:	
Oval base with coloured Swastika and horseshoe. Inscribed: *Good luck*, Base can be found in mother-of-pearl or blue lustre.	
2 sizes: 64mm.	25.00
85mm.	30.00
Hatbox, oval, with coloured swastika and horseshoe. Inscribed: *Good Luck*.	26.00
Pouffe, the cat's bow is found blue instead of usual red. Inscribed: *Good luck*. 90mm.	24.00
Black Cat and Kitten on ashtray with match holder. Inscribed: *Don't scratch me, scratch mother*. Can be in maroon lustre. 70mm.	40.00
Chimpanzee. 84mm.	19.00
Doe on oval stand. 118mm.	75.00
Bulldog, sitting, inscribed: *Bill Sykes dog*. 95mm long.	20.00
Bulldog, sitting, thin faced. Inscribed: *Model of Bill Sykes dog* and sometimes found also	14.50

inscribed: *My word if your're not off*. 51mm.	19.50
Bulldog, standing, inscribed: *My word if you're not off*; can be found inscribed: *Slow to start, but what a hold*. Inscribed add £8.00. 120mm long.	15.00
Dog (French Bulldog), sitting with pricked-up ears and blue eyes. 57mm.	12.50
Dog, Staffordshire Bull Terrier, inscribed: *My word if you're not off*. 100mm.	20.00
Dog, standing Collie. Inscribed: *Scotch Collie*. 110mm long.	40.00
Dog playing banjo, inscribed: *Some Band*. 83mm.	31.50
Bulldog looking out of kennel, inscribed: *The Black Watch*. Dog's head is coloured black. 90mm.	19.50
Dog (Puppy) in slipper. Puppy coloured brown. 100mm long.	30.00
Dog (Puppy) sitting with one ear raised. Can be found painted blue and in lustre, add £10.00. 83mm.	9.00
With black spots.	14.00
This puppy can be found on a hand mirror (silvered) inscribed: *Me twice*. 105mm long.	33.50
Dog, Scottie, begging, pink ears and red collar. Can be found coloured red, add £10.00, or in lustre. 74mm.	24.00
Dog, Scottie, begging, wearing a glengarry, some colouring. 105mm.	12.50
Can be found on thistle base. 105mm.	35.00
Dog, Scottie, sitting, wearing a tartan or orange tam-o'shanter with orange bobble. Also found in lustre. Add £6 for orange tam-o'shanter.	
2 sizes: 60mm.	11.00
80mm.	11.00
Dog, Black Scottie, wearing blue and orange tam-o'shanter on horseshoe tray inscribed *Jolly Good Luck*. 72mm high, 110mm long.	55.00
Dog, Scottish Terrier, standing with tail in the air. May be found inscribed: *As old Mrs Terrier said to her pup in all lifes adversities keep your tail up*. 100mm long.	19.50

Dog, Scottish Terrier. 120mm long. 20.00
Dog, standing, impressed on collar:
Caesar and inscribed: *I am the
Kings dog*. Some colouring.
106mm long. 40.00
Donkey, inscribed: *Gee up Neddy*.
110mm long. 40.00
Elephant, walking. 51mm high,
75mm long. 30.00
Elephant with raised trunk.
51mm high, 80mm long. 24.00
Fawn. 70mm. 30.00
Field Mouse, on base. 54mm. 16.00
Can be found fully coloured. 40.00
Fish (Salmon), 112mm long. 7.50
Fish ashtray, inscribed: *A plaice for
the ashes*. 120mm long. 7.50
Flamborough Donkey, with orange
and blue rosettes. 88mm (rare). 82.50
Monkey, sitting hands to mouth.
90mm. 24.00
Monkey holding yellow coconut,
brown face. 58mm. 25.00
Pig sitting on haunches, inscribed:
*Wont be druv or You can push, you
can shuv but I'm hanged if I'll be
druv*. 60mm. 17.50
Pig, standing, found inscribed: *Wont
be druv*. Also found entirely
coloured blue. for which add
£10.00. 65mm long. 12.50
Pig, very fat, standing, inscribed:
You can Push or You.....
85mm long. 15.00
Pig, fat and standing, found
inscribed: *Wont be druv*.
80mm long. 14.50
Pig, standing, fat, found inscribed:
You can push, etc. or *I'm the fellow
who pays the rent*. for which add
£20.00. 94mm long. 12.50
Pig, standing. 48mm. 12.50
Pig, sitting, wearing coloured
German Pickelhaube and with
Iron Cross on left breast.
Pepper Pot. Reg. No. 642626.
90mm. Very rare. 160.00
Piglet, standing. 70mm long. 10.00
Inscribed: *Wunt be druv*. 12.50
Rabbit, crouching with pricked ears.
65mm long. 8.50
Shetland Pony.
2 sizes: 138mm long. 35.00
150mm long. 35.00
Stag with large antlers on oval
stand. 146mm. Two moulds exist,

one looking left and one looking
right, but less of them around,
possibly because the antlers are
fragile. Can be found in lustre. 110.00
Squirrel eating nut. 70mm. 30.00
Teddy Bear. 85mm. 19.50
Terrapin. 75mm long. 15.00
Three Wise Monkeys on wall.
Inscribed: *Speak no evil, see no evil,
hear no evil*. 90mm. 13.00
Three Wise Monkeys, coloured
brown, on rectangular base with
the same inscription as above.
87mm long. 19.50
Welsh Goat on rocky base,
inscribed: *Yr Afr Cymreig* (The
Welsh Goat). No. 391. 96mm. 55.00
Wembley Lion on ashtray base,
some colouring. 60mm (This was
the stylised lion symbol of the
British Empire Exhibition and is
usually found with BEE crest). 28.00

Birds (including Eggs)
Bluebirds, two, coloured blue and
yellow, on ashtray base.
88mm wide. 30.00
Egg, cracked open on top.
77mm long. 7.50
Hen roosting. 60mm long. 11.00
Hen and Cock, salt, pepper and
mustard pots, some colouring.
70mm each 10.00
Chicken hatching from egg.
64mm long. 9.00
Egg cracked open, lying on side.
74mm long. 5.00
Owl, baby. 66mm. 15.00
Owl, wearing black mortar board
with red tassel. (Models with
Irish crests can be found with red
mortar boards.) 75mm. 20.00
Models can also be found fully
coloured. 22.50
Owl cream jug. 88mm. 10.50
Owl, pepper pot. 92mm. 20.00
Owl, fully coloured, on oval ashtray
base. 70mm. 30.00
Parrot, inscribed: *Pretty Polly*.
74mm. 14.50
Peacock. Can be found coloured
blue, add £10.00. 63mm. 16.00
Stork with pink beak, standing on
one leg. Can be found in lustre.
110mm. 30.00

Swan.

3 sizes: 55mm.		6.50
63mm.		7.50
76mm long.		7.50

Smallest can be found coloured red (add £10.00).

Swan pepper pot. 53mm.	6.00
Swan posy bowl. 78mm.	6.50
Woodpecker, comic, some colouring on wings, beak and feet. 60mm.	20.00
Woodpecker, fully coloured. 65mm.	40.00

Carlton made a series of 5 birds on green bases and these are listed below:

Cock standing on green base, some colouring to head. 85mm long.	27.50
Can be found coloured blue.	35.00
Goose standing on green base, yellow beak. Also found in lustre. 72mm.	32.50
Duck standing up, rather comic, on green base. 102mm.	40.00
Duck airing wings, green base, yellow beak. 80mm.	32.50
Turkey on green base, coloured beak and feet. Can also be found in lustre and red or blue. 70mm.	40.00

Great War

Many Great War models are found with the following Victory inscriptions: *The Victory of Justice, Armistice of the Great War signed Nov 11th 1918* and *Victory of Justice. Peace signed at Versailles June 28th 1919.* These add interest but not value.

Munitions Worker, inscribed: *Doing her bit* and *Shells and more shells,* some colouring. 140mm.	125.00
Nurse with red cross, inscribed: *A friend in need.* 150mm.	82.50
Old Bill, standing figure of Bruce Bairnsfather's cartoon character. Inscribed: *Yours to a cinder.* 138mm.	75.00
Can be found coloured.	125.00
Sailor, bust. Inscribed: *The Handy Man* and *HMS Dreadnought.* 85mm.	35.00
Sailor standing to attention with blue trim. Inscribed: *Handy Man.* 135mm.	75.00
Scottish Soldier with rifle, wearing glengarry, some colouring. 148mm.	135.00

Scottish Soldier with bagpipes, wearing bearskin, some colouring. Very rare. 148mm.	350.00
Scottish Soldier with rifle, wearing bearskin (busby) Some colouring. Very rare. 153mm.	250.00
Soldier standing to attention, inscribed: *Are we downhearted No!* and with verse *Its a long way to Tipperary.* 153mm.	75.00
Soldier standing to attention with ammunition belt worn over shoulder. 125mm (rare).	170.00
Biplane with movable propellor. 145mm long.	95.00
Can be found with coloured roundel and tail or just coloured tail.	145.00
Also found with coloured roundel and tail with skids instead of wheels. Very rare. 140mm long.	285.00
Biplane, with coloured roundels and tailplane with movable propellor, can have two crests. 2 sizes: 140mm long.	220.00
165mm long.	220.00
Monoplane, rounded fuselage and movable prop. 134mm long.	65.00
Monoplane, square fuselage and movable prop. 140mm long.	65.00
Zeppelin or Airship with moulded Iron Cross on side; can be found with cross painted black, or left white and coloured roundels on nose. 118mm long.	55.00
with coloured RAF roundels.	65.00
or coloured French roundels.	75.00
British mine sweeper whose splendid work will live forever in the annals of British history. 115mm long.	47.50
Can be found inscribed: *HMS Gowan Lea, HMS Peggy* or *HMS Minesweeper.*	65.00
Can be found with 'SH' inscribed on sail.	
A very rare version exists inscribed: *HMD Indian Summer.*	95.00
Battleship. 120mm long, 38mm wide in middle, 3 funnels, 2 guns fore, 2 guns aft.	30.00
Battleship. 34mm wide in middle. No large guns. 110mm long.	30.00
Battleship, 2 funnels, 4 guns fore, 4 guns aft. 160mm long. Named:	

HMS Canada,
HMS Australia,
HMS Marlborough   75.00
Battleship, 3 funnels, 4 guns fore, 2
guns aft. 160mm long. Named:
HMS Australia,
HMS Renown,
HMS Iron Duke,
HMS Princess Royal,
HMS War Spite,
HMS Inflexible.   75.00
Not named.   55.00
Battleship, 3 funnels, 2 guns fore, 4
guns aft. 170mm long. Named:
HMS Lion,
HMS Tiger.   75.00
Battleship, 3 funnels, 4 guns fore, 2
guns midships, 2 guns aft. 167mm
long. Named:
HMS Lion,
HMS Queen Elizabeth.   65.00
All the above can be found with
the following Victory inscription
only: Great War 1914-18. The
German Fleet surrendered 74
warships Nov 21st 1918.
Battleship, 3 funnels. Both bow and
stern rolled inwards. 115mm long.   30.00
Battleship with high prow. 140mm
long. Inscribed: HMS Humber,
Model of British Monitor.   55.00
Has also been found with same
Victory inscription as above and
not named.   45.00
Named.   55.00
Battleship, with high prow, two rear
guns pointing upwards, pinnacle
with bulbous base instead of
funnel. 144mm long. Scarce.   75.00
Can also be found with transfer
of 'HMS Lusitania' and inscribed:
The Lusitania sunk by German
submarine off the Irish coast May
7th 1915. Lives lost 1275, saved 703. 85.00
Battleship, wide with two funnels.
120mm long.   30.00
HM Hospital Ship Anglia, Model of
with 2 funnels, often found with
further detailed inscription:
Model of British Hospital Ship whose
voyage was disregarded on three
occasions by the German
Submarines. 165mm long. (Has
been found wrongly named as
HMS Tiger and as RMS Lusitania).   75.00

RMS Lusitania, 4 funnels. Found
with details of sinking: The
Lusitania was sunk by a German
Submarine May 7th 1915. Lives lost
1198, or the numerically incorrect
inscription: Sunk by German
Submarine off the Irish Coast, May
7th 1915. Lives lost 1275, Saved 703.
168mm long.   75.00
(Has been found wrongly named
as HMS Anglia).
British Submarine, Model of, blunt
nosed, often found without this
inscription but with E9 on side.
Submarines found unnamed are
found with the following
inscription: Great War 1914-18. 150
German U Boats surrendered Nov
20th 1918. With or without
pinnacle. 140mm long.   40.00
Submarine, pointed nose and fish tail,
inscribed: E9. 146mm long.
(Much rarer than blunt nosed
model).   43.00
British submarine, Model of, half-
submerged, inscribed: E9.
124mm long.   55.00
Ambulance with 3 red crosses and
WD on radiator. 100mm long.   35.00
Armoured Car with Rolls-Royce
type front. 120mm long.   200.00
Difficult to find in perfect
condition.
Armoured Car with 3 guns on
turret, inscribed: RNAS.
116mm long.   160.00
British Anti-Aircraft Motor, Model of,
inscribed: RNAS. 121mm long.   160.00
Tank with trailing steering wheels,
inscribed: HMLS Creme de
Menthe. 130mm long.   30.00
Also inscribed: The British Tank
successfully used against the
Germans, Combles, Sept 1916.   30.00
Tank with no steering wheels,
inscribed: HMLS.
4 sizes: 80mm long found with
           Tank Corps crest.   95.00
           95mm long.   60.00
           134mm long.   30.00
           156mm long.   40.00
134mm & 156mm sizes are
inscribed HMLS Creme-de-Menthe
and 130 and can be found with
Victory inscriptions. Also The

British Tank gave them hell at Marne 1918
and *Buy War Bonds. The British
Tank successfully used against the
Germans, Combles, Sept. 1916.*
The 134mm size can be found
with Tank Corps and Fearnaught
crests.   100.00
Tank Bank, as largest size tank above
but with slot for coins. Two sizes
of slot. Inscribed: *Buy War Bonds,*
and can be found with *Combles*
and *Marne* inscriptions.
156mm long.   55.00
HM Whippet Tank. 121mm long.   135.00
Italian Fiat Tank, not named.
100mm long. (Very rare).   400.00
Vickers Tank, not named. 126mm
long (rare). The latest model
manufactured, approx. 1928-32.   260.00
British Machine Gun, Model of. MG in
green wreaths on barrel. 2
moulds, one with open stand.
100mm long.   30.00
British Naval Gun, Model of. 88mm
long (very rare).   195.00
British Trench Mortar, Model of.
Mounted on steps and barrel at
an angle. 66mm.   19.50
Trench Mortar, not named, with
horizontal barrel. 60mm.   17.00
Field Gun, found inscribed: *French
75.*
3 sizes: 130mm long.   17.00
        148mm long.   17.00
        155mm long.   17.00
If named.   20.00
Field Gun with screen and sight-
hole, inscribed: *French 75.*
2 sizes: 115mm long.   20.00
        145mm long.   28.00
British 15" Shell. Model of. 90mm.   17.00
Cannon Shell, Model of. No. 606.
75mm.   7.50
Bullet. 80mm.   6.00
German Incendiary Bomb, Model of.
75mm.   25.00
British Hand Grenade. 83mm.   20.00
Floating Mine. Model of. 83mm.   55.00
British Searchlight, Model of.
Sometimes found inscribed: *The*   31.50
Zeppelin Finder. 68mm.   Inscribed 40.00
Capstan, Model of, with brown rope.
70mm.   11.50
Bandsman's Drum, mustard pot,
found in lustre. 45mm.   7.50
Australian Hat. 75mm long.   12.00

Inscribed: *Anzacs for ever.*   19.50
Colonial Hat, often found unnamed.
95mm dia.   10.50
Can be found inscribed: *Anzacs
for ever.*   20.00
If inscribed: *Colonial Hat.*   26.00
Forage Cap. 80mm long.   17.50
Glengarry with coloured thistle.
78mm long.   16.00
Glengarry with rosette. 93mm long.   40.00
Officer's Peaked Cap, coloured
band. 78mm long.   22.50
Territorials Hat, coloured hat band.
85mm dia.   30.00
Can be found with solid base.   40.00
Pair of folded blankets, orange &
black border, or red and blue
stripes. 56mm long.   125.00
Kitbag, open neck, with verse.
72mm.   19.50
Kitbag, closed neck, with verse.
72mm.   19.50
Kitbag as Pepper Pot. 72mm.   19.50
Bell Tent. 66mm. Can be found   16.00
named *Tommies Bungalow.* 70mm.   20.00
Blighty. Map of England and Wales,
with verse *Take me back to dear Old
Blighty.* 115mm.   65.00
Kitchen Range, with black kettle but
no teapot. Inscribed: *Keep the
home fires burning till the boys come
home.* 70mm.   16.00
Kitchen Range with black kettle and
brown teapot. Inscribed: *We've
kept the home fires burning till the
boys came home.*
2 sizes: 70mm.   16.00
        85mm long.   16.00
*Shrapnel Villa, Tommies Dugout
somewhere in France.* (From Bruce
Bairnsfather's cartoons).
83mm long.   43.00
Scarborough Lighthouse, Model of,
with rectanglar building showing
shell holes from Great War. Can
be found with blackened holes.
98mm. (Rare).   80.00
Blackpool War Memorial. 130mm.   56.50
Brighton War Memorial. 105mm long.
(Building, not a statue).   100.00
Cenotaph, inscribed: *The Glorious
Dead* with 2 green wreaths.
3 sizes: 105mm.   6.00
        110mm.   7.00
        146mm.   8.00

Clacton-on-Sea War Memorial.
Unglazed angel on glazed base.
148mm. 47.50
Cranbrook War Memorial. 140mm. 135.00
Douglas War Memorial. Can be
found with lustre finish. 160mm. 85.00
Dunbar War Memorial. 123mm. 110.00
Edith Cavell, statue, inscribed:
Brussels dawn October 12th 1915.
Sacrifice. Humanity. (Lustre).
2 sizes: 140mm. 23.00
163mm. 23.00
Elgin War Memorial. 165mm. 120.00
Feltwell War Memorial. 140mm. 110.00
Florence Nightingale, 1820-1910 The
Lady of the Lamp. Parian top.
175mm. 40.00
High Wycombe War Memorial, not
named. 148mm. 160.00
Northallerton War Memorial.
115mm. 82.50
Ripon War Memorial, found with
Ripon Hornblower inscription.
115mm. 75.00
Tunbridge Wells War Memorial,
soldier unglazed on glazed plinth
carrying a rifle with fixed
bayonet. With inscription: *Our*
Glorious Dead 1914-18. Honour,
Gratitude, Praise. 170mm. 120.00
Ulverston War Memorial. 146mm. 175.00

Home/Nostalgic
Anvil on tree stump base. 76mm. 6.50
Baby lying on side holding paint pot
with dirty cheeks. Sometimes
inscribed: *Mothers Darling.* Some
colouring. 125mm long. 125.00
Baby, similar to one above, with no
paint pot, holding dress. *Mother*
Darling. 136mm long. 145.00
Basket of coloured fruit. (Lustre).
88mm. (Almost Art Deco). 20.00
Bellows. 95mm. 7.50
Book with lock. 66mm. 6.50
Cigarettes, matches and ash, container
with cigarette on lid. 85mm long. 15.50
Clock, shaped. 83mm. 16.00
Coal Hod. 85mm. 4.00
Coal Hod, solid. 42mm. 12.50
Coal Scuttle. 60mm. 4.00
Dewsbury blankets, pair of. *Let*
Dewsbury blankets keep the world
warm. 35mm. 110.00
Dog Kennel. 62mm. 4.50

Dust Pan. 94mm long. 8.00
Inscribed: *Who said dust.* 10.50
Fireplace, with a kettle and teapot in
the hearth, and dogs and clock on
the mantelpiece. (Lustre). Found
inscribed: *By my Ain Fireside* or
East, West, Home is best. 85mm. 27.50
Fireplace with clock and dogs on
mantelpiece, cauldron on fire and
black cat by side. Inscribed as
above. 80mm. 20.00
Flat Iron, can be found in lustre.
2 sizes: 60mm. 12.50
77mm. 12.50
Frying Pan. Rd. No. 537474.
110mm long. 17.00
Garden Trug. 78mm long. 16.50
Girl, Toddler, with outstretched
arms on circular plinth, inscribed:
Diddle'ums. Some colouring to
face and bonnet. 130mm. 80.00
Grandfather Clock, Model of,
inscribed: *Make Use of Time.....*
No. 389.
2 sizes: 105mm. 10.50
135mm. 13.00
Grandfather Clock, inscribed: *Gude*
morn.
3 sizes: 88mm. 16.00
105mm and 135mm. 16.00
Kettle, fixed lid, inscribed: *Polly put*
the kettle on, we'll have some tea.
80mm. 18.00
Lantern, inscribed: *Watchman what*
of the night? 83mm. 10.50
(The) Old Armchair, solid arms, with
verse or inscribed: *Jolly Good*
Luck. 88mm. 7.50
(The) Old armchair, open 'barley
twist' arms, with verse. 120mm. 12.50
Pillar Box GVR, found inscribed: *If*
you haven't time to post a line here's
the pillar box. 73mm. 10.50
inscribed 16.00
Pillar Box *ERVII.* 72mm. 19.00
Rocking Chair. 98mm. 19.50
Saucepan with lid. 100mm long. 10.50
Shaving Mug. 58mm. 5.50
Sofa. 90mm long, 64mm high.
(Lustre). 19.50
Spinning Wheel, found inscribed:
Model of ye olde spinning wheel or
more rarely: *The exact model of 14th*
Century spinning wheel. 74mm. 20.00
Stool, three-legged. 40mm. 5.50

Sundial, shaped. 80mm.	7.50
Sundial, bulbous. 76mm.	5.50
Sundial, round, inscribed: *Model of ye olde English sundial*, and *What' o'clock: lifes but a walking shadow.* No. 525.	
3 sizes: 120mm.	12.50
130mm.	13.00
140mm.	16.00
Sundial, square. Inscribed: *Let others tell of storms & showers, I'll only count the sunny hours.* 86mm.	7.50
Time Glass. 60mm.	10.00
Thimble. 40mm.	25.00
Trug or wooden basket. 78mm long.	14.50
Valise (or travelling case) with 2 straps.	
2 sizes: 55mm.	4.00
70mm long.	6.00
Village Water Pump, 2 varieties:	
Round. 88mm.	16.00
Square. 100mm.	16.00
Warming Pan, inscribed: *Sally warm the bed.* No. 392. 127mm long.	13.00
Water Pump, wooden. 80mm.	7.50

Comic/Novelty

Altar Inkwell with two orange and black candle holders and Buddha-like figure as cover for inkwell. Rare complete. Can be found inscribed: *Sox Kik the god of luck and cheerfulness.* Add £10.00 if inscribed. (Lustre). 90mm long.	40.00
Ashtray, with cigarette transfer, inscribed: *Who burnt the cloth?* 110mm dia.	23.00
Baby Girl Handbell, with metal clapper. 100mm.	19.50
Beaver, man with very long beard on base, some colouring. 120mm.	95.00
Billiken, flat faced grotesque type. 63mm.	5.00
Billiken sitting on high backed chair with thumbs raised, inscribed: *Thumbs up.* 84mm.	11.00
Billiken without chair. 84mm.	7.50
Black Girl in hip bath, inscribed: *I'se making ink.* Can be lustre. 80mm long.	56.50
Black Girl in hip bath, different from above, with high back, same inscription. 85mm long.	56.50
White.	40.00
Choir Boy Handbell. 88mm.	19.50

Clown, bust, inscribed: *Put me amongst the girls.* Some colouring. 75mm.	25.00
Humpty Dumpty: see sports.	
I'm forever blowing bubbles. Pears advert Blue Boy blowing bubbles. Clothes blue, bubble and bowl lustre. Can be found all in lustre. 110mm.	75.00
Ye Jester awake, Ye jester asleep double faced bust.	
2 sizes: 70mm.	19.50
84mm.	25.00
(Only larger size found inscribed)	
John Citizen, man carrying sack inscribed: *Housing, unemployment, taxes.* Hat and face coloured.	
95mm.	125.00
white.	82.50
Negro Minstrel, bust, verse by Eugene Stratton. 85mm.	
white.	16.00
coloured face.	34.50
Oval Rich Tea, brown biscuit on white base.	26.00
Policeman hailing: *From.....* 138mm.	25.00
Policeman with raised hand, inscribed: *A policeman's lot is not a happy one.* 140mm.	56.50
Sack of Meal with mouse peeping out. Mouse can be coloured grey. 75mm.	19.50
Suffragette Handbell inscribed: *Votes for Women* and *She shall have Votes.* 100mm.	35.00
Truck of Coal, *Black diamonds from...* or *Black Diamonds* rarely inscribed *Brought down from Sunderland,* add £10.00. Can be found in lustre. 2 sizes:	
60mm long, 95mm long	25.00
Weighing Machine inscribed: *Try your weight.* 120mm.	26.00
Yes we have no bananas, oval dish with yellow bananas. 115mm. Can be found in lustre.	13.00

Cartoon/Comedy Characters

Jackie Coogan, coloured figure of boy film star, attached to white tree trunk, ink well with lid. 73mm.	47.50
Harry Lauder, bust, with red bobble on hat and coloured thistle.	
80mm.	30.00
All white.	26.00

Ally Sloper, bust, inscribed: *Vote for Sloper etc.* Some colouring.

2 sizes: 85mm.	40.00
100mm.	56.50

Bonzo Dog, standing upright, not named. Red tongue. 110mm.   30.00

Bonzo Dog, with fly on his tail. Inscribed: *When you are on to a good thing stick to it.* Can be found unnamed.   115.00

Felix the Cat on oval base, inscribed: *Felix kept on walking.* Coloured Felix, swastika and horseshoe on base. 75mm.   150.00

Felix the Cat on lustre or rust armchair, with Felix inscription.

Coloured Felix. 75mm.	82.50
White Felix.	56.50

Felix the Cat on ashtrays (various shapes).   75.00

Felix the Cat on (lustre) pillar box, with Felix inscription. Coloured Felix. 115mm.   82.50

Felix the Cat on lustre sofa, with Felix inscription. Coloured Felix. 90mm long.   82.50

Felix the Cat on *Hatpins* box and lid. 80mm long.   56.50

Felix the Cat on Trinket box, with Felix inscription.

Coloured Felix. 93mm long.	85.00
White Felix.	56.50

Felix the Cat on rectangular base, a much larger and well modelled Felix than the above, with Felix inscription. 82mm (very rare).

Coloured Felix.	150.00
White Felix.	82.50

Winkie the Gladeye Bird, some colouring. 68mm.   16.00

Woody Woodpecker, fully coloured. 63mm.   40.00

Alcohol

Beaker, inscribed: *Tak a Thimblefull.* No. 153. 45mm.   4.00

Beer barrel on stilts. XXX in red on sides. 57mm.   5.50

Bottle with solid top. 92mm.   6.50

Bottle with cork. 2 sizes:

70mm and 94mm.	7.50
Can be found with Bass sign on reverse and *Bass & Co.'s. Pale Ale.*	11.00

Drunkard leaning on lamp-post, fully coloured on ashtray. Inscribed: *Show me the way to go home* and *Swat a night Boys Hic, Snow Usse Hic.* (Lustre.) 112mm.   65.00

Gin bottle, inscribed: *Have a drop of gin old dear.* 95mm.   20.00

Hand holding beaker, inscribed: *Good health.* Some colouring. 88mm long.   14.50

Hip Flask.   7.50

Man sitting with beer barrel and glass, some colouring. (Lustre.) Inscribed: *Beer Hic Beer Hic Glorious Beer Hic.* 70mm.   55.00

Monk holding beaker, with verse: *A Jovial Monk am I.* 113mm. Can be found with black cap, add £3.00.   16.00

Mr. Pussyfoot, holding umbrella with one foot on bottle of Scotch, inscribed: *No home in Scotland.* 135mm.   30.00
(Mr. Pussyfoot was an American Prohibitionist).

Soda Syphon. 100mm.   12.50

Thistle Vase. *Just a wee deoch and doris, just a wee drap thats a'.* 50mm.   4.00

Toby Jug, with verse: *No tongue can tell. No heart can sing How I love a drop of drink.* Can be found inscribed: *This jug is an exact copy in miniature of the old Toby jug.*

No. 413. 75mm.	12.50
Can be found coloured.	16.00

Whisky Bowl, inscribed *Scuab* and *As'i* coloured cross and thistles on handles. 123mm dia.   7.50

Sport/Pastimes

Five pieces have been found labelled British Sports Series. The ashtrays labelled in this way have been listed separately.

British Sports Series

Cricketer holding bat, with stumps, on ashtray base. Inscribed: *Play M.C.C. The home of cricket formed 1787.* Coloured. Rd. No. 685380. 105mm.   130.00

Games Spinner and Match Holder on shield ashtray, inscribed: *Put and take: yer ash: a match.* 90mm long.   56.50

Goal with Keeper and Ball on ashtray,
   inscribed: *League Football first
   played 1888*. Some colouring.
   100mm long.   150.00
Golfer standing with Club on ashtray.
   94mm.   75.00
   Coloured version.·   85.00
Humpty, Dumpty sat on a Wall.
   Humpty on wall on ashtray, some
   colouring. With inkwell inset.
   97mm.   160.00
Tennis player holding Racquet aloft
   in front of net. Inscribed: *40 Love*.
   Some colouring.
   Regd. No. 684704. 83mm.   145.00

Other Sporting Items
Cricket Bag. 105mm long.   12.50
Cricket Bat. 118mm long.   75.00
Cricketer carrying bat, flat figurine
   on green base. Some colouring.
   115mm (rare).   130.00
Curling stone, inscribed: *Soop-up*.
   61mm dia.   14.50
F.A. Cup., can be found in yellow.
   100mm.   14.00
   named   26.00
Footballer with football, arms
   outstretched, some colouring.
   110mm.   85.00
Golf Ball, can be found inscribed: 7.50
   *The ancient game of golf was first
   played in 1448*. 50mm. Add £5.00.
Golf Club, can be found inscribed:
   Fore, or as above or both. 75mm.   19.00
Jockey standing on base, silks can
   be blue/black, yellow/blue, red/
   black, green/black or orange/
   black. 121mm.   110.00
Jockey on Racehorse, rectangular
   base, silks can be blue/green,
   blue/brown, green/yellow or
   red/yellow. Very occasionally the
   horse is found painted black. Can
   also be found with inscription:
   for example: *Ala Baculia: St Leger
   first run 1876*. 110mm long.   75.00
Jockey on Racehorse (comical) with
   real hair tail (often missing) on
   ashtray base, some colouring.
   Inscribed: *Horsey keep your tail up*.
   102mm.   30.00
Jockey on racehorse wearing
   coloured silks on horseshoe base.
   Inscribed: *Humorist winner of the
   Derby 1881 Donoghue Cup.*   105.00

Racehorse on oval base.
   2 sizes: 118mm long.   125.00
            140mm long.   50.00
Roller Skate. 120mm long.   40.00
Tennis Racquet. 140mm long.   19.50
Trophy. (Lustre). 130mm.   17.50

Musical Instruments
Upright Piano, open coloured
   keyboard, Dolphin feet.
   64mm high, 90mm long.
   Marked keyboard.   20.00
   Plain keyboard.   19.00

Transport
Charabanc, inscribed: *Over the hills
   and far away*. 'DN999' on radiator.
   148mm long. Found in lustre.   41.50
Double Decker Bus, with driver and
   outside staircase, impressed:
   *Putney-Charing Cross: Globe
   Theatre John Bull Thursday:
   General*. 'DN999' on radiator.
   126mm long.   170.00
Luggage Trolley, inscribed: *Luggage
   in Advance* and/or *LMS Railway to
   Timbucktoo*. Can be found in
   lustre.
   2 sizes: 75mm long.   40.00
            85mm long.   45.00
Motorbike and sidecar with rider.
   112mm long.   75.00
Motorscooter on oval base.
   115mm long.   47.50
Open Sports Car, 'DN999' on
   radiator. 106mm long.   40.00
Punt, with two women, some
   colouring. 113mm long.   75.00
Saloon Car, 'DN999' on radiator.
   130mm long.   65.00
Stephenson Locomotive, with
   detailed inscription: *Locomotion
   1825. This Engine was built by Geo.
   Stephenson and Son, and was used
   at the opening of the S. and D. Rly.
   Sept 27th 1825*. 88mm.   125.00
Locomotive. 120mm long.   115.00

Modern Equipment
Gramophone in Cabinet, black
   record on turntable, inscribed:
   Music hath charms. Found in
   lustre. 92mm. Can be found
   coloured blue, add £10.00.   75.00
Gramophone, square with Horn,
   inscribed: *HMV* or *His Masters*

Voice, with transfer of 'HMV' dog and notes of music. 96mm. — 40.00
If lustre add £6.00.

Gramophone with dog listening to horn, on oval base. Inscribed: *His Masters Voice.* Some colouring. 88mm long. Very rarely found in lustre. — 70.00

National cash register with '£.s.d.' Found unnamed but with '£.s.d.' (lustre). 70mm. — 20.00
Plain. — 17.00

Radio Operator, inscribed: *Listening in.* Some colouring. 85mm. — 95.00

Radio Operator with microphone, inscribed: *Listening in.* Some colouring. 85mm. — 95.00

Radio Operator with horn, inscribed: *Listening in.* Some colouring. 85mm. — 110.00

Telephone, stick type, inscribed: *Hello, Hello* or rarely *All alone by the telephone.* 115mm. — 23.00

Treadle sewing machine, found inscribed: *Singer.* 80mm. — 24.00

Footwear
Boot.
2 sizes: 50mm. — 5.50
72mm long. — 6.50
Tall laced Boot. 85mm. Particularly fine. — 14.00
Lancashire Clog with verse: *There's many a factory lass wi' clogs on her feet.* 100mm long. — 7.50
Riding Boot. 65mm. — 16.00
Boot pin box. — 8.50
Sabot. 100mm long. — 7.50
Slipper wall pocket. 105mm long. — 6.50

Hats
Bishop's Mitre. 70mm. — 13.00
Straw Boater Hat, red/black band. 104mm long. — 19.00
Boy Scouts Hat. 95mm dia. — 20.00
Top Hat. 40mm. — 5.50

Miniature Domestic
Barrel Jug. 47mm. — 3.00
Butter Dish & lid, buttercup knob. 55mm. — 15.00
Cake Plate on stem. 50mm. — 3.50
Cheese Dish (one piece). 45mm. — 10.50
Cheese Dish, fluted with cover. 50mm. — 8.50

Coffee Pot with lid. No. 271. 78mm. — 7.50
Kettle. 60mm. — 7.50
Tea set on tray. Tray 115mm long. — 22.50
Teapot with lid. 40mm. — 5.50
Teapot with lid. 50mm. — 5.50
Teapot with lid. 65mm. — 8.50
Teapot with lid with swan shaped handle. 70mm. — 14.50
Can be found inscribed *Polly put the kettle on.* — 16.00
Thistle Tea Pot with lid, lustre. 76mm. — 16.00

Carlton also made a whole range of small vases, pin or ashtrays, pill boxes and trinket boxes in club, diamond, heart and spade shapes. They can be found with crest or transfer views. Very few articles for domestic use, plates, cups etc. have been found but this is probably because they were used and broken.
Price range: — 2.00 to 8.00.

Domestic
Candleholder. 118mm. — 3.00
Candlesnuffer. 65mm. — 3.00
Dice Pin Box and lid, with black spots. 50mm square. — 26.00
Hair Pins rectangular box and lid. 90mm long. — 7.50
Hair Tidy and lid with *Pins* tray. (Lustre). 85mm. — 7.50
Hatpin Holder in shape of a thistle on leaves. 80mm. — 10.50
Hatpin Holder, square, scalloped base. 97mm. — 12.50
Horse's Hoof Inkwell with lid. Rd. No. 538564. 95mm long. — 12.50
Horse's Hoof Pin Box and lid. 98mm long. — 4.00
Mustard Pot, EPNS rim. 58mm. — 5.50
Mustard Pot with lid. 60mm. — 5.00
Preserve Pot with coloured pear and two leaves on lid. Inscribed: *Preserve.* (Lustre). 85mm. — 10.50
Sugar Sifter, EPNS rim, 147mm. — 8.50

Miscellaneous
Hand holding crinkle topped flower vase (not a tulip as usually found). 85mm. — 5.50
Fully coloured. — 14.50
Hand bell with porcelain clapper. 100mm. — 7.50

Horseshoe. 115mm. 3.00

Horseshoe photo frame. Inscribed:
The Best of Luck. 125mm. 13.50

Jug. Inscribed: *Measure for Measure.*
45mm. 6.50

Carmen China

Trademark used for E.A. Green, Rugby by
J.A. Robinson & Sons Ltd, Arcadian
Works, Stoke-on-Trent (Usual trademark:
Arcadian).

For details of this china and manufacturer
see Arcadian China.

Although most models and 'smalls' found
with this mark have a Rugby crest, other
English crests are also discovered. E.G.
Green, whose name often appears below
the Carmen mark, was either a wholesaler,
or more probably J.A. Robinson used this
mark to supply other buyers.

All known models indicate that this mark
was not used after the Great War. No
devices other than crests have been
recorded. Stock numbers where used
would be the same as Arcadian models.

Carmen Models
Ancient Artefacts
Model of Old Butter Pot. 44mm. 4.00
Model of Vase found near Winchelsea.
75mm. 3.00

Monuments
*Tom Hughes Monument, Rugby
School.* 140mm. 30.00

Seaside Souvenirs
Bathing Machine 'Morning Dip
7 a.m.'. 65mm. 7.50
Eddystone Lighthouse. 125mm. 7.50
Lighthouse, *Sailor Beware.* 140mm. 12.50
Scallop Shell on 3 tiny feet.
90mm long. 3.50

Animals
Dog, Labrador Puppy, inscribed:
Daddy wouldn't buy me a bow-wow.
75mm.   10.00
Dog, Scottish Terrier. 66mm long.   13.00
Hare. 75mm long.   15.00
Shetland Pony. 125mm long.   30.00
Tortoise. 69mm long.   9.00

Birds (including Eggs)
Egg with flat base. 44mm.   4.00
Hen roosting. 54mm.   7.50

Great War
Model of Tommy on Sentry Duty.
105mm.   82.50
Standing Sailor, hands on hips.
125mm.   80.00
Standing Nurse *Soldiers Friend.*
126mm.   75.00
Monoplane. 114mm long.   65.00
Battleship, 3 funnels and tiny gun
fore and aft. 100mm long.   17.50
Torpedo Boat Destroyer, not named.
108mm long.   23.00
Jack Johnson. Shell. 90mm.   8.50
Tommy's Hut. 104mm long.   47.50
Bomb dropped from Zeppelin.
80mm.   17.00
Bandsman's Drum. 53mm.   10.50
Officers Peaked Cap with coloured
badge and hatband. 65mm dia.   15.50

Home/Nostalgic
Chair, high-backed. 90mm.   6.50
Grandfather Clock, with
inscription: *Make use of Time.*
110mm.   12.00

Comic/Novelty
Clown, bust, inscribed: *Put me
amongst the girls.* 90mm.   25.50

Sport/Pastimes
Golf Ball with inscription. 45mm.   12.50

Musical Instruments
Banjo. 150mm long.   10.50

Footwear
Slipper. 105mm long.   7.50

Domestic
Candlesnuffer, conical. 65mm.   3.50
Circular Match Holder. 53mm.   5.50

Cascade China

Trademark used for a retailer on china manufactured probably by Taylor & Kent Ltd. Florence Works, Longton (Usual trademark Florentine)

Cascade Model
Home/Nostalgia
Book. No.72. 57mm.   6.50
Vase. 57mm. (Crest of Castleford).   2.50

Cauldon China

'CAULDON IVORINE' or 'CAULDON PARIAN CHINA' may also be impressed or printed.

Trademark used by Cauldon Ltd, Stoke-on-Trent.

For details of the history of this firm see Arcadian China.

As Harold Taylor Robinson amalgamated most of his concerns and restyled them Cauldon Potteries Ltd in 1920, this mark can be found impressed or printed on china which also carries any other mark he was entitled to use, these include Arcadian, Goss and Willow. The Cauldon mark was mainly used on domestic china only one of which has been found with a crest, but plates, cups and saucers and other items were obviously overstamped with other marks and crests applied to fill orders from 1920 onwards.

One 'Cauldon' model with a crest has been recorded in several sizes. This is a model of the Queen's Doll's House, which is most appropriate as Cauldon had been commissioned to produce a miniature breakfast set for the house, each tiny piece having a royal monogram. The same model of the Doll's House can be found marked Arcadian.

Late transfer decorations found on china marked Arcadian can also be found on Cauldon domestic wares, which include small floral designs and the coloured tropical birds.

Cauldon Models
Buildings – White

Queen's Doll's House, found both glazed and unglazed.

5 sizes:	75mm (also with lid).	30.00
	95mm (also with lid).	40.00
	118mm.	47.50
	125mm.	52.50
	146mm.	57.50

Full inscriptions can be found on the base of these models sometimes with Wembley arms outpressed.

Domestic

Posy Ring in beige. 115mm wide.	5.00
Tea Plate. 155mm dia.	2.00

Celtic Porcelain

Ceramic China

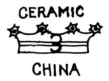

Trademark used by the Nautilus Porcelain Co., Possil Pottery, Glasgow.

Only four pieces of china have been recorded carrying this mark and these have Scottish crests. Some form of numbering system appears on the base, but these could well be paintresses marks. (The log is marked '11'.) Nothing more can be recorded about this obscure mark until more items are found.

Celtic Models
Countryside
Log Vase. 32mm.   9.00

Alcohol
Carboy.   9.00

Hats
Top Hat match holder & striker.   11.00

There is also a range of crested
   small vases.   3.00

Trademark used by an unknown British manufacturer, possibly the Ceramic Art Co. (1905) Ltd., Crown Pottery, Stoke. This manufacturer also produced a few items for a Chorley retailer, called Sandifords. (See Sandifords Ceramic China entry). The quality is similar to that of Royal Vale or Royal Ivory. Only a few smalls have been found so far, and these have the crests of St. Andrews, Dunkeld and Stornoway.

£3.00 upwards.

Challenge China

Trademark used by an unknown manufacturer (but probably Taylor & Kent Ltd)
for a retailer possibly in the Birmingham
area.

Only two pieces known –
Jug. 83mm with Birmingham crest.   4.50
Lancashire Clog. 85mm long.   6.50

Chelson China

1914-1919

Trademark used by New Chelsea Porcelain
Co. (Ltd), Bagnall Street, Longton.
This firm is not known to have produced
crested china as such, but they did
manufacture Great War commemoratives
on small domestic pieces and 'smalls'. The
commemorative takes the form of a black
transfer print of HMS Lion, with four
coloured flags of the Allies and inscribed:
For Honour and Liberty. Some items carry
the further inscription: *God Save the King.*
Peace commemoratives were also made.
These have a transfer print of Britannia,
with the flags of the Allies and the
inscription: *Peace 1914-1919 Liberty Truth
Justice Honour.* Some bird transfers, very
similar to those used in the Arcadian
range, have been recorded.

Value from £5.00 upwards.

Christop China

No details of mark available.

Trademark used by an unknown manufacturer for a retailer in the Colonies. Manufacturer possibly Sampson Hancock (and Sons), Bridge Works, Stoke (usual mark Corona) as this firm used the circle and buckle device in several of its trademarks.

This mark has only been found on one small flat sided vase, inscribed: *Souvenir, settler's centenary. Grahamstown.* and with a crest of Cape of Good Hope.   12.50

Civic

Trademark used by Taylor and Kent (Ltd)., Florence Works, Longton. (Usual trademark Florentine). The products are very similar to IVORA WARE models.
For details of this manufacturer see Florentine China.

Civic Models
Ancient Artefacts
Chester Roman Vase (not named).
62mm.   3.00

Seaside Souvenirs
Whelk Shell. 90mm long.   5.00

Animals
Cat sitting with long neck. 105mm.
   (This is a model of a Destroyer's
   Ship's mascot which became
   popular during the Great War).   10.00
Elephant, kneeling. 60mm.   22.50
Manx Cat. 90mm.   19.50
Toad. 75mm long.   19.50

Great War
Bandsman's Drum. 55mm dia.   10.50

Home/Nostalgic
Watering Can. 75mm.   6.50

Sport
Cricket Bag. 110mm long.   12.50

Miniature Domestic
Tea Pot and lid. 68mm.   7.50

C.J.B. & Co

Clarence China

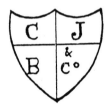

Trademark used by Sampson Hancock and
Sons, Bridge Works, Stoke and later at the
Gardon Works, Hanley. (Usual trademark
Corona).

The majority of pieces recorded are
small vases.   3.00

Great War
Red Cross Van. 98mm long.   25.00

Mark used by Arkinstall & Son Ltd.,
Arcadian Works, Stoke on Trent. (Usual
mark Arcadian).

Clarence Models
Ancient Artefacts
Model of Jug in Kendal Museum dated 1602.
No. 210. 74mm.   4

Home/Nostalgic
Grandfather Clock. Inscribed: *The time o' day.*
110mm.   12

Comic/Novelty
Bust of Negro with Eugene Stratton verse.
Black face, some colouring. 95mm.   30

Clarence Crest China

c1914–c1925.

Trademark used by Beresford Bros., Clarence Works, High Street, Longton. The models either bear a close resemblance to H & L (Willow Art) models or are the same. There must have been some connection between these two firms, both working in Longton. It is common to find firing flaws in this china.

This firm was established in 1900 to produce china and fancy goods. Very little is known about the firm; no mark was registered and the first reference found in the Pottery Gazette is an advertisement in 1920. In 1921 a further advertisement announces Beresford Bros as makers of 'View Ware. "A present from . . . ", also Crest Ware'. there is no reference to this firm after 1921 and the Clarence Works beloned to Crown Clarence Porcelain Co. after 1932. One can only assume that Beresford Bros became bankrupt as so many other firms did in the thirties, or that the firm changed its name to Crown Clarence.

This mark is most often found on small vases and domestic ware. The very small range of models bore a close resemblance to those being made by other Longton firms most notably Hewitt and Leadbeater (H and L or Willow Art China). It is possible that some of these models were purchased from H and L before being decorated and glazed but none has actually been found impressed H and L so it is more likely that designs for models were copied or bought from a freelance modeller.

A commemorative saucer has been found with a transfer print of The Four Flags of the Allies with the inscription: 'For right and freedom' and one suspects that Beresford Bros made a range of such domestic items. Only one transfer print has been recorded, a coloured Kingfisher with the inscription: 'Happy Days at . . . '. The two-handled vase with this inscription and blue edging can be found on Willow Art 'smalls', and again leads one to look for a connection between Beresford Bros and Hewitt and Leadbeater, but apart from both firms working in Longton no other evidence of such a connection can be found.

No numbering systems appear to have been used.

Clarence Models
Ancient Artefacts
Canterbury Vase, *Model of Roman Vase found near Canterbury original in Canterbury Museum.* No. 285.
66mm.   4.00
Highland Whisky Bowl. Model of.
90mm long.   4.00
Loving cup, 3 handled. 40mm.   3.00

Buildings – White
Windmill. 85mm.   34.50

Monuments (including Crosses)
Baron Burton statue. 130mm.   25.50

Historical/Folklore
James V chair. 100mm.   7.50
Man in the Moon. 55mm.   19.50

Traditional/National Souvenirs
Welsh Hat with blue band. 55mm.   5.00

Animals
Cat, sitting. 78mm.   10.00
Dog, Dachsund, sitting. 75mm long.   40.00
Elephant, standing. 78mm long.   17.00
Hare. 67mm long.   12.50
Pig, standing. 95mm long.   19.50

Birds
Swan. 57mm.   6.50

Great War
Soldier standing to attention,
  inscribed: *Our Brave Defender.*
  130mm.   47.50
Nurse, inscribed: *A friend in need.*
  130mm.   40.00
Monoplane with revolving prop.
  150mm long.   65.00
Tank with trailing wheels.
  130mm long.   17.50
Field gun with screen. 114mm long.   19.50
Bandsman's Drum. 58mm.   10.50
Kit Bag, with inscription: *Pack up*
  your troubles in your old kit bag.
  70mm.   19.50
Tommy's Steel Helmet. 76mm long.   21.00
Kitchen Range, with pot on fire
  inscribed: *Keep the home fires*
  burning. No. 199. 78mm long.   13.00

Comic/Novelty
A Truck of Coal from.. Wagon of black
  coal. 70mm.   19.50

Sport/Pastimes
Trump indicator (2 piece). 110mm dia.   30.00

Alcohol
One Special Scotch, Bottle. 88mm.   7.50

Footwear
Ladies heeled Shoe, blue bow.
  115mm long.   10.50

A small range of domestic china
  was produced bearing colour
  transfers of good quality.   £6.00 upwards.

Clays

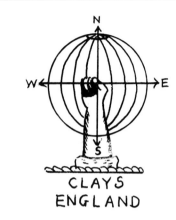

CLAYS
ENGLAND

Trademark used on crested china
  manufactured by Hewitt Bros. (Usual
  trademark Willow Art).
For details of Hewitt Bros china see Willow
  Art China.
This trademark is very perplexing, a very
  similar mark having been used by another
  Longton firm – Green and Clay, Staff
  Street, Longton. This firm went out of
  business in 1891. The models found with
  the Clays mark as above are certainly
  made by Hewitt Bros and some have been
  found impressed 'H Bros. Willow'. One
  can only guess that there must be some
  family connection between the two firms
  indicating that the mark was inherited.
  Another alternative thought is that
  Harold Taylor Robinson inherited the
  mark during his Empire Building days
  (see Arcadian). Later when Hewitt Bros
  sold out to him he could have used the
  Clays mark on some unprinted but
  impressed Willow Wares. This obviously
  needs much more research as it is one of
  the fascinating mysteries which make
  crested china marks so interesting.
One transfer print has been recorded, being
  of a colour kingfisher with the inscription:
  Happy days at . . . Exactly similar prints
  can be found marked Willow Art and
  Clarence (see Clarence Crest China).
Stock numbers are given where known.

Clays Models
Buildings – White
Chesterfield Parish Church.
110mm long.   40.00

Historical/Folklore
Bell inscribed: *Curfew must not ring*
tonight. 72mm.   7.50
'Burns Chair, Dumfries' as corner
seat. 77mm.   15.00
James the Fifth Chair. 104mm.   7.50
Sir Walter Scott's Chair, Abbotsford.
80mm.   7.50

Animals
Cow, kneeling. 115mm long.   47.50
Dog, Terrier, standing. 95mm long. 14.50
Elephant, walking. 70mm long.   13.00
Lion, walking, open mouth.
121mm long.   24.00
Pig, standing. 96mm long.   10.00

Birds
Wise Owl, with verse. 98mm.   14.50

Great War
Soldier, with rifle, inscribed: *Our*
brave defender. 132mm.   47.50
Battleship, impressed: *HMS Lion.*
140mm long.   30.00
Submarine, impressed: *E4.*
116mm long.   19.50
British Tank, Model of, with trailing
wheels. No. 107. 125mm long.   17.50
Field Gun & Screen. 110mm long.
                          19.00
Officers Peaked Cap. No. 100.
75mm dia.   11.00

Home/Nostalgic
Pillar Box. *GVR.* 76mm.   17.00

Cartoon/Comedy Characters
Baby, with arms outstretched,
inscribed: *Cheerio.* Some
colouring on face. 125mm. (Great
War cartoon character, could be
'Pooksie'.)   30.00

Alcohol
Barrel, on stand. 52mm long.   5.50

Clifton (Grille)

Trademark used by a branch of J.A. Robinson
Ltd, Stoke-on-Trent. Subsequently
Cauldon Ltd. (Usual mark Arcadian).
This trademark was not registered, but the
china was produced in the Arcadian
Works at the same time as Arcadian and
Swan models (Clifton pieces have been
found with badly obliterated 'Arcadian'
marks.) The few Clifton models which
cannot be recognised as Arcadian are
invariably found in the Swan range. A
three-handled loving cup with crests of
Edward VII and Queen Alexandra and
details of their lives, reign and the 1901
census has been found with the Clifton
mark. This is very much in the early Swan
style and exactly the same loving cup has
been found marked Swan. One could
therefore suspect that this mark was
offered by the firm of C. Ford (the makers
of Swan China) instead of the usual Swan.
Clifton is uniformly finer than Arcadian or
Swan China and it obviously was a higher
class range. The crests are painted with
much more care as are the coloured
models. Very few late models are found
and it likely that the mark was not used
after 1920. (There is one exception listed
here, 'A Box of Chocolates' is from a
Willow mould and this would not have
been used in the Arcadian Works until the
mid-twenties; why this piece was marked
Clifton will remain a mystery.)
Some view ware has been found and also
these Military badges: Royal Military

College, Camberley, Royal Staff College, Camberley, Coldstream Guards, Oxford & Bucks Light Infantry, Lincolnshire Regiment, Royal Air Force, Royal Field Artillery and 2nd Life Guards. Otherwise all recorded models carry crests.

Numbering System Many of the Clifton models are numbered. Printed or painted stock numbers can be found, and these numbers are listed where known. The stock numbers occasionally correspond with the numbers found on similar Arcadian or Swan models, but this range seems to have been stocked separately. Paintresses' marks are initials painted on the base, where the stock number is also painted, the initial being placed at the end of the numbers. (Beware of the initials O and I.)

Clifton Models
Parian/Unglazed

Bust of Edward VII with inscription. Wearing suit, no hat. 128mm.	45.00
Bust of King George V, glazed circular base, with inscription: *King George V born June 3rd 1865, ascended the throne May 6th 1910.* 135mm.	47.50
Bust of Queen Mary, glazed circular base, with inscription: *Queen Mary born May 26th 1867.* 135mm.	47.50
Bust of *HRH Prince of Wales*, unglazed on circular glazed base. Midshipmans uniform. 132mm.	75.00
Bust of Napoleon on glazed square base. 136mm.	55.00

Ancient Artefacts

Most inscriptions begin:*Model of*, so this will not be repeated throughout the list.

Ancient Tyg. No. 58. 70mm.	4.00
Ashbourne Bushel, inscribed: *His Majesty King Charles 2nd's Royal Standard Bushel fastened to the Market Cross in the year 1677.* 95mm dia.	10.00
British Bronze Pot, Ancient. 71mm.	4.00
Cambridge Jug, inscribed: *Model of Roman Jug found at Cambridge.* 60mm.	4.00
Canterbury Roman Vase, 2 shapes:	

No. 22. 63mm (with handle);	4.00
No. 29. 60mm (no handle).	4.00
Carlisle Salt Pot. No. 110. 40mm.	4.00
Chester Roman Vase. No. 131. 60mm.	4.00
Chinese Vase originally in Hanley Museum. 58mm.	4.00
Derby Roman Vase, inscribed: *Roman Vase found at Little Chester, Derby.* No. 26. 63mm.	4.00
Dorchester Jug, inscribed: *Old Jug found in North Street, Dorchester.* No. 17. 55mm.	4.00
Egyptian Vase, Ancient, about 230BC. No. 155. 45mm.	4.00
Exeter Vase. 65mm.	4.00
Fountains Abbey Cup. No. 94. 50mm.	3.00
Glastonbury Bowl. No. 65. 40mm.	4.00
Glastonbury Vase. No. 642. 55mm.	4.00
Hastings Kettle. No. 237. 62mm.	3.00
Irish Bronze Pot. No. 62 50mm.	4.00
Loving Cup originated by Henry of Navarre King of France. 3 handled. 2 sizes: 40mm.	4.00
50mm.	4.00
Newbury Leather Bottle, inscribed: *Leather bottle found on battlefield of Newbury 1644 now in museum.* No. 83. 65mm.	4.00
New Forest Roman Jug, not named. No. 174. 67mm.	3.00
Nose of Brasenose College, Oxford (not found numbered). 103mm long.	12.50
Pompeian Vessel, not found named. 43mm.	3.00
Portland Vase in British Museum. No. 57. 60mm.	4.00
Puzzle Jug, original in South Kensington Museum with usual verse. No. 147. 70mm.	5.50
Roman Salopian Ewer found at Uriconium, now in Shrewsbury Museum. 75mm.	4.00
Southwold Jar, (not found numbered). 95mm.	4.00
Wedgwood Vase inscribed: *Ancient Roman Vase in the Wedgewood Museum.* 65mm.	4.00
Winchelsea Roman Cup (3 handles).	4.00
West Malling Stoup, Elizabethan. 74mm.	10.00

Buildings – White

Highland Cottage, Model of. 60mm.	20.00

Monuments (included Crosses)

Baron Burton monument. Inscribed:
Michael Arthur first Baron Burton.

2 sizes: 130mm.	30.00
160mm.	30.00

Historical/Folklore

Ancient Coaching Hat, Model of.

No. 687. 68mm long.	7.50
Jenny Geddes Stool, not named. 42mm.	5.50
Witches Cauldron with verse. 47mm.	5.50

Traditional/National Souvenirs

John Bull bust, eyes and mouth coloured. 100mm.	25.00
Melton Mowbray Pie, The, pie with moulded pastry adornments, with verse. 50mm.	16.00
Thistle Vase. 93mm.	3.50
Ladies of Llangollen. 115mm.	30.00

Welsh Lady, bust, with inscription:
*Wales! Wales! My Mother's sweet
home in Wales* etc. With black

Welsh hat. 80mm.	20.00
Welsh Leek. 95mm.	5.50

Welsh Tea Party,

2 sizes: 55mm.	35.00
95mm.	40.00

Seaside Souvenirs

Lifeboat, inscribed: *Margate Lifeboat, friend to all nations.* 118mm long.	20.00
Clam shell menu holder. 62mm.	10.50
Mr. Punch, bust, some colouring – red hearts on cheeks. Rd. No. 524786 80mm.	30.00

Countryside

Acorn. 42mm.	7.50
Haystack, circular. 58mm.	6.50

Animals

Bear and Ragged Staff, impressed: *WARWICK* on base. No. 339. 85mm.	30.00
Cat, angry, standing with arched back, green eyes. 62mm.	10.50
Cat, long necked and sitting, can be inscribed: *My word if you're not off.* 108mm.	16.00
Elephant walking. Can be found inscribed: *Baby Jumbo.* No. 237. 70mm.	30.00

Frog, open mouth and green eyes, inscribed: *Always croaking.* 80mm.	20.00
Hare. No. 10. 73mm high, 80mm long.	15.00
Lion, walking. Inscribed: *King of the Forest.* 110mm long.	18.00

Sussex Pig, Model of, standing
inscribed: *You can push or you can
shuv but I'm hanged if I'll be druv.*
No. 148.

2 sizes: 78mm long.	12.50
94mm long (fat).	14.50
Polar Bear, standing. 135mm long.	65.00

Pony, Shetland.

2 sizes: 105mm long.	25.00
120mm long.	30.00
Teddy Bear, sitting. 90mm.	19.50

Birds (including Eggs)

Chick emerging from egg.

72mm long.	9.00
Cockerel, standing. Inscribed: *Cock O'th'North* 100mm.	20.00
Owl. 69mm.	12.50

Great War

Despatch rider, Model of, on motorbike. 120mm long.	75.00

Sailor, bust, inscribed: *HMS
Dreadnought* and *The handy man.*

95mm.	34.50
With verse: *Hearts of Oak.*	37.00

Sailor, bust, impressed: *HMS Queen
Elizabeth.* 86mm. | 34.50

Soldier standing to attention with rifle over shoulder. 137mm.	95.00

Soldier, bust, inscribed: *Territorial*
with verse *'It's the Soldiers of the
King'.* 95mm. | 47.50

Monoplane, movable prop.

155mm long.	65.00

Battleship, impressed *HMS Lion.*

140mm long.	22.50
Tank, Model of. 116mm long.	19.50

Tank with inset wheels.

127mm long.	19.50
Red Cross Van. 90mm long.	30.00

Howitzer (not found named).

115mm long.	16.00
Field Gun with Screen. 112mm long.	23.00
Trench Mortar. 70mm long.	17.50

Bomb dropped from Zeppelin, Model of.

80mm.	17.00
Canister Bomb, Model of. 60mm.	17.50
Colonial Hat, Model of. 88mm wide.	16.00

Glengarry. 90mm long.	19.50
Officers Peaked Cap. 65mm long.	10.50
Kitbag with verse: *Pack up your troubles*. 75mm.	15.00
Anti Zeppelin Candle holder 62mm.	17.50
Sandbag. 73mm long.	22.50
Trench Lamp. 67mm.	13.00

Home/Nostalgic

Anvil on circular base. No. 25. 68mm.	5.50
Bellows. 95mm long.	11.50
Bucket. No. 92. 75mm.	3.00
Dustpan. 110mm long.	9.50
Flat Iron Stand. 70mm.	3.00
Grandfather Clock, Model of a, inscribed: *Make use of time let not advantage slip. Shakespeare.* No. 209. 108mm.	12.00
Pillar Box, inscribed: *G V R if you haven't time to post a line here's the pillar box.* 60mm.	16.00

Comic/Novelty

2 Black boys heads popping out of box, inscribed: *Box of chocolates.* Some colouring. 60mm.	75.00
Clown figure candlesnuffer, baggy suit, hands in pockets. 102mm.	47.50
Clown, standing, hands on hips, wearing baggy suit. 104mm.	47.50
Clown, bust, inscribed: *Put me amongst the girls.* Some colouring. No. 12. 80mm.	25.00
Policeman on duty, with verse. 148mm.	34.50
Suffragette Handbell. Inscribed: *Votes for Women. This one shall have a vote.* 105mm.	47.50

Cartoon/Comedy Characters

Ally Sloper, bust. Inscribed: *Good Health Old Man.* 90mm.	40.00

Alcohol

Barrel on stilts. 60mm.	5.50
Monk, holding glass with verse. 112mm.	19.50

Sport/Pastimes

Football. 50mm dia.	6.50

Musical Instruments

Banjo. 152mm long.	10.00
Lute, 162mm long.	35.00

Transport

4 Seater Open Car, folded down hood. 140mm long.	30.00

Hats

Straw Boater, coloured ribbon. 95mm long.	17.50
Luton Boater, not found named. 78mm dia.	8.50

Footwear

Ankle Boot. No. 251. 85mm long.	5.50
Oriental Slipper. No. 352. 105mm long.	6.50

Miniature Domestic

Cheese Dish and lid, inscribed: *Cheddar Cheese.* 50mm.	20.00

Domestic

Cone candlesnuffer. 68mm.	3.50

Recorded Numbered Ornamental Wares

No. 16. Globe Vase. 46mm.	3.00
No. 37. Vase, wide mouth. 50mm.	3.00
No. 40. Trinket Box and lid, horseshoe shaped. 65mm long.	4.00
No. 45. Trinket Box and lid, spade shaped. 40mm.	4.00
No. 63. Pot on 3 small feet. 41mm.	3.00
No. 72. Jug. 60mm.	3.00
No. 74. Jug. 82mm.	3.00
No. 88. Jug with banded neck. 75mm.	3.00
No. 100. Vase. 53mm.	3.00
No. 141. Vase. 47mm.	3.00
No. 144. Vase. 50mm.	3.00
No. 145. Vase. 53mm.	3.00
No. 146. Vase. 50mm.	3.00
No. 215. Vase. 60mm.	3.00
No. 216. Vase. 60mm.	3.00
No. 217. Vase. flat bottomed. 37mm.	3.00
No. 303. Vase. 52mm.	3.00
No. 305. Beaker. 34mm.	3.00
No. 532. Jug. 70mm.	3.00
No. 579. Loving Cup.	3.00
No. 587. Taper Vase. 60mm.	3.00
No. 666. Crinkle topped vase. 40mm.	3.00
Found not numbered. Trinket Box and lid, heart shaped. 40mm.	4.00

Clifton China

WH & S
L.

1908-27 (with slight variation).

Trademark used by Wildblood, Heath and Sons (Ltd), Peel Works, Longton. The models show great resemblance to those of H & L – Willow Art, also working in Longton and later wares are identical to Arcadian models.

Wildblood, Heath and Sons (Ltd) made china, mostly hotel and badge ware from 1899 to 1927. Crested china was produced from around 1907 when they first advertised Arms Ware. The production of arms ware seems to have been a small sideline for this firm as few models are found with this mark. Early wares tend to be domestic but in 1920 the firm were advertising china miniatures with crests and most of the named models were made at that date. Many of these models resemble Willow Art China made by Hewitt and Leadbeater also in Longton. There is no known connection between the two firms. so one can only speculate whether designs for moulds were bought, sold or borrowed! For the most part the china is heavy and the crests are crudely coloured.

A few pieces of view ware have been recorded, including a nice 'Cat and Fiddle, Buxton' inn sign. These are usually domestic items but transfer prints can be found on other models. Great War inscriptions and commemorative transfers are not found, but one interesting Military crest, 'The Royal Field Artillery' has been recorded.

Numbering system. Hand painted stock numbers are found on models and these are given where known. Paintressses' marks are usually initials painted underneath the stock number.

Clifton China Models
Parian/Unglazed
Bust of Queen Alexandra on round
    base. 137mm.   47.50

Ancient Artefacts
Loving Cup. 39mm.   3.00
Egyptian Urn, Model of. No. 130.
    48mm.   4.00

Buildings – White
Wainhouse Tower. 135mm.   55.00

Monuments (including Crosses)
Burns, Statue on square base.
    177mm.   30.00
Burton Statue, Burton on Trent.
    Inscribed: *Michael Arthur first*
    Baron Burton, born 1837. Died 1909.
    2 sizes: 130mm.   30.00
              158mm.   35.00

Historical/Folklore
Burns chair, Model of. No. 49. 90mm.   7.50

Traditional/National Souvenirs
John Bull, bust of. 90mm.   25.00

Seaside Souvenirs
Lighthouse. 110mm.   5.00

Animals
Cat in Boot. No. 65. 68mm.   14.50
Cheshire Cat, still smiling, green right
    eye. 80mm.   7.50
Donkey. *Hee-Haw.* 120mm long.   43.00
Elephant, walking. 75mm.   17.00
Lion. 112mm long.   12.50
Shetland Pony. Inscribed: *A Native of*
    Shetland. 110mm long.   23.00

Birds
Canary on Rock, unnamed Norwich
    Warbler. No.23. 98mm.   13.00

Great War
Sailor, standing at attention.
    Inscribed: *Our Brave Defender.*
    130mm.   55.00

Monoplane with movable prop.
155mm long.   65.00
Beta Airship. 55mm.   55.00
Battleship, impressed: HMS Lion.
140mm long.   30.00
Liner converted to Troop Ship, not
named. 135mm long.   95.00
British Tank, Model of. 140mm long.   14.50
British Tank, Model of, with trailing
steering wheels. No. 120.
130mm long.   17.50
Field Gun with Screen. No. 214.
115mm long.   19.00
Shell. No. 114. 70mm.   5.00
Kit Bag with verse: *Pack up your
troubles.* 72mm.   20.00
Bugle. 72mm long.   19.50
Drum. 65mm dia.   10.50
Tommy's Steel Helmet. 75mm long.   20.00

Home/Nostalgic
Anvil. 88m long.   7.50
Shaving Mug. 65mm.   6.50
Watering Can. No. 126. 75mm.   6.50

Comic/Novelty
Billiken, The god of luck. 75mm.   7.00
Inscribed   10.50

Cartoon/Comedy Characters
Standing Baby inscribed: *One of the
B'Hoys.* Saluting, coloured face,
160mm. Refers to the Alsager
B'Hoys.   40.00

Alcohol
Barrel on legs. No. 85. 60mm.   4.00
Barrel on stand. No. 83. 63mm long.   5.50

Musical Instruments
Lute. 160mm long.   35.00

Miniature Domestic
Cream jug. 74mm.   2.50

Domestic Wares
Hexagonal and octagonal salt pots
can be found inscribed: *Salt.* Jugs,
beakers and small vases can also
be found.   from £2.50

Miscellaneous
Bell. No. 12. 55mm.   5.50
Hand holding Tulip. 80mm.   5.00

Colleen China

Trademark unidentified but could possibly
be Belleek. It is similar to Shamrock China.

National Souvenirs
Bust of *John Redmond MP 1914.* (The
bust is hollow and has a Wexford
crest). 137mm.   55.00

Domestic
Water Cooler. 63mm.   3.00

Collingwood

Columbia China

COLLINGWOOD
MADE IN
ENGLAND

Columbian
China

1924-30.

Trademark used by Collingwood Bros (Ltd.),
St. George's Works, Longton.
Collingwood Bros manufactured china from
1887 to 1957. The firm was not known to
produce crested ware, but they did make
'smalls' with the Wembley Lion symbol to
celebrate the Wembley British Empire
Exhibition 1924. Such souvenirs are very
popular not only with crested china
collectors but collectors of British Empire
Exhibition memorabilia.

from £6.50

Trademark used by an English manufacturer
for export to British Columbia.
Only one small square vase measuring
60mm has been found with this mark and
a crest of British Columbia.
Any of the firms known to have made
crested china for the Colonies could have
produced this china.

Columbia Model
Vase. 60mm.   4.00

Coral Porcelain

Trademark used by the Coral Porcelain Co. also known as the Scottish Porcelain Co. This would appear to be a Scottish manufacturer producing for the Scottish market.

A range of 'smalls' with Scottish crests was produced, in addition to the model below.

£3.00 upwards

Coral Model
Home/Nostalgic
Cradle on Rockers. 60mm long.
(Similar to Nautilus).   9.50

The Corona China

Mark used between c1910-1937. The mark is sometimes found without the manufacturers name but with the addition at the base of the initials RBW – These may possibly be retailers initials.

Trademark used by Sampson Hancock (& Sons), Bridge Works, Stoke and later at the Garden Works, Hanley (renamed Corona Pottery).

Sampson Hancock and Sons was an old established firm of earthenware manufacturers, founded in 1858. On May 9th, 1900 Mr Sampson Hancock a prominent Wesleyan died, and the business was then carried on by his sons. The firm made domestic pottery of all kinds and later introduced high class semi-porcelain and ivory ware to their range, producing an extensive range of decorated dinner ware, toilet ware, flower pots, vases and jugs for the home, Australian and colonial markets. Before the Great War they were represented in London by M.V.V. Adams and had showrooms at 9 Charterhouse Street, Holborn Circus. Hancocks seem to have produced crest china in quantity as an emergency measure to see them through the war years when skilled labour was unavailable. Unlike other established potters they do not appear to have advertised this line, although as early as 1906 they announced that they made 'Art Trinket Wares'. Hancocks exhibited their 'Corona Ware' at the 1920 British

Industries Fair but there is no indication that crested china formed a large part of the display. In 1924 the firm bought out a large part of the display. In 1924 the firm brought out a parian statuette of 'Our Prince', in civilian clothes complete with walking stick, modelled by P. Bryant Baker. The statuette came in three sizes and was specially designed to be sold to visitors to England for the British Empire Exhibition. (No record can be found of the firm actually exhibiting at Wembley in 1924 or 1925.) As yet no parian or unglazed models marked Corona have been recorded including 'Our Prince', although a glazed model of the Prince of Wales at his Investiture exists marked 'Duchess', which was another trademark used by the firm (see DUCHESS CHINA).

S. Hancock and Sons (Potters Ltd), Hanley, a titled used from 1935, was put into the hands of the Receiver, R.E. Clark on 23rd March, 1937 – yet another victim of the Depression.

The Corona models are not very original, showing the usual range of animals, Great War and miscellaneous souvenirs in reasonably fine china with pleasant crests. It seems likely that the firm stopped making china miniatures in the early twenties as models have not been found decorated with other devices. There are a few pieces bearing coloured views but these are small pots and jugs and would have been made before the War. Hancocks did make a large number of Great War commemoratives: usually four flags of the Allies and inscribed: 'European War 1914'. These have an unusual border of European flag bunting around the necks of vases and jugs. Also transfer prints of Generals decorated in the same way have been found and probably other Great War leaders were commemorated similarly. The following WWI transfers/badges have been found with Corona or Duchess marks:

1st Life Guards
Black Watch
12th Lancers
Royal Irish
Royal Engineers (2 types, one with 1 figure, another with 3 figures)
Union Jack (with Jellicoe inset)
"Waiting" (sailor and ship)

5th North Staffs
The Man in Khaki
The King's Own Yorkshire Light Infantry
The 13th County of London
Princess of Wales Yorkshire Regiment
The Royal Standard (2 type with General French or Kitchener inset)
The 1st Grenadier Guards

Numbering system. Early crested models and Great War commemoratives can be found with gold or black painted stock numbers. These are recorded where known in the following lists. Paintresses' marks are a series of coloured dots or squiggles found near the trademark.

Corona Models
Ancient Artefacts

Aberdeen Bronze Pot. 58mm.	4.00
Canterbury Leather Bottle. No. 156.	4.00
Glastonbury Bowl. 42mm.	4.00
Hastings Kettle. 57mm.	3.00
Lincoln Jack. No. 123. 57mm.	4.00
Loving Cup, 3 handled. 70mm.	4.00
Newbury Leather Bottle, not named. 72mm.	3.00
Puzzle Jug. No. 148. 70mm.	5.50
Shrewsbury Roman Salopian Ewer. 60mm.	4.00

Buildings – White

Ann Hathaway's Cottage. 95mm long.	13.00
Blackpool Tower. 139mm.	9.50
Bottle Oven (inside of). 82mm.	19.50
Bridge, with grassy banks. 134mm long.	20.00
Canterbury Cathedral, West Front. 137mm.	40.00
Clifton Suspension Bridge. 115mm long.	75.00
Cottage. 60mm long. (This is identical to the model usually found marked British Manufacture.)	7.00
Crosthwaite Church, Keswick. 110mm long.	60.00
St. Osyth Priory, unnamed. 75mm.	45.00

Monuments (including Crosses)

Bunyan's Statue. 165mm.	18.00
Tom Hughes Monument, Rugby. 136mm.	30.00
John Ruskin Memorial. 105mm.	12.50

Historical/Folklore

Mary Queen of Scots Chair Edinburgh
  Castle. 80mm.   6.50
Noah's Ark. 95mm long.   5.00

Traditional/National Souvenirs

Welsh Harp. 90mm.   7.50
Welsh Hat, can be found with
  longest place name round brim.
  45mm.   5.00
    With wording   7.50

Seaside Souvenirs

Bathing Machine. 71mm.   8.50
Canoe. 102mm long.   7.50
Lighthouse, not named. 105mm.   5.50
Lighthouse, with steps. 115mm.   6.50
Beachy Head Lighthouse, black band.
  150mm.   7.50

Animals

Camel, 1 hump, kneeling. 114mm
  long.   13.00
Cat sitting with ruff around neck.
  105mm.   17.50
Cat, sitting, bow around neck, some
  colour. 100mm.   10.00
Cheshire Cat. 95mm.   6.50
Manx Cat. 60mm.   16.00
Bulldog, standing. 112mm and
  120mm long.   15.00
Bulldog, standing, with black collar
  and Union Jack on back. (Very
  rare). 130mm long.   145.00
Cow Creamer.   16.00
Dog, King Charles Spaniel, begging.
  69mm.   10.50
Fish Vase. 60mm.   5.00
Lion, lying down. 140mm long.   19.00
Mouse, eating nut. 44mm.   19.00
Piglet, kneeling. 65mm long.   9.00
Pig, standing. 84mm long.   10.00
Pony, Shetland. 110mm long.   22.00
Rabbit with raised ears. No. 166.
  63mm long.   6.50
Teddy Bear, sitting, can be found
  completely brown with no crest.
  No. 194. 85mm.   19.50
    Brown   30.00
Tortoise. 72mm long.   9.00

Birds

Swan. 85mm.   6.50
Swan, posy holder. 87mm long.   5.00

Great War

Monoplane, Bleriot type with
  movable prop. 145mm long.   65.00
British Airship on base.
  128mm long.   35.00
Zeppelin. 134mm long.   30.00
Battleship. 120mm long.   20.00
Lusitania. 163mm long.   82.50
Submarine, inscribed: *E4*. Size
  varies. 102mm–120mm long.   19.50
New submarine, Model of. 146mm
  long. (This is the submarine
  usually named E5 by other firms).   19.50
Red Cross Van. 98mm long.   30.00
Renault Tank. No. 272. 100mm long.   75.00
Tank with inset trailing wheels.
  100mm long.   20.00
Field Gun.
  3 sizes: 120mm long.   17.50
            130mm long.   19.50
            140mm long.   23.00
Field Gun with Screen. 120mm long.   23.00
Mills Hand Grenade. 69mm.   19.50
Cannon Shell. 100mm.   5.00
Cannon Shell Pepper Pot. 112mm.   9.50
Torpedo, Model of. No. 285.
  145mm long.   55.00
Bandsman's Drum. No. 208.
  63mm dia.   5.00
Officers Peaked Cap. 60mm long.   10.50
Bell Tent, hexagonal tent with open
  flaps. No. 209. 85mm.   16.50
Gurkha Knife. 140mm long.   20.00
Flash Lamp. No. 323. 88mm.   10.50
Water Bottle. 68mm.   13.00
Grandfather Clock, same mould as
  usual Grandfather clock but
  clockface transfer at 3.25,
  inscribed: *World War 1914-1919*.
  Peace signed 3.25pm June 28th 1919.
  128mm.   56.50
Cenotaph. Whitehall. 145mm   5.50
Romsey War Memorial. 160mm   90.00
Rushden War Memorial. 158mm.   90.00
A small series of vases with portraits of
  General French, Lord Kitchener
  and Admiral Jellico set in the
  Union Jack or Royal Standard
  flag marked *1914* are worth 17.50
  to 30.00
A similar series of transfer prints of
  soldiers in regimental uniforms
  marked *1914* are worth 30.00 upwards.

Home/Nostalgic

Alarm Clock, with detailed face.	
85mm	30.00
Armchair. 62mm.	12.50
Baby in Bootee. 80mm long.	11.00
Baby's Cradle. 80mm long.	11.00
Cigarette Case. 72mm long.	13.00
Flask, rectangular with sloping shoulders. No. 242. 65mm.	5.00
Grandfather Clock. 128mm.	9.00
Hip Bath. 95mm long.	10.50
Jardiniere, on fixed stand.	
2 sizes: 82mm.	5.00
97mm.	5.00
Pillar Box, with verse. No. 171.	
2 sizes: 60mm.	11.00
74mm.	14.50
Policeman's Lamp. 70mm.	10.00
Sofa, 3-seater. 95mm long.	14.50
Tobacco Pouch. 77mm wide.	9.50
Watering Can. 70mm.	6.50
Writing Slope/Desk top. No. 268.	
53mm.	8.50

Comic/Novelty

Man's Head cream jug. 76mm.	10.50

Sport/Pastimes

Tennis Racquet. 132mm long.	13.00
Bishop chess piece.	
2 sizes: 61mm.	20.00
90mm.	20.00
King chess piece. 115mm.	25.00
Knight chess piece. 70mm.	16.00
Pawn chess piece.	
2 sizes: 61mm.	25.00
90mm.	25.00
Queen chess piece. 84mm.	24.50
Rook chess piece. 68mm.	11.00

Musical Instruments

Banjo. 140mm long.	10.00
Double Bass. 150mm long.	32.50
Harp. 92mm.	6.50
Upright Piano. 63mm.	16.00

Modern Equipment

Gas Cooker. 70mm.	10.00
Gramophone, square with no horn, arm on middle of record. Crest is on the front edge. 57mm.	15.00

Footwear

Ladies Button Boot. No. 149. 65mm.	8.50

Ladies 18th Century Shoe. No. 146.	
90mm long.	7.50
Lancashire Clog.	
2 sizes: 70mm long.	5.00
102mm long.	6.50
Lancashire Clog. Square toe and gilded buckle. 60mm long.	8.50

Hats

Top Hat. 45mm.	5.50

Miniature Domestic

Cheese Dish. 1 piece. 60mm x 80mm.	6.50
Cheese Dish and cover. 60mm.	6.50
Coffee Pot and lid. 75mm.	7.50
Cream Jug, ornate. 78mm.	4.00
Fluted Jug. 47mm.	3.00
Fluted Bowl. 65mm diameter.	3.00
Kettle with lid. 70mm & 87mm.	10.00
Tea Pot with lid, pattern in relief.	
No. 122.	
2 sizes: 60mm.	7.50
65mm.	7.50

Domestic

Candlestick square top and base.	
83mm.	3.00
Candlestick round top and base.	
85mm.	3.00
Pepper Pot. 80mm.	7.50
Salt Pot.	
2 sizes: 84mm.	7.50
95mm.	7.50
Tea Caddy and lid. 92mm.	12.50

Miscellaneous

Horseshoe, on slope. 70mm long.	3.00
Horseshoe, wall plaque.	
60mm long.	3.00

Coronet Ware

F. P. & S

−Mark used c1910-1921 but without initials before 1917.

F. L™

Mark used 1921-c1924

Originally it was thought that Coronet Ware was produced by Ford and Pointon Ltd, Norfolk Works, Hanley, who became a member of the J.A. Robinson and Sons Ltd group (see ARCADIAN) in 1919. However, further research into the ware has revealed that pieces have in every case originated either from Taylor and Kent (Florentine) or J.A. Robinson & Sons Ltd (Arcadian).

It is most probable that Coronet Ware is a trademark for a wholesaler 'F.P. & S.', or possibly Ford & Pointon were the wholesalers. The firm of Pointon and Co Ltd at the Norfolk Works was sold in 1917, and a new company, Ford and Pointon Ltd

was formed. Pointon and Co Ltd were basically tableware manufacturers but along with practically every other firm of this kind had begun to make crested china miniatures sometime just before or during the Great War.

At Ford and Pointon Ltd crest china production would have continued along with other decorative items and tableware. In 1920 at the British Industries Fair, J.A. Robinson showed a 'New range of Coaching Scenes in the Ford and Pointon China'. When J.A. Robinson was amalgamated with Cauldon Potteries Ltd in 1920, Ford and Pointon was described as making 'Fords' china – useful and ornamental, and a selection of these wares were exhibited at the B.E.E. in 1924 as part of the Cauldon display. This mark was not used on arms ware for more than a year or two at the Cauldon Place Works. The firm seems to have ceased to exist after the Cauldon/Coalport merger in 1933.

Two early commemoratives have been recorded, 'Festival of Empire, Crystal Palace 1911' and 'Shakespearian Exhibition, Earls Court 1912'. Flags of the Allies Great War commemoratives are found inscribed: 'War 1914', and two military badges are known – The Kings Own Yorkshire Light Infantry and the Australian Commonwealth. There is no evidence of any other forms of decoration being used on models other than coloured views and these are rare. (No numbering system seems to have been used).

Coronet Models
Ancient Artefacts

Eddystone Jug. 58mm.	3.00
Fountains Abbey Cup, not found named. 48mm.	3.00
Guernsey Milk Can. 100mm.	4.00
Puzzle Jug. 70mm.	5.50
Roman Oil Lamp. 100mm long.	4.00
Salisbury Kettle. 95mm.	4.00
Shrewsbury Roman Salopian Ewer. 60mm.	4.00

Buildings – White

Cottage. 50mm.	14.00

Monuments (including Crosses)

Iona Cross, on square base. 108mm.	10.50

Irish Round Tower. 106mm.	12.00
Wallace's Memorial at Stirling.	
120mm.	40.00

Historical/Folklore

Executioner's Block and Axe. 50mm.	20.00
Judge, bust. 60mm.	14.00
Man in Pillory. 103mm.	17.00
Man in Stocks. 102mm.	25.00
Mother Shipton. 72mm.	8.00

Traditional/National Souvenirs

Welsh Hat. 57mm.	5.50
Welsh Hat with blue band & gold	
tassles. 80mm.	7.50

Seaside Souvenirs

Bathing Machine. 78mm.	10.00
Bathing Machine with figure in	
doorway. 75mm.	14.50
Bermudan rigged Sailing Boat.	
125mm.	17.00
Houseboat. 90mm long.	5.00
Yacht. 125mm.	12.50
Whelk Shell. 95mm long.	3.00
Beach Chair. 84mm.	12.50
Punch and Judy Booth, with Punch	
and dog Toby. (rare)	
2 sizes: 90mm.	55.00
110mm.	60.00
Punch, bust, with red nose.	
83mm.	30.00

Countryside

Milk Churn, 2 handles and lid.	
70mm.	5.00
Pine Cone on side. 90mm long.	4.00

Animals

Camel with 1 hump, kneeling.	
56mm.	13.00
Cat, large and furry, snarling.	
93mm.	55.00
Cat, long necked. 103mm.	6.50
Cat, Manx. 64mm.	19.50
Cat, angry. 80mm.	10.50
Cat, sitting inscribed: *The Cheshire*	
Cat, always smiling. 88mm.	7.50
Cat, sitting, bow round neck.	
70mm.	10.00
Dog, Pekinese on cushion, begging.	
70mm.	8.50
Dog, spaniel type, standing.	
76mm long.	10.50
Dog, Staffordshire Bulldog. 100mm.	20.50

Dolphin Vase. 102mm.	5.50
Elephant, kneeling. 60mm.	20.00
Fish, open mouthed.	
2 sizes: 102mm	4.00
120mm long.	5.00
Frog, open mouthed and green eyes.	
60mm.	16.00
Frog Jug. 47mm.	6.50
Monkey, wearing coat, sitting.	
75mm.	13.00
Mouse playing Mandolin, on base.	
80mm.	24.50
Pig, standing, inscribed: *The pig that*	
won't go. 84mm long.	12.50
Pig, standing. 95mm long.	11.00
Polar Bear, walking. Inscribed:)	
SAM. 93mm long.	55.00
Pony, inscribed: *Shetland Pony.*	
74mm.	25.00
Rabbit sitting, ears flat.	
74mm long.	8.50
Seal, with ball on nose.	
85mm long.	17.50
Teddy Bear. 96mm.	30.00
Toad with closed mouth. 50mm.	19.50
Tortoise. 72mm long.	9.00

Birds

Bird on rock. 90mm.	14.50
Hen, roosting. 55mm	7.50
Kingfisher. 80mm.	30.00
Kingfisher cream jug. 60mm.	5.50
Owl. 70mm.	10.50
Pelican cream jug. 80mm.	5.50
Swan posy holder. 90mm long.	5.00
Swan. 75mm.	7.50

Great War

Bust of Sailor. 90mm.	30.00
Tommy in Bayonet Attack. 130mm.	130.00
British Airship, on base.	
130mm long.	20.00
Monoplane with movable prop and	
cross hatching. 145mm long.	55.00
Monoplane with movable prop and	
no cross hatching. 170mm long.	55.00
Battleship. 115mm long.	16.00
Torpedo Boat Destroyer, Model of.	
105mm long.	19.50
Submarine, inscribed: *E5.*	
130mm long.	16.00
Armoured Car with turret. 95mm.	30.00
Red Cross Van. 90mm long.	25.00
Tank. 110mm long.	13.00

Tank with large gun turrets.
120mm long. 21.00
Tank with inset steering wheels.
116mm long. 15.00
Field Gun. 145mm long. 19.00
Canister Bomb. 60mm. 13.00
German Aerial Torpedo.
80mm long. 30.00
Observer Sausage Baloon. 82mm. 47.50
Cannon Shell. 76mm. 3.00
Zeppelin Bomb. 78mm. 11.00
Bandsman's Drum. 55mm dia. 5.00
Bell Tent. 10.50
Ghurka Knife. 110mm long. 20.00
Hand Grenade. 60mm. 13.00
Glengarry. 90mm long. 16.00
Peaked Cap. 63mm long. 9.00
Sandbag. 70mm. 13.00
Solar Topee. 60mm. 16.00
Telescope, folded. 70mm. 17.00
Trench Lamp. 70mm. 13.00
Tommy's Hut, unnamed. 105mm long. 40.00
Shell. 130mm. 4.00
Water Bottle. 63mm. 13.00
Dartford War Memorial (rare).
163mm. 85.00
Cenotaph. 100mm. 4.00

Home/Nostalgic
Anvil on wooden stump. 66mm. 5.50
The Old Armchair, with verse. 86mm. 7.50
Broom head. 105mm long. 20.00
Coal Bucket. 63mm. 4.00
Coal Scuttle, ornate. 68mm. 4.50
Dustpan. 100mm long. 6.50
Flat Iron. 75mm long. 12.50
Frying Pan. 115mm long. 7.50
Garden Roller. 83mm long. 7.50
Grandfather Clock. 127mm. 10.50
Kennel. 52mm. 6.50
Lantern. 86mm. 5.50
Pillar Box.
2 sizes: 60mm. 8.00
78mm. 8.00
Policeman's Lamp. 70mm. 10.00
Portmanteau. 80mm long. 4.00
Shaving Mug. 58mm. 5.50
Sofa. 82mm long. 10.50
Stool, 3 legged. 40mm. 5.50
Torch. 10.50
Watering Can. 70mm. 5.50
Wicker Chair. 92mm. 8.50

Comic/Novelty
Baby in Hip Bath. 100mm long. 11.00

Billiken, sitting. 64mm. 6.50
Boy on Scooter. 95mm. 16.00
Bust of Mrs Gamp the suffragette,
double faced smiling and fierce.
90mm. 25.00
Clown, bust. 65mm. 8.50
Truck of Coal. 90mm long. 15.00
Jack in the Box. 95mm. 16.00

Alcohol
Barrel on stand. 56mm. 5.50
Bottle of Champagne in Ice Bucket.
85mm. 7.50
Carboy. 75mm. 3.00
Drunkard, bust of (looks rather like
Ally Sloper). 74mm. 19.50
Toby Jug. 63mm. 6.50

Sport/Pastimes
Cricket Bag. 110mm long. 9.00
Cricket Bat. 115mm long. 40.00
Football. 50mm. 6.50
Golf Ball. 42mm. 7.50
Golf Ball on Tee. 63mm. 12.50
Golf Club head. 90mm long. 10.50
Tennis Racquet. 95mm long. 7.50
Castle Chess Piece. 87mm. 4.00

Musical Instruments
Grand Piano. 82mm long. 16.00
Guitar. 152mm long. 12.00
Harp. 95mm. 5.50
Piano, upright. 65mm long. 12.50
Tambourine. 68mm dia. 4.50

Transport
Saloon Car. 85mm long. 30.00
Motor Horn: *Pip Pip*. 90mm long. 22.50

Modern Equipment
Radio Horn. 93mm. 18.00
Square Gramophone. 55mm. 15.00

Footwear
Boot. 70mm. 5.00
Ladies Ankle Boot. 76mm long. 6.50
Ladies 18th Century Shoe.
95mm long. 7.50
Sabot with turned up toe.
90mm long. 5.00

Miniature Domestic
Cheese Dish. 2 pieces. 50mm. 6.50
Coffee Pot with lid. 80mm. 7.50

Cup and Saucer. 40mm.   5.00
Tea Pot with lid. 70mm.   7.50

Domestic
Oil Lamp. 103mm long.   5.00
Salt Pot, octagonal. 85mm.   3.00
Serviette ring.   4.00
Tea Pot with lid. 95mm.   5.50

Craven China

Trademark used by Wiltshaw and Robinson
Ltd, Carlton Works, Stoke-on-Trent (usual
trademark Carlton).

For details of this firm and the china
manufactured see CARLTON CHINA.

Wiltshaw and Robinson Ltd seem to have
only used this mark during the Great War
and a few years afterwards. They do not
seem to have used the mark for a specific
retailer as crests recorded are from all over
Britain. Great War models can be found
with 'The Victory of Justice Armistice of
the Great War signed Nov 11th 1918'
inscription.

Craven Models
Animals
Cat sitting, blue bow. 56mm.   12.00
Rabbit, crouching. 60mm long.   8.50

Great War
Cannon Shell. 75mm.   7.50
British Searchlight. 70mm.   31.50
Glengarry, with coloured thistle.
    78mm long.   16.00
Kitbag. 72mm.   19.50

Home/Nostalgic
Old Warming Pan. Inscribed: *Sally
    Warm the Bed.* 130mm long.   13.00
Sundial on circular base. Inscribed:
    What-o-clock. 127mm.   13.00

Musical Instruments
Lute. 158mm long.   30.00

Footwear

Ankle Boot, laces undone.
    78mm long.   6.50
Shoe Posy Holder. 100mm long.   6.50

Crown China

Trademark used by Wiltshaw and Robinson
    Ltd, Carlton Works, Stoke-on-Trent (usual
    trademark Carlton).
For details of this firm and the china
    manufactured see CARLTON CHINA.
This mark seems to have been used up to the
    twenties as an alternative trademark to
    Carlton. No view ware or other transfer
    devices have been found on pieces
    marked Crown.

Crown Models
Buildings – White
Cottage, two chimneys. 50mm.   10.50
Brick cottage, one chimney, on
    rectangular base. 48mm.   12.00

Traditional/National Souvenirs
Blackpool Big Wheel. 82mm.   14.00
Irish Harp, surmounted by crown,
    decorated with green shamrocks.   12.50
Jenny Jones, Welsh lady, standing
    figure with black hat, brown
    basket and red and green shawl.
    147mm.   35.00
Welsh Hat, with orange or gilded
    band. 44mm.   5.00

Seaside Souvenirs
Motorboat with driver on waves.
    120mm long.   22.50
Lifeboat. 113mm long.   12.50

Countryside
Milk Churn. 62mm.   5.00

Animals
Black Cat on oval base. 85mm.   30.00
Dog playing Banjo, inscribed: *Some
  band*. 83mm.   31.50
Dog (puppy), sitting with one ear
  raised. 83mm.   9.00
Dog, Scottie, wearing a Tam-
  o'shanter, some colouring. 82mm.   11.00
Pig, inscribed: *You can push....*
  85mm long.   15.00
Welsh Goat on rocky base,
  inscribed: *Y afr Cymreig* 98mm.   55.00

Birds
Bird cream jug. 84mm.   5.50
Hen, roosting. 60mm long.   11.00
Owl, wearing black mortar board
  with red tassel. 75mm.   20.00

Great War
HM Hospital Ship Anglia, Model of
  with 2 funnels. 165mm long.   75.00
Minesweeper. *SH* and blue stripe.
  115mm long.   47.50

Home/Nostalgic
Armchair, ornate with barley twist arms.
  120mm.   12.50
Bellows, ornate. 93mm long.   7.50
Grandfather Clock, inscribed: *Make
  use of time. Let not advantage slip.*
  135mm.   13.00
Portmanteau. 55mm long.   4.00
Rocking Chair. 96mm.   19.50
Sundial square or bulbous,
  inscribed: *Let others tell of storms
  and showers I'll count the sunny
  hours*. 90mm.   7.50
Sundial, circular. 76mm.   5.50
Sundial, bulbous. *What O'Clock* and
  Life's but a walking shadow. 130mm.   13.00
Village Pump, round. 76mm.   7.50
Water Pump with trough.
  75mm.   11.00

Comic/Novelty
I'm forever blowing bubbles. Pears
  advert Blue Boy blowing bubbles.
  Clothes blue, bubble and bowl
  lustre. 110mm.   75.00
Truck of Coal, *Black diamonds from...*
  95mm long.   25.00

Alcohol
Beer Barrel on stilts. XXX in red on
  sides. 57mm.   5.50

Bottle. 90mm.   6.50
Toby Jug, with verse. 79mm.   12.50

Sport/Pastimes
British Sports Series
Golf club head *FORE, The Ancient
  Game of Golf was first played in
  1448*. 65mm.   18.50
Tennis Player holding Racquet in
  front of net, inscribed: *40 Love.*
  Some colouring. 83mm.   125.00
  Can be found on ashtray base.

Transport
Luggage Trolley inscribed: *Luggage
  in Advance,* etc. 80mm long.   40.00
Motorbike and Sidecar with rider.
  102mm long.   75.00
Open Sports Car, inscribed: *DN999.*
  105mm long.   40.00

Footwear
John Waterman's Clog. 100mm long.   18.50

Modern Equipment
Gramophone in Cabinet, black
  record on turntable, inscribed:
  Music hath charms. 92mm.   75.00
Gramophone with dog, inscribed:
  His Masters Voice. 90mm long.   70.00
Telephone, stick type, inscribed:
  Hello, hello. 115mm.   23.00
Treadle Sewing Machine. 72mm.   24.00

Miniature Domestic
Tea Pot with lid. 90mm.   7.50

Domestic
Hair-pins, ornate box and lid.
  100mm long.   7.50

Miscellaneous
Horseshoe. 105mm long.   3.00

Crown Derby

Trademark used by Crown Derby Porcelain
Company Ltd.

Crown Derby Models
Footwear
Lady's Slipper. 98mm long.   20.00

Crown Devon

Trademark used by S. Fielding and Co (Ltd),
Railway Pottery, Devon Pottery, Stoke.
This factory specialised in lustre ware
with a yellow sheen.
S. Fielding and Co established in 1879, are
earthenware manufacturers. The firm
were not kown to produce a range of
crested china and only a small number of
models have been recorded. They would
all appear to be souvenirs from the Isle of
Man. The mark above was registered in
1930 but was probably used long before
that.

Crown Devon Models
Buildings – White
Tower of Refuge, Douglas IOM, also
found in lustre and always with a
Douglas Crest. 68mm.   30.00

Traditional/National Souvenirs
Legs of Man, lustre. 101mm.   13.00

Animals
Cat, Manx. 78mm.   17.50

Home/Nostalgic
Shaving Mug. 90mm.   5.50

Transport
Racing car with driver and co-
driver, coloured, inscribed: *Manx*
International Motor Car Race.
140mm long.   135.00

Domestic
Butter Pot. Lidded wooden tub,
  inscribed 'Manx Butter Pot'.
  No. 695. 100mm.   12.00
Dish. 81mm dia.   3.00
Gravy boat with Legs of Man
  handle with matching saucer
  (pottery). 135mm long.   20.00
Pot and lid bearing a colour transfer.
  86mm.   5.00

The Crown Duchy English China

Trademark probably used for a Morecambe
  retailer by an unknown English manufacturer, but probably Taylor and Kent
  (Ltd.), Florence Works, Longton. (Usual
  trademark Florentine).

Crown Duchy Models
Birds
Chicken. 63mm long.   9.00

Alcohol
Tankard. 74mm.   4.00

Miniature Domestic
Teapot and lid. 50mm.   7.50
Teapot and lid. 72mm.   7.50

A range of domestic ware all with
  Morecambe crests was produced.

C & SC

C & S . C

Trademark used by Taylor and Kent (Ltd.), Florence Works, Longton. (Usual trademark Florentine), for agents Collins & Sons, Chelmsford.

See Florentine China for details of the firm.

The three crests recorded so far are of Durban, Chelmsford and Saffron Walden. Saffron Walden is close enough to Chelmsford for Collins & Sons to have stocked this crest, but it is a mystery as to why a model with a Durban crest was given the C & S.C. mark. Taylor and Kent were known to export arms ware, and possibly used this mark on an extra model to complete an order.

C and SC Models
Seaside Souvenirs
Yacht. 127mm.   12.50

Home/Nostalgic
Baby's Cradle. 73mm long.   10.50

Domestic
Oil Lamp with lid. 95mm long.
    (arms of Chelmsford).   7.00

Crown Staffordshire

Trademark used by Crown Staffordshire Porcelain Co. Ltd, Minerva Works, Fenton. Subsequently Crown Staffordshire China Co. Ltd.

This very well known firm did not produce a range of crested china, but, like most famous firms, could not disregard the prevailing fashions. A miniature milk jug and sugar basin with crests have been recorded and this would seem to indicate that a little miniature domestic ware was made. No 'smalls' have been recorded, which is rather odd as most manufacturers would have added crests to small vases and jugs to satisfy customers' demands.

Crown Staffordshire Models
Miniature Domestic
Milk Jug.   3.00
Sugar Bowl.   3.00

Curzon Art

CW and Co.

Trademark probably used for a retailer by
   Hewitt and Leadbeater, Willow Potteries,
   Longton (usual trademark Willow Art).
This mark has been found on 'smalls' with
   World War I commemoratives.

Four flags of the Allies and the
   inscription: *United we stand.*   from 5.50

Trademark used by Charles Waine (and Co.),
   Derby Works, Longton (usual trademark
   Venetia China).
For further details see Venetia China.

CW and Co. Models
This mark has been found on a
   crinkle top vase with the
   inscription: *Festival of Empire,
   Crystal Palace, 1911.* 72mm.   7.50

Animals
Polar Bear. 105mm long,
   63mm high, rare.   50.00

Cyclone

CYCLONE
H. A. A. & S

CYCLONE
A.A.A.
L
CHINA

CYCLONE
A.A.A.

Three marks recorded may well have been used by different manufacturers.

Trademark used by a wholesaler of crested china manufactured by several well-known firms including Taylor and Kent and Wiltshaw and Robinson (usual trademarks Florentine and Carlton).
For details of the above manufacturers see Florentine China and Carlton China.
The initials AAA L are most certainly those of a large wholesaler who could have been based in London but was more probably in the Potteries at Longton. Models have been recorded as being identical to several well known ranges but most seem to have been made by Taylor and Kent and Wiltshaw and Robinson. A great number of 'smalls' and some domestic ware have been recorded but no transfer devices other than crests have so far been reported, indicating the mark was not used after the early twenties.

Cyclone Models
Ancient Artefacts

Ancient Tyg, one handle, not named. 70mm.	3.00
Chester Roman Vase, not named. 2 sizes: 50mm and 68mm.	3.00
Irish Bronze Pot, not named. 50mm.	3.00
Loving Cup, 3 handled. 38mm.	3.00
Salisbury Kettle, not named. 100mm.	3.00

Buildings – White

Blackpool Tower. 117mm.	10.50
Cottage. 70mm long.	6.50

Monuments (including Crosses)

Iona Cross, not named. 108mm.	10.50

Historical/Folklore

Man in Pillory. 105mm.	20.00
Man in Stocks. 103mm.	22.50

Traditional/National Souvenirs

Highland Quauch. 83mm dia.	4.00

Seaside Souvenirs

Bathing Machine. 76mm.	10.00
Bathing Machine with figure in doorway. 75mm.	14.50
Yacht, in full sail. 127mm.	12.50
Lighthouse. 100mm.	5.00
Whelk Shell. 100mm long.	5.00
Child sitting on Rock. 110mm.	16.00

Countryside

Milk Churn, 2 handles and lid. 70mm.	5.00

Animals

Cat, very plump with open mouth. 88mm.	13.00
Cat smiling, could be an unnamed Cheshire cat. 76mm.	6.50
Manx Cat. 90mm.	20.00
Dog in Kennel. 85mm.	8.00
King Charles Spaniels, two in top hat. 70mm.	15.00
Elephant kneeling. 82mm long.	15.00
Monkey crouching, hands to mouth. 90mm.	24.00
Pig, standing, inscribed: *The pig that won't go.* 85mm long.	10.50
Rabbit. 70mm long.	8.50
Seal with ball on nose. 75mm.	17.50
Terrapin.	13.00
Toad, very flat. 72mm long only 32mm high.	19.50
Tortoise. 75mm.	9.00

Birds

Fledgling cream jug. 68mm.	5.50
Kingfisher. 80mm long.	30.00
Owl, standing. 70mm.	13.00
Pelican cream jug. 83mm long.	5.50
Swan.	6.50
Swan posy bowl. 75mm long.	5.00

Great War

Submarine, inscribed: *E9*. Blunt nosed. 146mm long.	40.00
Armoured Car, with 3 guns on turret, inscribed: *RNAS*. 116mm long.	140.00
Tank. 125mm long.	17.50
Drum. 32mm.	5.00
Shell. 75mm.	3.00
Telescope, folded. 70mm.	13.00
Cenotaph, inscribed: *The blood of heroes is the seed of freedom*.	
2 sizes: 100mm.	5.00
140mm.	5.50

Home/Nostalgic

Old Armchair. 87mm.	7.50
Baby in hip bath.	
2 sizes: 90mm long.	11.00
103mm long.	12.50
Coal Bucket. 60mm.	5.00
Cradle on rockers. 58mm long.	10.50
Lantern. 65mm.	5.50
Oil Lamp. 60mm.	5.00
Pillar Box, inscribed: *I can't get a letter from you so send you the box*. 76mm.	14.00
Sofa. 82mm long.	17.00
Shaving Mug. 55mm.	5.50
Suitcase.	
2 sizes: 77mm long.	4.00
83mm long.	4.00
Watering Can. 70mm.	5.50

Comic/Novelty

Boy on Scooter. 106mm.	20.00
Jack in the Box. 90mm.	20.00

Alcohol

Toby Jug. 65mm.	6.50
Upright Barrel. 53mm.	3.00

Sport

Boxing Glove. 70mm long.	30.00
Cricket Bag. 110mm long.	12.50

Musical Instruments

Tambourine. 70mm dia.	6.50

Modern Equipment

Square Gramophone. No horn. Arm is on edge of record. Crest also on record. 53mm wide.	15.50
Radio Horn. 95mm.	25.00

Footwear

Lancashire Clog. 88mm long.	5.50
Oriental slipper. 100mm long.	5.00
Sabot. 95mm long.	5.00
Shoes, Ladies' 18th Century. 95mm long.	7.50

Domestic

Hairbrush Trinket Box with lid. 140mm long.	14.00

Miniature Domestic

Coffee Pot with lid. 65mm.	7.50
Teapot with lid. 75mm.	7.50

The Dainty Ware

Trademark used by a London wholesaler on crested china manufactured by a number of companies but mainly Taylor and Kent (usual trademark Florentine).

For details of Taylor and Kent see Florentine. EB and Co were almost certainly the initials of a London wholesaler. Although the majority of models marked The Dainty Ware were definitely made by Taylor and Kent, others seem to have been made by a number of other manufacturers. A 'Japan' crest has been found on a model of a mouse. The crests of the Allies were reproduced during the Great War by J.A. Robinson Ltd but any other manufacturer could have produced them if requested. Several B.E.E. 1924 and 1925 crests have been recorded with this mark, but they are unlikely to have been made by Taylor and Kent. Quite a number of 'smalls' have

been recorded but there are no clues as to their manufacturer. For the most part wares with The Dainty Ware mark are rather crude and were obviously sold very cheaply.

Dainty Ware Models
Ancient Artefacts

Carlisle Salt Pot, not named. 62mm.	3.00
Puzzle Jug. 60mm.	5.50
Salisbury Kettle. 100mm.	3.00
Three-handled Loving Cup. 38mm.	3.00

Historical/Folklore

Man in Pillory. 104mm.	20.00

Traditional/National Souvenirs

Welsh Harp. 97mm.	10.00

Seaside Souvenirs

Bathing Machine. 71mm.	11.00
Bathing Machine with figure on steps. 75mm.	14.50
Rowing Boat. 100mm long.	8.50
Yacht in full sail. 127mm.	12.50
Lighthouse on rocks. 95mm.	5.50
Whelk Shell.	5.00
Child sitting on rock. 110mm.	16.00

Countryside

Tree trunk section, hollow. 73mm long.	10.50

Animals

Bulldog in Kennel. 68mm.	10.50
Dogs, two King Charles Spaniels in a Top Hat. 70mm.	15.00
Dog, sitting, head on one side, blue eyes. 69mm.	8.50
Pup, sitting, red eyes, bow around neck. 77mm.	10.50
Fish, open mouth. 110mm long.	3.00
Mouse. 63mm long.	13.00
Pig, sitting. 63mm long.	8.50
Seal, with ball. 72mm.	17.50

Birds

Baby Bird cream jug.	
2 sizes: 48mm.	5.50
68mm.	5.50
Duck posy holder, yellow beak. 80mm long.	6.50
Hen, roosting. 63mm long.	7.50
Kingfisher, with long beak. 80mm.	30.00
Parakeet. 75mm.	10.50

Swan posy holder. 88mm long. 5.00

Great War
Tommy and his Machine Gun.
  75mm. 30.00
Tank. 164mm long. 22.50
Wide Tank. 120mm long. 20.00
Red Cross Van inscribed: *EH139*.
  90mm. 30.00
Battleship. 110mm long. 16.00
Drum. 30mm. 5.00
Pickelhaube or spiked military
  helmet. 16.00
Cenotaph. 142mm. 5.50

Home/Nostalgic
Baby in hip bath. 103mm long. 12.50
Book. 57mm. 5.00
Coal Scuttle. No. 165. 70mm. 3.00
Cradle on rocker. 58mm long. 9.00
Flat Iron. 77mm long. 12.50
Grandfather Clock. 130mm. 10.50
Invalid Feeder. 85mm long. 6.00
Lantern. 70mm. 5.50
Oil Lamp. 60mm. 5.00
Old Armchair, with usual verse.
  85mm. 7.50
Pillar Box. 76mm. 12.50
Policeman's Lamp. 70mm. 10.00
Portmanteau. 78mm. 4.00
Shaving Mug. 56mm. 6.50
Sofa. 80mm long. 10.50

Comic/Novelty
Boy on Scooter. 106mm. 20.00
Jack-in-a-Box. 91mm. 20.00

Alcohol
Champagne bottle in ice bucket.
  Something good. A bottle of the
  "boy". 85mm. 14.50

Sport/Pastimes
Boxing Glove. 65mm long. 30.00
Cricket Bag. 110mm long. 12.50
Cricket Cap. 65mm. 45.00

Musical Instruments
Tambourine. 70mm dia. 6.50

Transport
Charabanc with driver. 118mm long. 33.00

Modern Equipment
Square Gramophone with arm on
  edge of record. Crest also on the
  record. 57mm wide. 15.50

Footwear
Ladies Shoe with high heel and
  fluted tongue – 18th Century
  shoe. No. 187. 90mm long. 7.50
Lancashire Clog. 88mm long. 5.50
Sabot. 70mm long. 4.00

Miniature Domestic
Cheese Dish and cover. 75mm long. 6.50
Coffee Pot with lid. 63mm. 7.50
Kettle with lid. 80mm. 7.50
Tea Pot with lid, ribbed sides.
  85mm long. 7.50
Tea Pot with lid, shaped body.
  56mm high, 95mm long. 7.50

Domestic
Cake slice pin box and lid.
  140mm long. 14.00
Lily flower Vase. 120mm. 8.50

Derwent China

Devonia Art China

Trademark used for J.M. White, retailer in Matlock Bath by an unknown English china manufacturer.

Derwent Models
Ancient Artefacts

Fountains Abbey Cup. 60mm.	3.00
Loving Cup, 3 handled. 36mm.	3.00

Miniature Domestic

Beaker. 40mm.	3.00

Trademark used by Hewitt and Leadbeater for a Devon wholesaler or agent (usual trademark Willow Art).

For details of this firm and the china see Willow Art China.

It is likely that WB was based in Plymouth, and that Hewitt and Leadbeater and subsequently Hewitt Bros made crested ware for them for some time and in some quantity. There are Great War souvenirs and memorials, and some later models such as Black Cats. 'Black Cat' transfers were also made for the firm. A great number of 'smalls' have been recorded. Crests from all over Devon can be found and occasionally other places.

Numbering System. Willow models often carry stock numbers and where these are known they are the same.

Devonia Art Models
Ancient Artefacts

Glastonbury Roman Ewer. 60mm.	3.00
Loving Cup, 3 handled. 40mm.	3.00

Buildings – White

Citadel Gateway, Plymouth. 110mm.	30.00
Derry's Clock Tower, Plymouth.	
3 sizes: 125mm.	16.00
134mm.	18.00
156mm.	20.00

Monuments (including Crosses)
Plymouth Armada Memorial. inscribed:
Plymouth War Memorial. He blew with his winds and they were scattered.

2 sizes: 170mm	34.50
190mm.	30.00
Drake Statue, Plymouth. 160mm.	14.50
Mayflower Stone, 1620, Model of.	
90mm.	60.00

Historical/Folklore
Bell, inscribed: *Curfew must not ring*	
tonight. 70mm.	7.50

Traditional/National Souvenirs
Bagpipes. 118 long.	20.00
Welsh Hat. 58mm.	5.00

Seaside Souvenirs
Lighthouse, not named. 110mm.	5.00
Shell on stand, posy holder.	7.50
Scallop shell on coral hatpin holder.	
80mm.	10.50

Animals
Boar. 95mm long.	20.00
Black Cat, sitting on diamond shaped astray, inscribed: *Good luck* and *Ashtray.* Impressed No. 1016. 120mm long.	20.00
Cat, fluffy sitting. 75mm.	12.00
Cat standing with shield around neck. 75mm.	12.50
Dog, Bulldog, walking. 90mm long.	13.00
Dog, Bulldog, emerging from kennel, inscribed: *The Black Watch.* 70mm long.	19.50
Dog, Collie, sitting, bow round neck. 60mm.	12.50
Dog, Collie, standing with shield around neck. 60mm.	12.50
Dog, Labrador. 90mm.	12.50
Dog, Scottish Terrier, standing. 88mm long.	14.50
Elephant, walking. 52mm.	17.00
Elephant Jug. 70mm.	12.50
Lion, walking. 120mm long.	14.50
Pig, standing. 85mm long.	10.00
Pony, inscribed: *A native of Shetland.* 110mm long.	25.00
Rabbit, sitting, with alert ears. 60mm long.	7.50
Teddy Bear, sitting. 76mm.	19.50

Birds
Canary on rock. 98mm.	13.00
Chicken. No. 911. 40mm.	5.50
Swan posy bowl. 35mm.	5.00

Great War
Soldier, inscribed: *Our Brave Defender.* 130mm.	47.50
Standing Nurse inscribed: *A Friend in need.* 135mm.	40.00
Monoplane with revolving prop. 150mm long.	65.00
Airship, inscribed: *Beta.* 75mm long.	55.00
Battleship. 116mm long.	19.00
Battleship, impressed. *HMS Lion.* 140mm long.	30.00
Battleship, inscribed: *HMS Tiger* 160mm long.	55.00
Troop Carrier, Liner converted. No. 213. 140mm long (rare).	95.00
Tank, inscribed: *HMS Whippet Tank.* 120mm long.	95.00
Tank with inscriptions: *HMLS Creme de Menthe, Victory of Justice...* & *British Tank successfully...* 130mm long.	30.00
Tank with trailing wheels. 125mm long.	17.50
Field Gun with screen. 115mm.	19.00
Trench Mortar Gun. 100mm.	47.50
Officer's Peaked Cap. 80mm long.	10.50
Fireplace, inscribed: *Keep the home fires burning.* Some colouring. 100mm long.	17.00
Drum. 56mm dia.	10.50
Cheddar War Memorial, with inscription: *Praise God and remember the men of Cheddar who died for their country in the Great War 1914-1919.* 148mm.	170.00
Plymouth War Memorial. 120mm, 145mm.	125.00
Plymouth Naval War Memorial. 2 sizes which are slightly different models:	
140mm octagonal stepped base.	65.00
160mm 4 columns at base.	65.00

Home/Nostalgic
Coal scuttle, helmet shaped. No. 101. 53mm.	5.00
Sundial on circular base, with inscription: *'I mark not the hours'.* 118mm.	10.50
Sundial on square base. 84mm.	7.50

Comic/Novelty
Billiken. 60mm.	7.50
Sack of Meal with Mouse, inscribed:	

May the mouse ne'er leave yer meal
poke wi' a tear drop in its eye.
63mm.   14.50

Alcohol
Barrel. 50mm.   3.00
Barrel on stand. 59mm.   5.50
Whiskey Bottle. No. 134. 63mm.   6.50
Whiskey Bottle, inscribed: *One*
   Special Scotch. 88mm.   7.50

Transport
Cycle Lamp. 83mm.   55.00
Open Tourer, 4-seater. 112mm long.   40.00

Musical Instruments
Harp. 88mm.   6.50

Footwear
Lancashire Clog. 88mm long.   5.00

Miniature Domestic
Cheese Dish, 1 piece. 68mm long.   7.50
Cup and Saucer. 35mm.   5.50
Shaving Mug. 63mm.   5.50

Domestic
Pepper Pot, octagonal. 95mm.   3.00

Diamond China

Trademark used by a London wholesaler, the china being manufactured by several leading crested ware specialists, including Birks, Rawlins and Co., Hewitt and Leadbeater and A.B. Jones and Sons Ltd. (usual trademarks Savoy, Willow Art and Grafton).

The tradename Diamond China was registered by the Blyth Porcelain Co., Blyth Works, High Street, Longton. However, this firm used the initials B.P. Co. Ltd., and printed the diamond the other way up. So I think we can discount this manufacturer who never actually advertised crested wares.

H.M. and Co. Ltd, was in all probability a London wholesaler. Why the mark sometimes carries the initial W is rather a mystery. (It is just possibly the manufacturer's initial, see W.)

Some models with this mark are recognisably made by Birks, Rawlins and Co. (see Savoy China). All pieces from this factory are rejects, usually having bad firing flaws, in which event the value of such a piece will be reduced by 25%. Minor flaws can be discounted. Others are definitely made by Hewitt and Leadbeater (see Willow Art). Although the majority of known models and 'smalls' in this range were made by these two firms, there are a few models which were not. One model, a man with his feet and head protruding from a barrel looks very like a model made by A.B. Jones and Sons Ltd. (see Grafton China). Probably many firms supplied this wholesaler.

Crests are from all parts of the British Isles, but only early models and Great War souvenirs seemed to have been made, indicating that the mark was not used after the War.

One piece of view ware has been recorded which could have been produced by any of the potters mentioned above. A Great War commemorative is found with this mark, taking the form of a transfer of Four Flags of the Allies and inscribed: *United we stand*. This device was used by Willow Art. Stock numbers are given where known.

Diamond Models
Ancient Artefacts
Puzzle Jug. 66mm.	5.50

Historical/Folklore
Bunyan's Chair, Model of. No. 42. 90mm.	19.00
Mons Meg, Edinburgh Castle, Model of. 130mm long.	12.00

Traditional/National Souvenirs
Dutch Boy. 78mm.	10.50

Seaside Souvenirs
Bathing Machine. 60mm.	10.00
Lighthouse, on rocky circular base. 110mm.	5.50
Fisherman leaning into barrel. No. 395. 70mm.	30.00
Oyster Shell on shell base. 80mm long.	4.00
Scallop Shell. 76mm.	3.00

Animals
Cat in Boot, blue collar. 92mm long.	14.50
Elephant, walking. 52mm.	17.00
Grotesque animal. 100mm.	10.00
Pig, standing. 70mm long.	10.00
Rabbit, crouching. 89mm long.	8.50
Seal. 62mm long.	13.00

Birds
Canary. 100mm.	10.50
Duck, swimming. 67mm long.	13.50

Great War
Airship (observation Balloon), inscribed: *Beta*. 80mm long.	55.00
Battleship, impressed: *HMS Lion*. 140mm long.	30.00
Armoured Car. 125mm long.	80.00
Red Cross Van with 'Rolls Royce' front. 110mm long.	40.00
British Motor Searchlight, Model of. 103mm long.	145.00
Field Gun with screen. 55mm.	19.00
Trench Mortar Gun. 98mm long.	47.50
Cannon Shell. 73mm.	4.00
Balmoral Bonnett. 73mm dia.	20.00
French Trench Helmet. 80mm long.	40.00
R.F.C. Cap. 76mm long.	40.00
Glengarry.	
2 sizes: 78mm long.	16.00
100mm long.	18.00
New Zealand Hat. 80mm long.	20.00
Drum. 56mm dia.	6.00
Tent with open flaps. 70mm.	25.00

Alcohol
Barrel. 52mm long.	3.50

Miniature Domestic
Cheese Dish. 1 piece. 45mm long.	6.50
Cheese Dish and cover. 45mm long.	7.50

Disa Art China

"DISA"
ART
VALENTINE & SONS
CHINA
CAPE TOWN

Trademark used by Valentine and Sons, Cape Town. China manufactured by Hewitt Bros. (usual trademark Willow Art).
For details of china see Willow Art China.

A range of 'smalls' usually with Cape Town and area crests and one bowl with a crest of the Municipality of the City of East London have been recorded in addition to the models listed below.

Disa Models
Traditional/National Souvenirs
Dutch Girl. 78mm.   10.50

Animals
Monkey holding nut. 85mm.   17.00

Birds
Wise Owl winking, with verse: *An
    aged owl sat in an oak*, etc. 93mm.   14.50

Great War
Liner Converted to Troop Carrier.
    140mm long.   95.00
Kitbag with verse: *Pack up your
    troubles*. 75mm.   19.50
Pickelhaube. 51mm.   30.00

Home/Nostalgic
Anvil. 57mm.   5.50

Alcohol
Barrel, on side. 44mm.   3.50

Miniature Domestic
Coffee Pot with lid. 70mm.   7.50

Do! Do! Crest China

LL & L
D

Trademark used for a wholesaler, by Hewitt and Leadbeater and Birks, Rawlins & Co. (Usual trademarks Willow Art and Savoy).
This wholesaler – LL and LD – also used another mark (see Wy Not China) on wares manufactured by Hewitt and Leadbeater. The mouse found with the Do! Do! mark is known to be a Hewitt and Leadbeater mould. (See Willow Art China.)
However the elephant recorded was made by Birks, Rawlins and Co. (see Savoy China), but does not carry their stock number. It is quite possible that they used this mark however, their numbering system was nothing if not unreliable. Only a Great War commemorative crest of flags of the Allies has been found on models with this mark. This indicates that the mark was only used for a short time.

Do! Do! Models
Animals
Elephant, sitting. 70mm.   25.00
Mouse. 64mm long.   20.00

Dolphin

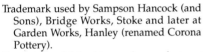

Trademark used by Sampson Hancock (and Sons), Bridge Works, Stoke and later at Garden Works, Hanley (renamed Corona Pottery).

For details of this china and manufacturer see Corona China.

Dolphin Model
Miniature Domestic
Cheese Dish and cover, circular.
85mm dia.   6.50

Doric Herald

Trademark used by Taylor and Kent (Ltd), Florence Works, Longton for the Glasgow wholesaler CR & Co. Glasgow. See also Atlas Heraldic and Caledonia China. (Usual trademark Florentine).

This mark seems to have been used on domestic pieces only.
Value   £2.00-£5.50.

Dougall's "Castle" Series

DRGM

DRGM

Trademark used for a retailer by Hewitt and Leadbeater. (usual mark Willow). Only one model known with Rothesay crest.

Monuments (including Crosses)
Highland Mary, statue on plinth.
  150mm.   25.00

Impressed mark found on German china.

Comic/Novelty
Locomotive and coaltruck,
  condiment set, lustre.
  130mm long.   13.00

The Duchess China

Can be found with H & CL under mark instead of S. Hancock & Sons above.

Trademark used by Sampson Hancock (and Sons), Bridge Works, Stoke and later at Garden Works, Hanley (renamed Corona Pottery). Many of its shapes carry the European War 1914 decoration with crossed flags and bunting to rim. Add £5 for pieces found with this decoration. (Usual trademark Corona).

For details of this firm and their products see The Corona China.

S. Hancock and Sons usually used the alternative mark Corona on crested ware, this mark having been registered as early as 1898. Most pieces recorded are 'smalls', decorative dishes and bagware and it would seem likely that the crests were added to pieces originally designed and marked to be sold plain. Although some English and Welsh crests are found, these pieces usually carry a Great War commemorative, four flags of the Allies with the inscription: *1914 European War.* Two interesting commemorative transfers have also been recorded: 'Soldier of the 12th Lancers' and 'Royal Engineers'. These models do not appear to carry stock numbers. The Rd. No. found on models refers to the mark and not the model, it is Rd. No. 330440.

Duchess Models
Ancient Artefacts
Puzzle Jug with verse. 70mm.   5.50

Salisbury Kettle. 110mm.   3.00

Buildings – White
Bridge, with grassy banks.
134mm long.   20.00

Historical/Folklore
HRH Prince of Wales, future Edward VIII, in his investiture costume, standing on base. 88mm long. (Very rare).   130.00

Traditional/National Souvenirs
A Cornish Pasty. 95mm long.   7.50
Welsh Hat. 55mm.   5.00

Seaside Souvenirs
Lighthouse. 110mm.   5.50

Countryside
Milk Churn with lid. 85mm.   5.00

Animals
Cat in boot, white bow.
96mm long.   12.50
Teddy Bear, sitting.
2 sizes: 75mm.   17.00
90mm.   18.00
Elephant. 74mm long.   17.00
Elephant Jug. 70mm.   12.50

Birds
Swan posy holder.   5.00

Great War
Battleship, four small twin funnels.
140mm long.   26.00
Picklehaube. 50mm.   30.00
Bell Tent. 70mm.   16.50

Home/Nostalgic
Shaving Mug. 55m.   5.50
Watering Can. 74mm.   5.50
Wooden Pail with rope handle.
64mm.   3.50

Comic/Novelty
Billiken, grotesque. 68mm.   4.00

Footwear
Lancashire Clog. 87mm long.   5.00

Miniature Domestic
Bagware Jug. 51mm.   3.00
Cheese Dish and cover. 65mm.   6.50

Cheese Dish and cover, circular.
    87mm dia.   6.50
Kettle with lid. 80mm.   10.00

Domestic
Inkwell with four grille holes.
    52mm.   12.50
Pepper Pot, octagonal. 94mm.   7.50

Eclipse China

Previously unknown work of an unknown
British wholesaler, possibly in the West
Country as the coat of arms on the only
known piece is Devizes. Probably
manufactured by Carlton China.

Home/Nostalgic
Time Glass. 60mm.   10.00

Eglinton China

Trademark used for a Scottish retailer by an unknown British manufacturer.

Traditional/National Souvenirs
Thistle vase. 50mm.   3.00

Animals
Fish. 125mm long.   3.00

Domestic
Rectangular box and lid, ornately
  carved. 94mm long.   8.50

Elite

Trademark of H.M. & Co. The two crests recorded with this mark are Weymouth, Melcombe Regis and Godalming.

Ancient Artefacts
London vessel found during
  excavations. 65mm.   4.00

Miniature Domestic
Cup and Saucer. 35mm.   5.00

Elite China Series

Trademark used for the retailer David S.
Butler of Derby (Forerunner of the Butler
Group of Companies) by Hewitt and
Leadbeater, Willow Potteries, Longton.
(Usual trademark Willow Art).
For details of china and manufacturers see
Willow Art China.
All crests found are Derby or its environs,
and pieces are often found impressed: H
AND L WILLOW ENGLAND.
Stock numbers where recorded are the same
as those found on Willow Art models.

Elite Models
Monuments (including Crosses)
Baron Burton Statue. 70mm.   28.00

Historical/Folklore
James V Chair.   7.50
Mary Queen of Scots Chair. 85mm.   6.50

Traditional/National Souvenirs
Cornish Pasty. 100mm long.   7.50

Animals
Cat, walking, with blue bow.
    80mm long.   10.50
Cat, fat and angry, tail in air. 80mm. 17.00
Lion, walking. 110mm long.   12.50
Rabbit. 57mm long.   7.50

Great War
Soldier with rifle, inscribed: *Our
    Brave Defender.* 132mm.   47.50
Nurse, with red cross on apron,
    inscribed: *A Friend in Need.*
    133mm.   40.00

Red Cross Van, red cross on side.
    No. 218. 84mm long.   30.00
Florence Nightingale Statue, Model of.
    No. 225. 185mm.   20.00
Mickleover War Memorial inscribed
    with 26 names of the fallen and *To
    the glorious dead of Mickleover
    1914-1919.* No crest. 135mm.   125.00

Home/Nostalgic
Grandfather Clock, inscribed. 112m.   10.50

Cartoon/Comedy
Baby with arms outstretched,
    inscribed: *Cheerio.* Some
    colouring on face. 125mm.   30.00
Billiken the God of Luck. 102mm.   10.50

Miscellaneous
Hand holding Tulip. 80mm.   5.00

Miniature Domestic
Cup and Saucer. 35mm.   5.00

Empire China

Trademark used for an unknown retailer or wholesaler on china manufactured by William Richie & Son Ltd, 24, 26 and 28 Elder Street, Edinburgh. (Usual trademark Porcelle).

Empire Models
Ancient Artefacts
Loving Cup, 2 handled. No. 47.
   41mm.   3.00

Seaside Souvenirs
Boat. 130mm long.   10.50
Whelk Shell. No. 451. 80mm long.   3.00

Great War
Bell Tent. 67mm.   16.00

Hats
Top Hat. 44mm.   5.50

Miniature Domestic
Cheese Dish and cover. 46mm.   6.50
Trinket Box, hexagonal, and lid.
   36mm.   4.00

Empire Gem

Trademark used by Schmidt and Co., Carlsbad (Bohemia) For further details of this china see Gemma.

A range of domestic and miniature ware was produced.
                Price £3.00-5.00

Miniature Domestic
Cheese Dish with curved lid.
   80mm long.   5.50

Empress China

Endor China

EMPRESS
CHINA

Trademark used by Schmidt and Co, Carlsbad (Bohemia) (Usual trademark Gemma).

Trademark used for a retailer by an unknown manufacturer, but possibly Birks, Rawlins and Co (Ltd), Vine Pottery, Stoke. (Usual trademark Savoy).

Empress Models
Ancient Artefacts
Chester Roman Vase, not named.
58mm.   3.00

Animals
The Cheshire Cat. 90mm.   7.50

Cartoon/Comedy Characters
Comedian, probably W.C. Fields,
red spotted nose, mouth and eye.
85mm.   30.00

Endor Models
Ancient Artefacts
Loving Cup, 3 handled. 41mm.   3.00

Traditional/National Souvenirs
Welsh Leek Vase. 90mm.   6.50

Domestic
Bagware Jug. 50mm.   3.00

England

English China

No details of mark available.

Trademark used by an unknown British manufacturer.

A 50mm flat jug on 4 small feet has been recorded.   3.00

Trademark believed to have been used by Alfred B. Jones & Sons Ltd., Grafton China Works, Longton, Staffs. (Usual trademark Grafton).

Several shapes of small vase have been seen.   Each 3.00

Scent bottle, rectangular with ribbed back. Franco-British Exhibition 1908. 76mm.   6.50

English Emporium China

English Herald China

Mark can also be found without the rectangular outline.

Trademark used by F. Phillips, Bazaar owner, china thought to have been manufactured by James Reeves, Victoria Works, Fenton. (Usual mark Victoria China).

For details of china and manufacturer see Victoria China.

Much crested ware was advertised as being suitable for the Emporium or Bazaar Trade, so it is rather appropriate that this mark was used. The china is exactly the same as that marked VICTORIA CHINA which was thought to have been made by James Reeves. Very few pieces have so been recorded and it is very likely that this type of china was usually sold unmarked.

English Emporium Models
National Souvenirs
Welsh Hat. 62mm.   5.00

Animals
Toad. 70mm.   16.00

Birds (including Eggs)
Bird Jug. 70mm.   5.50

Home/Nostalgic
Baby's Cradle. 60mm long.   14.00

Comic/Novelty
Suffragette Handbell, double-sided
    with clapper. 110mm.   47.50

Trademark used for the Southend/Westcliffe on Sea agent by Alfred B. Jones and Son Ltd., Grafton China Works, Longton. (Usual trademark Grafton). A number of small shapes were made.

Ancient Artefacts
Swedish Kettle, not named.   3.00

English Manufacture

English Souvenir China

ENGLISH
MANUFACTURE

Trademark used by an unknown English manufacturer.

A 75mm vase with two small handles has been found with this trademark.   2.00

Trademark used for The Golden West Exhibition, 1909, by an unknown English manufacturer. All carry the Golden West Exhibition crest, or the International Exhibition crest, used by Florentine.

English Souvenir China Models
Seaside Souvenirs
Whelk Shell. 95mm long.   7.50

Animals
Camel, with 1 hump, sitting. 110mm.   18.00
Cheshire Cat always smiling. 91mm.   7.50
Elephant, kneeling. 95mm.   20.00
Fish, with open mouth. 118mm long.   8.50

Home/Nostalgic
Anvil.   8.50

Cartoon/Comedy Characters
Ally Sloper, bust, not named. 85mm.   30.00

Musical Instruments
Tambourine. 68mm dia.   6.50

Miniature Domestic
Mug. 47mm.   7.50

Erin China

Trademark used for an Irish wholesaler by a British manufacturer.

Erin Models
Ancient Artefacts

Carlisle Salt Pot. 65mm.	4.00
Fountain Abbey Abbot's Cup, not named. 49mm.	4.00

Esbeco

Trademark used for the retailer S.B. & Co. possibly by Willow Art.

SB and Co. are not the initials of any china or earthenware manufacturer who are recorded as having made crested ware. The mark is probably that of a Scottish wholesaler. The models below may have been supplied by Hewitt and Leadbeater. (See Willow Art China).

Esbeco Models
Great War

Monoplane with movable prop. 67mm.	65.00
British Tank, Model of, with inset wheels. 95mm long.	15.00
HMS Lion, impressed battleship. No. 213.	30.00
Red Cross Van. No. 216H.	30.00

Home/Nostalgic

Anvil. 57mm.	5.50

Cartoon/Comedy

Baby with arms outstretched. Coloured face. Similar to Cheerio Baby. 122mm.	40.00

Domestic

Trefoil Cruet Set.	3.50

Etruscan China

Exceller

BRITISH
EXCELLER
R.B.W.
MANUFACTURE

Trademark used for a retailer or wholesaler AD, probably manufactured by Charles Waine, Longton. (Usual trademark Venetia).

This mark has not been found on crested ware but black transfer prints of HMS Achilles and HM Torpedo Boat have been found on a 63mm vase and a 40mm loving cup, with this trademark. No known china manufacturer used the initials A.D. so these models could have been made by almost any firm for a wholesaler or retailer, with these initials. They are more aptly described as earthenware than china and are very similar to the colour transfer ware made by Charles Waine, the mark too being remarkably similar to the 'Venetia' mark this firm used on miniatures and 'smalls' (see Venetia China).

Etruscan Models
Three-handled loving cup with
  black transfer *HM Torpedo Boat*.
  34'. 40mm.   12.00
Vase with black transfer of *HMS*
  Achilles. 63mm.   12.00

Trademark used for a retailer in the south of England, especially Worthing, by Sampson Hancock (and Sons). (Usual trademark Corona).

For details of this china see The Corona China.

It is possible that R.B.W. owned a chain of souvenir shops in southern seaside towns. Crests so far recorded are Worthing, Littlehampton, Brighton and Lewes.

Exceller Models
Ancient Artefacts
Canterbury Leather Bottle. 47mm.   3.00

Traditional/National Souvenirs
Laxey Wheel. 80mm.   40.00

Animals
Tortoise. 70mm long.   6.50

Birds (including Eggs)
Swan Posy holder. 80mm.   5.00

Great War
Flash Lamp. 90mm.   11.00
Ghurka Knife. 140mm long.   20.00

Home/Nostalgic
Armchair. 60mm.   12.50
Cradle on rockers, wicker.
  80mm long.   10.50
Tobacco Pouch. 75mm long.   9.50

Modern Equipment
Gas Cooker. 70mm.   10.00

Footwear
Lancashire Clog. 80mm long.   5.50

Excelsior

Trademark used by an unknown manufacturer.
This mark looks very like a manufacturer's
mark and not one used for a retailer. No
known manufacturer however used the
initials W.P. and S.L. The mark seems to
have been used only during the Great War
as all the 'smalls' found have the
commemorative: Four flags of the Allies.
Until more pieces are recorded it will be
impossible to even suggest a manufacturer.

A range of 'smalls' with
commemorative Four Flags of the
Allies was produced.
Value   from £5.00

Excelsior Models
Buildings – White
Laxey Wheel.   40.00

Animals
Pig, standing. 70mm long.   8.50

Home/Nostalgic
Grandfather Clock. 100mm.   9.00
Horn Lantern. 85mm.   5.50

Sport/Pastimes
Trophy Cup. 70mm.   10.00

Fairy Ware

Trademark used by Schmidt and Co., Carlsbad (Bohemia). (Usual trademark Gemma). These marks appear in blue, red, green or black.

For further details of this china see Gemma.

Schmidt and Co. used this mark as an alternative to the Gemma mark. A great number of small domestic items such as bowls, cups and saucers, vases and ink wells are found with the mark. The china is often very decoratively moulded. Models are often identical to those marked Gemma and pieces have been found with both marks. As Gemma is stamped over Fairy Ware it seems that the latter was an early mark, the models recorded also indicating that the mark was not used after the War.

Fairy Ware Models
Ancient Artefacts
Loving Cup, 3 handled. 39mm.   3.00
Puzzle Jug. 65mm.   5.50

Historical/Folklore
Coronation Chair. 100mm.   5.00

Seaside Souvenirs
Lighthouse on rocks. 105mm.   5.50

Animals
Cow cream jug. 103mm long.
(Probably a reproduction in
miniature of an early
Staffordshire 'creamer'.)   23.00
Dog, pug, lying, paws forward.   20.00
Dog, puppy, sitting with one ear
raised. 78mm.   9.00
Tortoise dish with lid. 80mm long.   7.50

Home/Nostalgic
Bucket with rope handle. 83mm.   3.00
Grandfather Clock, with arabic
numerals. 105mm.   8.50
Grandmother Clock, with arabic
numerals. 85mm.   5.50
Kettle, very ornate. 71mm.   7.50
Pillar Box, oval. 87mm.   10.50
Pipe, brown, on dish. 72mm long.   10.50
Shaving Mug, rope handle. 55mm.   5.50
Stool, 4 legs. 44mm.   4.00
Watering Can. 65mm.   5.50

Hats
Top Hat. 43mm.   5.50

Footwear
Sabot. 90mm long.   4.00

Miniature Domestic
Cheese Dish and cover. 55mm.   6.50
Cheese Dish and cover, two piece.   6.50
Cup and Saucer. 45mm.   5.00
Milk Jug. 40mm.   3.00
Teapot with lid, oval, ribbed sides.
48mm.   7.50
Teapot with lid. 60mm.   7.50
Teapot with lid. 85mm.   7.50

Domestic
Teapot, oval. 130mm long.   10.50

Miscellaneous
Mustard Pot and Lid on 4 gold feet.
64mm.   3.50
Winged Sphinx Jug. 85mm.   15.00

Famous Henley China

FAMOUS HENLEY CHINA

Trademark used by the retailer Hawkins, Henley-on-Thames, manufactured by Hewitt and Leadbeater, Willow Potteries Ltd, Longton. (Usual trademark Willow Art).

Famous Henley Models
Seaside Souvenirs
Eddystone Lighthouse, not named.
No. 135. 110mm.   5.00

Animals
Dog, Collie, standing, detailed fur.
105mm long.   23.00
Pig, standing.
2 sizes: 80mm.   10.00
94mm long.   12.50
Elephant, walking. 52mm.   17.00

Great War
Standing Soldier with rifle,
inscribed: *Our Brave Defender.*
130mm.   47.50

Home/Nostalgic
Watering Can. No. 126. 75mm.   5.50

Alcohol
Barrel. No. 100. 35mm long.   3.00

Miniature Domestic
Cheese Dish and cover. 50mm.   7.50

Fenton China

Mark used 1905-1912.

1900-1905.

Trademark used by E. Hughes and Co., Opal Works, Fenton.

E. Hughes and Co. was established in 1889 and were noted for their 'badge ware suitable for hotels, ships, clubs, schools and public institutions generally'. It is not therefore surprising that a firm making such wares would turn to the production of view and arms ware as soon as it became fashionable. The firm started producing 'Arms' ware in white china and in celadon well before 1900. In 1907 they began advertising Fenton China Arms Ware and offered to supply the arms of any town, city, county or college. During these years the firm produced a quantity of arms ware, mostly domestic items such as beakers, mugs, vases and shell trays. In 1908, Mr Edward Hughes died and although the firm went on advertising 'correct Heraldic china' for at least the next year they did not specialise in the production of these lines after that date, concentrating rather on tea sets and breakfast ware.

A considerable quantity of crested ware is found with the Fenton China mark but for the most part they are small vases, inkwells, dishes and jugs. Such items are very ornately moulded and look rather Victorian. Although the firm advertised view ware, none has as yet been recorded. (This is probably because such domestic pieces were used and have therefore not survived.) Fenton China was exported and one vase with a Canadian crest has been found.

Fenton Models
Ancient Artefacts
Chester Roman Vase. No. 480.

55mm.	3.00
Leather Bottle. 55mm.	3.00
Loving Cup. 39mm.	3.00
Loving Cup, 3 handles. 50mm.	3.00

Home/Nostalgic

Iron Trivet. 70mm.	4.00

Miniature Domestic

Cheese Dish and cover. 55mm.	6.50
Cup and Saucer. 35mm.	5.50

Domestic
Inkwell, square, with lid.

50mm wide.	12.50

A range of useful domestic items such as egg cups and sealing wax holders was produced.

Value	£2.00-£7.50.

Filey China

Trademark used on wares made for a Filey retailer by Taylor and Kent (Ltd), Florence Works, Longton. (Usual trademark Florentine).

Ancient Artefacts

Loving Cup, 3 handled. 39mm.	3.00

F.L.

Trademark used for a retailer on wares made by Sampson Hancock (& Sons), Bridge Works, Stoke and later at the Garden Works, Hanley. (Usual mark Corona).

F.L. Models
Great War
Tommy on Sentry Duty, model of.

110mm.	82.50
Battleship. 120mm long.	17.50

Birds (including Eggs)
Chick hatching from egg.

60mm long.	9.00

Florentine China

Can often be found without 'Made in England'.

Trademark used by Taylor and Kent (Ltd), Florence Works, Longton.

Taylor and Kent, a well known firm which survived the Depression, specialised in producing tableware, toy tea sets, commemoratives and while the craze lasted 'coat of arms ware', at reasonable prices. In 1911 the firm made front page news in the Potteries by persuading the Wallasey Coronation Committee to cancel an order for coronation mugs from a German firm and to fill the order themselves. They gained a great deal of kudos from this order. The firm could hardly have been aware of the longer struggle against Germany in which the whole country was about to embark. A sad sequence of events unfolds in the Pottery Gazette of the next few years. In 1914, Mr John Kent, the traveller for Taylor and Kent in the North of England and Scotland was called up for service. With the rank of Major he commanded the 1st Battery of the 2nd North Midland Division RFA. The company requested and encouraged customers to send their orders directly to the works. Major John Kent was regrettably killed in action in 1916, his death recorded with many others in the Gazette of that year (yet another victim of that pointless war).

By 1913, Taylor and Kent were making 'Coat of Arms ware and View china' as well as 'Tea sets, Breakfast sets and Domestic China'. A year later large extensions were made to the Florentine Works because of the extra orders the firm were receiving. The new oven could accommodate some 5,000 dozen of porcelain miniatures at each firing. The firm obviously specialised in heraldic, commemorative and view wares throughout the war years and continued into the early twenties. They were recognised as one of the leading Staffordshire firms for souvenir china and one of the biggest suppliers. By 1925, however, Taylor and Kent had recognised the need to emphasise other products and were advertising their 'excellent china tea and breakfast ware suitable alike for home and export trades'.

Florentine china is not particularly fine and was produced as cheaply as possible, often marked with the name or trademark of the wholesaler. The range of models is not particularly original and most of the novelty items are to be found in other manufacturers' lists. (There is a similarity to models made by J. Reeves (Victoria China). The firm supplied wares under a large number of trademarks, the most common including Caledonia, Coronet and Cyclone, which cannot be explained by any known connection between the firms.)

Florentine does present, however, a very representative selection of models but a surprisingly small number of Great War miniatures.

Taylor and Kent made a great amount of crested domestic ware including some early items to which pewter lids and tops were added. View ware made by the firm is pleasant but unmemorable and they also produced a range of transfer prints of a regional nature including 'Welsh costumes' (also found on models marked Victoria China).

Commemorative transfers of the Great War are often found on 'smalls' and models including the Triple Entente (Flags of Great Britain, France and Russia in shields). The only military badge recorded is RMC Camberley. There is also an interesting commemorative of the War Museum Exhibition, Crystal Palace.

Many models and 'smalls' are found with 'Lucky Black Cat' transfers but no 'Lucky White Heather' devices have been recorded.

Taylor and Kent produced small china figures and other novelties which were not crested before 1900 and after 1925, although many of these would be of interest to some collectors, they have not been listed here as they cannot be considered crested china. (No numbering system was used on Florentine china).

Florentine Models
Ancient Artefacts
Aberdeen Bronze Pot, not named. 58mm.	3.00
Chester Roman Vase, not named. 62mm.	3.00
Fountain's Abbey Cup. 50mm.	3.00
Irish Bronze Pot, not named. 52mm.	3.00
Loving Cup, not named. 39mm.	3.00
Puzzle Jug. 67mm.	5.50
Roman Lamp.	
2 sizes: 62mm.	3.00
100mm.	4.00
Salisbury Kettle, not named. 100mm.	3.00
Southwold Jar, not named. 100mm.	3.00
Windsor Urn, not named. 50mm.	3.00

Buildings – White
Blackpool Tower. 117mm.	8.50
Crofters Cottage. 70mm long.	17.00
London Bridge. 88mm long.	20.00
Marble Arch, not named. 50mm.	14.00
Old Pete's Cottage, near Ramsey. 75mm long.	25.00
St. Paul's Cathedral.	
2 sizes: 93mm.	19.50
130mm.	20.00
Tower Bridge. 105mm long.	25.00
Westminster Abbey, West Front. 85mm.	15.00

Monuments (including Crosses)
Caister-on-Sea, Lifeboat Memorial, impressed: *1903.* 150mm.	25.00
Glastonbury Tor. 90mm. (rare).	35.00
Great Rock of Ages, Model of. 135mm.	16.00
Iona Cross. 108mm.	10.50
Nelson's Column. 121mm.	47.50

Historical/Folklore
Brussels Boy, 120mm. Impressed: Mannekin pis.	82.50
Man in Pillory. 105mm.	20.00
Mother Shipton. 72mm.	8.00

Traditional/National Souvenirs

Laxey Wheel, Isle of Man, not named. 85mm.	40.00
Legs of Man in Lifebelt. 95mm.	16.00
Lincoln Imp on pedestal. 106mm.	8.50
Thistle Jug. 63mm.	3.00
Welsh Bardic Chair. 88mm.	19.50
Welsh Dragon Water Jug, with lid. 120mm.	13.00
Welsh Harp. 100mm.	10.00
Welsh Hat. 57mm.	5.00
inscribed with longest town name.	7.50
Indian Canoe. 110mm long.	14.00

Seaside Souvenirs

Child sitting on Rock, hand to mouth. 110mm.	16.00
Basket Beach Chair.	
2 sizes: 80mm.	16.00
100mm.	19.00
Bathing Machine. 76mm.	10.00
Bathing Machine with figure on steps. 75mm.	14.50
Houseboat. 57mm.	5.00
Houseboat, square. 90mm long.	5.00
Yacht, in full sail. 127mm.	12.50
Sea Waves on base. 57mm.	19.00
Fisherman, bust. 84mm.	20.00
Lighthouse, not named. 90mm.	5.00
Whelk Shell. 100mm long.	5.00

Countryside

Milk Churn and lid. 72mm.	5.00

Animals

Camel, kneeling. 95mm long.	13.00
Cat, Manx. 61mm.	19.50
Cat, sitting.	
2 sizes: 62mm.	10.00
112mm.	12.50
Cat, sitting, detailed fur. 90mm.	10.00
Cat, with long neck, sitting. 115mm.	10.00
Cheshire cat, The, inscribed: *Always smiling*. 115mm.	7.50
Cat with bandaged face. 88mm.	20.00
Cat in Top Hat. 65mm.	23.00
Dog, with bandaged face. 90mm.	23.00
Dog, Bulldog looking out of kennel. If with black face add £4.00. 73mm.	10.50
Dog, Bulldog, sitting. 56mm.	13.00
Dog, King Charles Spaniel, sitting. 68mm and 88mm.	11.00
Dog, King Charles Spaniel, sitting, begging on cushion.	

2 sizes: 70mm.	8.50
85mm.	13.00
Dog, lying in cradle. 90mm long.	12.50
Dog, puppy, sitting. 92mm.	12.50
Dogs, two King Charles Spaniels in a Top Hat. 65mm.	15.00
Dolphin Vase. 102mm.	5.50
Donkey, walking. 90mm long.	19.00
Elephant, kneeling.	
2 sizes: 82mm long.	20.00
95mm long.	23.00
Fish, inscribed: *Caught at....* 120mm long.	5.50
Fish, open mouthed. 115mm long.	3.00
Fish vase. 115mm.	5.50
Frog cream jug. 45mm.	6.50
Mouse, playing mandolin, on circular base. 90mm.	25.00
Pig, lying down, alert ears. 80mm long.	10.50
Pig, standing.	
2 sizes: 80mm.	10.50
95mm long.	10.50
Larger size found inscribed: *The pig that won't go*.	
Piglet, kneeling. 70mm long.	10.50
Polar Bear. 95mm long.	30.00
Pony, small. 105mm long.	19.50
Rabbit. 98mm long.	7.50
Seal, with ball. 72mm.	17.50
Shetland Pony. 66mm.	22.00
Toad, flat. 74mm long.	19.50
Tortoise. 74mm long.	9.00

Birds (including Eggs)

Baby Bird cream jug. 65mm.	5.50
Canary on Rock. 95mm.	14.50
Chicken, hatching from egg. 63mm long.	9.00
Hen roosting.	
2 sizes: 60mm long.	7.50
90mm long.	10.00
Kingfisher cream jug. 60mm.	5.50
Kingfisher with long beak. 80mm.	30.00
Owl. 75mm.	10.50
Parakeet. 75mm.	10.50
Parrot. 94mm.	14.50
Pelican cream jug. 83mm long.	5.50
Sparrow. 63mm.	19.50
Swan.	
2 sizes: 65mm.	6.50
80mm.	7.50
Swan posy holder. 88mm long.	5.00

Great War

Monoplane with 4 bladed movable prop. 175mm long.	110.00
Battleship. 175mm long.	40.00
Red Cross Van. 88mm long.	30.00
Tank with trailing wheels. 127mm long.	30.00
Tank. 125mm long. (wide variety).	20.00
Shell. 75mm.	5.00
Telescope, folded. 70mm.	13.00
Cenotaph, inscribed: *The blood of heroes is the seed of freedom.* 140mm.	6.50
Gravesend War Memorial. 140mm.	105.00
Great Yarmouth War Memorial, with inscription on all four sides. 2 sizes: 145mm.	22.00
175mm.	22.00
Matlock Bath Memorial, some colouring, 155mm, found without factory mark.	125.00

Home/Nostalgic

Baby in Bootee. 95mm long.	10.50
Baby in Hip Bath. 100mm long.	12.50
Bellows. 107mm long.	10.50
Case, Attaché. 60mm long.	5.50
Chamber Pot. 40mm.	3.00
Coal Bucket. 60mm.	5.00
Cradle on rockers.	9.00
Dolly Tub with two pegs and clothes protruding. 82mm.	26.00
Flat Iron. 76mm.	12.50
Garden Roller. 85mm long.	12.50
Grandfather Clock. 135mm.	10.50
Keys on Ring. 46mm.	20.00
Lantern. 65mm.	5.50
Oil Lamp and lid. 55mm.	5.00
Old Armchair, The. 85mm.	7.50
Oriental Lamp (Aladdin's Lamp). 2 sizes: 100mm long.	3.00
198mm long.	5.00
Pillar Box, inscribed: *I can't get a letter from you so send you the box.* 76mm.	12.50
Policeman's Lamp. 70mm.	10.00
Portmanteau. 77mm long.	4.00
Shaving Mug. 55mm.	6.50
Sofa, 3 seater. 82mm long.	10.50
Travel bag, with moulded decoration. 145mm long.	7.50
Watering Can. 68mm.	6.50

Comic/Novelty

Boy's head on container base, two side holes could be used for matches? 75mm long.	7.50
Boy on Scooter. 106mm.	20.00
Jack in the Box. 90mm.	20.00
Man, comic character standing with hands raised in front of him. Wearing straw boater, barrel body, solemn expression. 130mm.	55.00
Negro Minstrel, bust. 100mm.	19.50
Pierrot, hands and face flesh coloured, black pompoms on hat and costume. 125mm.	35.00
Pixie sitting on Flower Pot candlesnuffer. 180mm.	30.00
Pixie sitting on Thimble. 115mm.	30.00
Screw, inscribed: *You could do with a big fat screw.* (Wage rise). 75mm.	20.00
Suffragette Handbell, some colouring. *Votes for Women.* 108mm.	45.00

Cartoon/Comedy Characters

Ally Sloper, bust. Not named. 83mm.	25.00

Alcohol

Bottle of Champagne in Ice Bucket, inscribed: *Something good a bottle of the boy.* 85mm.	13.00
Carboy. 76mm.	4.00
Toby Jug. 65mm.	6.50

Sport/Pastimes

Boxing Glove. 65mm long.	30.00
Cricket Bag. 110mm long.	12.50
Golf Ball vase on brown base. 55mm.	14.50
Also found as a scent bottle.	14.00
Football. 70mm.	6.50

Musical Instruments

Grand Piano. 85mm long.	15.00
Tambourine. 70mm.	6.50

Transport

Charabanc with driver. 115mm long.	33.00
Motor Horn, inscribed. *Pip Pip.* 88mm.	20.00
Saloon Car. 88mm long.	40.00

Modern Equipment

Gramophone, hexagonal, with horn.
  90mm.   40.00
Gramophone, square, without horn.
  53mm.   15.50
Radio Horn, plain or fluted.
  2 sizes: 90mm.   25.00
            96mm (fluted).   28.00
            102mm.   18.00

Footwear

Lancashire Clog. No. 407.
  88mm long.   5.50
Oriental Shoe with pointed turned
  up toe. 95mm long.   5.00
Shoe, ladies, 18th century.
  95mm long.   7.50
Slipper, open with bow (Babies
  shoe) 100mm long.   20.00

Miniature Domestic

Bagware Vase. 50mm.   3.00
Cheese Dish, 1 piece. 45mm.   6.50
Cheese Dish and cover, 2 pieces.
  45mm.   6.50
Coffee Pot and lid. 63mm.   7.50
Cup and Saucer. 40mm.   5.00
Jug and Bowl, ornate, tulip pattern
  in relief. 55mm.   5.50
Kettle and lid. 85mm.   7.50
Tea Pot with lid. 3 sizes: 50mm,
  60mm and 70mm. All sizes.   7.50
Tea Pot with lid, squat and wide.
  88mm long.   7.50
Tea Pot with lid, ribbed sides. 80mm.   7.50

Domestic

Candlestick. 56mm.   4.00
Candlestick with Snake. 103mm.   7.50
Dragon Jug with lid. 120mm.   24.50
Hair Brush pin box and lid.
  145mm long.   14.00
Napkin Ring. 40mm.   5.50
Scent Bottle (contained
  'Wallflowers' scent) with metal
  top which unscrews. 93mm.
  Many other varieties now found.   12.50
Trowel pin box and lid. 140mm long.   14.00

The Foley China

1890-1910

1890-1910

Trademark used by Wileman and Co., Foley
  Potteries, and Foley China Works, Fenton,
  Longton, subsequently renamed Shelleys
  Ltd.
For all details of manufacturer and models
  produced please see Shelley China.

Fords China

c1920-30

Fords China Models

Alcohol

Soda Syphon. 100mm.   10.00

Miniature Domestic

Cup and Saucer, ornate. 60mm.   5.50

A range of domestic ware, trinket boxes,
    ashtrays, jugs etc.   2.00-6.50

In 1874, Charles Ford took over T & C Ford
    and produced Swan China at Cannon
    Street, Hanley. Ford also owned Ford &
    Pointon who produced Fords China at the
    Norfolk Works, Hanley. Both firms
    subsequently became branches of J.A.
    Robinson & Sons. (Usual trademark
    Arcadian).
This mark was mostly used on domestic
    ware, and only one model has been
    recorded. Jugs, trinket dishes, cups and
    ashtrays are found with crests, transfer
    views and sometimes coloured transfers
    of tropical birds found on Arcadian
    pieces. The only known model is most
    definitely from an Arcadian mould.

Foreign/Germany

Germany

Foreign

Impressed marks.

Austria, Bohemia and Czechoslovakia can
also be found.

Many German firms manufactured crested
china for the English souvenir market.
German wares tend to be somewhat
whiter and of poorer quality than British
made wares. These firms include:

Max Emanuel, The Mosanic Pottery,
Mittereich. (Usual trademark Mosanic).

Moschendorf, Hof, Bayern. (Usual
trademark PM and Rex).

Hutschenreuther, Probstzella, Thuringia.
(Usual trademark P).

Klösterle, Carlsbad. (Usual trademark Union
K).

Wilhelm Kutzscher & Co., Schwarzenberg,
Saxony. (Sometimes used the trademark
Princess China).

The models with impressed numbers would
appear to be made by Max Emanuel.
(Usual trademark Mosanic), as he was the
only German manufacturer known to use
stock numbers and registered numbers.
Foreign, Austria or Czechoslovakia
would be used after the Great War due to
the unwillingness of the British to buy
anything German. Nearly all of these
models can be found in various shades of
lustre, mostly yellow/brown, usually
with the lucky white heather decoration
or in full colour. They are often found with
no coat of arms.

A range of coloured fairings were
made, which although uncrested,
and collected by some crested
china collectors.   from 20.00

Germany/Foreign Models
Parian/Unglazed
Bust of General Booth, with beard.
  Inscribed: *The Salvation Army.*
  86mm.   40.00
Bust of Mussolini, in uniform on
  rectangular base. 130mm. Rare.   52.50
Souter Johnny (impressed). Sitting
  coloured figure. No. 5140/A.
  119mm.   30.00
Tam o'Shanter (impressed). Sitting
  coloured figure. No. 5140/B.
  Unglazed. 118mm.   30.00

Ancient Artefacts
Loving cup, 3 handled. 38mm.   3.00
Loving cup, 3 handled, with Nelson
  transfers. 40mm.   20.00
Irish Bronze Pot. 50mm.   3.00

Plymouth Jug, not named. No. 4580.
60mm. 3.00
Southwold Jug. No. 4687. 40mm.
(lustre). 3.00
Swindon Vase. No. 4557. Not
named. 58mm. 3.00

Buildings – Coloured
Robert Burn's Cottage Nightlight.
No. 5145. 130mm long. 30.00
Fairmaid's House Perth, Nightlight.
88mm. 65.00
Shakespeare's Cottage Nightlight.
112mm long. 29.50

Buildings – White
Bandstand. 2 sizes:
No. 3921. 75mm. 8.00
No. 3972. 90mm (lustre). 11.00
Birmingham Town Hall.
95mm long. 25.00
Blackpool Tower. No. 3484. 130mm. 11.50
Blackpool Tower cruet set (Tower is
salt pot, buildings either side
pepper and mustard – very
vulgar and therefore rather
appealing). 135mm. 7.50
Boston Stump. No. 193. 128mm. 24.00
Clock Tower. No. 7727. 7.50
Cottage. No. 7208. 65mm long.
(lustre). 6.50
Dunster Yarn Market. 24932.
95mm long. 26.00
Margate Clock Tower. No. 7213.
153mm. 7.50
Rye Medieval Gateway. No. 4412.
75mm. 40.00
Scarborough Clock Tower. No. 3560.
138mm. 8.50
St. Winifred's Well, Holywell.
No. 4195. 60mm. 28.00
Windmill, fixed sails. No. 7223.
90mm. 14.50
Windmill, fixed sails, with hoist and
rope. No. 4167. 110mm. 14.50
Whitby Abbey, Ruin. No. 4169.
2 sizes: 75mm. 110.00
175mm. 110.00

Monuments (including Crosses)
Banbury Cross.
2 sizes: No. 6895. 135mm. 15.50
No. 3295. 150mm. 19.50
or No. 4245.
Margate Lifeboat Memorial. No.
3562 or No. 7200. 125mm. 12.50

Statue of Drake, named, *King
Edward VII.* 125mm. 20.00
Ripon Market Cross. No. 4195.
125mm. 11.00

Historical/Folklore
Alladin on lamp. Coloured.
110mm long. 16.00
Banbury Cross, lady on a horse.
130mm. 30.00
Cinderella's Coach. No. 5800.
96mm. (Lustre). 27.50
Coronation Coach Inkwell with lid.
27.50
Mary Queen of Scot's Chair, not
named. No. 3604 or No. 3404. 73mm. 4.50
Ripon Hornblower. No. 4196. with
inscription. 123mm. 15.00

Traditional/National Souvenirs
Blackpool Big Wheel.
2 sizes: No. 7534. 80mm. 10.50
No. 3561. 90mm. 10.50
John Bull, standing figure. 19.50
Burns Cottage, interior. 17.50
Coronation Chair. No. 3583. 97mm. 4.00
Coronation Coach, (inkwell). 85mm. 27.50
Leaking Boot, Cleethorpes. (Statue ·
of boy holding boot, moulded to
chest). No. 4592. 130mm. 20.00
3 Legs of Man in Lifeboat – not
glazed. 13.00
Irish Colleen, standing by harp on
ashtray base. Coloured.
No. 20214. 80mm. 19.00
Irish Colleen with harp posy vase.
Coloured, no crest. No. 21585.
90mm. 19.00
Irish Colleen ashtray. Coloured.
No. 21586. 86mm. 19.00
Irish Man, sat on stool ashtray,
playing bagpipes. Coloured.
No. 21587. 87mm. 19.00
Highland Mary Statue. 138mm. 20.00
Souter Johnny, unglazed, beige.
115mm. 30.00
Scots Lad spill holder, in kilt, shirt,
bonnet, belt, with big feet.
116mm. 55.00
Scots Girl playing bagpipes on
ashtray base. Coloured figure, no
crest. No. 21587. 85mm. 19.00
Welsh Tea Party. Three Welsh ladies
taking tea. Coloured. 96mm. 20.00

Welsh Lady, standing figure.
No. 8498. 140mm. 18.00
Dutch Boy holding Flag. Coloured.
No. 8912. 92mm. 30.00
Dutch Boy with Wheelbarrow.
No. 5803. 95mm. 23.00
Dutch Girl with Wheelbarrow.
No. 5803. 95mm. (Pair). 23.00
Dutch Girl, fully coloured. No. 3053.
110mm. 30.00
Dutch Boy holding fish and net.
No. 2555. 155mm. 25.50
Gondola. No. 5660. 132mm long.
Can appear coloured (add £6.00)
No. 3803. 16.00
Indian Canoe. 104mm long. 10.50

Seaside Souvenirs
Ark. No. 7193. 90mm. 5.00
Bathing Hut. No. 4433. (Lustre). 64mm. 11.00
Bathing Hut with bather sitting
outside. No. 5668. 70mm long. 20.50
Bathing Hut. No. 6066. 60mm. 7.50
Bathing Hut Cruet Set. 4-piece.
Lustre. 85mm. 20.00
Canoe, paddle and flag. No. 5175.
150mm long. 9.00
Canoe, Indian. 104mm long. 10.50
Coracle tied to Stump. No. 1284.
90mm. 5.50
Galleon with bird at front. Swan on
sea beside it. 83mm. 23.00
Galleon, in full sail. Coloured front.
No. 916. 205mm. 30.00
Liner on back of oval ashtray. No.
5808. 80mm. If coloured add
£8.00. 17.00
Ship with 3 masts on waves.
(Lustre). 115mm. 20.00
Rowing Boat with rudder. No. 5176.
130mm long. 10.00
Steamboat Cruet Set. 4-piece. Some
colouring. 155mm long. 25.50
Yacht. Lustre. No. 1123. 115mm. 9.00
Yacht. No. 3482. 103mm. 12.50
Yacht. No. 4132. 113mm. 9.00
Yacht with waves, beige/rust.
No. 4422. 110mm. 9.00
Yacht, full sail on waves. No. 4438.
85mm. 10.50
Anchor, beige. 3 links of chain.
No. 5183. 75mm. 7.00
Fisherman behind ship's wheel.
125mm. 24.00
118mm. 17.50

Fisherman's Creel. No. 7192. 60mm. 4.00
Fisherman's Wicker Basket with net
overflowing with fish, beige/
rust. No. 5186. 66mm. 17.00
Fisherman, Bust, holding ashtray,
fully coloured. No. 4282. 12.00
Lifeboatman, standing figure.
3 sizes: No. 6528. 105mm. 14.50
No. 7200. 128mm. 14.50
No. 3562. 122mm. 14.50
Lighthouse. No. 3585. 90mm. 4.00
Lighthouse. No. 1585. 80mm. 4.00
Lighthouse. No. 11223. 110mm. 4.00
Lighthouse. 150mm. 4.00
Beachy Head Lighthouse, black band.
2 sizes: 100mm. 5.50
145mm. 8.50
Lighthouse (Beachy Head), yellow
rust lustre. No. 6474. 130mm. 6.50
Corbiere Jersey Lighthouse. No. 751.
100mm. 17.00
Shell dish, black edging.
145mm long. 3.50
Cockle shell dish. 115mm long. 4.00
Crab, Pin Box, in orange lustre.
No. 2191. 80mm long. 10.50
Boy on Lobster. No. 4426.
100mm long. 14.50
Boy in trunks on diving board.
No. 5799. 110mm. 23.50
Boy in skiff holding ice cream.
No. 4446. 17.00
Girl on rubber duck in sea. No. 5179.
85mm. 19.50
Black Boy on inflatable duck.
No. 5179. 78mm. 41.50
Girl wearing a hat on a donkey.
No. 4170. 110mm. 17.00
Girl riding a donkey. No. 4840.
115mm. 17.00
Boy riding a donkey. No. 4840.
115mm. Pair with above. 17.00
Mermaid sitting in whelk.
No. 4430. 100mm long. 22.00

**Bathing Beauties/Twenties
Flappers**
Found decorated in two styles –
white ware with clothes edged in
rust brown and the face and hair
coloured, or yellow/rust or other
shaded lustre. Value the same.

Bathing Beauty on ashtray. No.
4424. 95mm long (lustre).   23.00
Bathing Belles, two, on ashtray base
in relief in colour. Inscribed: *I'm
letting myself go. People think I'm
potty but what do I care?* 107mm.   35.00
Bathing Beauty on square ashtray.
110mm long.   20.00
Bathing Beauty on triangular
ashtray. No. 2578.
2 sizes: 75mm.   30.00
         90mm.   30.00
Bathing Beauty diving through
waves on lustre dish. 88mm long.   19.50
Bathing Beauty on oyster ashtray.
No. 4172. 75mm. (Lustre).   20.00
Bathing Beauty sitting up on lustre
shell, green costume. No. 4174.
70mm.   23.00
   Bathing Beauty reclining on shell,
   orange costume. No. 4173.
90mm long. (Lustre).   23.00
Bathing Beauty reclining on tummy
on lustre shell, orange costume.
100mm long.   25.00
Bathing Beauty reclining on oyster
ashtray, orange or purple
costume. No. 4027. 80mm.   23.00
Bathing Beauty sitting on oyster
shell. 80mm.   23.00
Bathing Beauty on slide – pair of
girls facing different ways both
with same No. 5801. Different
poses. 102mm. (Lustre).   each 24.00
Bathing Beauty sitting outside ridge
tent. 60mm.   20.50
Bathing Beauty peeping out of
Bathing Hut. Can be found with
right arm over head, or left arm
on shoulder. No. 4421. 104mm.   25.00
Bathing Beauty on Turtle. No. 4451.
100mm long. (Lustre).   25.50
Bathing Beauty paddling canoe,
with flag at back. No. 5174.
140mm long.   19.50
Bathing Beauty in canoe with
2-bladed paddle, no flag.
No. 3174. 140mm long.   19.50
Flapper on Stool with Scottie dog.
No. 5672. 108mm. (Lustre).   19.50
Flapper Pin Cushion Girl, four holes
in base. Blue costume, pink hat.
No. 5717.   25.50
Girl in Basket Chair. No. 8902.
74mm. (Lustre).   17.50

Girl with parasol in Basket Chair.
2 sizes: No. 4165. 120mm.   30.00
         No. 4074. 104mm.   23.00
Sunbather with parasol, reclining.   17.50
Girl in slacks on beach ball. 115mm.   20.00
Girl in sleeveless dress on sea shell.
No. 4430. 85mm. (Lustre).   20.00

Figures
Figures which are obviously seaside
souvenirs have been included in
that section. For Bathing Beauties
and Twenties flappers please see
'Bathing Beauties/Twenties
Flappers' heading. Some of the
figures below were obviously
made as a girl and boy pair.
Baby on Scottie Dog's back, holding
flag. No. 7148. Some colouring.
90mm long.   34.50
Child on red and white Dog,
holding flag. No. 3148. 80mm.   16.00
Child in Fez, riding elephant.
No. 7498. 80mm.   30.00
Two Children, skiing downhill on
slope. No. 5805. 95mm.   30.00
Two Children, on sledge on slope.
No. 5802. 95mm.   20.00
Two Children with a wheelbarrow
on slope. No. 6381. 90mm.   19.50
Boy on Swing, standing. No. 5809.
Some colouring. 110mm.   20.50
Girl on Swing, standing. No. 5808 or
5809. 110mm.   20.50
Boy Scout with dog. 100mm.   25.00
Girl Guide with cat. 103mm.   25.00
Boy with flag. No. 5798.   15.00
Girl with flag. No. 5798.   15.00
Boy, bathing dog in a tub, with
watering can and soap. 83mm.   25.00
Girl with pigtails, sitting on side of
oval wooden tub, holding two
kittens, with cat on other side.
Pair to the above.   25.00
Girl in shorts and t-shirt leaning
against globe. No. 5797. 105mm.   14.00
Boy in swimsuit leaning against
globe. No. 5797. 115mm.   14.00
Boy on square base, holding up
boat. 122mm.   23.00
Boy carrying umbrella and satchel.
No. 21669. 85mm.   25.00
Boy with begging pug dog.
No. 7062. 75mm.   20.00
Boy feeding birds beside a basket.   11.00

Boy on toy elephant on wheels,
coloured. No. 21686. 88mm. 25.50

Girl, sitting with dogs, on a stand.
No. 3147. 85mm. 22.00

Girl with mandolin. No. 20396.
103mm. 24.00

Girl with banjo, seated, coloured.
No. 20884. 85mm. 24.00

Girl in coloured dress, wheeling
barrow. No. 3321. 110mm. 25.50

Girl sitting on chaise longue.
No. 5667. 95mm long. 30.00

Girl on blue seat, metal screw
stopper on head scent bottle. No.
8596. 95mm. 22.00

Girl on horseback. No. 4428. 105mm. 16.50

Girl on horseback on oval base.
No. 4840.
2 sizes: 115mm. 14.50
128mm. 16.50

Girl on horseback in riding gear.
No. 4840. 113mm. 19.50

Huntsman on horseback, coloured.
No. 2445. 100mm. 28.00

Gentleman wearing top hat,
carrying umbrella on green
ashtray base. No. 20036. 70mm. 23.00

Country Gent on ashtray, coloured.
No. 20218. 83mm. 23.00

Man & woman (lovers) on bench
within pillars, with steps leading
up to it. 65mm. 20.00

Woman with basket on her back.
122mm. 30.00

Waiter in tailcoat, fully coloured, no
crest. No. 7061. 30.00

Countryside

Butterfly vase. 45mm. 6.00

Four Bar Gate with stile and
milestone. 50mm long. 6.50

Milkmaid holding churn. 124mm. 16.00

Pine Cone on side, lustre.
No. 7216. 90mm long. 7.00

Shepherd and Lamb by hollow tree
trunk. No. 846A. 75mm. 12.00

Shepherdess and Lamb by hollow
tree trunk. No. 846B. 75mm. 12.00

Stile with milestone, with heart and
initials. 100mm. 6.50

Animals

Butterfly on Vase. 98mm. 7.00

Cat with arched back. No. 8922. 65mm. 9.50

Cat in bandages, sitting. 90mm. 30.00

Cat, black on ashtray. No. 5002.
92mm long. 18.00

Cat, Cheshire. No. 6622. 70mm. 5.50

Cat and chimney pot. No. 7582.
52mm. 6.50

Cat, sitting. No. 6623. 55mm. 6.00

Cat, standing on hind legs, comical.
85mm. 40.00

Cat in long skirt and blouse with tie,
carrying tennis racquet. 100mm.
Rare. 65.00

Cat on trinket box. No. 5678, No.
5679 & No. 5819. Can be found in
lemon/rust lustre. 88mm long. 11.50

Cats, one large and one small either
side of a cauldron. 105mm long. 17.00

Cat, fat and miserable with bandage
over eye and bow on head.
No. 930. 80mm. 30.00

Cats, three in a laundry basket, or
possibly one kitten and two pups.
65mm. 27.50

Cat posy bowl, detailed fur.
No. 4394. 115mm. 11.00

Cat, grotesque with long neck,
overpressed; *Luck* in orange.
No. 3402. 132mm. 7.00

Cat, sitting, bow around neck.
Lemon/rust. 60mm. 9.50

Cat, singing, holding song sheet, left
paw on top of music. 65mm. 22.50

Cat and Rabbit in High Boot. 95mm. 20.00

Cat and Rabbit in pair of Boots.
83mm. 20.00

Cat with paw on Rat. 35.00

Cat peeping out of old Boot.
No. 6568. 98mm long. 14.50

Cat on back of Boot, mouse on toe.
No. 4720. 110mm long. 17.50

Cat, black ears, sitting, in lustre
slipper. No. 6980. 95mm long. 10.50

Black Cat with grey bow, on orange,
red or blue chair. No. 1925 or No.
7287 or 7887. *Good luck* in relief.
68mm. 23.00

Black Cat on sofa. No. 3767. 76mm. 12.00

Black Cat on orange chair, arched
back. No. 8767. 50mm. 9.00

Black Cat in orange basket.
No. 6231. 69mm. 15.00

Cow Creamer. No. 4394.
118mm long. 12.00

Cow's head cream jug. 80mm. 7.00

Cow, walking. 102mm long.	45.00
Dog, Pointer with coiled metal tail. 135mm long.	30.00
Dog, Pointer. 120mm long.	24.00
Dog in kennel. No. 3479. 70mm.	7.50
Dog in bandages, sitting. 90mm.	30.00
Dog in boot. No. 6568. 114mm long.	14.50
Dog, sitting, Spaniel. 67mm	8.50
Dog, Scottie, wearing Tam-o'shanter. 74mm.	7.50
Dog, Terrier, standing. No. 6630. 74mm long.	6.50
Pug Dog sitting with top hat matchholder. No. 3417. 78mm.	13.00
Dog, black on ashtray base. No. 1971. 100mm long.	11.50
Dog's head spill holder. 46mm.	8.50
Dog with dead hare in mouth, on rocky base, plaque. 140mm.	30.00
Dog, King Charles Spaniel, head to one side, holding red flower on leaf base. No. 11447. 82mm.	7.00
Dog with paw on Rat. 72mm.	35.00
Dog, puppy sitting. 70mm.	9.00
Dog, puppy on chaise-longue. No. 5894. 84mm long.	24.50
Dog, orange Scottie, sitting on purple lustre shoe. No. 349. 105mm long.	14.50
Dogs, mother and puppy on oval base. 80mm.	16.00
Dog standing, Chauffeur, smoking pipe wearing hat with glasses and long overcoat. 85mm.	47.50
Dog, or possibly a fox, standing, dressed in long travelling coat and flat cap, tied with scarf under chin. 82mm. (Possibly a pair to the chauffeur above).	55.00
Dog, sitting with arms folded, with left eye blackened and cauliflower right ear, wearing battered top hat, on lustre ashtray base. Fully coloured. No. 7018. 75mm.	22.00
Dog, sitting by Top Hat match-holder. 76mm. No. 3417.	21.00
Dog Mustard Pot and Spoon. 80mm.	10.50
Dogs, two Bullterriers sitting together. 80mm wide.	20.00
Black Dog on pink padded French Chair. No. 6590. 65mm.	15.00
Dog, puppy, on a shoe. No. 6980. 100mm long.	10.50

Donkey, ears laid back, standing on oval base, in harness. No. 3486. 88mm long.	12.50
Donkey in Harness. No. 6102. 93mm long.	17.00
Donkey. 90mm long.	19.50
Donkey and tree stump. No. 3486. 90mm.	11.00
Donkey, standing inscribed: *Carisbrooke Donkey*. 88mm long.	30.00
Elephant sitting, posy holder. No. 4391. 120mm long.	7.50
Elephant standing, posy holder. No. 4508.	7.50
Elephant with foot on ball. No. 3682. 95mm long.	40.00
Elephant with howdah. 70mm.	35.00
Elephant with howdah, Pepper Pot. 70mm.	20.00
Elephant standing, head raised. No. 6629. 75mm.	19.50
Elephant, trunk raised. No. 6629. 85mm long.	14.50
Fish, very ornate. 110mm long.	4.00
Fish. No. 6476. 180mm long.	7.50
Fish. No. 5011. 125mm long.	3.00
Fish, open mouthed. No. 6475. 143mm long.	3.00
Fish Pepper Pot, black facial features. 110mm long.	7.50
Fish on ashtray base, coloured. No. 11560. 83mm.	9.00
Fox, standing, wearing dress. 85mm.	40.00
Frog, yellow/green on white oval base. 60mm.	19.50
Frog on shell, the frog is usually brown or green on a lustre shell. No. 4450. 110mm long.	12.00
Two Goats standing by open tree trunks. 50mm.	12.50
Hare, sitting. 74mm.	7.50
Horse's head and horse shoe, ashtray. No. 3925. 44mm.	14.00
Jaguar, open mouthed, crouching on oval base. No. 934. 125mm long.	40.00
Lion on base. Left and right facing found. Obviously sold as a pair as they have the same No. 4166. 90mm long.	9.00
Lion on a plinth, sometimes beige. No. 4166. 115mm.	8.00
Lion Posy Holder, lying down. No. 4392. 125mm long.	9.00

Lobster Trinket Box, orange.
130mm long.   8.00
Monkey, sitting. No. 7198. 82mm.   10.50
Three Wise Monkeys on wall.
No. 7195. 80mm.   10.00
Pig, standing. No. 3566. 98mm long,
53mm high.   15.50
Pig, standing, posy holder, pink.
135mm long.   16.00
Pig, sitting on haunches. Pepper
Pot. 70mm.   16.50
Pig, sitting up with front trotters on
hips! Pink snout. 87mm.   40.00
Pig, gilded, peering over rim of cup.
55mm.   11.50
Pig, sitting, heavy china. 66mm.   14.00
Pig, standing. 98mm long.   19.50
Pig, lustre, in boat. 115mm long.   14.00
Polar Bear. No. 4439. 90mm.   30.00
Rabbit in clothes on sledge.
90mm long. (Saxony).   30.00
Seal on rectangular base. No. 4452.
127mm long.   14.50
Shetland Pony. 100mm long.   19.00
Snail. No. 5178. 112mm long.
(Lustre).   13.00
Snail. No. 7187. 92mm long.   12.50
Tortoise trinket box. No. 402 or 6625.
2 sizes: 78mm long.   7.50
85mm long.   10.50
Turtle Pin Box and lid. 128mm long.   16.00
Wild Boar, charging. Pepper Pot.
No. 9279. 85mm long.   18.50

Birds (including Eggs)
Egg Shell, empty. 60mm long.   3.00
Bird on edge of nest pin tray. 3 eggs.
No. 312. 58mm.   20.00
Bird on rock, head looking right.
80mm.   12.00
Can be found fully coloured.   20.00
Bird, possibly white throat.
Coloured brown. No. 887. 97mm.   14.50
Chicken, red comb. No. 6621.
80mm.   7.50
Chickens, two with flowers on vase.
Can be found with a lustre finish
or with chickens, flowers and
ladybird coloured on white
ground. No. 5806. 120mm.   7.50
Chick Pepper Pot. 67mm.   4.50
Chicks, two, yellow, on vase,
squawking at each other.
120mm.   25.00
Cock and two chickens on slope.
No. 5807. Some colouring.

95mm long.   30.00
Cockerel Pepper Pot. 74mm.   12.50
Duck, fully coloured, on lemon lustre
trinket box and lid.
75mm long.   15.50
Duck Jug. 130mm long.   6.00
Duck Ashtray. No. 5695.
110mm long.   7.50
Duckling Pepper Pot, can be found
coloured. 80mm.
Coloured.   19.50
White   15.50
Duckling wearing hat, carrying
umbrella, on leaf shaped base.
Yellow lustre on mauve base.
No. 11448. 85mm.   4.00
Fledgling, blue with orange beak on
ashtray base.   14.00
Goldfinch on rock. Coloured.
No. 877. 97mm.   23.50
Heron Posy Holder, No. 4445.
120mm long.   7.50
Owl on three books. No. 937.
100mm.   20.00
Owl on tree stump, with inscription.
115mm.   12.50
Squawking parrots, facing one
another. 100mm.   19.50
Parrot. No. 6626. 75mm long.   8.50
Peacock on oval ashtray. No. 4934.
80mm long.   15.00
Pelican, drooping beak. 92mm.   17.50
Penguin Pepper Pot. 82mm.   12.50
Pheasant, blue on yellow/brown
ashtray. No. 4934. 60mm.   13.00
Seagull, swooping down on fish in
sea, on ashtray base. No. 11015.
95mm.   16.00
Swan on water. No. 4169. 82mm.   6.50
Swan posy bowl, yellow beak.
93mm.   4.00
Swan posy bowl. No. 3486.
81mm long.   4.00
Turkey posy holder. No. 1361. 90mm.   9.00

Great War
Monoplane, with hole in body,
could be posy holder or pin
cushion. Lustre. 77mm long.   13.00
Monoplane with egg timer
propellor. No. 8488. 112mm long.   10.00
Monoplane with pilot. No. 7207.
100mm long.   30.00
Monoplane with gold fixed prop.
76mm long.   15.50

Monoplane in orange lustre.	
130mm long.	13.00
Air Ship, open top, posy holder.	
131mm long.	45.00
Airship Cruet set. 192mm long.	40.00
Ambulance, Red Crosses on sides.	
No. 854 or 3916. 80mm long.	28.50
Tank with forward facing guns and	
curved exhaust pipe on roof. No.	
8424 and No. 854. 110mm long.	43.50
Tank, small, no wheels.	40.00
Bucket Helmet. 55mm.	65.00
Pith Helmet. 57mm long.	30.00
French Soldier's Cap. 60mm long.	40.00
Mess Pot. 55mm.	65.00
Cenotaph with inscription.	
2 sizes: No. 6725. 110mm.	4.50
No. 6726. 148mm.	5.50
Clacton on Sea War Memorial.	
No. 8999. 125mm.	14.50
Great Yarmouth War Memorial.	
110mm.	16.00
130mm.	20.00
Matlock Bath War Memorial, often	
poor quality.	
3 sizes: No. 6655. 120mm.	11.00
No. 4194. 140mm.	15.00
No. 3924. 155mm.	16.50
Southsea War Memorial. No. 6660.	
2 sizes: 120mm.	20.00
160mm.	30.00
Worthing War Memorial. No. 6776.	
2 sizes: 108mm.	13.50
155mm.	15.50

Home/Nostalgic

Anvil. No. 6618.	
2 sizes: 60mm.	5.00
85mm.	5.50
Armchair. No. 6095. 76mm.	5.50
Armchair, upholstered. No. 6812.	
74mm.	8.50
Basket, blue bow and red roses on	
handle. No. 4714. 75mm.	5.00
Basket of coloured Fruit. No. 3918.	
85mm.	13.00
Bath on four splayed feet. No. 5188.	
115mm long.	10.50
Bellows Pin Box and lid. No. 2001.	6.50
Book, brass bound and open.	
No. 8470. 52mm.	6.50
Book, open, with heart in relief on	
front cover. 50mm. No. 8470.	10.50
Box Iron. No. 5671. 90mm long.	12.50
Carpet Bag, open top. 86mm.	5.00

Coffee Table, central stem. 60mm.	4.00
Chair, ornate. No. 3567. 105mm.	12.50
Chair, Lloyd Loom. 62mm.	11.00
Chair, padded high back. No. 6095.	
70mm.	8.50
Coal Scuttle. No. 6813. 55mm.	4.50
Fireplace, *There's No Place Like Home*.	
No. 2275. 65mm.	10.00
Grandfather Clock, inscription.	
Make use of Time. No. 3401.	
140mm.	8.50
Grandmother Clock. 88mm.	5.50
Clock with rope columns.	5.50
Jardiniere, fixed base. 88mm.	5.00
Mantle Clock, ornate. 85mm.	10.50
Mantle Clock with side wings.	
No. 4729. 72mm.	6.00
Mantle Clock. No. 4810.	
100mm long.	10.00
Pail with handle down. No. 5185.	
65mm.	6.50
Pedestal. No. 6905. 83mm.	2.00
Pipe, gold on orange dish.	
85mm dia.	8.50
Pocket Watch. No. 5184. 70mm.	24.50
Policeman's Lamp. 70mm.	6.50
Post Box. No. 6496. 75mm.	7.50
Post Box, oval, inscribed: *Letters*.	
88mm.	14.00
Sack of Meal. No. 1645. 80mm.	9.00
Shaving Mug.	
2 sizes: 30mm.	5.50
40mm.	5.50
Sofa, ornate. 70mm long.	10.50
Stool, blue lustre. 53mm.	4.00
Umbrella, coloured. 70mm.	12.00
Watering Can, heavily gilded. 103mm.	11.00
Watering Can, rust coloured.	
No. 1423. 87mm.	11.00
Watering Can. No. 4427. 90mm.	11.00
Wheelbarrow. No. 51277.	
135mm long.	13.00

Comic/Novelty

Black *Momma* candlestick, coloured.	
A present from... 100mm long.	24.50
Bride and Groom in large Shell.	
No. 5795. 105mm.	19.50
Cupid with wings standing at	
curtained window, his and her	
shoes on ledge. No. 753. 90mm.	17.50
Egg as house with rabbit peering	
out of barred window in egg.	
With standing rabbit in tailcoat	
alongside and a snail in front.	
65mm.	40.00

Bell Hop with 2 cases, telegram and bouquet. Posy Vase. Coloured. 105mm.   19.00

Boy dressed as Bell Hop with Globe. No. 5197. 98mm.   13.50

Girl dressed as Bell Hop with Globe. No. 5194. 98mm. (pair).   13.50

Boy dressed as Bell Hop, saluting, sitting on suitcase. 75mm and 97mm. No. 5804   19.00

Girl dressed as Bell Hop, sitting on suitcase. No. 5804. 75mm long. (pair).   19.00

Jester. 75mm.   6.50

Pierrot Mustard Pot, head as lid. No. 9301. 100mm.   81.50

Pierrot standing by open bag. No. 3315. 90mm.   12.50

Pierette standing by open bag. No. 3315. 90mm. (pair).   12.50

Pierette reclining on trinket box. No. 3498. 110mm.   17.50

Pixie on oval base. 60mm.   9.00

Policeman, fully coloured at front. No. 7083. 84mm.   25.00

Sack of Money, with figure 500,000 impressed in seal. No. 1645.   13.00

Sailor, comical, smoking pipe. Some colouring. No. 8959. 132mm.   28.50

Sultan sitting on bowl. No. 4834. 100mm.   16.00

Coal Truck. No. 3915. 75mm.   10.50

Coal Truck. No. 3916. 65mm long.   10.50

Cartoon/Comedy Characters

Bonzo salt pot, inscribed: *I'm Salt*, some colouring and in lustre. 80mm.   14.00

(This is a very true likeness of Bonzo, exactly like the drawings of him).

Alcohol

Toby Jug. No. 6608. 63mm.   8.50

Sport/Pastimes

Boy, footballer spill holder, fully coloured. No. 3476. 80mm.   30.00

Boy, tennis player match holder. No. 3414. 80mm.   20.00

Girl, tennis player match holder, partly coloured. No. 3414. 80mm.   20.00

Trophy and lid. 105mm.   12.00

Artist's Easel and brushes. No. 4841. 65mm.   2.00

Club card suit indicator. No. 3919. 80mm.   10.50

Musical Instruments

Grand Piano. No. 4168. 85mm long.   12.50

Guitar. 136mm long.   14.50

Upright Piano. No. 7134. (lustre). 70mm.   12.50

Transport

Girl in Car. No. 5774. 100mm long. (lustre).   30.00

Girl driving a van with gladstone bag and bundle on top. No. 5794. 85mm long.   26.00

Hot Air Balloon, square basket. 2 sizes: 65mm.   35.00
90mm.   40.00

Locomotive 2-4-4. Cruet set with black coal. No. 69627/34. 135mm long.   19.50

Motor Car, open top. No. 3917. 75mm long. (lustre).   13.00

Motor Car, open tourer. No. 1912. 92mm long.   16.00

Motor Car Cuet Set. 120mm long.   15.00

Luggage Trolley, loaded. 2 sizes: 65mm long.   19.50
80mm long.   20.00

Ornate Sleigh.   19.50

Passenger Monoplane. 85mm wide.   30.00

Petrol Can, impressed: *Motor Spirit*. No. 7214. 67mm.   17.50

Modern Equipment

Binoculars. No. 5187. 2 sizes: 60mm.   10.50
75mm.   10.50

Cruet Set Binoculars, in lustre. 70mm.   4.00

Folding Camera. No. 5182. 75mm.   24.00

Flat Iron.   8.50

Horn Gramophone. No. 7196. 42mm.   19.50

Horn Gramophone. No. 3563. 70mm long, 80mm high.   19.50

Dog listening by gramophone on beige oval ashtray. 115mm long.   30.00

Radio with horn. No. 5180. 70mm.   40.00

Treadle Sewing Machine. No. 5439. 72mm.   17.50

Hats

Boater, lustre. No. 4429. 97mm long.   8.50

Helmet with plumage. 48mm.	13.00
Top Hat Match Striker. 42mm.	5.50
Top Hat with brown umbrella on top. 60mm.	12.50

Footwear

Ankle Boot, open top.	
2 sizes: 130mm long. No. 3586.	8.50
105mm long.	6.50
Baby's Bootee, quilted, threaded with real ribbon. 52mm.	12.50
Ladies Boot. No. 1835. 70mm.	6.50
Dutch Clog. No. 2079. 70mm long.	5.00
Ladies Slipper. 150mm long.	7.50
Ladies 18th Century Shoe. 84mm long.	7.50
Lancashire Clog. No. 3587.	
2 sizes: 125mm long.	5.00
180mm long.	7.50
Oriental Slipper. No. 5428. 95mm long.	6.50
Ornate Ladies Shoe. No. 3322. 115mm long.	10.50
Sabot, with orange lobster in relief on side. 105mm long.	7.50

Miniature Domestic

Bowl. 40mm.	2.50
Cheese Dish and cover, traditional shape. No. 3403. 74mm.	5.00
Cheese Dish and cover, flat sloping top. No. 3043. 70mm long.	7.50
Cheese Dish and cover, shield shaped base, some colour. 85mm long.	8.50
Cheese Dish and lid, one-piece. No. 6114. 65mm long.	6.50
Cheese Dish and cover, handle on curved face. No. 6632. Lustre. 76mm.	7.50
Coffee Pot and lid. No. 3442. 65mm.	5.50
Cork Vase, 86mm.	3.50
Jug, fluted. 60mm.	2.50
Jug. No. 4683. 60mm.	2.50
Kettle and lid. (Lustre) 78mm.	7.50
Mug, two-handled. 38mm.	2.50
Tea Pot and Lid, wide base. 45mm.	7.50
Tea Pot and Lid, square base. No. 973. 120mm.	7.50
Tea Pot and Lid. No. 4866. 65mm.	7.50
Tea Pot and Lid. No. 9084. 65mm.	7.50
Tea Pot and Lid. No. 4809. 60mm.	7.50
Toast Rack. 74mm long.	8.50

Numbered Domestic Items

Candlestick. No. 358. 80mm.	3.00
Cone Vase. No. 4539.	2.50
Chamberstick. No. 5486. 45mm.	3.00
Inkwell with stopper - bound with metal for thermometer. No. 02169. 100mm long.	4.00
Heart shaped trinket box. No. 5098. 70mm wide.	3.00
Two handled vase. No. 5682. 65mm.	2.00
Square Plate. No. 32. 145mm.	3.00
Trinket Box, horseshoe shaped, bright yellow. No. 2356. 80mm long.	3.00
Pin Box and lid. No. 2001.	3.00

Miscellaneous

Cow Bell, porcelain clapper. 80mm.	4.50
Horse's Head and Horseshoe on ashtray base. Some colouring. 105mm wide.	6.50

FP & S

F. P. & S.

Furstenberg

FURSTENBERG
GERMANY

Trademark used by Ford and Pointon Ltd,
– Norfolk Works, Hanley, subsequently a
branch of J.A. Robinson and Sons, Ltd,
and later Cauldon Ltd. (Usual trademark
Coronet).
For details of this firm and the china
produced see Coronet Ware.
This mark was probably used by Ford and
Pointon Ltd before the Great War. The
mark is mostly found on small vases and
miniature domestic pieces. No view ware
or other transfer prints have been
recorded.

FP and S Models
Ancient Artefacts
Loving Cup, 3 handles. No. 19.
   38mm.   3.00

Historical/Folklore
Miner's Lamp. 70mm.   16.00

Home/Nostalgic
Baby's Cradle. 63mm long.   6.50

Musical Instruments
Tambourine. 72mm long.   6.50

Footwear
Boot. 35mm.   5.00
Oriental Shoe, with pointed toe.
   90mm long.   6.50

Miniature Domestic
Beaker. 39mm.   2.00
Cheese Dish and cover. 50mm.   5.50
Circular Trinket box and lid. 60mm.   4.00

Trademark used by a German manufacturer
for German Souvenir China.

This mark has only been found on a
   small 60mm vase with the crest
   Köln Rh. (Cologne).   5.00

Gaelic

The Garnion Ware

"Ɗéaɟcɑ Sɑɲ
ʈ-Siopɑ́iɲ"

THE
GARNION
WARE

Trademark used by an unknown manufacturer for the Irish market.

A pierced plate with the crest of Dublin has been found.   7.00

Mark used by an unknown manufacturer, thought to be foreign.

Only one small vase with a Guernsey crest has been recorded.   4.00

Gemma

Often found without 'Czecho-Slovakia' under mark, or just with the latter.

Trademark used by Schmidt and Co., Carlsbad (Bohemia). Almost all models can sometimes be found with a lustre finish.

Established in 1883, Schmidt and Co. were one of the biggest German exporters of crested china. Before the war AUSTRIA sometimes was printed under the mark but after the war it was more acceptable to print the name of the newly formed state of Czechoslovakia.

Schmidt and Co. used the Gemma mark mostly on miniatures, especially on domestic ones, but some useful domestic ware can be found with the mark including inkpots, pen stands, pill boxes, ribbon plates and salve pots. (One salve pot has been recorded with a silver rim with a Birmingham mark!). Some modern collectors look down upon the very white bodied German crested china that was popular in the period of its manufacture. This attitude is often unfair for, although much Gemma china is clumsy and cheap looking, there are some very delicate pieces especially in the miniature domestic range. Some of the coloured animals and lustre models are exceptionally appealing and inventive and should not be overlooked by collectors who like the later crested wares.

Gemma china sold very well in the twenties probably because it was so cheap, and so

many of these coloured and lustre finish models are to be found. 'Black Cat' transfers were also used and there are a great number of items with 'Lucky White Heather' usually on lustre but sometimes on a white body. The firm specialised in a yellow shaded lustre, tints varying in depth, but usually shaded from pale lemon, through orange to almost rust. Many bathing beauties are found in this yellow/orange to lustre marked only Germany, but it seems probable that they were made by this firm (see unmarked). Other shades of lustre found on Gemma models include pink, blue, dull orange and mother-of-pearl.

Schmidt and Co. also produced a range of view ware, and coloured and monochrome (black only) views can be found on Gemma models and 'smalls'. Some interesting transfer prints can be found on late miniature models including flowers, crinoline ladies and twenties beauties.

Three interesting commemoratives have been recorded, Festival of Empire, Crystal Palace 1911; Imperial Service Exhibition, Earls Court 1913 and War Museum Crystal Palace. Obviously no Great War commemoratives are to be found, as it was illegal to import German china at the time, but crests of King George V appear and the badges of HMS Dreadnought and HMS Illustrious. (No numbering system was used on Gemma models.)

Gemma Models
Ancient Artefacts

Chester Roman Vase. 65mm.	3.00
Loving Cup, 3 handled.	
3 sizes: 39mm.	3.00
50mm.	3.00
(can be found with	
silver rim).	10.50
68mm.	3.00
Puzzle Beaker. 64mm.	17.00
Puzzle Coffee Pot with inscription:	
Try your skill, this pot to fill and not	
to spill don't use the spout except to	
pour out. 64mm.	16.50
Puzzle Cup and Saucer, actually a	
beaker with a handle, with verse:	
Try how to drink and not to spill and	
prove the utmost of thy skill, or *Try*	
your skill this cup to fill but do not	

spill. You must not give the problem up till you succeed to Drain the cup.

35mm.	19.50
Puzzle Ewer. 70mm.	14.00
Puzzle Jug, with verse.	
2 sizes: 70mm.	5.00
80mm.	5.50
Puzzle Jug, no inscription but impressed with a shell pattern, lustre. 52mm.	10.50
Puzzle Milk Jug with verse. 42mm and 72mm.	15.00
Puzzle Loving Cup, 1 or 3 handled with verse. 46mm.	14.50
Puzzle Mug. 51mm.	14.00
Puzzle Sugar Bowl, 2 handles. 42mm.	12.00
Puzzle Tea Pot with verse. 45mm and 62mm.	20.00
Puzzle Teapot. 94mm long.	20.00
Puzzle Tankard. 50mm and 68mm.	10.50
Puzzle Watering Can. 48mm.	20.00
Sedan Chair, green. 127mm.	30.00

Quite a number of 'smalls' have been recorded, often in Victorian/Gothic style and very ornate, which may or may not be ancient artefacts – but are probably just ornamental!	2.50-4.00

Buildings – White

Blackpool Tower. 130mm.	8.50
First and Last Refreshment House, not named. Also found in yellow/orange lustre. 72mm long.	10.50
Cottage. 72mm long.	8.50

Historical/Folklore

Coronation Chair. Can also be found in yellow/orange lustre. 98mm.	5.00
Miners Lamp. 58mm.	16.00

Traditional/National Souvenirs

Kelly from the Isle of Man posy holder, with cat. Inscribed: *A present from the Isle of Man.* 115mm.	40.00
Manx Cats as handles of Miniature Domestic pieces: see 'Animals'.	
Manx Legs inside lifebelt. 85mm.	10.50
Manx Man, three legged with Manx cat on triangular base. 115mm.	47.50

Welsh Candlestick, Welsh lady handle. Black hat. 80mm dia.	20.00
Welsh Hat, often found with 'Welsh' transfer print, add £4.00. 75mm dia.	5.00
Welsh milk jug, Welsh Lady handle, some colouring.	
2 sizes: 54mm.	24.50
62mm.	26.00
Welsh Ladies' head cream jug. 72mm.	22.00
Welsh Lady, coloured, as handle of cream jug.	
2 sizes: 60mm.	24.50
90mm.	30.00
Welsh Lady, coloured, as handle of Cheese Dish and cover. 74mm long.	26.50
Welsh Lady, coloured, as handle of Tea Pot and lid. 68mm.	27.50
Welsh Lady, coloured, as handle of Mug. 55mm.	20.00
Welsh Lady, coloured, as handle of Watering Can. 65mm.	22.50
Welsh Lady, coloured, as handle of Coffee Pot and lid. 54mm.	27.50
Welsh Lady, coloured, as handle of Vase. 75mm.	30.00

Seaside Souvenirs

Bathing Machine money box. 83mm.	14.00
Yacht. 88mm high, 102mm long.	13.00
Beachy Head Lighthouse. Black band. 123mm.	10.50
Lighthouse. 95mm.	5.50
Lighthouse on Rock. 120mm.	5.50
Lobster Ashtray, red lobster forming handle. 63mm long.	10.00
Horn shaped lustre Shell on shell base. 80mm.	7.50

Countryside

Milk Churn with lid. 72mm.	4.00

Animals

Cat, sleeping, lying on side. Can be found inscribed: *Stop Yer Tickling Jock*, add £8.00. 83mm long.	24.50
Cat wearing boots (Puss in Boots). Cat has pink face and ears. 84mm.	40.00
Cat in Bowler Hat. Cat can be found coloured, add £10.00. 63mm.	20.00
Cat, Cavalier style with bows on boots, ruffles on trousers. 83mm.	30.00

Comical Cat, standing hands on hips, black features. 97mm.	20.00
Cat, Egyptian, lying down. 78mm.	24.00
Cat, sitting in Top Hat. 70mm.	23.00
Cat, in saucepan with black handle. 70mm long.	20.00
Cat, peeping out of frilled rim bowl. Cat's face coloured. 60mm.	30.00
Cat, peeping out of plain rimmed bowl. 58mm.	25.00
Cat, crouching, can have blue or yellow bead eyes. 50mm.	25.00
Cat, lying down. Comical. 90mm long.	30.00
Cat, sitting in ladies shoe, with shoe tongue flopping out. 80mm.	23.00
Cat, sitting, paw on rat. 80mm.	40.00
Cat, sitting, black features. 73mm.	24.50
Cat's head bowl. 57mm.	14.00
Manx Cat, sitting. 74mm.	25.00
Manx Cat, standing stretched. 94mm long.	30.00
Manx Cat, down on front paws, upright back paws. 98mm long.	35.00
Manx Cat handle on coffee pot or jug. Cat coloured.	
2 sizes: 76mm.	30.00
80mm.	30.00
Manx Cat as handle on a cup. Cat coloured. 48mm.	30.00
Manx Cat handle, coloured, on miniature Cheese Dish and cover. 76mm long.	30.00
Manx Cats, as two handles on a vase. 73mm.	30.00
Cow cream jug, some colouring. 127mm long.	23.00
Dog, cross-eyed, with fly on his nose. Can be found with some colouring. 76mm.	20.00
Dog, curled up on its side. 98mm long.	24.50
Can be found inscribed: *Stop Yer Tickling Jock.*	28.00
Dog, King Charles Spaniel, sitting. 83mm.	12.50
Dog, pug lying down. 92mm long.	20.00
Dog, pug sitting. 100mm long. Some colouring to face.	20.00
Dolphin Vase. 100mm.	11.00
Fish with open mouth. 140mm long.	4.00
Fish pin cushion holder. 106mm long.	5.00

Fish, pepper pot, black features. 110mm long.	5.00
Fish vase. 110mm long.	4.00
Frog Prince (Frog with crown on head) with colouring. 90mm.	35.00 / 47.50
Pig in Top Hat. Pig has pink muzzle and ears. 60mm.	22.50
Pig as above but with Chef's Hat. 93mm.	50.00
Pig in saucepan with black handle. Pig coloured pink as above. 57mm.	30.00
Pig, standing, hands on hips, pink muzzle and ears. Can also be found in yellow/orange lustre. 100mm.	30.00
Pig, sitting, can have pink muzzle and ears. 100mm long.	
With colouring.	19.50
Without colouring.	16.50
Pig, curled/lying, pink ears and muzzle. 82mm long.	30.00
Pig, pink, lying on edge of horseshoe ashtray. 65mm long.	19.00

Court Room Pigs
All coloured pink as follows:

Policeman, with black helmet with yellow badge. 80mm.	82.50
Barrister, with monocle. 80mm.	55.00
Prisoner, trotters padlocked. 80mm.	75.00
Witnesses, female with balmoral bonnet, male with bowler. 80mm.	80.00
Judge, robed. 80mm.	75.00
Jury Box of six Piglets. 120mm long.	130.00

Shetland Pony. 108mm long.	22.00
Tortoise trinket box and lid. 80mm long.	7.50

Birds (including Eggs)

Cockatoo on branch, some colouring. 102mm.	30.00
Hen Egg Basket, 2 pieces, red comb. 85mm long.	11.00
Swan. 80mm.	5.50
Swan posy holder. 90mm long.	5.00

Great War

Despatch Rider's Cap with Goggles. 65mm dia.	25.00
With colouring.	34.50

Home/Nostalgic

Armchair, straight backed. 50mm.	5.50

Bag, open on four feet.	6.50
Basket. 60mm and 90mm.	3.00
Basket, star-shaped. 65mm dia.	3.00
Bucket with looped handle. 80mm.	4.00
Bucket with rope handle. 51mm.	3.50
Clock, bracket. 76mm.	10.50
Coal Bucket and lid, ornate. 55mm.	6.50
Coal Scuttle, cylinder shaped.	
65mm.	5.50
Coal Scuttle, box shaped. 50mm.	4.50
Coal Scuttle, helmet shaped. 70mm.	4.50
Coal Scuttle, ornate. 76mm long.	4.50
Cradle on rockers. 60mm long.	9.00
Dressing Stool. 4 legged.	
62mm long.	5.50
Fireplace, inscribed: *There's no place*	
like home. Some colouring. 68mm.	10.00
Flat Iron. 71mm long.	10.50
Garden Trug. 80mm long.	3.50
Grandmother Clock. Can be found	
in yellow/orange lustre. 88mm.	5.50
Home Bank, you don't miss what goes	
in – what comes out will surprise	
you. Oval box with handle and	
slit. 58mm.	10.50
Not named.	5.50
Jardiniere. 80mm.	5.00
Jardiniere and stand. 165mm.	7.50
Jardiniere pot and stand. 121mm.	7.50
Mantel Clock, ornate. 85mm.	10.50
Pillar Box, oval. Can be found	
inscribed: *Letters,* or *Letter Box*	
add £3.00. 90mm.	10.50
Policeman's Lamp. 45mm.	10.00
Rocking Chair. 60mm.	12.50
Saucepan with silver lid and black	
handle. 70mm long.	10.50
Shaving Mug. 60mm.	5.50
Shaving Mug, square handle.	
40mm.	5.50
Shaving Mug, with raised shell	
pattern. 55mm.	6.50
Sofa, very ornate. 60mm.	8.50
Stool, circular with 3 legs. 55mm.	4.00
Table. 45mm.	5.50
Tobacco Jar with brown pipe on lid.	
70mm.	10.50
Trunk with separate lid. 60mm long.	5.50
Wash Bowl and Jug set. 58mm.	5.50
Washing Basket, with pierced sides.	
30mm.	3.00
Watering Can, also yellow/orange	
lustre. 70mm.	5.50
Wheelbarrow, also in yellow/	
orange lustre.	

3 sizes: 45mm.	5.50
63mm long.	6.50
95mm long.	6.50

Comic/Novelty

Briar Pipe, brown. 76mm long.	10.50
Briar Pipe, brown on leaf tray.	
72mm long.	10.50
Whistle, shaped as ewer. 45mm.	2.00

Alcohol

Beer Mug. 47mm.	4.00

Sport/Pastimes

FA Cup, not named. 68mm.	13.00
FA Cup and lid. 110mm.	10.00
Trophy, 2 handled with separate lid.	
150mm.	16.00

Musical Instruments

Tambourine ashtray with gilded	
discs. 68mm long.	6.50

Modern Equipment

Cash Register. 35mm.	16.00

Hats

Bowler Hat. 83mm long.	20.00
Fireman's Helmet. 74mm.	40.00
Peaked Cap, very large.	
118mm long. Unglazed.	10.50
Straw Boater. 75mm dia.	10.50
Top Hat, can be match striker.	
45mm.	5.50
Top Hat. 60mm, 110mm long.	5.50

Footwear

Boot, pierced eyelets.	
2 sizes: 88mm long.	5.50
135mm long.	7.50
Dinant Wooden Shoe. 80mm long.	7.50
Dutch Sabot. 88mm long.	4.00
Ladies Shoe with high heel and	
fluted tongue. Two different	
moulds. 75mm long &	
80mm long.	7.50
Ladies Shoe with pronounced heel	
& instep. 58mm, 98mm long.	10.00
Clog with buckle. 125mm long.	6.50
Lancashire Clog. 125mm long.	6.50
Shoe with lace holes. 90mm long.	6.50

Miniature Domestic

Complete tea sets can be found on
round or square trays. These

usually consist of teapot, sugar
bowl, milk jug and two cups and
saucers. Usually, except saucers,
each piece is crested but on really
small sets only the tray carries a
crest.   30.00
Cake Dish. Can also be found in
yellow/orange lustre. 70mm dia.   3.00
Stilton Cheese Dish and cover,
round. 45mm dia.   7.50
Cheese Dish and cover.
2 sizes: 63mm.   6.50
76mm long.   6.50
These can be found coloured, lustre,
beige and with transfers as well
as crested in the usual manner.
Cheese Dish with large handle to
cover. 77mm long.   14.00
Coffee Pot with lid, ribbed sides.
63mm.   7.50
Coffee Pot with lid with ornate
handle. 78mm.   5.50
Cup and Saucer. 40mm.   5.00
Found yellow.   add £4.00
Cylinder Box and lid, moulded
hinge, for cigarettes. Match
striker base. No. 2065½.
63mm.   3.50
Also found with fixed lid and
money box slot.   4.00
Dish. 40mm.   3.00
Dressing Table Set, miniature.
These usually comprise 1 tray, 2
candlesticks, 1 ring tree and 3
powder bowls with lids.   30.00
Kettle with lid, ornate. 66mm.   7.50
Kettle with lid, flat handle to use on
range. 90mm.   12.00
Kettle with lid. 75mm.   7.50
Kettle with lid, with 2 spouts.
63mm.   5.00
Meat Dish and lid, oval. 76mm long. 6.50
Milk Jug, square. 44mm.   3.50
Moustache Cup. 47mm.   6.50
Mug. 50mm.   2.00
Photograph Frame, glazed, with
cardboard backing. 94mm.   13.00
No backing.   7.00
Ribbon Plate, hexagonal.
78mm long.   5.00
Tea Pot, also found in yellow/
orange lustre.
4 sizes: 50mm.   7.50
60mm.   7.50

65mm.   7.50
70mm.   7.50
Tea Pot, square with lid. 64mm.   12.00
Tea Pot and lid, pearl lustre, shell
pattern. 82mm.   19.50
Tea Pot and lid, diamond shaped.
64mm.   14.00
Tea Pot and lid, with two spouts
(left/right pourer) and silver
handle. 67mm.   5.00

Domestic
Candlestick. 78mm dia.   3.00
Candlestick. 80mm.   3.00
Candleholder. 44mm.   3.00
Candleholder shaped match holder
with striking surface. 60mm.   5.00
Gravy Boat. 100mm long. 40mm.   5.50
Inkwell and lid, with pen rest.
65mm long.   12.50
Ink Stand and pen holder with lid. 11.00
Inkwell/Striker, ball-shaped. 40mm. 5.50
Mustard Pot and lid, on saucer base.
60mm.   3.00
Pepper Pot with ribbed sides.
83mm.   3.00
Ring Tree Candleholder. 70mm.   8.00
Tea Pot and lid, oval. 130mm long. 10.50
Toastrack.
2 sizes: 39mm.   7.50
70mm long.   13.00
Trefoil, salt, pepper and mustard
dish. 40mm.   3.50
Trinket Box and lid. 45mm.   3.00

Germany

Gladstone China

All details and listings of china marked 'Germany' will be found under 'Foreign/Germany entry.

Trademark used by Taylor and Kent (Ltd.), Florence Works, Longton (usual trademark Florentine).

For details of this manufacturer and china produced see Florentine China.

This mark was used mainly on domestic and miniature domestic items. No other decoration other than crests have been found on pieces with the mark.

Gladstone Models.
Miniature Domestic

Cheese Dish and cover. 50mm.	6.50
Mug, one handle. 35mm.	2.50
Hexagonal Vase. 77mm.	2.50
Ewer. 83mm.	2.50

Footwear

Ladies 18th century frilled shoe. 90mm long.	7.50

W.H. Goss

1862-1930.

Printed mark used on small bases also found as impressed mark.

Used from 1930. Can also be found with the following added; "Hand Painted," "Royal Buff," and "Cottage Pottery".

Trademark used by William Henry Goss (Ltd), Falcon Pottery, Stoke.

The prices and a full listing of every Goss piece known to the author will be found in the companion volume to this guide, *The Concise Encyclopaedia and Price Guide to Goss China* by Nicholas Pine.

Values of the thousands of crests and decorations to be found on Goss china appear in *The Price Guide to Arms and Decorations on Goss China* by the same author. Full details of marks, including 42 illustrations, will be found in chapter 2. of *The Price Guide to Goss China.*

Many pieces appear bearing either Arcadian, Willow Art, W.H. Goss or W.H. Goss England marks as the later period of crested china (1925-37) saw much merging of companies and liberal use of marks.

Any piece with the W.H. Goss or W.H. Goss England mark is worth a small premium over a similar piece not so marked and a priced list of Goss England, or Third Period items will be found in *The Price Guide to Goss China* previously referred to. New pieces are constantly coming to light however, and that list is by no means exhaustive.

The values of Arcadian and Willow Art models have increased rapidly over the past few years and the differential between these and examples marketed by the Goss factory has narrowed considerably.

W.H. Goss Ltd. were the originators of heraldic porcelain. So well known were their products that the term Goss was used to describe any make of crested china. The products of the Falcon Works are so popular with collectors that several books have been written about the firm.

The early history and the lists of models and other wares made by Goss are well covered in these books and so will not be repeated here. But I do feel it necessary to say a few words in praise of Adolphus Goss and to explore the connection between Goss and Harold Taylor Robinson (see Arcadian China).

William Henry Goss was an important potter in his day, developing the ivory porcelain body used for heraldic china. He was an industrious and studious man, very much the Victorian. The real hero must be his son Adolphus Goss who joined the firm in 1883, it was he who saw the commercial possibilities of heraldic china. The Goss firm had for sometime been decorating small ivory pots with crests of University Colleges and public schools for sale in local china shops and Adolphus rightly saw that these had much wider possibilities. The public interest in archaeology and heraldry could both be satisfied by producing for each town and city miniature historical shapes with applied local coats of arms. Adolphus not only searched the country's museums for suitable ancient artefacts to copy but also found local shops to act as agents. Each agent sold local souvenirs with the correct local crest, but could order other shapes if he so desired. (An exercise in mass-marketing that was years before its time). He also wrote several of the verses to be applied to china. In addition, he sketched and coloured some 2,500 transfer printed views and 6,000 coats-of-arms, all of which were sent to the factory with the order by Adolphus.

These heraldic porcelains became enormously popular not only in tourist areas, where they made the most perfect souvenir, but in towns and cities all over Britain. The Goss name became famous, but by 1906 many cheap pot versions were being made by other firms who didn't stop at ancient artefacts but applied crests to other, even comic miniatures. W.H. Goss never forgave Adolphus for thus debasing the Goss name: he would have preferred to have been remembered for his Parian wares. Without Adolphus however, the firm would not have prospered and in fact this became evident because in 1906 when William Henry died he left the firm to Adolphus' young brothers Victor Henry and William Huntley, and the story from then on is one of gentle decline.

W.H. Goss left Adolphus £4,000 and commissions, which was dutifully paid, but this left the company very badly financed. With no Adolphus the firm seemed to lack the commercial drive necessary to survive. Goss produced very few miniatures to commemorate the Great War, and although they produced a range of exquisite military badges and crests and even tried making dolls' heads, this period was really the beginning of the end. The other major crested ware manufacturers were making exciting and popular models and the people buying them were not concerned with the beauty of the china. Goss hopelessly failed to catch the style of crested souvenirs popular in the twenties, and so by 1930 the firm was in such financial trouble that the Falcon Works had been foreclosed on by the bank. The trustees of William Huntley sold the business, but obviously not the property to Cauldon Ltd, whose managing director was Harold Taylor Robinson. Mr Robinson arranged the purchase of the business of W.H. Goss from Caulton Ltd. for £2,500. He subsequently bought the Falcon Works from the mortgagee for £4,000. The bank lent him £6,000 to complete the purchase and he then formed W.H. Goss Ltd. The issued capital stood at £6,000 all in ordinary shares all allotted to Harold Taylor Robinson. He acted as director until May 1932 when the firm was put into the hand of the Receiver as the whole Taylor empire crashed. Of the 6,000 ordinary shares he gave 1,000 to his brother, 500 to his father, 500 to his wife, and 1,000 to a business friend. 2,000 shares were transferred to Royal Crown Derby Porcelain Co. Ltd, as part of some rather clever deal that Mr Robinson always seemed to be involved in. After 1930 the wares marked Goss cannot be considered to be really Goss, the china is not so fine and the moulds used could be from any firm in the Cauldon group. I have termed this the third period of Goss manufacture.

For history of the firm after 1932 please see Arcadian China.

Gothic China

Trademark used by James Reeves, Victoria
   Works, Fenton (usual trademark Victoria).

Traditional/National Souvenirs
Welsh Hat, blue cord and gold
   tassels, longest place name round
   brim. 51mm.   7.50

Grafton China

1900-1915

1920's on domestic ware.

1915-1933

Used after 1915 mainly on later domestic ware, in green or black.

NB Retailers name often appears above these marks for example MEW BROS, SANDOWN I.W.

This rather strange mark has been found on some small models. It could have been a mark used on small bases but as the initials ABJ and S are absent it is rather odd. It could have been used by a disreputable pottery to cash in on the good Grafton name.

Trademark used by Alfred B. Jones and Sons Ltd., Grafton China Works, Longton, Staffs.

NB. Although the Grafton stock numbering system is very reliable, several items have been found with the wrong numbers. The most usual number is given here. It is not unusual to find two models consistently given the same number.

A.B. Jones and Sons Ltd. are one of the firm firms that produced arms ware in any

great quantity, to have survived the 1930's and to be still in business today. (They are now trading as Crown Lynn Ceramics Ltd. and use the trademark Royal Grafton). Although Grafton China had a large share of the china souvenir market they always produced other domestic and ornamental lines and presumably they sold enough of these, especially abroad, to keep going through the Depression.

Alfred B. Jones of the Grafton China Works had taken his two sons, Messrs. N.B. and A.B. Jones, Jnr, into partnership on 1st January 1900, the firm was then known as A.B. Jones and Sons Ltd. At that time they announced 'The firm will still make tea and breakfast sets for the Home, Colonial and American Markets, their chief specialities'. They were, however, in 1900 already advertising 'Badge Ware and View Ware' and were obviously producing goods for the lower end of the market (hotel ware and small souvenir items).

By 1906 A.B. Jones and Sons were making a special line of 'Miniature ivory arms china with the arms of any County, City or Borough painted in correct heraldic colours'. The pieces included jugs, loving cups, trays, milk jugs and vases in innumerable shapes. They also supplied 'local views of any locality' and had introduced another interesting speciality the 'zoo' series, animals of all kinds in pure white china, but do not appear to have been applying arms to them at that time.

By 1909, Mr John Walker, their London Representative at the Showroom in Buchanan Buildings, Holborn, was able to display Grafton 'Transparent ivory arms ware' in several hundred different shapes 'antique, pleasing, artistic, useful, quaint and humourous'. So it seems that between 1906 and 1909 Grafton had begun applying arms to more interesting pieces than vases and milk jugs, presumably animals, ancient artefacts and other souvenir items.

As the craze for heraldic china grew, Grafton appeared to place greater emphasis on its production. In 1919 they introduced crested souvenirs of the Great War and a series of zoo-logical (sic) interest, including, many attractive models of elephants, monkeys, mice and what not else, in all sort of postures!' By 1920 they advertised the firm to the trade as makers of 'heraldic and view wares, miniature mascots, grotesques' and only 'also tea and breakfast ware'.

A.B. Jones were present at the British Industries Fair in 1920 and at the British Empire Exhibition 1924, displaying 'Tea, Breakfast, Dessert, Dinner and Coffee Services and Fancy Goods – coloured, Heraldic and Model Reproductions'. The firm still produces much the same kind of ware today, with the exception of heraldic china which they last advertised in the 1920's. Unfortunately in 1946 there was a fire at the Grafton works and all the records of crested china production were lost, so even this manufacturer, who did not go bankrupt or merge, can offer no detailed information on wares made in the early part of this century. In 1909 A.B. Jones offered in the Pottery Gazette to send 'coloured sheets of illustrations of Grafton China to anyone in the trade writing for them'. Regrettably none of these tantalising sheets have so far been found.

Grafton was one of the major producers of good quality heraldic china, perhaps rivalling Shelley as the main Goss competitor for the better end of the souvenir market. Certainly Grafton models are in the main rather more imaginative and clever than Shelley, and the china tends to be finer, indeed Grafton is porcelain, not earthenware or 'pot' as it is termed in The Potteries, and A.B. Jones were the only major manufacturer apart from W.H. Goss to produce heraldic china in porcelain. The arms on Grafton models are very well produced and the colours are much more muted and subtle, and therefore rather more attractive than on other china.

Because this firm worked quite independently of any other arms ware manufacturer its wares have a style and character of their own. This is particularly noticeable in the Great War and animal models. The soldiers produced as souvenirs of the Great War are in action: 'Over the Top' and 'The Bomb Thrower' are unlike anything produced by most other firms as are the series of children playing on the beach. The range of white crested animals includes many more grotesque and comical items than are usually found, and Grafton are the only manufacturers apart from Tuscan to add coloured glass bead eyes to their animals. Many amusing miniature coloured animals were made, but these are invariably made without a crest and so have not been listed here. The style is very obviously late 20's, when coloured china souvenirs became more popular. One can only assume that Grafton stopped using crests on such items earlier than the other major manufacturers who went on producing coloured pieces with crests long after the interest in heraldic devices had waned. (This is probably one of the reasons why A.B. Jones survived the Depression. Their souvenir ware must have looked very 'modern' in the 20's).

Only two military badges have been recorded – The Gordon Highlanders and the Tidworth Camp but the following commemoratives are found: Flags of Liberty; Franco-British Exhibition 1905; Latin-British Exhibition, Great White City 1912; British Empire Exhibition 1924/5. Some foreign crests have been found and these are usually marked 'Importe d'Angleterre', and were made for export.

Grafton seem not to have used 'Lucky Black Cat' and 'Lucky White Heather' devices or any other form of decoration on their models, other than coloured transfer views and regional souvenirs such as the 'Somerset Cuckoo'. (View ware too is well produced but the colours are much more vibrant than one would expect from this manufacturer). Black transfer prints are also found including two unusual portraits of the 'Prince of Wales, President of B.E.E. 1924' and the 'Duke of York, President of B.E.E. 1925' which are really commemoratives.

Numbering system. The numbers sometimes appearing on the base of Grafton pieces are stock numbers that occur consistently on certain models. On early china numbers are printed but they are mostly found painted in black and for that reason are not always easy to read. The letter that follows the numbers is obviously the paintresses' mark. The highest number found is 737, but anyone making a numerical list of known models will find that many numbers are missing. The models listed without numbers and domestic ware will account for many of the gaps but nothing has been found numbered 570-632 and one wonders if these were perhaps used on coloured models without crests. Stock numbers are given in the following lists.

Grafton Models
Parian/Unglazed

Bust of John Peel, inscribed: *D'ye ken John Peel with his coat so grey.* 120mm.	75.00
Bust of Albert I of Belgium, wearing hat, on glazed base, inscribed: *Albert I.* 125mm	65.00
Bust of *Allenby*, impressed, square glazed base. 145mm.	65.00
Bust of George V, inscribed: *George V.* 125mm.	47.50
Bust of David Lloyd George. No.415. 135mm.	55.00
Bust of *Foch*, impressed. Square glazed base. 135mm.	65.00
Bust of Field Marshal, Sir John French. 140mm.	55.00
Bust of Admiral Sir John Jellicoe. 140mm.	55.00
Bust of General Joffre. 155mm.	47.50
Bust of Lord Kitchener, with inscription and impressed on back: *Kitchener.* No. 395 102mm and 125mm.	40.00
Bust of General Pershing on square glazed base. 148mm	82.50
Bust of Lord Roberts, impressed on back: *Roberts.* 135mm.	47.50
Bust of *Sir Walter Scott,* impressed: *Scott,* on circular glazed base. 120mm.	17.50
Bust of President Wilson. 140mm.	75.00

Ancient Artefacts

These models are often found not named and are quite often decorated with a coloured transfer view rather than a crest.	
Ancient Kettle with 2 spouts, not found named. No.325. 52mm.	2.00
Aberdeen Bronze Pot. No. 217 and No. 280.	
2 sizes: 56mm.	2.00
65mm.	2.00
Ale Pot. No.176. 60mm.	4.00

Brading Vase. No.195. 35mm dia.	4.00
Brading Roman Vase. 5 vases of different shapes:	
No. 135. 60mm.	4.00
No. 136. 62mm.	4.00
No. 137. 62mm.	4.00
No. 139. 55mm.	4.00
No. 195. 30mm and 35mm.	4.00
Burial Urn, inscribed: *Ancient British Burial Urn excavated in Cornwall.* 64mm	4.00
British Vase. No. 17. 40mm.	4.00
Butter Pot. No. 185. 40mm.	4.00
Canterbury Pilgrim Bottle. Rd. No. 470749. No. 317. 52mm.	4.00
Chester Roman Vase. No. 165. 60mm.	4.00
This has been found inscribed wrongly:*Roman Lamp Pompeii 1st century AD.*	
Chinese Pilgrim Bottle. No. 269. 88m.	4.00
Chinese Teapot and lid. 2 different models:	
No. 70. 54mm.	4.50
No. 77. 54mm.	4.50
Chinese Vase. 3 vases of different shapes:	
No. 276. 86mm.	4.00
No. 278. 85mm.	4.00
No. 282. 75mm.	4.00
Collingbourne Ducis, Medieval Pilgrim Bottle found at. No. 181. 53mm.	4.00
Cyprus Vase. No. 120. 70mm.	4.00
Elizabethan Bushel, not named.	4.00
Ely Drinking Mug. 2 shapes:	
No. 186. 40mm.	5.00
No. 187. 39mm and 46mm.	5.00
English Wine Glass. 4 glasses of different shapes:	
No. 309. 75mm. (Ale glass)	5.00
No. 310. 75mm. (Goblet)	5.00
No. 311. 70mm. (Tumbler)	5.00
No. 312. 70mm. (Ovoid bowl)	5.00
Egyptian Pottery – these specimens were discovered by Doctor Flinders Petra (sic) *in Egypt, manufactured about 4,000 BC.*	
No. 155. 60mm.	4.00
No. 156. 50mm.	4.00
No. 157. 60mm.	4.00
No. 158. 51mm.	4.00
The following two models have this inscription and further inscriptions.	
Egyptian Bottle. No. 159. 57mm.	4.00

Egyptian Tear Bottle. No. 151.
42mm.   4.00
Egyptian Vase. No. 323. 45mm.   3.00
Guernsey Milk Can.   5.50
Hereford Kettle. This model has a
separate lid. No. 179. 80mm. (Can
be found wrongly numbered 174.)   10.50
Hythe Crowellian Mortar. 40mm.   3.00
London Vessel, inscribed: *Model of
vessel found during excavations in
London.* 7 different models:
No. 201. 85mm.   4.00
No. 202. 82mm.   4.00
No. 204. 44mm.   4.00
No. 205. 48mm.   4.00
No. 206. 45mm.   4.00
No. 207. 48mm and 84mm.   4.00
No. 208. 70mm.   4.00
Norman Pot, inscribed: *Norman pot
from original in Burley Hill
Museum.* No. 182. 45mm.   4.00
Oxford Jug. No. 179. 60mm.   5.00
Pompeian Lamp. No. 119. 59mm.   5.00
Pompeian Vase. No. 110. 35mm.   4.00
Pompeian 1st Century Lamp. No. 118.
75mm.   5.00
Portland Vases, not named. 50mm.
No. 150 and No. 530.   3.00
Loving Cup, not found named.
No. 145. 40mm.   3.00
Reading Roman Vase. 50mm.   3.00
Roman Lamp. No. 119. 60mm.   3.00
Roman Vase. No. 160. 48mm.   3.00
Romsey Bushel, Model of Ancient.
No. 149. 53mm.   7.00
Salisbury Kettle.
No. 173. 97mm.   3.00
No. 174 105mm.   3.00
(Can be found wrongly
numbered No. 179.)
Shakespeare's Jug. No. 124. 76mm.   4.00
Shrewsbury Roman Ewer, inscribed:
*Roman Ewer found at Uriconium
original now in Shrewsbury
Museum.* No. 175. 76mm.   4.00
Southwold Jar.   4.00
Swiss Urn, inscribed: *Urn from Swiss
Tacustrine Habitation.* No. 184.
40mm.   4.00
Swiss Urn. No. 185. 44mm.   3.00
Yaverland J.W. Roman Vase.
No. 125. 50mm.   3.00

Buildings - Coloured
Bell Hotel, Tewkesbury.
92mm long.   125.00
*Captain Cook's house Great Ayton re-
erected in Melbourne.* 95mm long
(rare)   145.00
Couch's House, Polperro, on roof, with
arms of Polperro.   100.00
House on the Props, Polperro.
100mm long.   100.00
Old Chapel, Lantern Hill, Ilfracombe.
72mm long.   65.00
Old Maids Cottage, Lee, Ilfracombe.
70mm long, 68mm high.   120.00
Old Toll Bar, Gretna Green.
125mm long.   220.00

Buildings - White
Bath Abbey. 112mm.   40.00
Bath Abbey, West front. 105mm.   55.00
Bargate, Southampton. 90mm.   25.00
The Tower, Blackpool. No. 521
2 sizes: 120mm.   14.50
135mm.   13.50
Carnarvon Castle. 90mm.   57.50
Citadel Gateway, Plymouth.
2 sizes: 105mm.   28.00
119mm.   47.50
*First and Last Refreshment House in
England,* Land's End, found
numbered 469 and 627.
75mm long.   16.00
Gynn Inn, Blackpool, inscribed:
*Model of Blackpools famous
landmark, the old Gynn Inn
demolished 1921.* No. 520.
125mm long.   135.00
Houses of Parliament. No. 424.
115mm.   47.50
Irish Round Tower (not named),
often has green shamrocks on
base. No. 417. 137mm.   10.50
with shamrocks and Irish crest   14.50
Lincoln Cathedral, West Front.
No. 368. 115mm.   25.00
Old Cornish Cottages. 125mm long.   47.50
Old Chapel, Lantern Hill, Ilfracombe.
75mm long.   20.00
Old Toll-Gate House, including path
with gate, inscribed: *Ye olde toll-
gate house.* No. 498. 130mm long.   78.00
Old Toll-Gate House, as above but
not on base with path and gate,
and not named. No. 502 and
No. 501. 63mm long.   40.00

*Oldest Chemists Shop in England
established 1790*, also can be found
inscribed: *Model of the oldest
pharmacy in England,
Knaresborough, Yorkshire.
Established in the reign of George 1st
1790*, some colouring. 97mm long.   65.00
Plas Mawr, Conway. 93mm (rare).   105.00
St. Pauls Cathedral, London.
2 sizes: No. 423. 145mm.   25.00
No. 633. 115mm.   16.00
Scarborough Castle Ruins, not
named. White unglazed on
glazed base. 104mm.   65.00
Skegness Clock Tower, not named.
127mm.   12.00
*Smallest House in Great Britain,
Conway.* No. 560. 92mm.   24.50
Tonbridge Castle. 88mm long.   30.00
Westminster Abbey, front. No. 422.
121mm.   30.00

Monuments (including Crosses)
Banbury Cross. 141mm.   19.50
Irish Cross, not named, green
shamrocks on base. No. 419.
138mm.   12.50
Lifeboat Memorial. No. 497. 120mm.   19.50
Lloyd George Statue, Carnarvon.
150mm.   65.00
Ramsgate Lifeboat Memorial
(Statue of Lifeboatman), not
named but often found with the
inscription: *Souvenir from the
Imperial Bazaar Albion Hill,
Ramsgate, which was twice wrecked
by Zeppelin bombs on May 17th 1915
and June 17th 1917* on base.
140mm.   30.00
Rufus Stone. 96mm.   5.50
(John) Ruskin Memorial Stone,
inscribed: *John Ruskin
MDCCCXIX-MDCCC* and
religious verse. No. 515. 120mm.   16.00
St. Anne's Lifeboat Memorial. No. 495.
161mm.   16.00
Sandbach Crosses. 130mm.   75.00
Southport Lifeboat Memorial.
121mm.   14.50

Historical/Folklore
Antique Horn Workbox, Model of, plus
lid. No. 308. 70mm long.   16.00
Antique Bureau. 64mm.   11.00
Burn's Chair. No. 667. 88mm.   7.50

Charles I bottle with removable
head lid, not named and thought
by some collectors to be Guy
Fawkes. No. 209. 96mm.   40.00
Coaching Hat, not named. No. 213.
60mm long.   7.50
Lady Warrior in duck boat, holding
shield & sword. 125mm.   110.00
President Wilson's Grandfather's Chair.
No. 491 and 492. 75mm.   14.50
Ride a cock horse to Banbury Cross
(lady on horse). No. 569.
106mm long.   40.00
Robin Hood. 135mm.   100.00
St. Thomas A Becket Dec. 29th 1170.
137mm.   145.00
*Saint Wilfred of Ripon Patron Saint of
the City of Ripon.* 136mm.   145.00
Ye Old Chertsey Bell. 57mm.   10.50
Winged Horse on base, possibly
Pegasus. 85mm.   14.50

Traditional/National Souvenirs
Blackpool Big Wheel, not named.
2 sizes: 78mm.   10.50
100mm.   14.50
Cornish Pasty. No. 340. 95mm and
110mm long.   7.50
A Cornish Pasty. No. 578.
90mm long.   8.50
Gretna Green Anvil. No. 552. 67mm.   10.50
John Peel, Bust. 72mm.   30.00
Leaking Boot, Cleethorpes, statue of
boy, boot joined to hand by
string. 156mm.   64.00
Lincoln Imp on pedestal. 108mm.   12.00
Prime Cheddar Cheese. 38mm.   10.50
Cheddar Cheese with floral
decoration and verse. Never
found factory marked. 60mm dia.   11.00
With crest instead of transfer.   12.50
Ripon Horn Blower, often found not
named, inscribed: *The horn is
blown every night at 9. Formerly it
denoted that the watch was set for
the night.* 136mm.   16.00
Toby Jug, coloured. English. 80mm.   30.00
Toby Jug, coloured. Irish. 80mm.   30.00
Toby Jug, coloured. Scots. 80mm.   30.00
Toby Jug, coloured. Welsh Lady.
76mm.   30.00
Welsh Harp. No. 418. 90mm.   10.00
Welsh Hat, with blue band and bow,
found with longest Welsh place

name printed round brim.
No. 383. 50mm.

With longest place name	7.50
Plain	5.00
Welsh Milk Can. No. 479. 103mm.	5.00
Yarmouth Bloater. 115mm.	5.50
Dutchman, sitting cross legged and holding cheese. No. 230. 85mm.	24.00

Seaside Souvenirs

Bathing Machine. No. 256. 2 sizes. 55mm long.	11.00
65mm long.	12.50
Boat with billowing sail, inscribed: *Polly*. No. 448. 115mm long.	30.00
Boat, flat bottomed with bird's head as figurehead. No. 442. 80mm long.	6.50
Houseboat, rectangular. No. 401. 73mm long.	14.00
Lifeboat. No. 332. 110mm long.	9.50
Fisherman, bust on round, waisted plinth. No. 254. 116mm.	16.00
Lifeboatman, bust. No. 234. 109mm.	35.00
Rowing Boat, can be found inscribed: *Sant Cybi* (patron saint of Holyhead) on models with a Holyhead crest, *Robin Hoods Bay and Whitby*. No. 169. 130mm long.	9.50
Inscribed	12.00
Fisherman's Creel with lid. No. 292. 72mm long.	6.50
Beachy Head Lighthouse, with black band. No. 3. 135mm.	14.50
Eddystone Lighthouse. No. 315. 102mm.	7.50
Lighthouse, with steps on base and gilded windows. No. 47. 145mm.	7.50
Lighthouse, miniature candlesnuffer. No. 64. 71mm.	6.50
Lighthouse pepper pot. 108mm.	6.50
Shell dish. No. 533. 63mm long.	4.00
Shell with handle. No. 536. 54mm.	4.00
Oyster Shell, on coral legs. No. 496. 51mm.	5.50
Shell dish with handle. No. 537. 80mm.	5.50
Shell Jug. No. 524 on 3 tiny whelk shell feet. 76mm.	12.50
Whelk Shell, 5 sizes: No. 57. 80mm long.	5.00
No. 65. 45mm long.	5.00
No. 65. 85mm long.	5.00
No. 428. 70mm long.	5.00
No. 528. 115mm long.	7.50

Bathing Beauty, reclining, wearing swimsuit and mob-cap, holding parasol. 135mm (uncommon).	120.00
Boy holding model yacht, on beach base, coloured hair and yacht. No. 563. 85mm.	120.00
Boy in swimsuit, swimming on a rectangular blue 'sea' base. Hair and eyes coloured. No. 565. 120mm long.	75.00
Girl kneeling on 'beach' base with red bucket and spade, brown hair and red hat brim. No. 564. 75mm (563-565 are all quite rare). Coloured	125.00
White	82.50
Toddler on Donkey. 85mm and 109mm.	150.00
Deep Sea Diver. No. 261. 105mm.	195.00

Countryside.

Axe in Tree Stump. No. 61. 80mm.	10.50
Milk Churn with handle. No. 625. 53mm.	5.50
Milk Can and lid. No. 417. 106mm.	5.50
Milk Can and lid. No. 478. 72mm.	5.50

Animals

Some Grafton animals were given tiny glass bead eyes, more often than not these are missing, leaving small holes. Even without these beads the models remain very attractive, but obviously a complete model is more desirable and £4 to £10 should be added for models having glass eyes. The range of large comical cats with these coloured bead eyes and coloured bows are particularly appealing but are hard to find.

Bear, dressed as boy, standing on shell tray. 85mm.	47.50
Bear and Ragged Staff. No. 224 2 sizes: 85mm.	40.00
100mm.	40.00
Both versions can have bead eyes.	
Water Buffalo, lying with head turned, curved horns. 110mm. (very rare).	90.00
Bull, yellow, flat on base. (Art Deco). 65mm.	47.50
Calf, not named, but mostly found with cartoon transfer of farmer	

and wife behind gate with calf on
the other side (add £7.00).
No. 287. 100mm long. 20.00

Camel, 2 humps. No. 242.
125mm long. 40.00

Cat, Cheshire, inscribed: *The
Cheshire Cat* and *Always smiling*. 1
yellow glass eye. No. 288. 86mm. 11.00

Cat, Cheshire, can have red mouth
and nose, one bead eye (green or
red) and one eye closed,
inscribed: *The Cheshire Cat*. Found
with and without separate shield
carrying crest.
2 sizes: No. 228. 86mm. 8.50
No. 171. 100mm. 12.00

Cat, crouching and angry. No. 211.
55mm. 30.00

Cat, crouching, fat and angry with
tail in the air. Found with bead
eyes. No. 303. 88mm long. 30.00

Cat in Jar, inscribed: *From Chicago
Perishable*. No. 277. 80mm. 47.50

Cat singing, red mouth and green
bow. 75mm. 33.00

Cat Scent Bottle, sitting with
removable head. No. 229. 93mm. 40.00

Cat, sitting and comical, green bow
and tail at front with bead eyes
(blue or green). No. 319.
2 sizes: 88mm. 24.50
103mm. 28.50

Cat, sitting and winking. No. 612.
2 sizes: 80mm red or orange
bow. 24.50
105mm yellow bow. 26.50

Cat, blue, on roof of house. *Music on
the tiles*, unglazed, no crest.
Rd. No. 668183. 12.00

Cat, sitting and comical, yellow
bow. Found with verse: *As I was
going to St.Ives*. No. 351. 94mm. 26.50

Cat, sitting and comical, green bow
and tail at front, with bead eyes.
No. 339. 154mm. 30.00

Cat, sitting and comical, yellow bow
and tail at back, with bead eyes.
No. 344 or No. 420 (no colouring
£20.00). 146mm. 30.00

Cat, sitting, winking with both
thumbs in *Thumbs Up* position,
Orange bow, thumbs painted
black. 83mm. 40.00

Cat, sitting, tail at back, yellow bow.
No. 320. 104mm. 30.00

Cat, standing, arched back and tail
in the air with green bow.
No. 303. 100mm. 30.00

Cat, standing, arched back, small
tail, green bow. No. 527. 78mm. 30.00

Cat, standing and comical, blue bow
and green eyes. 88mm long. 30.00

(Cat) Kitten. No. 211. 50mm. 26.00

Lady Cat, upright, wearing coat and
bonnet and carrying handbag,
bow to neck. 90mm. 160.00

Cat salt pot, red open mouth and
green bow tied at back. No. 729.
92mm. 16.00

The Jersey Cow, often found not
named. No. 545. 60mm. 47.50

Cow, long-horn, sitting down.
No. 646. 150mm long. 75.00

Bulldog, British, inscribed: *Slow to
start but what a hold*. 83mm. 25.00

Bulldog, standing with feet wide
apart. No. 391. 51mm. 13.00

Bulldog, sitting, can have bead eyes
(yellow, red or green). No. 250.
2 sizes: 88mm. 40.00
102mm. 45.00

Bulldog pepper pot. No. 250. 80mm. 25.00

Dog in boater and clothes. 88mm. 43.00

Dog in top hat and clothes. 95mm. 45.00

Dog, scent bottle with head lid.
No. 232. 100mm. 40.00

Dog, Greyhound, standing with
front legs on small oval base.
No. 709. 102mm long. 47.50

Dog, with 2 heads, one head is
smiling and the other is sad. Two
varieties. Sometimes found with
a paper tag around neck
inscribed: *Two heads are better than
one*.
No. 645. 38mm. 100.00
No. 646. 63mm. 100.00

Dog, King Charles Spaniel, sitting.
No. 390. 53mm. 16.00

Dog, kneeling, wearing a green cap.
No. 488. Can be found coloured
with match holder. 85mm. 65.00
White. 47.50

Dog salt pot, sitting, large head,
blue stripes to ears, red nose.
75mm. 14.00

Dog, Labrador Pup, sitting with
bead eyes (yellow or green). Can

be found painted yellow or blue.

Painted. No. 355. 85mm. — 30.00

White. — 20.00

Dog, Puppy, sitting, one ear raised and scratching with back leg. (Often found coloured with no crest.) No. 410. 85mm. — 16.00

Coloured — 20.00

Dog, running, with fly or bee on tail, some colouring. 95mm long. — 47.50

A stylised version of this was made as a menu holder, coloured yellow and white. (late) 80mm long. — 40.00

Dog, Scottie, standing. No. 432. Can be found with bead eyes. 94mm long. — 26.00

Three varieties of dog, all with some colouring and marked *Swains Studdy Series* are as follows:

Dog, yawning, on ashtray base. 105mm long. — 25.00

Dog, with ball in mouth, on ashtray base. 105mm. — 25.00

Dog, yawning. 46mm. — 30.00

Dog, with ball in mouth. 46mm. — 30.00

Elephant, circus, standing on forelegs on stool. No. 231. 105mm. — 115.00

Elephant, sitting and comical. No. 438. 127mm. — 40.00

Found coloured purple or green. — 65.00

Elephant, sitting with trunk raised, comical. No. 102. 75mm. — 47.50

Elephant, walking. No. 426 or No. 470.

3 sizes: 50mm. — 40.00

65mm. — 47.50

80mm. — 47.50

Can be found coloured purple or red.

With colouring. — 45.00

Elephant, with sandwich boards, crest one side and inscribed: *Turn me round* on the other. 102mm. — 100.00

Fish, curved vase. No. 196. 57mm. — 5.50

Fish, curved tail and open mouth. No. 392. 105mm long. — 5.50

Fish, curved with bead eyes. No. 196. 125mm long. — 5.50

Fish, curved. No. 197. 70mm. — 9.50

Fish, curved body and open mouth. No. 393. 80mm long. — 8.50

Fish. No. 244. 110mm long. — 4.50

Fish, straight and scaly. No. 247.

2 sizes: 88mm long. — 4.50

115mm long. (bead eyes) — 7.50

Fish, straight and fat with open mouth. No. 341. 102mm long. — 4.00

Fish, straight with open mouth. No. 97. 100mm long. — 4.00

Fish, straight and thin. No. 302.

2 sizes: 76mm long. — 4.00

112mm long. — 5.50

Large size can be found with bead eyes.

Fox with bead eyes (yellow). No. 462.

2 sizes: 80mm long. — 50.00

140mm long. — 56.50

Fox, without bead eyes (i.e. model designed without them). 135mm long. — 50.00

Can be found painted red.

Fox with pheasant on stand. No. 434. Can be found painted red. 139mm long (late). — 60.00

Fox crouching. No. 467. 76mm long. — 75.00

Frog, with closed mouth, hands on chest, sitting on back legs. Can be found with bead eyes. No. 204. 72mm. — 30.00

Lion, standing. 105mm long. — 16.00

Monkey, can be found with bead eyes.

No. 242. 87mm. — 13.00

No. 286. 70mm. — 13.00

Can be found painted yellow, red, green or blue. — 20.00

Monkey, sitting, wearing coat. No. 245. 62mm. — 13.00

Can be found painted yellow or blue. — 20.00

Mouse, sitting up. No. 210. 42mm. — 20.00

Mouse, sitting up, holding nut, yellow bead eyes. No. 243. 43mm. — 25.00

Mouse. No. 222. 68mm. (Candlesnuffer). — 20.00

Mouse on cheese, can be found purple or blue with pink ears. No. 459. 55mm (late). — 37.50

Mouse sitting on pudding. 66mm. — 55.00

Pig, fat, lying asleep, inscribed: *Wunt be druv.* No. 421. 83mm. — 22.00

Pig, running, red bead eyes. No. 416. 87mm. — 30.00

Pig, sitting, long pointed nose and long ears tilted forward. No. 263. 90mm long. — 30.00

Pig, sitting with raised ears and miserable expression. No. 203. 70mm. — 40.00

Pig, sitting and laughing, inscribed:
Wunt be druv. No. 338. 65mm.   47.50
Pig, sitting, is much fatter than the
above, inscribed: *Wunt be druv.*
No. 341. 95mm long.   25.00
Pig, sitting up on hind legs, found
inscribed: *Wunt be druv,* or *I won't
be drove.*
No. 417. 70mm.   30.00
No. 420. 80mm.   33.00
Pig, standing, fat and inscribed:
Wunt be druv. No. 342.
98mm long.   30.00
Pig, standing, can be found with no
inscription but normally found
inscribed: *Wunt be druv* or *I won't
be drove.* No. 343. 70mm long.   14.00
Pig, standing, inscribed: *Wunt be
druv.* 88mm long.   15.00
Pig, fat. 95mm long.   14.50
Polar Bear. No. 102.
105mm long.   47.50
Polar Bear, standing on rocky base.
117mm long.   56.50
Polar Bear, baby, lying on its back
holding back foot, red eyes,
yellow lustre. 50mm wide,
60mm high.   65.00
Pony, not named. No. 493.
2 sizes: 70mm.   20.00
          105mm long.   25.00
Very rarely largest size found
inscribed: *New Forest Ponies.*   30.00
Rabbit, sometimes with yellow bead
eyes. No. 240. 112mm long.   13.00
Can be found painted brown.
Rabbit trinket dish, pink eyes.
No. 734. 120mm long.   15.50
Rabbit, crouching, head tucked in.
No. 102. 30mm.   75.00
Rat, sitting up. Candle snuffer.
No.210. 65mm.   30.00
Seal. No. 402. 70mm long. (This is a
very delicate model).   17.50
Snail. No. 328. 80mm long.   15.00
Squirrel holding nut, can be found
with bead eyes. No. 327. 75mm.   30.00
Terrapin. No. 253. 92mm long.   13.00
Wallaby, 90mm.   75.00

Birds (including Eggs)
Bird/fledgling, some colouring. No.
435. 65mm. (very plump and
pretty).   25.00
Grotesque Chick posy holder with
orange legs, (late). No. 737.
68mm.   29.00

Comical Bird match holder, orange
legs, yellow eyes, large beak,
(late). 65mm.   40.00
Birds, two with long beaks and
spread wings in the form of a tall
taper vase. 145mm.   13.00
Chicken half out of egg, can be
found with bead eyes. No. 326.
73mm long.   12.50
Chick Ashtray with compartment to
hold matches, striker on tail.
Some colour. 80mm.   32.50
Cockerel salt pot, some colouring.
62mm. No. 727.   40.00
Cock on circular base. No. 454.
100mm (pair with hen).   19.50
Duck, swimming, occasionally
found inscribed: *Aylesbury duck.*
No. 377. 96mm long.   19.50
Inscribed.   27.50
Duck posy holder, comical, yellow
beak. No. 442. 80mm.   40.00
Duck posy or cigarette holder, some
colouring. No. 732 115mm long.   30.00
Duck match holder, striker and
ashtray. Some colouring. No. 735.
80mm.   32.50
Hen, on circular base, can be found
in orange. No. 453. 100mm (pair
with cock).   19.50
Hen, roosting on basket base.
82mm.   10.50
Kingfisher on base. No. 670. 62mm.   40.00
Owl on rocky base. No. 687. 132mm.   60.00
(very impressive model).
Penguin. No. 329. 88mm.   30.00
Swan, head under wing. No. 409.
85mm long.   19.50

Great War
Prince of Wales in uniform, one
hand in pocket, cigarette in other.   500.00
American Soldier (Doughboy),
squatting. 80mm.   160.00
Two Models found fully
coloured.   400.00
Also appears painted black
except for cigar. No. 85. 80mm.   200.00
British Territorial Bulldog, seated
figure of Tommy with bulldog
face, red and blue bands on hat.
No. 262. 88mm.   160.00
Cavalry officer, standing. No. 411A.
128mm. Very rare.   500.00
Kitchener bust (glazed) on circular
base, inscribed: *Lord Kitchener of*

Khartoum creator of British Army
1914/1918. Born June 24th 1850.
Died serving his country June 5th
1916 by the sinking of HMS
Hampshire off the Orkneys. No. 395.

2 sizes: 100mm.	40.00
130mm.	40.00

See also *Parian* Section.

German officer match holder,
caricature of head inside with
life-belt, some colouring. No. 214.
95mm dia.

Plain	30.00
Coloured	47.50

Or could it possibly be the
Kaiser?

Sailor, seated and holding a model
submarine, blue on hat band
impressed: *Victory*. Is often found
inscribed: *Weve got 'U' well in
hand*. — 110.00

Can also be found fully coloured.
No. 452. 80mm. (very rare). — 150.00

Soldier leaving Trench, inscribed:
Over the top. No. 433. 118mm. — 145.00

Soldier throwing Hand Grenade,
inscribed: *The Bomb Thrower*.
No. 425. 140mm. — 145.00

Soldier throwing Hand Grenade,
without the ammunition box
which must have been added for
stability. A forerunner of above.
One example known. 140mm.
(Very rare). — 300.00

Biplane, fixed prop. No. 450. 145mm
long. (Very rare). 2 versions –
open wing ends and closed
wing ends. — 200.00

Monoplane, fixed prop. No. 414.
135mm long. — 55.00

HMS Dreadnought, ship with high
prow. No. 408. 142mm long. — 75.00

Same ship with same stock
number found inscribed:

HMS Gosport	75.00
HMS Victory.	75.00
No name.	40.00

HMS Iron Duke. No. 431.
155mm long. — 85.00

Submarine, inscribed:*E9*. No. 406.
145mm long. — 40.00

Motor Ambulance with curtains,
inscribed: *Motor ambulance car
given by Staffordshire china
operatives. British Red Cross*

*Society: St John Ambulance
Association. Load not to exceed 1
driver, 1 attendant and patients.*
No. 397. 98mm long. — 55.00

Motor Tractor, inscribed: *Model of
motor tractor used on western front*.
No. 456. 80mm long. — 170.00

Renault Tank. 100mm long. — 65.00

Tank with steering wheels,
inscribed: *H.M. Landship Creme de
Menthe*. No. 413. 118mm long. — 22.50

Tank, no steering wheels, inscribed:
H.M. Landship Creme de Menthe.
No. 413. 98mm long. — 24.50

Also found inscribed: *Model of
Whippet Tank*. 98mm long. (Rare). — 70.00

Whippet Tank, inscribed: *Model of
Whippet Tank*. No. 449.
115mm long. — 115.00

Alpine Gun with moving wheels,
inscribed: *Model of Alpine gun*.
No. 394. 105mm long. (Very rare). — 250.00

Desert Gun. No. 430. 155mm long. — 75.00

Field Gun on Sledge, inscribed:
French 75. No. 412. 160mm long. — 47.50

German Gun captured by British.
No. 403. 153mm long. — 40.00

Trench Howitzer (found with
Ramsgate Imperial Bazaar
inscription. See Monuments.
Ramsgate Lifeboat Memorial)
No. 404. 75mm long. — 17.50

Cannon Shell. No. 400. 76mm. — 5.00

Cannon Shell, inscribed:*Jack
Johnson*. No. 399. 90mm. — 12.50

German Incendiary Bomb. No. 405.
80mm. — 17.00

Mills Hand Grenade with removable
metal pin, often found without
inscription. No. 411 or No. 117.
83mm. — 25.00

Bandsman's Drum. No. 235. 45mm. — 9.00

Bell Tent with open flaps, with or
without base. No. 239. 65mm. — 16.00

Boot with Puttee. No. 389. 75mm. — 22.00

Anzac Hat with blue band.
110mm long. — 25.00

Colonial Soldier's Hat. No. 238.
89mm long. — 19.00

Water Bottle. No. 234. 80mm. — 13.00

Cenotaph, inscribed: *MCMXIV-
MCMXIX - The Glorious Dead* and

3 coloured flags on reverse.
2 sizes: 138mm.   12.00
   (Flags add £12.00).
155mm.   16.00
   (Flags add £12.00).
Glandford Brigg War Memorial.
114mm.   160.00

Home/Nostalgic

Anvil candlesnuffer, never found
   factory marked. 56mm.   8.50
Anvil on heavy base. No. 552.
70mm.   7.50
Baby crawling naked, brown hair,
   blue eyes. No. 544. 120mm long.   95.00
Baby sitting up. No. 481. 63mm.   30.00
Baby's Rocking Cradle. No. 294.
   62mm long.   12.00
Basket with handle. No. 29. 52mm.   3.00
Cabin Trunk. 56mm long. No. 351.   7.50
Flat Iron. No. 162. 65mm long.   12.50
Flower Basket. No. 244. 65mm.   6.50
Grandfather Clock. No. 396. 110mm.   16.00
Handbell, no clapper. 82mm.   7.00
Horn Lantern, inscribed. No. 306.
   76mm.   8.50
Laundry Basket. No. 534.
   75mm long.   6.50
Rocking Horse. 125mm long.   47.00
Shaving Mug. 40mm.   6.50
Tub, hole in top. No. 149. 45mm.   4.00
Village Water Pump. No. 331. 80mm.   10.50
Watering Can.   6.50
Wing Chair. No. 389. 73mm.   15.00

Comic/Novelty

Billiken. No. 291. 44mm.   5.50
Boy, grotesque, sitting cross-legged,
   top of head on egg-cup. 62mm.   30.00
Boy Scout holding bugle. 133mm.   140.00
Boy Scout saluting. 133mm.   140.00
Chinese Man Pepper Pot, some
   colouring. No. 726. 70mm. (There
   must be a matching Salt Pot).   17.50
Fu Hing God of Happiness, Chinese
   Priest standing upright, holding
   baby, some colouring. 115mm.   55.00
Gladiators Head, Candlesnuffer.
   No. 228.   30.00
Head on a rock, comic, could be
   Kitchener wearing a pharaoh's
   headress. 67mm.   30.00
Head, comic salt pot, miserable face
   and droopy bow tie. No. 255 or
   No. 250. 85mm (matches below).   16.00

Head, comic pepper pot, happy face
   and perky bow tie. No. 258.
   85mm. (matches above).   16.00
Knave Candlesnuffer. No. 101.
   90mm.   55.00
Lemon with lid, stalk handle.
   No. 62. 60mm.   16.00
Pierrot, sitting cross-legged on box
   playing banjo, some colouring.
   Found with inscription: *As I was
   going to St. Ives.* No. 566.
   103mm.   82.50
Policeman, cylindrical body
   covered by cape. No. 427. *Special
   Constable.* 115mm.   130.00
Teapot with face of General Kruger,
   spout and handle form arms,
   some colouring. No. 264. 48mm.   80.00
Watch Stand, Father Time head with
   beard forming legs. No. 154.
   110mm.   40.00

Cartoon/Comedy Characters

Bonzo Dog, pepper pot. 80mm.   25.00
Sunny Jim with red bow tie and
   black topper. 86mm.   47.50

Alcohol

Barrel, upright as pepper pot.
   No. 17. 69mm.   15.00
Bottle with cork. No. 715. 68mm.   6.50
Champagne Bottle. No. 221. 102mm.   10.00
Champagne Bottle pepper pot.
   No. 225. 102mm.   10.00
Man in Barrel, head and feet
   protruding, inscribed: *No beer.*
   No. 429. 115mm.   19.00
Soda Syphon. No. 313. 93mm.   10.00
Tankard. 80mm.   3.00
Toby Jug, red, staff in left hand.
   65mm.   25.00

Sport/Pastimes

Footballer with ball on small base.
   130mm.   80.00
Golfer holding bag of golf clubs,
   comic figure, inscribed: *The
   Colonel.* No. 352. Cigarette is often
   broken off. Can be found in green
   cap. 90mm.   38.50
   Can be found fully coloured.   52.50
Comical Golfer in baggy trousers,
   bent over ball with clubs, about
   to put, on tray base. 72mm.   215.00
Golf Ball salt pot. 52mm.   6.50

Golf Ball pepper pot. No. 293.
52mm.   6.50
Tennis player, lady holding racquet
(reputedly Suzanne Lenglen).
133mm.   100.00
Dice, Trump Indicator, heart,
diamond, club and spade and no
trump on five sides. 35mm.   23.00

Transport
Charabanc, with 5 rows of seats,
inscribed: *Dreadnought*. No. 568.
100mm long.   45.00
If inscribed   55.00
Mons Bleriot, bust, inscribed: *First
man to fly across the channel in an
aeroplane July 25th 1900*. 85mm.   82.50
Punt with two girls aboard with
wooden pole. 115mm long.   55.00

Modern Equipment
Horn Gramophone, square base.
No. 641. 92mm.   33.50

Hats
Bowler Hat. No. 710. 93mm long.   30.00
Top Hat. No. 189 and No. 213.
37mm.   7.50
Fireman's Helmet. No. 66. 65mm.   30.00

Footwear
Boot. No. 237. 80mm long.   8.50
Lancashire Clog, sometimes found
inscribed: *Model of Lancashire
Clog*. No. 407. 90mm long.   5.50
If inscribed   6.50
Sabot. No. 212. 80mm long.   5.00
Also appears with manufactured
hole for wall hanging. Same
price.
Oriental Shoe, pointed. No. 170.
3 sizes: 80mm long.   6.50
           95mm long.   6.50
           104mm long.   6.50
Shoe, lady's 18th century. No. 50.
83mm long.   8.50
Slipper Wall Pocket. 100mm long.   7.50

Miniature Domestic
Beaker. No. 73. 52mm.   2.00
Candleholder, circular. No. 80.   3.00
Cheese Dish and cover (2 pieces)
No. 78. 65mm long.   11.00
Cup and Saucer, fancy. No. 107.
48mm.   5.50

Cup and Saucer, No. 108.
110mm dia.   5.50
Cup and Saucer. No. 122. 67mm dia.   5.50
Cup. No. 147. 39mm.   2.00
Milk Jug. No. 72. 40mm.   3.00
Mug with handle. No. 36. 48mm.   3.00
Mug with handle. No. 143. 41mm.   3.00

Numbered Domestic and Ornamental Wares
No. 2. Vase. Ivy covered. 60mm.   3.50
No. 3. Jug, elongated spout. 80mm.   2.50
   Also Vase. 88mm.   3.50
No. 4. Dish, crinkle edged. 69mm.   2.50
   or Jug. 75mm.   2.50
No. 5. Vase. Bagware. 45mm.   3.00
No. 6. Cauldron. 41mm.   2.50
No. 8. Vase. 61mm.   2.50
No. 9. Vase, shaped edge. 62mm.   2.50
No. 10. Vase, shaped, with cruciform
   top. Can be found coloured red.
   70mm.   2.50
No. 11. Vase. 66mm.   2.50
No. 12. Jug. 72mm.   2.50
No. 13. Jug. 67mm.   2.50
No. 16. Vase. 37mm   2.50
No. 17. Crinkle-top Jug. 30mm.   3.00
No. 18. Hexagonal Vase. 63mm.   2.50
No. 19. Vase, shaped. 65mm.   2.50
No. 20. Vase, 2 handled. 68mm.   2.50
No. 21. Jug, ornate. 75mm.   3.50
No. 22. Vase, bulbous, with
   ornamental shoulders. 50mm.   2.50
No. 23. Vase, with moulding. 60mm.   2.50
No. 25. Vase, 2 handles. 60mm.   2.50
No. 27. Vase, bulbous. 60mm.   2.50
No. 28. Ewer. 55mm.   2.50
No. 29. Churn. 52mm.   3.00
No. 30. Vase. 50mm.   2.50
No. 31. Beaker. 62mm.   2.50
No. 34. 3-handled Loving Cup.
   47mm.   4.00
No. 36. Tankard Mug. 66mm.   2.50
No. 37. 2-handled mug. 45mm.   3.50
No. 38. 3-handled Loving Cup.
   48mm.   4.00
No. 44. Jug. 60mm.   2.50
No. 45. Jug, Bagware. 40mm.   3.00
No. 52. Ewer. 80mm.   2.50
No. 53. Ewer. 76mm.   2.50
   also Vase. 50mm.   2.50
No. 55. Pot and lid, ribbed. 60mm.   4.00
No. 57. Jug, fluted base. 68mm.   3.00
No. 60. Vase, 2 handled. 38mm.   2.50
No. 64. Vase. 60mm.   2.50

No. 65. Posy Bowl. 68mm long.   2.50
No. 67. Tray, diamond shaped.
   121mm long.   3.00
No. 68. Tray, heart shaped.
   100mm long.   3.00
No. 70. Oil Lamp & Lid. 93mm long.   5.50
No. 71. Tray, club shaped.
   100mm long.   3.00
   or Vase, 2 handles. 40mm.   2.50
No. 72. Jug. 40mm.   2.50
No. 73. Beaker. 33mm and 52mm.   2.50
No. 74. Pot with 3 blunt feet. 47mm.   2.50
No. 75. Jug. 39mm.   2.50
No. 80. Miniature circular
   Candleholder.   3.00
No. 82. Diamond pin box and lid.
   90mm long.   5.50
No. 83. Heart shaped pin box and
   lid. 63mm dia.   5.50
No. 84. Spade or Heart shaped pin
   box and lid. 68mm.   5.50
No. 85. Club shaped pin box and
   lid. 68mm.   5.50
No. 86. Bowl. 48mm dia.   2.50
No. 87. Vase, fluted and one
   handled. 30mm.   2.50
No. 88. Vase. 40mm.   2.50
No. 91. Vase. 39mm.   2.50
No. 92. Tray, hexagonal. 69mm dia.   3.00
No. 94. Vase. 44mm.   2.50
No. 95. Vase, Globe with crinkle top.
   43mm.   2.50
No. 96. Vase, Taper. 45mm.   2.50
No. 99. Dish, Trefoil. 80mm wide.   3.00
No. 100. Tray, spade shaped.
   78mm long.   3.00
No. 102. Ewer (But Polar Bear found
   with same No.)   2.50
No. 104. Vase. 65mm.   2.50
No. 105. Pitcher with high looped
   handle. 64mm.   2.50
No. 106. Jar. 60mm.   2.50
No. 118. Wine Bottle. 72mm.   3.00
No. 121. Vase, bulbous, 2 handles.
   60mm.   2.50
No. 125. Pot, round. 52mm.   2.50
No. 127. Vase, long necked. 62mm.   2.50
No. 128. Vase. 70mm.   2.50
No. 129. Long narrow-necked Vase.
   73mm.   3.50
No. 130. Bowl with handle.   2.50
No. 131. Basket, ornate. 123mm long.   8.50
No. 140. *Hair Tidy* and lid. 90mm.   9.50
No. 141. *Hair Pins*, oval box & lid.
   120mm long.   6.50

No. 143. 1-handled Mug. 40mm.   4.00
No. 144. 2-handled Mug. 40mm.   3.50
No. 145. 3-handled Loving Cup.
   39mm.   4.00
No. 149. Tobacco Jar with lid,
   inscribed: *Tobacco* on lid.
   120mm.   10.00
No. 152. Vase with ornate heron
   handles. 145mm.   6.50
No. 155. Cylinder vase. 60mm.   2.50
No. 157. Ribbed Jug. 70mm.   2.50
No. 161. Fluted Jug. 62mm.   7.50
No. 177. Vase, bulbous. 40mm.   2.50
No. 191. Vase. 70mm.   2.50
No. 200. Aberdeen Bronze Pot.
   55mm.   3.00
No. 205. Jug. 45mm.   2.50
No. 212. Square-topped Vase. 68m.   2.50
No. 242. Stamp Box and lid.
   47mm long.   5.50
No. 260. Vase, 2 handles. 37mm.   4.00
No. 263. Salve Pot and lid.
   45mm dia.   4.00
   also Hexagonal Vase. 55mm.   3.00
No. 267. Round Pot and lid.
   45mm dia.   4.00
No. 273. Vase, square neck. 78mm.   2.50
No. 278. Shaped Vase. 80mm.   3.00
No. 296. Circular Box and lid.
   43mm dia.   4.00
No. 297. Pill Box and lid, oval.
   45mm long.   4.00
No. 298. Pill Box and lid,
   rectangular. 45mm long.   4.00
No. 299. Pill Box and lid, 5 sided.
   28mm.   4.00
No. 300. Stamp Box and lid, 5 sided.
   50mm dia.   5.50
No. 301. Vase, bulbous. 50mm.   2.50
No. 302. Vase. 48mm.   2.50
No. 311. Vase. 50mm.   2.50
No. 314. Vase. 39mm.   2.50
No. 316. Triangular Chest and lid.
   70mm long.   9.00
No. 318. Pill Box and lid, decorated
   with angel's heads. 63mm.   8.50
No. 323. Tall narrow Vase. 45mm.   2.50
No. 325. Urn with spout, handle and
   lid. 48mm.   4.50
No. 348. Jug. 63mm.   2.50
No. 349. Jug, slim. 66mm.   3.00
No. 358. Sauce Boat. 105mm long.   5.00
No. 359. Vase, 2 angular handles.
   80mm.   3.00

No. 360. Pin Tray, triangular.
85mm long.   3.00
No. 367. Pin Box, oval. 90mm long.   3.00
No. 372. Jug, slim neck. 76mm.   2.50
No. 373. Jug, long necked. 75mm.   2.50
No. 374. Jug, fluted base. 73mm.   2.50
No. 375. Vase, double mouthed.
63mm.   2.50
No. 378. Sauce Boat. 120mm long.   6.50
No. 379. Jug with stem. 70mm.   2.50
No. 386. Ashtray, triangular on 3
feet. 75mm dia.   2.50
No. 387. Candlestick. 160mm.   3.00
No. 500. Casket with lid. 84mm
long, lions head handles.   11.50
No. 502. Mustard Pot with lid and
spoon. 70mm.   5.50
No. 504. Vase, octagonal. 60mm.   2.50
No. 505. Vase. 56mm.   2.50
No. 506. Vase, octagonal. 54mm.   2.50
No. 507. Taper Vase, octagonal.
60mm.   2.50
No. 524. Whelk Shells Jug. 76mm.   2.50
No. 526. Bowl, 2 handled.
118mm wide.   9.50
No. 526. (Also). Decagon Jug (10
sided). 55mm high, 110mm long.   7.50
No. 529. Vase, with moulding.
45mm.   2.50
No. 530. Vase. 50mm.   2.50
No. 531. Vase, curious wedge
shaped. 50mm.   2.50
No. 532. Vase, ribbed. 53mm.   2.50
No. 533. Grain Scoop. 60mm long.   7.50
No. 534. Oval woven Basket
without handle. 75mm long.   6.50
No. 535. Vase, shaped. 52mm.   2.50
No. 589. Vase. 112mm.   5.50
No. 590. Tray. 150mm long.   3.00
No. 616. Cylinder lip salve pot and
lid. 30mm.   4.00
No. 622. Vase. 121mm.   2.50
No. 634. Vase, wide top. 34mm.   2.50
No. 649. Vase, hexagonal wide top.
51mm.   2.50
No. 650. Vase, hexagonal wide top.
55mm.   2.50
No. 651. Vase, octagonal. 58mm.   2.50
No. 652. Vase, hexagonal shaped
top. 57mm.   2.50
No. 653. Vase, pentagonal tapered.
57mm.   2.50
No. 654. Vase, hexagonal wide top.
51mm.   2.50
No. 656. Vase, thin.   2.50

No. 657. Vase, bulbous hexagonal
base. 44mm.   2.50
No. 658. Vase, octagonal. 50mm.   2.50
No. 659. Triangular Pot. 42mm.   4.00
No. 660. Vase. 52mm.   2.50
No. 669. Font Vase. 83mm.   11.00
No. 671. *Salt* Pot. 82mm.   8.50
No. 672. *Pepper* Pot, shaped. 84mm.   8.50
No. 676. Cream Jug. 60mm.   2.50
No. 681. Salt Pot, egg-shaped.
45mm.   4.00
No. 682. Pepper Pot. 45mm.   4.00
No. 712. Vase, shaped. 68mm.   2.50
No. 713. Vase. 70mm.   2.50
No. 714. Vase. 69mm.   2.50
No. 715. Narrow Vase. 68mm.   2.50

Not numbered
Candlesnuffer, Anvil, not factory
marked. 56mm.   7.50
Egg Cup. 60mm.   6.50
Gravy Boat. 126mm long.   7.50
Pill Box, ivy leaf shaped.
57mm long.   3.50

Miscellaneous
Bell, miniature. No. 250. 55mm.   6.50
Handbell, no clapper.
2 sizes: No. 15. 82mm.   7.50
No. 265. 51mm.   4.50
Bell. No. 153. 86mm.   6.50
Horse's Hoof. No. 236. 72mm long.   5.50

Granic China

Grays Sports China

Trademark used by an unknown manufacturer but possibly Sampson Hancock
(and Sons), Bridge Works, Stoke and later
at the Garden Works, Hanley (usual
trademark Corona).

Granic Models
Crinkle edged vase. No. 262. 55mm.   4.00

Footwear
Ladies high boot, ornate. 30mm.   10.50

Mark registered in 1911 but used 1908
onwards.

Trademark used by A.E. Gray & Co., Glebe
Works, Mayer Street, Hanley.
A.E. Gray and Co. were earthenware
manufacturers – the company was
renamed 'Portmeirion Potteries Ltd' in
1961.
The firm does not appear to have made
crested china but the mark is included
here because the 'Sports China' series
very much appeals to collectors of pre-
Great War souvenir china. Vases, jugs and
beakers are found with transfer prints of
footballers in the colours of League teams.
Each transfer design is registered, the
earliest registration number being from
1907-8.

from £30.00 each

The Griffin China

Trademark used by the London wholesalers, Sanderson & Young, 21 Red Lion Square. Manufactured by several potteries, probably branches of J.A. Robinson & Sons (Coronet Ware), and Taylor and Kent (Florentine).

Sanderson & Young were quite well known wholesalers who could have sold wares produced by any English manufacturer, probably several manufacturers supplying models during the same period. Crests recorded indicate that the models were sold in the South of England, and, judging by models recorded this mark was not used during and after the Great War. No view ware or other transfer devices have been found.

Griffin Models
Ancient Artefacts

Fountains Abbey, Abbot's Cup, not named. 49mm.	3.00
Lichfield Jug. No. 60. 62mm.	3.00
Loving Cup, 3 handles. 39mm.	3.00
Irish Bronze Pot. 50mm.	3.00
Newbury Leather Bottle, inscribed: *Leather bottle found at Newbury 1644 on Battlefield now in Museum.* No. 83. 65mm.	4.00
Salisbury Kettle. 100mm.	4.00
Scarborough Jug, inscribed: *Jug about 600 years old found in the Ancient Moat of Scarborough.* 50mm.	4.00

Buildings - Coloured

Cottage. 95mm.	17.50

Monuments (including crosses)

Iona Cross. 110mm.	10.50
Sailor's Stone, Hindhead. 94mm.	10.50

Traditional/National Souvenirs

Welsh Hat, blue cord. 55mm.	5.00

Seaside Souvenirs

Yacht, in full sail. 127mm.	12.50

Countryside

Milk Churn and lid. 85mm.	5.00

Animals

Cat, *The Cheshire Cat Always Smiling.* 88mm.	7.50
Cat, Manx. 83mm long.	16.00
Camel, one hump. 88mm.	13.00
Dog in wicker cradle. 90mm long.	14.50
Pig, standing. 90mm long.	11.00
Toad. 72mm long.	19.50

Birds (including Eggs)

Hen, roosting. 54mm.	7.50
Parrot. 78mm.	8.50
Swan Posy holder. 80mm.	5.00
Baby Bird cream jug. 66mm.	5.50

Home/Nostalgic

Coal Scuttle. 75mm.	3.50
Coal Scuttle, helmet shaped. 60mm.	4.50
Lantern. 70mm.	8.50
Pillar Box. 75mm.	8.00
Shaving Mug. 55mm.	5.50
Suitcase, closed. 80mm long.	4.00
Telescope, folded. 70mm.	13.00
Watering Can.	5.50

Comic/Novelty

Boy on Scooter. 115mm.	16.00

Sport

Cricket Bag. 115mm long.	9.00

Musical Instruments

Drum. 57mm dia.	5.00
Tambourine. 68mm dia.	4.50

Footwear

Lady's 18th Century Shoe. 90mm long.	7.50
Oriental Slipper. 95mm long.	4.00

Miniature Domestic
Teapot and lid. 52mm.   9.50

Domestic
Candle Holder. 77mm dia.   3.00
Napkin ring.   4.00

Grimwades

Trademark used by Grimwades Ltd, Winton,
Upper Hanley and Elgin Potteries, Stoke.
Earthenware firm more noted for hotel and
domestic ware. Obviously made this one
late piece for export.

Grimwades Models
Jug. No. 1823. 69mm. Crest
Dominion of Canada   4.50

Grimwades also produced a range of beige
Great War miniature domestic pieces of
some interest.
The War Time Butter Dish (for a family of ten),
inscribed: *Made by the girls of Staffordshire
during the winter of 1917/18. When the boys
were in the trenches, fighting for Liberty and
Civilisation. Special message from Rt. Hon. D.
Lloyd George, Prime Minister: 'I have no
hesitation in saying that economy in the
consumption and use of food in this country is
a matter of the greatest possible importance to
the Empire at the present time'*. 110mm dia.
The War Time Bread and Butter plate, similar
inscription. 200mm dia.
The Patriotic Sugar basin for a family of ten with
a message from Lloyd George. 40mm.
Approximate value of pieces in this
range.   15.00-20.00

Grimwades also produced a range of
Victory & Peace commemoratives.

Grosvenor Crest China

Great War
Burford War Memorial. *In grateful
memory of the men of Burford who
fell in the war of 1914-1918.*
130mm.   170.00
Campden War Memorial. 146mm.   185.00

Grosvenor Series

Trademark used by Arkinstall & Son Ltd.,
Arcadian Works, Stoke on Trent. (Usual
trademark Arcadian).

Grosvenor Series Models
Ancient Artefacts
*Egyptian Pottery Discovered by Dr
Flinders.* 50mm.   4.00

Home/Nostalgic
Open Umbrella. 35mm.   14.50

Grosvenor Ware

Trademark used by Sampson Hancock (& Sons), Bridge Works, Stoke and later at the Garden Works, Hanley (renamed Corona Pottery. Usual trademark Corona).

For details of this mark and the manufacturer see The Corona China.

This mark was used as an alternative to the Corona trademark; as crests are found from all over Britain it is unlikely to have been a mark specially used for any specific wholesaler or retailer. No commemorative crests, view ware or transfer devices have been found on models. The mark appears to have been only used during the Great War.

Numbering System. Models can be found with gold or black painted stock numbers. These are recorded, where known, in the following lists:

Grosvenor Models
Ancient Artefacts

Canterbury Water Bottle. 50mm.	4.00
Guernsey Milk Can and lid. 95mm.	5.00
Jersey Milk Can and lid. 53mm.	5.00
Leather Jack. 58mm.	3.00

Buildings - White

Blackpool Tower, on heavy detailed base. 127mm.	9.00
Clifton Suspension Bridge. 120mm long.	75.00

Traditional/National Souvenirs

Laxey Wheel. 80mm.	40.00
Welsh Harp. 90mm.	7.50

Seaside

Lighthouse on rocky base. 150mm.	17.00

Animals

Cat, sitting, large ruff of fur. 100mm.	17.50
Cat, black, on horseshoe (from Arcadian registered series mould). 74mm.	75.00
Cow Creamer. No. 376. 130mm long.	16.00
Fish. 88mm long.	3.50
Lion, lying down. No. 369. 150mm long.	35.00
Pig, standing. No. 158. 84mm long.	10.00
Tortoise. 70mm long.	9.00

Great War

Submarine, inscribed:*E4.* 110mm long.	19.50
Renault Tank. 100mm long.	75.00
Torpedo, Model of. 150mm long.	55.00
Ghurka Knife. 140mm long.	20.00
Bell Tent. No. 209. 85mm.	16.50
Newnham War Memorial. 140mm. (rare).	150.00

Home/Nostalgic

Baby in Bootee. 80mm long.	11.00
Cigarette Case. 70mm long.	13.00
Desk Top. 35mm.	7.50
Grandfather Clock. 123mm.	9.50
Hip Bath. 92mm long.	10.50
Jardinière on fixed stand. 92mm.	5.00
Tobacco Pouch. 75mm long.	9.50
Watering can. 72mm.	5.50
Post Box. 62mm. Inscribed *I can't get a letter...*	11.00

Sport/Pastimes

Tennis Racquet. 136mm long.	13.00
Castle Chess Piece. 65mm.	11.00
Knight Chess Piece. 72mm.	20.00
Pawn Chess Piece. 60mm.	25.00

Musical Instruments

Piano with open lid. 60mm.	12.50

Modern Equipment

Gas Cooker with match striker top. 70mm.	10.00

Footwear

Ladies 18th Century Shoe. 90mm long.	7.50

Miniature Domestic
Column Candlestick. 100mm.   3.00

Miscellaneous
Horseshoe on slope. 70mm long.   3.00

Gwalia Ware

GWALIA
PORCELAIN

Oldbury, Knighton,
& Llandrindod Wells.

Trademark used for a Llandrindod Wells
    retailer by an unknown manufacturer.
    Only 2 pieces recorded, bearing
    Llandrindod Wells crests.

Gwalia Models
Ancient Artefacts
Chester Roman Kettle, not named.   4.00
Loving Cup, one handled. 40mm.   4.00

H & L

H & L

Impressed mark used 1905-1919.

Impressed mark used by Hewitt & Leadbeater, Willow Potteries, Longton. Usual trademark Willow Art, these impressed initials are often found on models that also carry the Willow Art mark.

For details of this firm see Willow Art and Willow China.

Early in its history this firm specialised in parian ware, which carried the impressed mark 'H & L'. Many busts also carry the printed trademark Willow Art China so they will be found listed under that heading. Several other models have been recorded with only this impressed mark, but as they are normally found with the Willow Art mark they too will be found listed under that heading.

The models listed below have not been found with a printed mark and are not normally found with crests.

H & L Models
Parian/Unglazed

Bust of *Bourne*. 154mm.	55.00
Bust of *Clowes*. 150mm.	55.00
Bust of Albert King of the Belgians, square base, unglazed. 172mm.	75.00
Bust of Sir John French. 168mm.	75.00
Bust of Field Marshall Lord Kitchener. Impressed 'C.S. *Chadwick copyright Sep 11th 1914*. 170mm.	95.00
Bust of Lord Roberts on square glazed or unglazed base. 170mm.	75.00

Bust of *Shakespeare* on square base.

3 sizes: 105mm.	17.50
112mm.	17.50
126mm.	40.00
Bust on square base, unknown. 174mm.	95.00
(Possibly Sir John Jellicoe).	

Buildings - Coloured
Ann Hathaway's Cottage

3 sizes: 60mm long.	16.00
105mm long.	30.00
125mm long.	30.00
Mason Croft, Residence of Miss Marie Corelli. 73mm.	110.00
Shakespeares House. 50mm long.	16.00

Historical/Folklore

Font in which Shakespeare was baptized, Model of. 95mm dia.	15.50
Lincoln Imp, not named. 130mm.	8.50

Cartoon/Comedy Characters

Dr Beetle and Sunny Jim, sitting on striped armchair with rose and brown colouring. 95mm.	65.00

H & S

Animals
Pig, sitting with inscription: *You may push...* 75mm.   12.50

Great War
Battleship, impressed: *HMS Lion.*
   140mm long.   30.00
Submarine. 120mm long.   20.00
Tank. 125mm long.   14.50

Home/Nostalgic
Coal Scuttle. 53mm.   4.50
Garden Trug. 70mm.   7.50

Trademark used for a Plymouth retailer by Hewitt & Leadbeater, Willow Potteries, Longton (usual trademark Willow Art).

For details of this china and the manufacturer see Willow Art China.

As two of the models recorded are to be found in Plymouth it is almost certain that the 'P' in the 'H & S.P' stands for Plymouth. It is quite possible that H & S had a number of shops in English resorts, or that Hewitt & Leadbeater used pieces with this mark to complete other orders. The mark does not appear to have been used after the Great War and no transfer devices of any kind have been recorded.

H & S Models
Unglazed
Bust of Field Marshall Lord
   Kitchener on square base. 170mm.   95.00

Buildings - White
Derry's Clock, Plymouth.
   2 sizes: 132mm.   18.00
        150mm.   20.00
Hastings Castle Ruins. 100mm.   25.00

Monuments (including Crosses)
Burns, statue on square base.
   170mm.   30.00
Drake, statue, Plymouth.
   160mm.   16.00

Historical/Folklore
Church Bell, inscribed: *Curfew must not ring tonight.* 70mm.   7.50

Hamilton China

Heathcote China

SALTBURN ʙʏ ᴛʜᴇ SEA

Trademark used for H. Hamilton, Milton & Amber, Saltburn, for products of J.A. Robinson & Sons Ltd. (Coronet Ware).
These models are always found with the Saltburn by the Sea crest and were sold in that town by H. Hamilton whose trademark they bear.

Hamilton Models
Ancient Artefacts
Puzzle Jugs. 67mm.   4.00

Seaside Souvenirs
Two curling waves on an octagonal base, inscribed: *The glad sea waves.*
50mm.   19.00

Animals
Kneeling Camel.   13.00

Birds (including Eggs)
Kingfisher. 77mm.   30.00

Comic/Novelty
Jack-in-the-Box. 90mm.   20.00

Miniature Domestic
Shaving Mug. 57mm.   5.50

Domestic
Sugar Basin. 53mm.   3.00

Trademark used by H.M. Williamson & Sons, Bridge Pottery, Longton.
Domestic manufacturer not known to have made crested souvenirs, only domestic wares found:

Cup and saucer with Burgh of
Stirling crest with early mark.   3.00
Cup and saucer with Troon crest
with late mark.   3.00
Coffee Can and saucer, with the 4
Flags of the Allies. 56mm.   12.00

Herald China

Heraldic China

Trademark used for a wholesaler or retailer probably by Alfred B. Jones & Sons Ltd, Grafton China Works, Longton, Staffs. (Usual trademark Grafton).

Herald Models
Ancient Artefacts
Aberdeen Bronze Pot, not named.
    60mm.   3.00

Animals
Pig, sitting. Inscribed: *Wunt be druv.*
    90mm long.   30.00
Shetland Pony. No. 493.
    103mm long.   23.50
Squirrel. 70mm.   30.00

Traditional/National Souvenirs
Dutchman, sitting cross legged
    holding cheese. 85mm.   24.00

Domestic
Diamond pintray. 120mm long.   3.00

Trademark used by Sampson Hancock (and Sons), Bridge Works, Stoke. (Usual trademark Corona).
For details of this firm and china manufacturer see The Corona China.
As very few models have been found with this mark and all of them would have been made before 1910 it is probable that the mark was used before the more familiar Corona trademark. Most of the pieces found with the 'Herald' mark are 'smalls'. One small vase has been found with a monochrome (brown) transfer print of Ellen Terry, this piece is also inscribed: 'Jubilee Souvenir 1856-1906'. Most models and 'smalls' carry seaside crests.

Heraldic Models
Ancient Artefacts
Exeter Vase. No. 129. 70mm.   3.00
Shakespeare's Jug. 55mm.   3.50

Animals
Bulldog in Kennel. 66mm.   15.00

Birds (including Eggs)
Baby Bird cream jug. 70mm.   5.50

Home/Nostalgic
Oil Lamp. 34mm.   3.00

Alcohol
Barrel on legs.   4.00
Tankard. 70mm.   3.00

Sports/Pastimes
Queen, chess piece. 90mm.   20.00
King, chess piece. 108mm.   20.00

Footwear
Ladies 18th Century Shoe.
   105mm long.   7.50

Heraldic China

Trademark used by an unknown manufacturer.

Only two items found.

Animals
Sitting Bulldog. 50mm.   14.00

Miscellaneous
Jug. 42mm. (Whitehead crest).   3.00

Herald Series

Trademark used for William Holmes & Co, fancy goods importers, Glasgow, on china manufactured by Alfred B. Jones & Sons Ltd, Grafton China Works, Longton, Staffs. (Usual trademark Grafton).

For details of this china and the manufacturer see Grafton China.

Several models and some domestic ware are found with this printed mark, most have Scottish crests, but some have been found with N. Irish crests. One model has been found with a colour transfer view of Portaskaig, Islay.

Numbering System. Where stock numbers occur they are the same numbers as found on 'Grafton' models. Numbers where known are listed below.

Herald Series Models
Ancient Artefacts
Chester Roman Vase. 60mm.   4.00

Seaside Souvenirs
Whelk Shell. 83mm long.   5.00

Animals
Cheshire Cat, The. Always Smiling.
  One green glass eye. 86mm.   11.00
Bulldog, sitting. No. 250. 88mm.   40.00
Dog, King Charles Spaniel, sitting.
  No. 390. 55mm.   16.00
Dog, Puppy, sitting with one ear up,
  scratching with back leg. No. 410.
  85mm.   16.00
Frog, sitting upright, hands on
  tummy. No. 204. 74mm.   24.00

Monkey sitting wearing coat.
  70mm.   13.00
Pig, sitting. No. 341. 90mm long.   25.00
Shetland Pony, not named. 105mm
  long. (This model can be found
  with a crest of Shetland.)   23.50

Birds (including Eggs)
Duck, sitting. No. 47. 90mm long.   19.50

Great War
Tank, no steering wheels, inscribed:
  HM Landship Creme-de-Menthe.
  No. 413. Rd. No. 659588.
  98mm long.   24.50
Hand Grenade with removable pin.
  83mm.   25.00
Cannon Shell, inscribed: *Jack
Johnson.* No. 339. 90mm.   12.50
Bell Tent with open flaps. No. 239.
  65mm.   16.00
Killin War Memorial, with extended
  base and railings. 160mm.   130.00

Alcohol
Champagne Bottle. 100mm.   10.00

Footwear
Sabot with hanging hole.
  80mm long.   5.00

Miscellaneous
Ashtray on three tiny feet. No. 386.
  86mm long.   2.50
Horses Hoof vase. 45mm.   4.50
Stamp Box and lid. No. 300.
  50mm across.   5.50

E. Hughes and Co. China

Trademark used by E. Hughes & Co., Opal
  Works, Fenton. (Usual trademarks Fenton
  & Royal).
For details of this china and manufacturer
  see Fenton China and Royal China.
This mark has only been found on domestic
  ware and the two pieces listed below. The
  mark was only used for a short time
  during the Great War of which a
  commemorative has been recorded, this is
  a design with six Flags of the Allies and
  inscribed: 'In Freedoms Cause'.

Hughes China Models
Seaside Souvenirs
Oyster Shell dish. 130mm long.   4.00

Miniature Domestic
Cheese Dish and cover. 70mm long.   6.50

Domestic
Egg Cup. 62mm.   6.50

Other Domestic ware found too.   2.50-10.00

Iceni Crest China

Trademark used for wholesalers by J.A.
  Robinson & Sons, subsequently Cauldon
  Ltd. (Usual trademark Arcadian).
For details of this china and manufacturer
  see Arcadian China.
This mark appears to have been used from
  around 1920 to 1925. Crests are found from
  all over England. Coloured transfer views,
  Poppies and 'Lucky Black Cats' transfers
  are found on 'smalls' with this mark. Stock
  numbers where used are the same as
  Arcadian numbers.

Iceni Models
Ancient Artefacts
Cadogan Tea Pot.   12.50
Goodwin Sands Carafe. 82mm.   3.00

Buildings – White
Cottage. 62mm long.   10.50

Monuments (including Crosses)
Caister on Sea Lifeboat Memorial.
  150mm.   25.50

Seaside Souvenirs
Lighthouse. 150mm.   9.00

Animals
Cat, sitting and smiling grotesque,
  (rather similar to Cheshire Cat).
  75mm.   7.50
Black Cats, 3 on sledge.
  118mm long.   135.00
Frog, open mouthed. 58mm.   16.00
Sussex Pig, Model of, sitting
  inscribed: *You can push or you can
  shuv but I'm hanged if I'll be druv.*
  No. 148. 88mm long.   17.00
Sussex Pig. Model of, standing.
  Inscribed as above. No. 148.
  88mm long.   14.50

Birds (including Eggs)
Chick, breaking out of egg.
  63mm long.   9.00
Hen, red comb. 80mm.   10.50
Owl. 67mm.   12.50
Pelican. 76mm.   40.00

Great War
Monoplane, movable prop.
  149mm long.   65.00
Tank. 100mm long.   45.00
German Incendiary Bomb. 80mm.   17.00
Clip of bullets, Model of. 87mm.   17.50
Colonial Hat, Model of. 88mm.   16.00

Home/Nostalgic
Chair, highbacked. 90mm.   6.50
Coal Bucket. 55mm.   5.00

Sport/Pastimes
Football. 46mm.   6.50
Knight chess piece. 64mm.   14.50

Footwear
Ankle Boot. 74mm long.   5.00

Domestic
Candlestick, square. 35mm.   3.00

Imperial

Trademark used by Wedgwood and Co (Ltd), Unicorn and Pinnox Works, Tunstall, on cheaply produced souvenir wares.

This firm, which is often confused with the famous Josiah Wedgwood and Sons Ltd, manufactured much cheaper earthenwares. The firm specialised in table and domestic ware but obviously turned their hand to crested and view wares when these lines became good sellers. They were already making badged ware, so producing crests would be no problem. The firm began using an 'Imperial' mark in 1909 but used a much more elaborate mark than the one above on tableware. Unlike other manufacturers they did not make models to commemorate the Great

War, and it seems likely that the firm was not geared to making these models. There is no evidence that crested ware was produced after the war, and most pieces found with this mark are 'smalls', generally rather heavy and cheaply made. Colour transfer view ware is reasonably well produced, but found on the same heavy pottery 'smalls' and domestic ware.
It is interesting to note that during his most successful period, 1920 to 1930, Harold Taylor Robinson managed to gain some financial control over this firm (see Arcadian China).

Imperial Models
Ancient Artefacts

Chester Roman Vase. 55mm.	3.00
Lincoln Jack, not named. 54mm.	3.00

Animals

Dog, sitting. 70mm.	10.00
Elephant, walking. 52mm.	17.00
Pig, standing, fat. 93mm long.	19.50

Birds (including Eggs)

Pelican jug.	5.50

Home/Nostalgic

Coal Scuttle. 35mm.	4.00
Suitcase. 79mm long.	4.00

Sport

Football. 65mm.	6.50

Hats

Top Hat. 40mm.	5.50

Footwear

Dutch Sabot. 83mm long.	4.00

Impero

Jmpero

JMPERO

IMPERO

Trademark used by the German manufacturer Kutzscher & Co, Schwarzenberg, Saxony on crested china for export to Britain.
This mark is mostly found on buildings and monumnets and traditional souvenirs usually carrying the crest of the town for which they were designed which is very much what one would expect from a German manufacturer. Models would be made from photographs, postcards or local drawings. The two elephants on the sledge are often found unmarked and is a most attractive comic model.
Impero models are made from the usual white 'hard china' so much scorned by English manufacturers, but the models are very nicely detailed, and for the most part desirable.

Impero Models
Ancient Artefacts

Puzzle Jug with inscription. 68mm.	5.50

Buildings – White

Boston Stump Church. 125mm.	20.00
Grimsby, The Tower. 170mm.	20.00
Lincoln Cathedral, west front.	
No. 824. 120mm.	20.00
Clock Tower, Skegness. 124mm.	7.50
York, *Bootham Bar.* 135mm.	15.00

Monuments (including Crosses)

Captain Cook's Monument, Whitby.	
135mm.	40.00

Captain Scott, figure on square base.

2 sizes: 135mm.	22.50
150mm.	22.50
Hall Cross, Doncaster. 158mm.	22.50
Hull Fisherman's Memorial with inscription. 125mm.	10.50
Hull Soldiers' War Memorial, with inscription: *Erected to the memory of the men of Hull who fell in the late South African War*. 120mm.	22.50
King Edward VII. 125mm.	15.00
Laceby Monument. 145mm.	30.00
Lincoln Stonebow. 105mm long.	23.50

Traditional/National Souvenirs

Devil looking over Lincoln. 95mm.	14.50
The Lincoln Imp. 112mm.	7.50
The Fiddler, York. 120mm (rare).	40.00

Seaside Souvenirs

Fisherman. 112mm.	16.00
Lifeboatman, standing. 110mm.	16.00
Spurn Lighthouse. 147mm.	17.00
The Lighthouse, Flamborough. 125mm.	17.00
Withernsea Lighthouse. 135mm.	17.00

Animals

Two Elephants on Sledge. Comic. 70mm.	75.00
A Native of Shetland, Shetland Pony. 80mm.	20.00

Birds (including Eggs)

Swan posy bowl. 74mm.	5.00

Ionic Heraldic

Trademark used for the Glasgow wholesaler CR & Co. by an unknown manufacturer, but probably Taylor & Kent. (Usual trademark Florentine).

The two other marks with the initials C.R. and Co G. were thought to have been used by Taylor and Kent (Florentine China) for a Glasgow wholesaler. See Atlas Heraldic China and Caledonia China. The 'smalls' and two models found with the 'Ionic' trademark are not recognisably made by Taylor and Kent, but it is probable that they made them. All items carry Scottish crests.

Ionic Models

Animals

Pig, fat. 70mm long.	10.00

Home/Nostalgic

Bucket with rope handle. 75mm.	3.50

Domestic

Beaker. 80mm.	2.50

Ivora

Trademark used by William Richie and Sons
Ltd., on a range of domestic ware. (Usual
trademark Porcelle). The products are
similar to Florentine and very good
quality.

For details of this china and manufacturer
see Porcelle.

Many British manufacturers during the early
twentieth century described their wares
as 'Ivory'. Ivory ware, Ivory porcelain and
Ivory china are terms found in many
advertisements in the pottery gazette at
that time. The only manufacturer, other
than William Ritchie known to have used
the initials W.R. was William Ridgway
whose marks were later re-issued by
Ridgways, Bedford Works, Shelton. It is
unlikely that this firm would have used
the term 'British Made', 'Made in
England' being the accepted form.

William Ritchie however did use 'British
Manufacture' as part of their Porcelle
mark and 'British Make' on Mermaid. As
the firm were known to use several marks
it seems likely that Ivora Ware was the
mark they used for domestic ware.

Most pieces found with this mark could be
described as 'smalls' or domestic ware.

Ivora Models
Ancient Artefacts
Three-handled loving cup. 38mm.   3.00

Historical/Folklore
Miner's Lamp. 70mm.   20.00

Home/Nostalgic
Coal Bucket. 70mm.   4.00

Footwear
Boot. 65mm long.   5.00

Hats
Top Hat matchstriker. 45mm.   5.50

Miniature Domestic
Cheese Dish and cover. 50mm.   6.50
1-handled mug. 36mm.   2.00

**NB: Badly printed marks which
appear to by *Ivyknot?* are
Wyknot? (See Wy not?).**

Ivy China

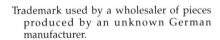

Trademark used by a wholesaler of pieces produced by an unknown German manufacturer.

Seaside Souvenirs
Lifeboatman. 125mm.   14.50

JBC

Trademark used for a Manchester wholesaler by Hewitt & Leadbeater, Willow Potteries, Longton. (Usual trademark Willow Art).

JBC Models
Historical/Folklore
Model of James' the Fifth Chair at
Stirling Castle. 100mm.   7.50

Traditional/National Souvenirs
Welsh hat, blue band.   5.00
Can be found with the longest
place name round brim. No. 75.
57mm.   7.50

Animals
Pig, fat and standing. Tail forms a
circle and rejoins the body.
80mm long.   12.50

Alcohol
Bottle inscribed: *One Special Scotch.*
90mm.   7.50

Miscellaneous
Hand holding Tulip vase. 80mm.   4.50

JBM

JP

Trademark used for the Manchester wholesaler JB & Co by Sampson Hancock (& Sons), Bridge Works, Stoke. (Usual trademark Corona).

JBM Model
Footwear
Ladies Button Boot. No. 149. 65mm.   8.50

Trademark used by a French manufacturer for the French souvenir market.

One Vase, 70mm high, has been recorded with this mark with the crest Boulogne Sur Mer.   4.00

J.R. & Co.

JW

Trademark used by an unknown manufacturer.

Unfortunately we have no details of the piece of crested china found with this trademark.

Trademark used for a retailer by J.A. Robinson Ltd. (Usual trademark Arcadian).

For details of this china and manufacturer see Arcadian China.

Unfortunately the crests on the three pieces recorded have not all been noted, but one suspects the town begins with the letter R. One military badge has been recorded, this being the Devonshire Regiment.

JW Models
Great War
Tommy and his machine gun, Model of.

130mm.	40.00
Red Cross Van. 80mm long.	30.00

Footwear

Dutch Clog. 102mm long.	5.00

Kahess China

No details of mark available.

Trademark used by Wiltshaw and Robinson
 Ltd., Carlton Works, Stoke-on-Trent.
 (Usual trademark Carlton).

Kahess Model
Great War
Edith Cavell Monument, unglazed
 figure on glazed base. 160mm.   19.00

Kangaroo Art China

Trademark used for the retailer Valentine &
 Sons, Melbourne by an English
 manufacturer, most probably Hewitt &
 Leadbeater. (Usual mark Willow/Willow
 Art).

Kangaroo Art Models
Animals
Kangaroo. 113mm.   75.00

Great War
Nurse, inscribed: *A Friend in Need.*
 130mm.   40.00

Kangaroo Brand

China manufactured by Wiltshaw & Robinson Ltd. Under the usual Carlton mark the following trademark can be found:
Made in England for G.F. Lucas S.F. Cal Kangaroo Brand.
The one model found has a crest of the Panama California Exposition. The model was found in California and was obviously made for that market.

Kangaroo Brand Model
Animals
Polar Bear, walking. 125mm long.   55.00

Keltic

BRITISH MAKE

Trademark used by Taylor and Kent (Ltd), Florence Works, Longton, (usual trademark Florentine), for Irish and Scottish retailers. Some pieces are similar to Nautilus Porcelain.

Keltic Models
Ancient Artefacts
Loving Cup. 3-handled. 40mm.   3.00
Puzzle Jug. 68mm.   5.50

Historical/Folklore
Old Armchair, with verse. 90mm.   7.50
Miners Lamp. 69mm.   14.00

Seaside Souvenirs
The Glad Sea Waves on base. 50mm.   17.00

Animals
Camel, kneeling. 95mm long.   13.00
Pig, standing. 95mm long.   10.50

Home/Nostalgic
Coal Scuttle. 65mm.   5.00
Policeman's lamp. 70mm.   10.00
Shaving Mug. 55mm.   6.50

Sport
Boxing Glove. 65mm long.   30.00

Footwear
Shoe, Ladies' 18th Century.
    95mm long.   7.50

Miniature Domestic
Teapot with lid. 70mm.   7.50

Kensington China

KENSINGTON ENGLISH CHINA

Trademark used by Royal Crown Pottery Co., Burslem, a branch of J.A. Robinson Ltd. (Usual trademark Arcadian and Willow Art).

No information is available on the history of this firm and the mark was not registered. The Bevington Brothers established a firm called the Kensington Fine Art Pottery Co in 1892 but this was a very short lived partnership, that was dissolved in 1899. The Kensington Pottery Ltd. was established in 1922 in the same Kensington Works in Hanley, and later at Burslem. The name 'Royal Crown Pottery' was not registered until 1952-7 by Trentham Bone China Ltd and has no connection with the earlier.

Many of the models with this mark are recognisably from Arcadian and Willow Art moulds, so it is most likely that this was one of the small firms bought and sold by Mr Harold Taylor Robinson between 1903 and 1920. (See Arcadian China). Many of these models carry the same stock numbers as Willow Art models and so it seems that either crested ware was produced for the firm at the Willow Pottery or that the mark was used in the same works. (Stock numbers where known will be listed below). Only town and resort crests have been found on Kensington models, 'smalls' and domestic ware.

Kensington Models

Ancient Artefacts

Carlisle Salt Pot. 50mm.	3.00

Monuments

Lifeboat memorial. 130mm.	6.50

Historical/Folklore

English Folksong Bride beside chest. No. 036. 93mm.	40.00
James V Chair, Stirling Castle. 105mm.	7.50
Mary Queen of Scots Chair, *Edinburgh Castle.* 80mm.	6.50

Traditional/National Souvenirs

Welsh Hat. No. 75. 57mm.	5.00

Seaside Souvenirs

Lighthouse, octagonal. 112mm.	5.50

Animals

Cat, Cheshire, inscribed: *Still smiling.* No. 159. 95mm.	7.50
Cat, haunched. 70mm.	10.50
Dog, sitting with shield. 80mm.	12.50
Elephant, walking. No. 113. 52mm.	13.00
Open mouthed Fish. 128mm long.	3.00
Teddy Bear, sitting. 90mm.	19.50
Shetland Pony. 108mm long.	22.00

Great War

Sailor, standing. Inscribed: *Our Brave Defender.* 127mm.	55.00
Nurse, inscribed: *A friend in need.* 130mm.	40.00
Battleship, impressed: *HMS Lion.* 140mm long.	30.00
Model of New Submarine.	20.00
British Tank. 90mm long.	14.50
Red Cross Van. 58mm.	30.00
Field Gun, with screen. 115mm long.	19.00
Oficer's Peaked Cap, brown band. 84mm long.	17.50
Kitchen range with cooking pot, inscribed: *Keep the home fires burning.* 77mm.	13.00

Home/Nostalgic

Coal scuttle. 52mm.	4.00
Grandfather Clock, inscribed: *Make use of time let not advantage slip. Shakespeare.* No. 149. 128mm.	10.50
Watering Can. 70mm.	12.00

Comic/Novelty

Pixie, crouching on a rectangular base. 78mm. (Could well be the Chester Imp).	20.00

Alcohol

Barrel on stand. 58mm.	4.00

Sport/Pastimes

Tennis Racquet, with tennis ball. 138mm long.	19.50

Transport

Open Tourer. 115mm long.	40.00

Footwear

Clog. 70mm long.	5.00

Miscellaneous

Hand holding Tulip. No. 74. 80mm.	4.50

Kent Bone China

Trademark used by Taylor and Kent, Florence Works, Longton. (Usual trademark Florentine). The only piece recorded with the above trademark is heavy and very white.

Domestic

Egg Cup, with arms of Aberdeen. 45mm.	6.50

King China

Kingsway Art or Crest China

Trademark used for a retailer or wholesaler by Alfred B. Jones and Sons Ltd., Grafton China Works, Longton, Staffs.

For details of this china and manufacturer see Grafton China.

Only one small fluted vase, 64mm high has been found with this mark. It is very well produced, the china is delicate and the crest of Swansea is beautifully printed and painted. The black painted stock number and paintresses mark are indisputably Grafton. Like most Grafton stock numbers it is difficult to read accurately, the number could be 206, 266 or 286. (206 and 286 have both been found on other Grafton models, but any of these could have been as badly printed).

Vase. 64mm.   3.50

024 and 36 015 are stock numbers and paintresses marks.

Trademark used for W.H. Smith by Hewitt and Leadbeater and Arkinstall and Son. (Usual trademarks Willow Art and Arcadian). The standard of quality is very high.

For details of this china and manufacturer see Willow Art China and Arcadian China.

Hewitt and Leadbeater obviously supplied a large range of crested ware for this customer. Crests recorded come from all over Britain and the initials W.H.S. and S. stand for W.H. Smith and Sons whose head office at that time was in Kingsway, W.C., London. The numbers which are found in the mark are either to indicate a particular order or possibly the paintress as it would have been a valuable order and checked more carefully than usual. The same numbers occur on several models and are normally prefixed by 0. Numbers

012, 024 and 030 are most common. (These numbers are not found on Willow Art models, where painted stock numbers also occur on models these are the same.)
The range of models indicate that Hewitt and Leadbeater supplied W.H. Smith until the end of the Great War. Some Naval crests have been recorded, these being HMS Ceres, HMS Hood, and HMS Valiant. No view ware or other transfer devices have been found on models with this mark. Domestic ware and many 'smalls' have also been recorded.

Numbering System. The numerals from the mark are not recorded as they are found on many different models. Painted stock numbers are listed below.

Kingsway Models
Ancient Artefacts

Loving Cup, three-handled. 40mm.	3.00
Pilgrims Bottle.	3.00
Salt Maller, Model of.	3.00

Buildings – White

St. Botolph's Church, Boston. 112mm.	47.50
Westminster Abbey, west front. 115mm.	24.00

Monuments (including Crosses)

Princetown Lifeboatmans Monument. 130mm.	40.00
Maiwand Memorial. 98mm.	20.00

Historical/Folklore

Bunyan's Chair. 92mm.	19.00
Burn's Chair, Dumfries. 85mm.	7.50
English Folksong Bride beside chest. 93mm.	40.00
James V Chair, Stirling Castle. 100mm.	7.50
Mary Queen of Scots Chair, Edinburgh Castle, Model of. 75mm.	6.50
Man in the Moon. 50mm.	20.00

Traditional/National Souvenirs

Bagpipes with turquoise ribbon. 118mm long.	22.50
Burns and Highland Mary, sitting on a rock. 112mm.	30.00
Souter Johnny (impressed), some colouring. 130mm.	47.50
Welsh Lady, bust, with black hat. 110mm.	19.00

Welsh Leek. 55mm.	3.50
Dutch Boy. 80mm.	10.50
Dutch Girl. 78mm.	10.50

Seaside Souvenirs

Yacht in full sail. 122mm.	12.50
Lifeboat on rocks. 110mm long.	14.00
Lifeboat, blue and yellow ropes. 116mm long.	12.50
Lighthouse. No. 027. 140mm.	5.00
Lighthouse on base, not named. 110mm.	5.00
Withernsea Lighthouse, octagonal. No. 174. 192mm.	8.50
Eddystone Lighthouse, Model of. 86mm.	6.50
Crab. 83mm long.	13.00
Scallop Shell on rocky base. 82mm.	7.50
Whelk Shell, inscribed: *Listen to the Sea.* 93mm long.	3.00

Countryside

Acorn. 56mm.	5.50
Milk Can and lid.	5.00
Pine Cone. 87mm.	4.00

Animals

Cat, Cheshire, inscribed: *Still smiling.* 95mm.	7.50
Cat, sitting.	
2 sizes: 57mm.	10.00
67mm.	13.00
Cat, standing, with blue bow. 70mm.	10.50
Dog, Bulldog sitting. 54mm.	17.00
Dog, black Bulldog emerging from kennel. No. 30. Inscribed: *The Black Watch.* 73mm long.	19.50
Dog, Dachshund. No. 021. 75mm long.	40.00
Dog, Scottie, wearing a Glengarry. Some colouring.	
2 sizes: 58mm.	12.50
87mm.	13.50
Dog, Scottish Terrier, standing. 90mm long.	14.50
Elephant, sitting with trunk in air. 97mm.	40.00
Elephant, walking. 98mm.	17.00
Elephant Jug. No. 78. 70mm.	12.50
Hare. 77mm long.	12.50
Monkey, holding a Coconut. No. 429. 80mm.	17.50
Three Wise Monkeys, with usual verse. 77mm.	15.00

Pig, sitting. Inscribed: *You may...*
75mm.   12.50
Pig, sitting on haunches, inscribed.
80mm.   11.00
Pig, standing, double chin. No. 014.
96mm.   19.50
Pig, fat, standing. 82mm long.   16.50
Rabbit, sitting. 70mm long.   7.50
Ram with curly horns.
90mm long.   43.00
Teddy Bear. 75mm.   19.50

Birds
Chick, fluffy, large feet. 70mm.   17.00
Goose. 95mm.   22.50
Owl. 115mm.   14.50
Swan. No. 012. 65mm.   6.50

Great War
Standing soldier inscribed: *Our
brave defender.* 130mm.   47.50
Submarine. *E4.* 125mm long.   19.50
Red Cross Van. 87mm.   30.00
Field Gun with screen.
115mm long.   19.00
Officer's Peaked Cap.
70mm dia.   10.50
Bugle. 70mm.   19.50
Drum. No. 030. 60mm dia.   10.50
Cenotaph, unglazed, green wreaths,
no crests. 140mm.   10.00
Edith Cavell Statue. 115mm.
(Impressed 507).   15.00
*Edith Cavell, Nurse. Patriot and
Martyr, Memorial Statue, Norwich.*
115mm. (Found impressed 296).   23.00
Florence Nightingale Statue, Model of.
160mm.   20.00

Home/Nostalgic
Anvil. 70mm long.   7.50
Basket. No. 244. 80mm long.   3.50
Bell, inscribed: *Curfew must not ring
tonight.* No. 107. 65mm.   7.50
Book. No. 76. 60mm.   5.50
Bureau. 80mm long.   20.00
Extinguisher. 65mm.   2.50
Flat Iron. No. 018. 65mm.   12.50
Pillar Box, inscribed: *GVR* and *If you
haven't time to post a line, here's the
pillar box.* No. 18. 80mm.   17.50
Pillar Box, impressed: G.R.
No. 203 and 024. 90mm.   25.00
Roll topped Desk. No. 030, reported
from Shelley range. 86mm.   16.00

Sundial, circular, with round base,
and inscription: *I Mark not the
hours.* 118mm.   10.50
Sundial, on square base. 94mm.   7.50
Sundial, circular base. No. 205 and
024. 93mm.   7.50
Thimble, large. *Just a thimble full.*
52mm.   19.50

Comic/Novelty
Baby with outstretched arms,
inscribed: *Cheerio.* No. 024.
128mm.   30.00
Billiken. 68mm.   7.50
Hammer Head match holder.
Inscribed: *My speciality is striking.*
82mm long.   13.00
Sack of Meal with mouse, inscribed:
*May the mouse ne'er leave yer meal
wi' a tear-drop'n its e'e.* 63mm.   14.50

Alcohol
Beer Barrel. 60mm.   3.00
Foaming Tankard, inscribed: *The
more we are together the merrier we
will be.* 58mm.   6.50
Whisky Bottle, inscribed: *A Special
Scotch.* 100mm.   7.50

Sport/Pastimes
Football. 48mm.   6.50
Golf Ball. 45mm.   5.50
Diamond, trump indicator. No. 009.
65mm.   4.00
Spade, trump indicator. 70mm.   4.00

Transport
Cycle lamp, reported from Shelley
range. 83mm.   50.00

Footwear
Clog. 70mm long.   5.00
Lancashire Clog. 78mm long.   5.50
Sabot/Clog. No. 152.
90mm long.   5.00
Shoe with blue painted bow.
115mm long.   13.00

Miscellaneous
Club pintray. No. 009.
58mm long.   3.00
Diamond pintray. No. 009.
58mm long.   3.00
Handbell. 82mm.   6.00
Hand holding Beaker. 50mm.   5.50

Kyle Series

From 1913

Trademark used by Charles Waine (& Co.), Derby Works, Longton. (Usual trademark Venetia).
For further details see Venetia China.

Kyle Series Models
Great War
Biplane with fixed prop.
    150mm long.   75.00

Transport
Tram. 50mm.   135.00

LAB

Mark used for a retailer by J.A. Robinson Ltd., Stoke-on-Trent. Subsequently Cauldon Ltd. (Usual trademark Arcadian).

LAB Models
Vase, with Arms of Seaford.
    62mm.   4.00
Vase, with Arms of Selsey.
    85mm.   4.00

Lawrence Sheriffe Ware

Leadbeater Art China

"LAWRENCE SHERIFFE" WARE

Trademark used by an unidentified manufacturer.

Lawrence Sheriffe Ware could have been produced by any of the major crest china makers, but none in fact advertised such a line. The only piece recorded with this mark also carried the retailers mark Hands and Son, Rugby, with a crest of Rugby. This would be correct, as Lawrence Sheriffe was founder of Rugby School and a benefactor of that town.

Lawrence Sheriffe Models
Ancient Artefacts
Loving Cup, 3 handles. 37mm.   4.00

1920-4

Trademark used by Edwin Leadbeater, Drewery Place, Commerce Street, Longton. Same quality and 'feel' as Panorama China, H & L and R & M of Longton.

Mr Edwin Leadbeater was the son of the senior partner of Robinson and Leadbeater ('R & L', makers of parian ware) and worked for that firm until 1905 when he left to go into partnership with Mr Arthur Hewitt, his brother in law. Hewitt and Leadbeater at Willow Potteries was a reasonably successful firm specialising in arms ware (see Willow Art and Willow China). Edwin Leadbeater left this partnership and started up on his own at Drewery Place in November of 1919, to manufacture heraldic china and ivory porcelain. It was a small one oven pottery started on £300 capital. This business was very short lived, but there is a surprising amount of information in the *Pottery Gazette* about Drewery Place during this period, quite out of proportion to its size and importance. While he was a partner at Hewitt and Leadbeater that firm too was often mentioned in the Gazette, one can only speculate as to whether Mr Leadbeater was a friend of the Editor or just very good at selling himself as newsworthy.

In 1920 the *Pottery Gazette* reported:
'. . . he has some 80 different models in small-wares to offer, which he is

decorating with crests, coat-of-arms, and various emblematic devices. These goods he is offering to all branches of the distributing trades, laying himself out specially for those retailers who can buy only in relatively small quantities. Apart from the tiny miniatures, which used to be popular selling lines at 6½d, Mr Leadbeater is bringing out models of monuments, notable buildings etc, for souvenir and commemorative purposes. These are quaintly tinted up by hand, very often quite realistically, although they are always very moderate in price. It is surprising how quickly, with enterprising zeal, some of these new models can be produced. A little time ago, Mr Leadbeater was asked by a big buyer to copy a model for a seasonal trade. Within 10 days the first sample was in the buyer's hands, and the latter was prompted to admit that it reminded him of how the German manufacturers of such wares used to handle their enquiries in the years before the war'.

In adverts for the trade at that time Mr Leadbeater announced that he specialised in arms china, miniatures, reproductions of War Memorials and historical buildings.

Edwin Leadbeater became bankrupt early in 1924, his business having run at a loss since it started. He had borrowed a great deal of money from friends and business acquaintances, and even £50 from a Bailiff to try to keep going, as he was still getting orders. Mr Leadbeater said he found he was 'selling his stuff too cheaply'.

Leadbeater Art China is often very heavy and on the whole not very well finished, but what it lacks in quality it makes up for in originality. The firm obviously got a large number of orders for War Memorials in the early years after the war and some of these were not modelled by any other manufacturers.

The firm collapsed before the vogue for 'Lucky Black Cats', 'Lucky White Heater' and other transfer devices, so these are not found marked Leadbeater. No commemoratives or view wares have been recorded either. However there is some evidence that some view ware marked 'Wagstaff and Brunt' was made by Edwin Leadbeater (see Panorama).

Numbering System. Painted stock numbers were sometimes used and where these have been recorded they will be found in the following lists. The paintresses' mark is the number painted directly below the stock number.

Leadbeater Art Models
Parian/Unglazed

Bust of *Burns.* 175mm.	40.00
Bust of *Pope Pius XI.* 190mm.	80.00
Bust of *Scott* on column base. 172mm.	23.00

Buildings – Coloured

Christchurch Priory.	125.00
Gate House, Stokesay Castle. 120mm long.	150.00
Ann Hathaway's Cottage. 95mm long.	30.00
Irish Cottage. 105mm long.	110.00
Isaac Walton's Cottage, Shallowford. 114mm long.	110.00
Old Church, Bonchurch. 108mm long.	230.00
Old Market Hall, Church Stretton 1617-1839. 100mm.	130.00
The Tan House, Little Stretton. 109mm long.	125.00

Buildings – White

Ann Hathaway's Cottage, not named.	
2 sizes: 58mm long.	16.00
144mm long.	18.00
Burns Cottage, with inscription. 70mm long.	17.50
Margate Clock Tower, Margate. 150mm.	20.00
Old Church, Bonchurch. 110mm long.	130.00

Monuments (including Crosses)

Limerick Monument, inscribed: *The treaty of Limerick signed AD 1696.* 120mm.	75.00
Margate Lifeboat Memorial. 160mm.	20.00
Plymouth Armada Memorial, with inscription: *He blew with his winds and they were scattered.* No. 107. 168mm.	35.00
Sir Walter Scott. Statue. 178mm.	16.00

Historical/Folklore

Bunyan's Chair. 95mm.	19.00
James Vth Chair, Stirling Castle, Model of. 102mm.	7.50
Mary Queen of Scots Chair. 85mm.	6.50

Traditional/National Souvenirs

Welsh Hat. No. 57. 60mm.	5.00

Seaside Souvenirs

Lifeboat. 100mm long.	12.50
Lighthouse. 110mm.	5.00

Animals

Cheshire Cat, inscribed: *Still smiling*.	
2 sizes: 85mm.	7.50
115mm.	8.50
Dog, sitting, with bow, black eyes. No. 77. 75mm.	10.50
Dog, labrador, sitting. 76mm.	10.50
Dog, Pug, sitting , long-necked, coloured features. 116mm.	19.50
Dog, with long neck, possibly Staffordshire Bull Terrier. 115mm.	17.00
Lion, walking. 114mm long.	14.50
Pig, fat. 102mm long.	16.00

Birds (including Eggs)

Chick posy holder. 60mm long.	6.50
Duck posy holder, with yellow beak. 45mm high, 80mm long.	11.00

Great War

Red Cross Van. No. 105. 88mm long.	30.00
Cumberland and Westmorland War Memorial. 148mm.	170.00
Derby War Memorial. 150mm.	110.00
Harrogate War Memorial, an unglazed obelisk on base with spiral steps. 153mm.	130.00
Nottingham War Memorial. 150mm.	110.00
Nurse Cavell, Memorial. 200mm.	115.00
Crich Stand, Notts and Derby War Memorial. 150mm.	160.00
Florence Nightingale 1820-1910 Statue. 175mm.	20.00
Ulster War Memorial, Thiepvel, with inscription: *They died that we might live*. 140mm.	215.00

Home/Nostalgic

Anvil. No. 78. 58mm.	7.50
Grandfather Clock, inscribed: *Make use of time, let not advantage slip*. 143mm.	15.50

Comic/Novelty

Jester, double faced bust, happy / sad. 85mm.	8.50
Monk, standing. 91mm.	16.00

Sport/Pastimes

Cricket Cap. 67mm long.	45.00
Footballer with ball on plinth. Inscribed: *Play up*. Fully coloured figure with blue shirt, white shorts and brown football. 158mm.	110.00

Footwear

Sabot. 80mm long.	5.00

Limoges

LIMOGES

FRANCE

An undistinguished range of domestic ware and small vases was made by this famous French manufacturer with the exception of the following. They are distinctly greyish white with transferred coats of arms.

Limoges Models
Seaside Souvenirs
Crab Pin Box. 60mm wide.   10.00

Home/Nostalgic
Watering Can. 75mm, 100mm long.   5.50

Comic/Novelty
Boy's Cap Money Box. 80mm long.   18.00

Transport
Open Motor Car. 90mm long.   15.00

Domestic
Match striker pot with lid (striker is
    on inside of lid).
    102mm long.   5.00

Lion Brand

Trademark used by an Australian retailer supplied by an unknown British manufacturer. Only one small model has been recorded, this having a New South Wales coat of arms. It is of similar quality to Royal Vale and Royal Ivory China.

Ancient Artefacts
Lichfield Jug. 60mm.   5.00

Lion China

Liverpool Rd Pottery

LIVERPOOL RD POTTERY LTD FINE BONE CHINA

Trademark used by Wiltshaw & Robinson, Ltd., Carlton Works, Stoke-on-Trent. (Usual trademark Carlton).

For details of this china and manufacturer see Carlton China.

Lion Models
Monuments (including Crosses)
Rock of Ages, with inscriptions.
82mm.   7.50

Animals
Dog (Puppy) sitting on a silvered
   hand mirror, inscribed: *Me twice.*
   105mm long.   33.50
Pug Dog with coloured features.
   115mm.   17.00

Trademark used by Liverpool Rd. Pottery Ltd., Stoke.

No information is available on this firm. They were not known to register a mark and do not appear under this name in the directory of British Pottery Manufacturers published in the Twenties and Thirties. C.J. Biss & Co. (see Unmarked) worked at 82 Liverpool Rd, Stoke during the Twenties; it is just possible that this firm used the name 'Liverpool Rd. Pottery Ltd'.

Liverpool Models
Seaside Souvenirs
Scallop Shell standing upright.
   110mm long. (This carries a map
   as well as a crest of Norfolk).   17.50
Scallop Shell. 110mm.   5.50
Scallop Shell flower holder. 60mm.   5.50

Transport
Open Motor Car. 90mm long.   40.00

Miscellaneous
Dish. 110mm dia.   3.00

Lochinvar

or with Nicholson and Carter in place of N & C.

Trademark used for the retailers Nicholson & Carter by Hewitt and Leadbeater, Willow Potteries, Longton. (Usual trademark Willow Art).

Lochinvar Models
Traditional/National Souvenirs
Welsh Hat. No. 75. 54mm.   5.00

Great War
Field Gun with screen. 115mm.   19.00
Bell Tent with open flaps. 85mm.   16.00

Alcohol
Whiskey Quaich or bowl. No. 110.
100mm long.   5.00

Locke and Co

c1895-1900

c1900-1904

Trademark used by Locke and Co (Ltd) Shrub Hill Works, Worcester.

The firm was established in 1896, the first manager being Edward Locke who had been Manager of the Potting Dept at Royal China Works, Worcester. After liquidation in 1902 they were prevented by the Worcester factory from describing their wares as Locke Worcester. Production eventually ceased in 1915.

It made a small range of what they described as Arms ware. In 1904 they advertised 'A variety of arms ware in heraldic colours on ivory ground, and there are original shapes amongst them.'

Many 'smalls' and some domestic ware are

found with this mark. The porcelain is very fine and the crests well produced. Some vases and jugs have been found with cream, biscuit and buff grounds, these are particularly attractive. The porcelain was exported and one Australian crest has been recorded. A coloured transfer print of the Flag of the Admiralty has been found and view ware was also produced by the firm.

Numbering System. Stock numbers were used but unfortunately these have not been recorded. Stock numbers where known are given in the list below.

All of the following models can be found in bisque – a biscuit coloured ground, as well as white.

Locke Models
Ancient Artefacts
Bath Roman Ewer, not named.

No. 46. 70mm.	7.50

Chester Roman Vase, not named.

No. 78. 55mm.	7.50

Hastings Kettle, not named.

2 sizes: 48mm.	7.50
No. 67. 64mm.	7.50

Irish Bronze Pot, not named. No. 99

or 66! 40mm.	7.50

Leather Jack, not named. No. 36.

72mm.	7.50

Newbury Leather Bottle, not

named. No. 84. 70mm.	7.50
Roman Lamp. 100mm long.	7.50

Traditional/National Souvenirs
Welsh Hat. No. 61. 56mm.	10.50

Home/Nostalgic
Thimble. 35mm.	17.50

Alcohol
Tankard, very ornate. 70mm.	7.50

Sport
Trophy. 65mm.	13.00

Hats
Top Hat, matchstriker. No. 52.

45mm.	7.50

Footwear
Dutch Sabot. No. 19.

3 sizes: 60mm long.	9.00
80mm long.	9.50
90mm long.	10.00

Miniature Domestic
Beaker. No. 51. 51mm.	7.50
Cream Jug with rope handle. No. 80.	
54mm.	7.50
Cup and Saucer. 78mm dia.	9.50

Numbered Ornamental and Domestic Wares
Some of the following may well be Ancient Artefacts, not named:

No. 3. Vase. 38mm.	7.50
No. 9. Vase. 78mm.	7.50
No. 10. Bowl. 33mm.	7.50
No. 13. Vase, circular, could have a lid. 40mm.	7.50
No. 14. Vase. 53mm.	7.50
No. 16. Large Pot. 65mm.	7.50
No. 17. Jar with separate lid. 70mm.	7.50
No. 18. Vase. 53mm.	7.50
No. 20. Vase. 83mm.	7.50
No. 21. Vase. 110mm.	7.50
No. 26. Ewer/Jug. 70mm.	7.50
No. 27. Vase. 74mm.	7.50
No. 28. Vase. 50mm.	7.50
No. 29. Vase. 62mm.	7.50
No. 31. Vase. 60mm.	7.50
No. 34. Tyg, one handle. 72mm.	7.50
No. 36. Vase. 41mm.	7.50
No. 37. Ewer. 70mm.	7.50
No. 39. Vase. 60mm.	7.50
No. 40. Diamond mouth Vase. 67mm.	7.50
No. 41. Cream Jug. 63mm.	7.50
No. 42. Cone Vase. 64mm.	7.50
No. 43. Vase. 43mm.	7.50
No. 47. Jug. 55mm and 70mm.	7.50
No. 51. Beaker. 51mm.	7.50
No. 53. Vase. 54mm.	7.50
No. 54. Vase. 70mm.	7.50
No. 55. Ewer. 78mm.	7.50
No. 55. Vase with two long handles. 80mm.	7.50
No. 58. Vase, Bagware. 53mm.	7.50
No. 60. Vase. 60mm.	7.50
No. 62. Vase. 62mm.	7.50
No. 69. Vase, 2 handles. 60mm.	7.50
No. 70. Vase, 2 handles. 70mm.	7.50
No. 74. Ewer. 59mm.	7.50

No. 79. Ewer. 62mm.   7.50
No. 80. Ewer, small twisted handle.
   53mm.   7.50
No. 85. Narrow necked Vase.
   90mm.   7.50
No. 87. Vase. 85mm.   7.50
No. 89. Ewer, 1 handle. 82mm.   7.50
No. 90. Vase. 78mm.   7.50
   (This appears to be the same
   model as No. 9).
No. 95. Vase, with 2 handles.
   63mm.   7.50
No. 101. Vase. 2 handles. 68mm.   7.50
No. 102. Vase. 50mm.   7.50
No. 103. Oval Vase, fluted top.
   67mm.   7.50
No. 112. Vase, narrow neck.
   97mm.   7.50
No. 113. Two handled Vase.
   62mm.   7.50
No. 116. Vase, two handles.
   72mm.   7.50
No. 118. Beaker with shallow fluted
   top. 60mm.   7.50
No. 120. Vase. 74mm.   7.50
No. 121. Vase. 83mm.   7.50
No. 178. Crinkle-top Ball Vase.
   58mm.   7.50
No. 754. Vase. 105mm.   7.50
No. 827. Beaker. 115mm.   7.50
No. 857. Base of Pepper or Salt Pot.
   63mm.   7.50

**Non numbered ornamental and
Domestic Wares**
Ball Vase, swirled, crinkle top.
   67mm.   7.50
Fairy Beaker. 32mm.   7.50
Wall Pocket. 85mm.   7.50

Lynton China

LYNTON CHINA

MADE IN ENGLAND

Trademark used by an unknown retailer on an Arcadian and Carlton mould.

Lynton Models
Animals
Black Cat on wall. Gosport crest.
   70mm.   75.00

Alcohol
Toby Jug, coloured features.
   73mm.   14.50

M

Macintyre

ENGLAND

Trademark used by an unknown English manufacturer.

This very obscure and unusual mark has only been found on one Great War Commemorative.

No manufacturer was known to use the initial M in 1914, and no firm used a mark anything like the unicorn above.

The colour transfer print of five flags and a field gun is found on a mug with a large handle. 59mm high. Inscribed: *Allies United 1914*.   17.50

Trademark used by James Macintyre & Co. Ltd, Washington Works, Burslem. (Usual trademark Argonauta Porcelain).

See Argonauta Porcelain for further details.

The Macintyre mark Argonauta Porcelain is exactly the same as the one above with the addition of Argonauta Porcelain printed above. It is very probable that this mark is just a badly printed version of that.

Macintyre Models
Ancient Artefacts
The Salisbury Jug from the original found in a barrow on Salisbury Plain. Reg. No. 134142. 137mm.   20.00

Domestic
Eggcup fixed to small saucer with two depressions inscribed: *salt* and *pepper*. Saucer also holds two eggs (salt and pepper pots) one white and one speckled brown. 66mm.   13.00
Inkwell, stippled.   14.00
Tea Pot. 130mm.   10.50

Small vases have also been found with this mark and china was also produced for manufacturers to add silver mounts. These seem to be very early/pre 1905.   3.00-10.00

Miscellaneous
Fleur de Lys shaped vase. 42mm.   4.00

M.C.G.

C McDMann & Co Ltd

Trademark used by an unknown wholesaler.
  Probably of German manufacture.

M.C.G. Model
Footwear
Dutch Sabot. Orange lustre.
  88mm long.   7.50

Retailer's mark used by Arkinstall & Son,
  Arcadian Works, Stoke-on-Trent. (Usual
  trademark Arcadian)

Only two small Arcadian shapes
  found:
Ewer with The Forts, Boxhill crest.
  52mm.   4.00
Vase with scroll handles, also with
  The Forts, Boxhill crest, in blue as
  is the retailer's mark underneath   4.00

Marine Art China

Trademark used by Hewitt & Leadbeater, Drewery Place, Commerce St., Longton, for a Brighton retailer. (Usual marks Willow and Leadbeater).

Marine Art Model
Birds (including Eggs)
Chick posy holder. 60mm long.   7.50

Marque Deposée

Trademark used by an unknown French manufacturer of French hard paste porcelain.
Only one model has been recorded so far and this has the crest of Anvers Antwerpen.

Marque Deposée Model
Footwear
Sabot with pointed toe.
    100mm long.   5.00

Maxim China

Trademark used by Max Emanuel & Co., Mitterteich, (Bavaria). (Usual trademark Mosanic).

This German firm was established around 1900 and as early as 1901 were advertising their hard paste china miniatures in the *Pottery Gazette*. (The wares were shown in Shoe Lane, Holborn and do not appear to be crested.) Max Emanuel and Co. were well known producers of pink souvenir wares and obviously turned to making crested souvenirs as soon as they would sell. The models illustrated in 1901 include comic or grotesque cats and dogs, which English manufacturers were not making at this early date. Many of the unmarked animals and buildings of German origin were probably made by this firm.

Maxim Models
Seaside
Beachy Head Lighthouse, black
band. 145mm.   11.00

Footwear
Sabot, pointed toe. 93mm long.   5.00

A range of 'smalls' and a trinket
box.   2.00-5.50

Mayfair Ware

Trademark used by Sampson Hancock (& Sons), Bridge Works, Stoke and later at the Garden Works, Hanley (usual trademark Corona).

Mayfair Models
Animals
Bulldog, standing. 125mm long.   17.50

Great War
Tank with inset wheels.
100mm long.   19.50

Meir Arms China

1912-1930

Trademark used by Barker Bros. Ltd., Meir
  Works, Barker Street, Longton.
Barker Bros, manufacturers of china and
  earthenwares, were established in 1876
  and are still working today. Like most
  established firms they made a range of
  arms china during the Great War when
  skilled labour was unavailable. They did
  not advertise at this time and it probably
  reflected in their small production. By 1919
  they were advertising 'Teddy Tail'
  Nursery China and had obviously turned
  their attention to the childrens' market.
Most models found are 'smalls' or domestic
  ware. The arms ware is more pot than
  china.

Meir Models
Ancient Artefacts
Loving Cup, 3-handled. 40mm.	3.00
Puzzle Jug with verse. 70mm.	5.50

Buildings - white
Open Tower. 116mm long.	38.00

Historical/Folklore
Mary Queen of Scots Chair.	
75mm.	6.50
Mons Meg, Edinburgh Castle, Model of.	
57mm.	12.00

Seaside Souvenirs
Eddystone Lighthouse. 109mm.	5.50

Animals
Cat in Boot. 88mm long.	14.50
Cheshire Cat, inscribed: *Still Smiling.*	
90mm.	7.50
Pig, standing. 88mm long.	10.50
Tortoise. 70mm long.	9.00

Birds
Canary on rock, yellow. 115mm.	20.00

Great War
Red Cross Van. 85mm long.	30.00
Tank.	14.50

Alcohol
Barrel. 52mm.	3.00

Home/Nostalgic
Watering Can. 75mm.	6.00

Transport
Open Sports Tourer. 116mm long.	37.50

Footwear
Sabot. 92mm long.	5.00
Lancashire Clog. No. 33.	
2 sizes: 70mm long.	5.00
115mm long.	5.50

Miniature Domestic
Cheese Dish and lid. 70mm long.	6.50
Vase, bud-shaped. 35mm.	3.00

Miscellaneous
Hand holding a Tulip. 83mm.	5.00

Melba Bone China

Melba China

Trademark used by Mayer & Sherratt, Clifton Works, Longton.

This mark is only found on late crested domestic ware.   from 3.00

Original china made by Mayer & Sherratt, Clifton Works, Longton. Over printed mark used by Sampson Hancock (& Sons), Bridge Works, Stoke. (Usual trademark Corona).

It seems likely that Mayer and Sherratt produced china which was later decorated with crests by S. Hancock perhaps to fill an urgent order!

This Melba china mark is earlier than the Melba mark above left which was used from about 1925.

This mark has been found overstamped 'Grosvenor Ware'. (Usual trademark also Corona).

Domestic Wares
Cream Jug. 60mm with a Chesham Crest.   4.00

Mermaid

Trademark used by William Ritchie and Sons
   Ltd, 24, 26 and 28 Elder Street, Edinburgh.
   (Usual trademark Porcelle).
For further details of this china and
   manufacturer see Porcelle.

Mermaid Models
Animals
Camel, kneeling. 90mm long.   13.00

Great War
Tank, sometimes inscribed: *HMS*
   Donner Blitzen, with details of
   Ancre. 130mm long.   30.00

Home/Nostalgic
Water Pitcher. 75mm.   2.50

Sport/Pastimes
Cricket Bag. 110mm long.   12.50

Footwear
Ladies 18th Century Shoe.
   80mm long.   7.50

Domestic
A range of domestic ware was
   produced.   3.00-5.00

The Milton China

Alternative mark found on domestic ware with transfer prints.

Trademark used by Hewitt Bros., Willow Potteries, Longton, on china for a London wholesaler (G.G. & Co.).

For details of this china and manufacturer see Willow Art China.

This trademark appears to have been used after the Great War, until at least 1926. No view ware has been found with this mark which indicates its later date, Willow view ware was made before the war. One military badge has been recorded, the Royal Flying Corps. Many 'Lucky Black Cat' transfer devices are found, usually with red or blue edging and rims.

Numbering System. Stock numbers where recorded are not necessarily the same as those found on Willow Art pieces. Milton China was probably offered as a separate range. Stock numbers where known are listed below. Single painted numbers found on models are paintresses' marks.

Milton Models
Ancient Artefacts

Aberdeen Bronze Pot, not named.	
52mm.	3.00
Ancient Tyg, 2 handled.	3.00
Loving Cup, 3 handled. 55mm.	3.00

Monuments (including Crosses)

Drake Statue, Plymouth. 160mm.	13.00
Fisherman's Memorial. 132mm.	12.50
Hull Fisherman's Memorial.	20.00

Historical/Folklore

Bunyan's Chair. 90mm.	19.00
Crown. 60mm.	20.00
Sword in decorative scabbard. No. 374. 135mm long (rare).	72.50
Model of Mons Meg, Edinburgh Castle. 130mm long.	11.00
Sir Walter Scott's Chair. 88mm.	7.50

Traditional/National Souvenirs

Bagpipes with turquoise ribbon. 115mm long.	20.00
Welsh Hat. 54mm & 62mm.	5.00
Dutch Girl, standing. 76mm.	10.50

Seaside Souvenirs

Bathing Machine. Can be inscribed: *A Morning Dip.* 70mm long.	7.50
Lighthouse, octagonal. 114mm.	5.50
Shell on coral base. 93mm.	5.00

Animals

Bear, Polar, standing upright. 95mm.	40.00
Cat, standing, chubby. 70mm.	16.00
Cheshire Cat, inscribed: *Still Smiling.* 90mm.	7.50
Dog, Scottie, wearing a glengarry. 60mm.	13.50
Donkey with saddle. No. 904.	
2 sizes. 105mm long.	40.00
120mm long.	40.00
Elephant, with trunk in the air. 80mm long.	40.00
Elephant, (trunk down). 75mm long.	17.00

Elephant Jug. 70mm. (Trunk is handle).   12.50
Frog, with open mouth. 60mm.   16.00
Lion, poised to pounce, red roaring mouth. 83mm long.   23.00
Lion, standing. 115mm long.   14.50
Lion standing on ashtray, inscribed: *Ash Tray* and *Who burned the tablecloth*. 110mm long.   20.00
Lion, roaring at mouse, sitting on apple. Inscribed: *Much Ado About Nothing*. Some colouring.   82.50
Pig, standing. 95mm long.   19.50
Pig, sitting, inscribed: *You may push and...* 72mm.   16.00
Rabbit, sitting with ears flat on back. 54mm long.   7.50
Ram, with curly horns. 90mm long.   43.00

Birds (including Eggs)
Chicken, very fluffy. No. 325. 65mm.   17.00
Swan. 69mm.   6.50

Great War
Nurse, inscribed: *A friend in need.* 130mm.   40.00
Aeroplane Propeller. Rarely factory marked. 150mm long.   25.00
Airship (Observation Balloon) not named, 80mm long.   40.00
Submarine, impressed: *E4*. 116mm long.   19.50
British Tank, Model of. 98mm long.   17.50
Red Cross Van. 90mm long.   30.00
Field Gun. 116mm long.   17.00
Incendiary Bomb, rope handle. 82mm.   11.00
Bandsman's Drum with cording. 60mm.   10.50
Bugle. 70mm.   19.50
Kit Bag with verse: *Pack up your troubles.* 74mm.   19.50
Telescope. 70mm.   13.00
Kitchen Range, pot on fire. Inscribed: *Keep the home fires burning.* Some colouring. No. 6. 80mm long.   13.00

Home/Nostalgic
Anvil. 60mm.   7.50
Book. 60mm.   5.00
Coal Scuttle. 65mm.   4.50
Shaving Mug. 55mm.   5.50

Watering Can. No. 126. 74mm.   8.50
Wheelbarrow. 105mm long.   10.50

Comic/Novelty
A truck of coal from... Wagon of black coal. 90mm long.   30.00

Cartoon/Comedy Characters
Baby, saluting, inscribed: *One of the b'hoys.* Some colouring. 160mm. (Great war cartoon character could be 'Pooksie').   40.00
Baby, sailor, on circular base inscribed: *SHIP AHOY.* Some colour. 150mm.   82.50
Dr. Beetle, impressed: Charlie Tolkard's character in Daily Mail. 142mm.   82.50

Alcohol
Barrel on its side. 53mm long.   3.50

Sport/Pastimes
Racehorse. 102mm.   75.00

Musical Instruments
Guitar. 163mm long.   10.50

Footwear
Ladies' 18th century shoe. 90mm long.   7.50
Slipper wall pocket, blue bow. No. 259. 150mm long.   12.50

Miniature Domestic
Coffee Pot and lid.   7.50
Jug, bagware, no colour. No. 161 or 191. 55mm.   2.50
Mug, one handled. 38mm.   2.50
Tea Pot with lid. 53mm.   7.50

Domestic
Hair Pins oval fluted box and lid. 105mm long.   5.00

Moore Bros

Mark used from 1891.

MOORE BROS.
STAFF
R⁰ N⁰
442279

Mark used from 1891-1905.

Trademark used by Moore (Bros).), St Mary's Works, Longton.

A range of 'smalls' with a Christmas crest and a sprig of holly have been recorded.   10.50

The Moore England mark can be found on very Victorian/ornate looking smalls, one being a 94mm crinkle ball vase with NR monogram in blue.

Mosanic

MOSANIC
MADE
IN
BAVARIA

Impressed mark.

Trademark used by the German firm, Max Emanuel & Co., The Mosanic Pottery, Mitterteich, Bavaria. They exported a range of brown/stone unglazed buildings to Britain.

Max Emanuel & Co. produced souvenir china for the British market. The buildings marked Mosanic are unusual in that they are usually a drab brown colour and are unglazed. The models although very attractive and detailed are rather heavy. They were made before the war and several models have been found with the mark defaced, one can only speculate whether this was done by unhappy owners or disgruntled retailers who still held German stock at the beginning of the war. These models are usually found without crests, but some crested examples exist.

One could properly argue that this range, being a type of brown stoneware and uncrested has no place in this book, but Mosanic pieces are eagerly collected by heraldic china buffs and so have been included.

Numbering System. Stock numbers are impressed above the mark, registration numbers at the side. Model numbers are four figure and begin with 0. The Registration numbers are six figure and begin with 5 or 6. Where these have been recorded they are listed below.

All models unglazed and brown/stone coloured.

Mosaic Models
Buildings

Abbots of Buckfast Town House,
inscribed: *Ye olde town house of ye
Abbots of Buckfast ye close Exeter.*
No. 0372. Rd. No. 567827.
100mm long. — 40.00

Aberdeen, Old Machor Cathedral.
No. 1313. Rd. No. 55628(?).
75mm long. — 40.00

Aberystwyth, The College. No. 0350.
Rd. No. 561630. 110mm long. — 40.00

Bank of Ireland. No. 0365. Rd. No.
587364. 129mm long. — 40.00

Birmingham Town Hall. 72mm long. — 40.00

Town Hall, Bradford. No. 554743. — 40.00

Bridlington Priory Church. No. 7533.
65mm. — 40.00

Burns Cottage. 113mm long. — 35.00

Canterbury Cathedral. No. 0326. Rd.
No. 558188. 112mm long. — 35.00

Carlisle Cathedral. No. 0361 Rd. No.
576552. 97mm long. — 40.00

Chester Cathedral. No. 0340 Rd. No.
559941. 100mm long. — 40.00
Two varieties with east and west
transepts transposed.

Christchurch Priory. Rd. No. 562002
2 sizes: No. 0345I. 98mm long. — 40.00
No. 0345II. 133mm long. — 40.00

Crosthwaite Church, Keswick Rd. No.
0382. No. 579266. 127mm long. — 40.00

Crystal Palace. No. 0386 Rd. No.
58157(?). 170mm long. — 47.50

Dartmouth, The Old Butterwalk
No. 0375. Rd. No. 576629.
105mm long. — 40.00

Douglas, Tower of Refuge.
75mm long. — 35.00

Durham Cathedral. No. 0353.
No. 570731. — 40.00

Edinburgh Castle. No. 0337. Rd. No.
559939. 113mm long. — 40.00

Exeter Cathedral. No. 0348. Rd. No.
564035. 150mm long. — 35.00

Exeter Guildhall, inscribed: *Ye olde
Guild Hall of ye Ancient and Loyal
Cittie of Exeter.* 65mm. — 35.00

*Exeter, St Mary's Steps & Stepcote
Hill.* No. 0304. Rd. No. 598554.
93mm long. — 40.00

Fairmaids House, Perth. No. 0318. Rd.
No. 558196. 72mm. — 40.00

Gloucester Cathedral. No. 0347 Rd.
No. 579265. 120mm long. — 40.00

Guy's Cliff, The Mill. No. 0309 Rd.
No. 554739. 93mm long. — 40.00

Halifax, Parish Church. No. 0323 Rd.
No. 558194. 90mm long. — 40.00

*Harrogate, Royal Pump Room, Old
Sulphur Well.* No. 1301. Rd. No.
554744. 60mm. — 35.00

Hathaways Cottage, Stratford
No. 0378. Rd. No. 576880.
120mm long. — 30.00

Hereford Cathedral. No. 0325. No.
558195. 92mm long. — 40.00

Hexham, The Abbey. No. 0371. Rd.
No. 581571. 109mm long. — 40.00

Hawarden Castle. No. 0335 Rd. No.
559936. 110mm long. — 40.00

Hawarden Church. No. 0333 Rd. No.
559934. 85mm long. — 35.00

*Hawarden, Gladstone Memorial Public
Library.* No. 0330. No. 559937.
115mm long. — 40.00

Hawthorns Hotel, Centenary Fetes,
Bournemouth 1910. — 45.00

Houses of Parliament. No. 0398 Rd.
No. 599955. 70mm. — 40.00

Iffley Church. No. 0360. Rd. No.
587402. 113mm long. — 40.00

Kirk Braddon Church. Rd. No.
557800. 80mm long. — 40.00

Lancaster Castle. No. 0363.
No. 578553. 130mm long. — 40.00

Lichfield Cathedral. No. 0352 Rd. No.
580372. — 40.00

Lincoln Castle. No. 0315. Rd. No.
556282. 110mm long. — 40.00

Londonderry Cathedral. No. 0391.
No. 587036. — 40.00

Lowther Castle. No. 0317. Rd. No.
566283. 105mm long. — 40.00

Madame Tussauds. No. 0388.
No. 582363. — 45.00

Malvern Priory. No. 0322. Rd. No.
558186. 95mm long. — 40.00

Manchester Cathedral. No. 0356. Rd.
No. 100mm long. — 40.00

Marble Arch (white). No. 0422 90mm. — 20.00

Molls Coffee House, Exeter. No. 6936.
70mm long. — 40.00

Newark Castle. No. 0307 Rd. No.
554738. 108mm long. — 40.00

Medieval Bridge, Newcastle on
Tyne. No. 0392 No. 591208. — 40.00

Newcastle Cathedral. No. 0343 Rd.
No. 560727. 95mm long. — 40.00

Newcastle-on-Tyne, Black Gate.
No. 0389. No. 585808. 80mm long.   40.00
Newcastle-on-Tyne, The Castle. No.
0307, 0419 or 0390. Rd. No. 554738
or 585809. (it is possible that there
is more than one model). 95mm.   40.00
Plas Newydd, Llangollen, No. 0319.
No. 521568.86mm long.   40.00
Ripon Cathedral. No. 0385 Rd. No.
580773. 109mm long.   40.00
Robinson Brewers Ltd, Ho'ton (Ales &
Stout). No. 0379. 112mm long.   40.00
Rowton Tower, inscribed: King
Charles stood on this tower Sep 2nd
1645 and saw his army defeated on
Rowton Moor. No. 0327.
No. 558197. 85mm.   40.00
St Andrews's Home, Folkestone.
No. 0331. No. 559935. 54mm.   40.00
St Johns Church, Perth. No. 0357 Rd.
No. 568187. 85mm.   40.00
St Mary's Church, Scarborough.
No.0303. 97mm long.   40.00
St. Mary's Church, Taunton. No.
0403. No. 604413.   40.00
St Patrick's Cathedral. No. 587037.
103mm.   40.00
St Pauls Cathedral, not named. Two
numbers recorded, No. 0387 and
No. 7332. Rd. No. 564098.
88mm long.   30.00
St Tudno's Church, Llandudno.
No. 0303. Rd. No. 564142.
84mm.   40.00
Salisbury Cathedral. No. 0351. Rd.
No. 567854. 105mm long.   40.00
Scarborough, The Castle. No. 0398.
78mm.   40.00
Shakespeares House, Stratford-on-
Avon. No. 0380. Rd. No. 576829.
110mm long.   25.00
Tintern Abbey. No. 0328.
No. 558187.   40.00
Upleatham Church. No. 0381 Rd. No.
582362. 97mm long.   40.00
Wells Cathedral. No. 583280.
105mm long.   40.00
Westminster Abbey. No. 0341. Rd. No.
560726. 110mm long.   40.00
Whitby Abbey. No. 0370. Rd. No.
578552. 105mm long.   40.00
Winchester Cathedral. No. 0430 Rd.
No. 632519. 144mm long.   40.00

Worcester Cathedral. No. 0334.
No. 564564.   40.00
York Minster. Rd. No. 556287.
2 sizes: No. 0312. 82mm long.   35.00
No. 0312II. 138mm long.   40.00

Monuments (including Crosses)
The Cross, Banbury. No. 0316. No.
536284 and No. 556281.
110mm.   35.00

Historical/Folklore
Christchurch, Rogers Tomb, Trinket
box and lid. Inscribed: WE WERE
NOT SLAYNE BUT RAYSD,
RAYSD NOT TO LIFE, BUT TO
BVT BURIED TWICE BY MEN
OF STRIFE WHAT REST COULD
LIVING HAVE WHEN DEAD
HAD NONE AGREE AMONGST
YOU HEERE WE TEN ARE ONE.
HEN: ROGERS DIED APRILL
17.1641: IR No. 0429. No. 632133.
113mm long.   40.00
Old Norman Font, St Mary's Church
Steps, Exeter. No. 0376. Rd. No.
579668.   26.00
Scott Memorial, Edinburgh.
No. 0332. No. 559938.   25.00
Westminster Abbey Coronation Chair.
116mm.   16.00

Seaside Souvenirs
Corbierre Lighthouse, Jersey, Model of.
No. 0419. Rd. No. 558636. 84mm.   20.00
Flamborohead Lighthouse. 67mm.   30.00

Moschendorf

Mother Shipton China

MOSCHENDORF
BAVARIA

Trademark used by the German firm Hof-Moschendorf (Bayern).

This mark has only been found on a crested tea plate. 150mm wide.   3.00

Trademark used for the retailer J.W. Simpson, Dropping Well, Knaresborough by Wiltshaw and Robinson Ltd, Carlton Works, Stoke-on-Trent. (Usual trademark Carlton).

For details of this china and manufacturer see Carlton China.

All models found with this mark have either a crest of Knaresboro' or Mother Shipton, accompanied by the inscription: 'Near to the Knaresboro Dropping Well. I drew breath as records tell'. Models can be found in lustre. Some 'smalls' and models are found with a hand coloured transfer print of Mother Shipton surrounded by a ship, aeroplane, train, telephone or radio wires, inscribed: *Prophecies of Mother Shipton.*

Such items usually have the following verse on the reverse: 'Around the world thoughts shall fly. In the twinkling of an eye. In the air shall men be seen, carriages without horses shall go, iron in the water shall float, as easy as a wooden boat'. No wonder Mother Shipton was so popular as a folklore figure in 1920.

Stock Numbers where found seem to be those found on Carlton models.

Mother Shipton Models
Ancient Artefacts
Loving Cup, 3-handled. 42mm.   4.50

Historical/Folklore
Knaresborough Dropping Well, with colouring and inscription. 103mm. (White £19.00).   27.50

Mother Shipton, with some
colouring.
3 sizes: 92mm.   30.00
         110mm.   47.50
         190mm.   55.00
Mother Shipton with some
colouring, standing on lustre oval
base. 90mm.   30.00
Mother Shipton, some colouring,
standing on ashtray base, with
inscription.   30.00

Countryside
Tree trunk hatpin holder. 115mm.   10.50

Animals
Cat, sitting wearing black top hat
and bow tie. 85mm.   16.00
Cat, blue collar, on cushion. 82mm.   12.00
Bulldog, French. 55mm.   12.50
Stag, with antlers. 217mm.   110.00

Great War
Munitions Worker, inscribed: *Doing
her bit. Shells and more shells.* Some
colouring. 140mm.   125.00
French 75mm Field Gun.
125mm long.   17.00
Edith Cavell, statue, inscribed:
*Brussels dawn October 12th 1915.
Sacrifice, Humanity.* 163mm.   23.00

Home/Nostalgic
Frying Pan. 110mm long.   17.00
Suitcase. 36mm. With inscription:
*Near to the Knaresboro' Dropping
Well*   8.50
Warming Pan. No. 392. 127mm long.   13.00

Comic/Novelty
I'm forever blowing bubbles. Pears
advert Blue Boy blowing bubbles.
Clothes blue, bubble and bowl
lustre. 110mm.   75.00

Alcohol
Toby Jug, with inscription. 70mm.   7.50

Musical Instruments
Upright Piano open keyboard.
64mm.   18.50

Footwear
Boot, with prophesies verse. 72mm.   6.50

Myott

Trademark used by Myott Son & Co. of
Hanley, Stoke-on-Trent.

One piece of crested ware has ben recorded
from this manufacturer.

Domestic
Teaplate 130mm dia. decorated with
Flags of the Allies, a field gun
and inscribed: *Allies United 1914.*   8.00

Nautilus Porcelain

1903-1913

GLASGOW

1907-1913

Trademark used by the Nautilus Porcelain Co., Possil Pottery, Glasgow.

This firm, established in 1896, and for sometime restyled the Possil Pottery Co., was disbanded in 1913. Based in Glasgow, the Nautilus Porcelain Co. made many Scottish crested pieces, but English crests can be found, the firm having showrooms in 47, Holborn Viaduct, London. The company specialised in producing ornamental porcelain, tea sets, dessert services, trinket sets and figures, so naturally they quickly turned to arms and view ware. The Nautilus Porcelain Co. were making a special feature of these as early as 1903, and by 1907 were producing large quantities. Crests were applied to a range of domestic porcelain ware as well as a 'large assortment of small fancy china pieces'.

Nautilus is fine china and some pieces of 'egg shell' lightness can be found. The crests and the very small quantity of view ware that has survived are very well produced. 'Smalls' with the early mark often have a black transfer print of a tudor rose, thistle or tartan shield on the reserve, and these can be found hand painted.

Obviously the range of models is small as the firm went out of business before the Great War, but there are many 'smalls' and much domestic ware to be found, and these are well worth looking for as they are of such good quality.

Numbering System. No stock numbers are printed on the china. The painted numbers on the base are paintresses' works numbers, 10 and 14 being most often found.

Nautilus Models
Ancient Artefacts

Aberdeen Bronze Pot. 65mm.	7.50
Hastings Kettle. 52mm.	7.50
Irish Bronze Pot. 50mm.	7.50
Loving Cup, three handled.	
4 sizes: 37mm.	7.50
39mm.	7.50
40mm.	7.50
50mm.	7.50
Puzzle Jug. 70mm.	10.50

Monuments (including Crosses)

Iona Cross. 162mm.	16.00

Traditional/National Souvenirs

Irish Wooden Noggin. 57mm.	9.00
Highland Whisky Bowl. Can have 2 or 3 handles. 60mm dia.	10.50
Thistle Jug. 64mm.	8.50

Countryside

Milk Churn. 76mm.	8.50

Animals

Pig, fat and standing. 70mm long.	17.50
Pig, tiny and fat. 67mm long.	24.00

Home/Nostalgic

Coal Bucket. 58mm.	8.50
Coal scuttle, cylindrical on bow feet. 70mm long.	10.50

Dust Pan. 50mm long.	14.00
Garden Urn. 63mm.	7.50
Miner's Lamp. 63mm.	22.00
Watering Can, flat top. 50mm.	10.00

Alcohol

Carboy. 70mm.	9.00

Musical Instruments

Tambourine. 70mm dia.	10.00

Footwear

Dutch Sabot. 90mm long.	10.50
Old Boot. 63mm long.	10 50
Oriental Slipper. 92mm long.	10.50

Hats

Balmoral Bonnet, not named. 75mm dia.	26.00
Top Hat, match striker. 46mm.	11.00

Miniature Domestic

Beaker. 39mm.	7.50
Candlestick. 52mm.	9.00
Cheese Dish and cover. 70mm long.	13.00
Cup. 39mm.	4.00
Diamond mouth Vase. 80mm.	7.50
Jug, barrel shaped. 52mm.	7.50
Jug, shaped. 45mm.	7.50
Milk Jug, tall and ornate. 95mm.	10.00
Mug, one handle. 40mm.	7.50
Tea pot with lid. 2 sizes: 48mm.	11.00
55mm.	11.00

Domestic

Bamboo Spill Holder. 103mm.	8.00
Hatpin Holder. 105mm.	17.00
Match Holders:	
Straight-sided. 57mm.	7.00
Ridged. 50mm.	7.00
Pin Tray, leaf-shaped with twig handle. 120mm long.	10.50
Vase, two-handled. 74mm.	7.50
Vase, long neck, fluted top, 2 small handles. 125mm.	7.50
Vase, two-handled. 170mm long, 100mm high.	7.50

Nelson China

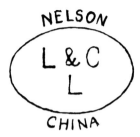

Trademark used for a Liverpool retailer by an unknown English manufacturer but probably a branch of J.A. Robinson & Sons. (Usual trademark Arcadian).

Nelson Models
Seaside Souvenirs

Bathing Machine. 65mm.	10.00

Great War

Model of a pair of Field Glasses. 60mm long.	17.00

Ness

New Chelsea Staffs

"NESS CHINA"

Trademark used for an Inverness firm by
Schmidt and Co., Carlsbad (Bohemia).
(Usual trademark Gemma).

Ness Models
Seaside
Lifeboat with lifebelt on side. No.
536 or No. 636. 130mm long.   12.50

Great War
French Infantry Helmet. 60mm long.   25.00

Trademark used by the New Chelsea
Porcelain Co. Longton.
For further details of this china and manu-
facturer see Chelson China.

A 54mm vase decorated with a bird
transfer has been found with this
trademark.   12.50

Niagara Art China

NIAGARA ART CHINA

Trademark used by Hewitt and Leadbeater, Willow Potteries, Longton, subsequently Hewitt Bros. (Usual trademark Willow Art).

Niagara Art Models
Traditional/National Souvenirs
Dutch Girl. 75mm.   10.50

Great War
Tommy's Steel Helmet. 76mm long.   24.50

Footwear
Lace-up Riding Shoe. 115mm long.   10.00

Norfolk Crest China

Mark has also been found with CHEST rather than crest, obviously a misprint.

Trademark used for W.H. Smith & Sons by Hewitt & Leadbeater, Willow Potteries, Longton - subsequently Hewitt Bros. (Usual trademark Willow Art).
For details of this china and manufacturer see Willow Art China.
This is the second mark used by Hewitt and Leadbeater for W.H. Smith and Sons, the other being Kingsway Art China. This appears to be a later mark, used from the end of the Great War to the mid-twenties. A half pint mug has been recorded with the Norfolk mark, it has a colour transfer print of H.M.S. Iron Duke, an aeroplaine, the Flags of the Allies and a peace inscription. Black Cat transfers are also found indicating the later date and some models could have come from Arcadian moulds once the firms had combined.
Stock numbers where found would be the same as Willow Art models.

Norfolk Models
Parian/Unglazed
Bust of Burns on column base.
    170mm.   40.00

Buildings - White
Shakespeare's House. 59mm long.   10.00

Monuments (including Crosses)
Sir Robert Peel statue. 168mm.   30.00

Historical/Folklore

James V Chair. 101mm.	7.50

Traditional/National Souvenirs

Thistle Vase. 58mm.	3.00
Welsh Hat, with blue band. No. 75. 57mm.	5.00

Seaside Souvenirs

Lifeboat. 95mm long.	12.50
Lighthouse, not named. No. 135. 105mm.	5.00

Animals

Cat, on cushion, playing fiddle, holding bow. 110mm. inscribed: *Cat and Fiddle, Buxton.*	40.00
Cat, standing, chubby, looking left, tail up. 76mm.	16.00
Dog, Bull Terrier, standing. 60mm.	12.50
Dog, sitting, bow at neck. Brown eyes. No. 22. 76mm.	12.50
Dog, sitting, head to one side. No. 23. 70mm.	13.00
Dog, wearing medallion.	13.00
Elephant, walking. 52mm.	17.00
Elephant, walking, trunk over head. No. 113. 53mm.	20.00
Pig, standing. 85mm long.	10.00
Pony inscribed 'A Native of Shetland'. 105mm long.	25.00

Birds (including Eggs)

Duck posy holder, yellow beak. 80mm long.	7.50
Hen egg cup. 76mm long.	8.50
Swan, open back. 63mm.	7.50

Great War

Battleship, impressed: HMS Lion. 140mm long.	30.00
British Tank. 102mm long.	14.50
Tank with trailing wheels. 123mm long.	17.50
Red Cross Van. No. 712. 88mm long.	30.00
Military Cap. 80mm dia.	13.00
Kitbag with verse. 74mm.	19.50
Nurse Cavell, War Memorial statue. 194mm.	82.50
Matlock Bath War Memorial. 182mm.	40.00

Florence Nightingale statue.

3 sizes: 160mm.	20.00
175mm.	25.00
180mm.	25.00

Home/Nostalgic

Grandfather clock, inscribed: *Make use of time let not advantage slip. Shakespeare.* 128mm.	10.50

Comic/Novelty

Jester, double faced bust. Some colouring.	
3 sizes: 65mm.	8.50
80mm.	9.00
90mm.	12.50
Monk, jovial and plump. No glass. 90mm.	12.50
Monk, jovial and holding glass. 70mm.	8.50

Sport

Cricket Cap. 67mm long.	75.00

Footwear

Lancashire Clog. 88mm long.	5.50

Domestic

Hatpins holder. 124mm.	12.50

Noritaké

Noritaké

Made in Japan.

A selection of coloured vases were made, many with a transfer print of St Annes with a crest in foreground and some with crests of London or Blackpool. There is very little Japanese souvenir ware around and certainly the British Potteries did not see the Japanese as much of a threat as they did the Germans.   8.50

Dish, shaped. 140mm dia.   7.50

Nornesford China

Trademark registered in 1920 and used by a Longton firm, probably R.H. and S.L. Plant (Ltd), Tuscan Works, Longton. (Usual trademark Tuscan).

Nornesford Models
Seaside Souvenirs
Lighthouse.   5.50

Animals
Bulldog in kennel. 65mm.   18.50
Cheshire Cat, with brown bead
    right eye. 90mm.   11.00
Fish with open mouth and bead
    eyes. 120mm long.   8.50

Birds (including Eggs)
Chick hatching from egg.
    70mm long.   7.50

Home/Nostalgic
Anvil on base. 60mm.   7.50
Bellows. 105mm.   12.50
Loaf of Bread. 55mm.   20.00
Pillar Box. No. 181. 73mm.   8.00
Shaving Mug. 53mm.   5.50
Wee Willie Winkie Candle Snuffer.
    90mm.   20.00

Hats
Top Hat. No. 173. 45mm.   5.50

One and All

Trademark used by J.A. Robinson & Sons, Stoke-on-Trent. (Usual trademark Arcadian).

Most china found with this mark are 'smalls' with 'Lucky Black Cat' transfers, and were produced by J.A. Robinson Ltd. This mark is very like a mark used by Cauldon for Pearsons of Blackpool. (See Palatine China).

These models often have Cornish crests.

One and All Models
Ancient Artefacts

Salisbury Jack, not named. 50mm.	3.00

Buildings - White

Anne Hathaway's Cottage. 105mm long.	16.00

Seaside Souvenirs

Sea-Shell Pin Tray, 3 tiny feet. 75mm long.	4.00

Animals

Black Cat with double base. 76mm.	160.00
Black Cat on jug. 85mm.	55.00
Bulldog, sitting. 50mm.	25.00
Crocodile. 127mm long.	75.00
Dog, Collie lying down. 78mm long.	19.50
Teddy Bear. No. 27. 65mm.	19.50
Squirrel, eating nut. 60mm.	30.00
Tortoise. 60mm long.	9.00

Birds (including Eggs)

Cockerel on circular base. Some colouring. 90mm.	19.50
Goose. 95mm.	30.00

Home/Nostalgic

Cauldron with handle. 82mm.	3.00
Fire Bucket. 53mm.	4.00
Grandmother Clock. 110mm.	10.50
Ring Stand. 52mm.	8.50

Comic/Novelty

Black Boy and Girl on log, coloured. 75mm long.	82.50
Jester, sitting on heart shaped ashtray. 65mm.	65.00

Transport

Petrol Can, impressed: *Motor Spirit*. 55mm.	16.00

Footwear

Ladies Ankle Boot. 72mm long.	5.00

Miscellaneous

Domed Jam Pot and cover. 80mm.	5.00

Oxford Art China

P

Trademark used for an Oxfordshire retailer by Hewitt & Leadbeater, Willow Potteries, Longton. (Usual trademark Willow Art). For details of this china and manufacturer see Willow Art China.
One model found with this mark has a Barrow-in-Furness crest which seems to indicate that the W. & Co. in the mark had a chain of gift shops, the original shop being in Oxford.

Oxford Art Model
Historical/Folklore
Sir Walter Scott's Chair, Abbotsford.
80mm.   7.50

Home/Nostalgic
Grandfather Clock inscribed: *Make use of time...* 124mm.   10.50

Footwear
Lancashire Clog.   5.00

Trademark used by Hutschenreuther, Probstzella, Thuringia (not the more famous Bavarian firm of the same name). Trademark can be found without the crown.
This mark is found on 'smalls', ancient artefacts and domestic ware with crests and coloured transfers from all over Great Britain. The ware is the continental hard china, and the models recorded indicate that the mark was used before the Great War.

P Models
Ancient Artefacts
Aberdeen Bronze Pot. 68mm.	3.00
Ancient Tyg, 2 handled.	3.00
Loving Cup, 3 handled & 2 handled. 38mm.	3.00
Puzzle Jug. 67mm.	5.50

Home/Nostalgic
Cauldron. 40mm.	3.00
Shaving Mug. 55mm.	5.50
Suitcase. 90mm.	4.00

Miniature Domestic
Cheese Dish and cover, 2 pieces. 55mm.	6.50
Tea Pot with lid. 65mm.	7.50
Tea Urn with lid, tapered. 65mm.	8.50

Domestic
Candlestick and snuffer. 85mm dia.	5.50
Oviform Pepper Castor. 70mm.	3.50

Palantine China

Trademark used for Pearsons, of Blackpool by J.A. Robinson Ltd. (Usual trademark Arcadian).

For details of this china and manufacturer see Arcadian China.

This mark was probably used for a 'Palatine Bazaar' in Blackpool, as only Blackpool crests have been recorded. This mark is very similar to one used in the mid-Twenties, on Willow Art moulds indicating that both marks were used by the Cauldon group. (See One and All). The models below seem to be earlier than the 'One and All' models, indicating that the mark was re-used later.

Palatine Models
Animals
Dog, sitting with a tear on cheek.
    80mm.   30.00

Great War
Armoured Car, Model of.
    120mm long.   40.00
Red Cross Van, inscribed: *EH139.*
    88mm long.   30.00
Tank, Model of. 115mm.   17.00

Palmer

Trademark used by Hewitt and Leadbeater, Willow Potteries, Longton. (Usual trademark Willow Art.) This piece was obviously ordered by their Buckingham agent and it bears the arms of the town.

Palmer Model
Comic/Novelty
Billiken sitting. 78mm.   7.50

P.A.L.T.

Panorama

Trademark used by a German firm on domestic wares, after the Great War.
This mark has been found on domestic ware with crests from all over Great Britain. The use of 'Czecho-Slovakia' as the country of origin proves that the mark was used after 1920.

Domestic ware only.   from £3.00

Trademark used by Wagstaff and Brunt on china manufactured by Edwin Leadbeater, Commerce Street, Longton, who also made Leadbeater Art China and H & L.
For details of this china and manufacturer see Leadbeater Art China.
Wagstaff and Brunt were registered as pottery manufacturers from 1880 to 1927 but most of the wares stamped with their name appears to have been made by other manufacturers. They specialised in commemorative china, and it could well be that they were dealers rather than manufacturers. The miniatures marked 'Panorama' were definitely made by Edwin Leadbeater, who could possibly have taken this contract with him from Hewitt and Leadbeater. I suspect the trademark Panorama was chosen because the range was intended to be only view ware. Many pieces marked Panorama carry coloured transfer views rather than a crest, but crests do occur. Apart from the usual views of castles and sea fronts there are some transfers of War Memorials to be found, including The Cenotaph, Stoke under Ham and Hemyock War Memorials. Stock numbers where they are used coincide with Leadbeater Art stock numbers.

Panorama Models
Many of these wares are found with
  a transfer print view rather than a
  crest.   Add £5.00

Unglazed/Parian
Burns and Highland Mary. 125mm. 30.00
Bust of Dickens, on circular glazed
   base. 170mm. 35.00

Ancient Artefacts
Model of Bowl found in lake village
   Glastonbury. 65mm dia. 3.00

Monuments
Drakes' Statue. 153mm. 17.50
Sir Robert Peel statue on large
   plinth. 165mm. 55.00

Historical/Folklore
Bunyans Chair, Model of. 95mm. 12.50
Model of Mons Meg Edinburgh Castle.
   130mm long. 11.00
Sir Walter Scott's Chair at Abbotsford.
   No. 85. 80mm. 7.50

Traditional/National Souvenirs
Welsh Hat. No. 57. 60mm. 5.00

Seaside Souvenirs
Lighthouse Pepper Castor. 110mm. 10.50

Animals
Cat sitting, left ear raised, one green
   eye. 105mm. 9.50
Labrador sitting, red eyes. 74mm. 12.50
Dog, Pug, sitting. 67mm. 10.50
Dog, Staffordshire Bull Terrier,
   sitting. 115mm. 17.00

Birds (including Eggs)
Chick. 33mm. 4.00
Crested Tit Posy Holder.
   80mm long. 8.50
Duck, open wings.
   80mm long. 12.50

Great War
Red Cross Van. No. 103.
   88mm long. 30.00

Home/Nostalgic
Anvil. No. 78. 58mm. 7.50

Comic/Novelty
Monk. 95mm. 16.00

Alcohol
Toby Jug. 74mm. 6.50

Sport
Cricket Cap. 67mm long. 45.00
Footballer, coloured holding brown
   ball on white plinth. Inscribed:
   Play Up 166mm. 110.00

Paragon China

PARAGON
CHINA
ENGLAND

Trademarks used by Star China Co., Atlas
Works (and other addresses), Longton.
Subsequently Paragon China (Co) Ltd.

The star mark was used on
domestic wares with the Great
War commemorative, Four Flags
of the Allies with inscription: *For
right and freedom.*   from £5.50

The crown mark is found on smalls
with ordinary crests.   2.00

Park, For the People, China

PARK,
FOR THE PEOPLE
CHINA

Mark used by unknown English manufacturer for a charity, (possibly) in
Newtown, Mid-Wales.

This mark has been found on
several 'smalls' all with a
Newtown crest, apart from one
with the crest of Machynlleth –
about 30 miles from Newtown.
Could they have been sold at a
charity or fund raising bazaar?   4.00

Patriotic China

PATRIOTIC
x BR & C x

CHINA
STOKE ON TRENT

Trademark used during the Great War by Birks, Rawlins and Co (Ltd), Vine Pottery, Stoke. (Usual trademark Savoy).

For details of this china and manufacturer see Savoy China.

The items with this mark so far recorded carry military crests and were obviously made to commemorate the Great War. The teapot listed below has a colour transfer with the verse 'A soldier of the King' and a crest of the "11th Welsh". Some domestic ware has also been found with this transfer and crest. Another pot has the crest of Seaford Camp and the crest of the 13th Manchester has also been recorded. These pieces are obviously of great interest to the Great War collector and one would assume that there must be further crests to record.

Patriotic Models
Range of wares all with military crests and Great War inscriptions.
£7.50 upwards

Parian/Unglazed
Bust of Admiral Sir David Beatty. Union Jack and laurel wreath. Inscribed: *To Victory*. Verse at rear *Be Briton still to Briton true.* 150mm.   65.00

Animals
Bulldog standing. Identical Union Jack and Laurel Wreath. Inscribed: *To Victory* and verse as on the bust. 135mm long.   65.00

Lion, walking with Burns verse: *Be Briton still to Briton true.* 135mm long.   22.00

Miniature Domestic
Beaker. 80mm.   7.00
Tea Pot with lid. 65mm.   13.50

Pearl Arms China

The middle initial could possibly be a 'C' and not a 'G'.

Trademark used for a wholesaler by Hewitt Bros, Willow Potteries Ltd, Longton. (Usual trademark Willow Art).

For details of this china and manufacturer see Willow Art China.

The initials A.G.R. & Co. Ltd. were used by the firm of A.G. Richardson and Co., Gordon Pottery, Tunstall, Staffs, established in 1915. This firm manufactured Crown Ducal ware and did not advertise crested miniatures. The models with the Pearl Arms mark are undoubtedly from the same moulds as those marked Willow Art. Whether this range was made for another manufacturer or retailer or was an alternative trademark used by Hewitt Bros must remain a mystery. The use of the initials A.G.R. or A.C.R. and the diversity of crests seems to indicate that the range was made for another manufacturer.

No military crests, transfer devices or views have been recorded on china with this mark. Domestic ware and 'smalls' are often found. Stock numbers where they occur coincide with those found on Willow Art models.

Pearl Arms Models
Ancient Artefacts

Carlisle Salt Pot, not named. 46mm.	3.00
Nottingham Urn, not named. No. 172. 45mm.	3.00
Puzzle Tea Pot. 56mm.	20.00

Monuments (including Crosses)

Lifeboat Memorial. 132mm.	16.00

Historical/Folklore

James V Chair, Stirling Castle. 100mm.	7.50
Man in the Moon. 55mm.	20.00
Mary, Queen of Scots Chair, Edinburgh Castle, Model of. 75mm.	6.50
Royal Crown. 55mm.	30.00

Traditional/National Souvenirs

Blackpool Big Wheel. 100mm.	12.00
Welsh Hat with longest Welsh place name around brim. No. 75. 55mm.	7.50

Seaside Souvenirs

Rowing Boat on rocks. 110mm long.	14.00
Lighthouse. 105mm.	5.00
Mermaid seated on rock combing hair. 105mm.	30.00

Animals

Cat, angry, tail in the air. Bow not coloured. 80mm long.	17.00
Cat, sitting. 70mm.	10.00
Cat sitting in boot, blue bow. 88mm long.	14.50
Cat, standing, blue bow. 80mm.	10.00
Cat, standing, chubby. 70mm.	16.00
Bulldog, black, emerging from kennel, inscribed: *The Black Watch*. 70mm long.	19.50
Dog, Collie, standing. 85mm.	23.00
Dog, Scottie with tam-o'-shanter. 95mm.	10.50
Elephant, walking. 52mm.	17.00
Elephant, cream jug. 72mm.	12.50
Fish. 128mm long.	5.00
Hampshire Hog with inscription. 100mm long.	14.00
Mouse. 62mm.	20.00
Pig standing. 95mm long.	12.50
Pig, sitting, inscribed: *You may push me* etc. 73mm.	16.00
Pig, standing. 85mm long.	12.50
Rabbit, right ear erect. 66mm long.	7.50

Birds (including Eggs)

Canary on rock. 98mm.	13.00
Swan, with head on breast. 58mm.	6.50

Great War

Sailor, inscribed: *Our brave defender.*
130mm. 55.00
Monoplane, with movable prop.
150mm long. 65.00
Monoplane, with fixed prop.
146mm long. 55.00
Battleship, 4 funnels.
127mm long. 19.00
Battleship, 3 funnels. Impressed
HMS Lion. 140mm long. 30.00
British Tank, Model of, with trailing
wheels. 130mm long. 17.50
British Tank, Model of.
92mm long. 14.50
Bugle. No. 370. 70mm. 19.50
Kit Bag with verse: *Pack up your
troubles in your old kit bag.*
74mm. 19.50
Officer's Peaked Cap.
70mm dia. 11.00
Pickelhaube. (German spiked
helmet). 50mm. 30.00
Fireplace inscribed: *Keep the home
fires burning.* Some colouring.
100mm long. 17.00

Home/Nostalgic

Anvil. 60mm. 7.50
Basket, oblong with handle.
76mm long. 3.50
Book, leather bound. 60mm. 5.00
Bucket. 65mm. 3.50
Coal scuttle, helmet shaped. No. 101.
53mm. 5.00
Grandfather Clock, inscribed: *Make
use of time let not advantage slip.*
Shakespeare. 128mm. 10.50
Pillar Box, outpressed: *G.R.*
90mm. 25.00
Shaving Mug. 55mm. 6.50
Sundial, circular on square base,
with inscription: *I mark not the
hours.* 98mm. 7.50
Watering Can. 72mm. 8.50

Comic/Novelty

Billiken, the God of Luck, often found
unnamed. 73mm. 7.50
Billiken, the God of Luck, sitting on
high-backed chair. 100mm. 10.50

Alcohol

Barrel, on its side. 55mm long.   3.50
Whiskey Bottle with cork, inscribed:
One special scotch. 88mm. 7.50

Transport

Open Tourer, 4 seater. 114mm long. 40.00

Hats

Policeman's Helmet. 17.50

Footwear

Lancashire Clog. 88mm long. 5.50
Sabot. 73mm long. 4.00

Miniature Domestic

Cheese Dish and cover. 45mm. 7.50
Cup and Saucer. 35mm. 5.50
Coffee Pot with lid. 69mm. 7.50

Miscellaneous

Hand holding a tulip. 80mm. 5.00

Phoenix China

Podmore China

1921-c1927 on crested china

Trademark used by Podmore China Co., Elm Street, Hanley.

A Mr A.J. Podmore of the Tunstall Art Pottery Co. in 1920 announced that in consequence of the expiration of his lease the blocks, moulds and cases and other implements connected with his range of useful and ornamental pottery were for disposal. In 1921 The Podmore China Co. was established in Hanley and one can only assume that Mr A.J. Podmore had found new premises. (This indication of the sale of moulds in Staffordshire helps to explain why so many firms produced similar if not identical models during this period.) The Podmore China Co. continued until 1941 when it became Sylvan Pottery Ltd.

Podmore China Co. produced crested china miniatures from 1921 to at least the middle if not late twenties. No early historical shapes have been recorded and the whole range of models seems to be from the twenties and not earlier. The range includes some coloured models including two delightful children at the seaside which would have sold well in the mid-twenties. The models are rather on the large and heavy side but well finished and

Trademark used by Thomas Forester & Sons (Ltd.), Phoenix Works, Longton.

A range of crested domestic ware was produced.

Miniature Domestic

Wash Bowl. 50mm.	2.50
Wash Jug. 80mm.	2.50

Domestic

Teaplate. 180mm dia.	2.00

painted. Some 'Lucky White Heather' transfers have been found on models and 'smalls' but no other transfer devices, views or commemoratives have been recorded.

(No stock numbers are found on Podmore China, the small dots and dashes in colour found on the base are paintresses' marks.)

Podmore Models
Unglazed/Parian

Bust of *Bunyan*, square unglazed base. 135mm.	20.00
Bust of Burns, on square unglazed base with crest. 150mm.	20.00
HRH, Prince of Wales, in uniform, standing on square base. Parian or glazed on glazed base. 155mm.	80.00

Buildings - Coloured

Bell Hotel, Abel Fletcher's house in John Halifax Gentleman.	
2 sizes: 67mm.	30.00
85mm.	40.00

Buildings - White

Bell Hotel, Abel Fletcher's house in John Halifax Gentleman. 67mm.	26.00
Big Ben. 101mm.	12.50
Blackpool Tower. 130mm.	11.50
Bunyan's Cottage. 90mm long.	24.00
Clifton Suspension Bridge.	
190mm long.	75.00
God's Providence House, Chester. AD1652.	
2 sizes: 70mm.	20.00
90mm.	20.00
Hastings Clock Tower. 167mm.	10.50
Leicester Clock Tower. 184mm.	25.00
Lincoln Cathedral, West front.	
106mm.	30.00
Margate Clock Tower. 143mm.	13.00
Matlock Bath, The Tower.	
120mm.	130.00
Ross on Wye Town Hall.	
106mm.	47.50
Rowton Tower (*King Charles Tower, Chester*). 80mm.	30.00
St. Albans, Clock Tower. 125mm.	43.00
St. Pauls Cathedral. 105mm.	15.50
Westminster Abbey. 127mm.	40.00

Monuments (including Crosses)

Banbury, The Cross. 158mm.	28.00

Black Watch Memorial.	
130mm.	65.00
Bunyan's Statue, Model of.	
2 sizes: 173mm.	17.00
206mm.	19.00
Nelsons Column. 140mm.	40.00
St Albans Statue. 160mm.	47.50

Historical/Folklore

Armour, breast plate. 75mm.	35.00
Bunyan's Chair. 99mm.	12.00
Burns Chair, Model of. 93mm.	7.50
Mary Queen of Scots Chair in Edinburgh Castle, Model of.	
80mm.	6.50
Mother Shipton, standing figure.	
75mm.	8.00
Mother Shipton, figure with black cat arching its back at her feet. Coloured features. Can be found inscribed: *Near to the Knaresborough Dropping Well I first drew breath as records tell.* 118mm.	11.00
Tewkesbury Cross Stocks and Whipping Post. 105mm (rare).	50.00

Traditional/National Souvenirs

Blackpool Big Wheel. 95mm.	14.00
Chester Imp, recumbent.	
100mm long.	30.00
Lincoln Imp sitting on pedestal.	
105mm.	6.50
Dutch Girl on ashtray base. Fully coloured. 100mm.	22.00

Seaside Souvenirs

Lifeboat with deep blue cord.	
115mm long.	11.00
Lifeboat collection box.	
170mm long.	60.00
Yacht. 111mm.	13.00
Lifeboatman on plinth.	
142mm.	16.00
Beachy Head Lighthouse, with black band. 120mm.	11.00
Needles Rocks and Lighthouse, Isle of Wight. 125mm long.	40.00
North Foreland Lighthouse, Broadstairs. 128mm.	25.00
Oyster Shell on coral base.	
80mm.	4.00
Whelk Shell, inscribed: *Listen to the sea.* 100mm long.	5.00
Fish Basket. 70mm long.	10.00

Child, sitting with knees under chin,
wearing bathing suit. Impressed:
Splash me. Some colouring.
140mm (rare).   85.00
Child, with blonde hair, standing on
rock draped in towel. Some
colouring. 115mm. and 140mm.   75.00

Animals

Cat, standing with arched back and
tail up. Coloured eyes and
mouth. 110mm.   12.50
Cat, with human face and wearing a
black cap. Inscribed: *Puss Puss*.
105mm.   40.00
Cat, grotesque with long neck,
named in orange *Luck*. 136mm.   8.50
Cat with long neck and funny face.
125mm.   10.00
Cat on round pouffe. Inscribed:
Luck. 80mm.   9.50
Bulldog, French, sitting. 65mm.   13.00
Dog, Scottie, looking out of kennel.
77mm.   10.50
Inscribed: *Black Watch*.   12.50
Dog, black with green bow.
70mm.   16.00
Dog, possibly St. Bernard, sad,
sitting. 48mm.   19.50
Dog, Scottie, wearing a tam-
o'shanter, orange pom-pom.
75mm.   10.50
Dog, sitting. 68mm.   8.50
Dog, with letter, sitting next to a
bright red pillar box on ashtray.
Inscribed: *Sorry I've missed the
post*. 90mm.   65.00
Dog, terrier, standing.
80mm long.   14.50
Elephant. 64mm long.   20.00
Pig, standing. 100mm long.   17.00
Shetland Pony. 100mm long.   22.00

Birds (including Eggs)

Cock, standing, red comb.
65mm.   12.00
Cock with red comb, on green base.
45mm.   13.00
Hen on green base.
70mm long.   13.00
Hen, with red comb. 66mm.   12.50
Kingfisher, coloured, on pearl lustre
trinket tray. 82mm long.   30.00
Penguin. 88mm.   11.50

Great War

Monoplane with revolving prop.   65.00
Grandfather Clock, same mould as
usual Grandfather clock but
clockface at 3.25, inscribed: *World
War 1914-1919, Peace signed 3.25pm
June 28th 1919*. 137mm.   56.50
Cenotaph, inscribed: *The Glorious
Dead. MCMXIV-MCMXIX*. Green
wreaths.
   3 sizes: 84mm.   4.00
                   130mm.   6.50
                   165mm.   7.50
Edith Cavell Memorial, London.
Inscribed: *Edith Cavell Brussels
dawn October 12th 1915. Humanity
Sacrifice*.
   2 sizes: 142mm.   14.50
                 170mm.   16.00
Edith Cavell Statue, Norwich.
165mm.   35.00
Leek War Memorial. *Model of War
Memorial Leek, presented by Sir
Arthur & Lady Nicholson*. 158mm.   90.00
Matlock Bath War Memorial. Often
found unnamed. 190mm.   30.00
Ad Astra, R.A.F. Memorial. *Unveiled
by HRH Prince of Wales July 16th
1923*. 152mm.   85.00
Rushden War Memorial. *Their names
liveth for ever, To keep in mind those
from this town who gave their lives
in the Great War. 1914-1918*.
155mm.   75.00
Blackpool War Memorial, inscribed:
*1914 in memory of our glorious dead
1918*. 145mm.   155.00

Home/Nostalgic

Baby's Bootee. 52mm.   12.50
Baby's Cradle. 65mm long.   6.50
Basket. 72mm long.   4.00
Grandfather Clock, with
inscription: *Make use of time*
120mm.   10.50
140mm.   10.50
Fireplace with clock on mantelpiece,
inscribed: *Home sweet home. East
or west home is best*. Some
colouring. 98mm.   16.00

Comic/Novelty
Billiken, sitting on high backed chair,
  inscribed: *The God of things as they
  ought to be.*
  102mm.   7.50
  Inscribed   8.50
The Bridegroom, God Help Him.
  145mm.   40.00
Child, some colouring, standing on
  ashtray base. 95mm.   30.00
  Fully coloured   35.00
Sack of Coal, some colouring.
  2 sizes: 60mm.   12.50
          95mm.   12.50
  Can be found inscribed: *If you
  can't afford a truck – buy
  a sack.*   16.00
Schoolboy, comic coloured face.
  100mm.   40.00

Cartoon/Comedy Characters
*Mr Pussy Foot. All water!! we don't
  think.* Standing by a pump, some
  colouring. 96mm.   30.00
Wilfred Wilfred, coloured.   35.00

Alcohol
Beer Barrel on stand, fixed.
  60mm.   4.50
Toby Jug with verse. 88mm.   10.50
Toby Jug with verse on base,
  red nose. 88mm.   12.50

Sport
Golf Ball, inscribed: *The ancient game
  of golf was first played in 1448.*
  40mm.   10.00
The Sprinter, gangly athlete with
  comic face, kneeling, on oval
  base. 98mm.   47.50

Musical Instruments
Double Bass. 140mm long.   33.00

Transport
Charabanc. 127mm long.   40.00

Modern Equipment
Horn Gramophone. 93mm.   20.00

Footwear
Lancashire Clog. 73mm long.   5.00

Miniature Domestic
Cheese Dish, 1 piece. 50mm.   6.50

Cheese Dish and cover.
  71mm long.   5.50

Miscellaneous
Hand holding a tulip. 95mm.   5.00
Horseshoe Pintray. 80mm long.   3.00
Vase, ornate with buttercups in
  relief. 110mm.   5.00

Poppyland

POPPYLAND
CHINA
ENGLISH
B.A.WATTS
SHERINGHAM

Trademark used by Taylor and Kent Ltd, Florence Works, Longton. (Usual trademark Florentine.)

The only piece recorded is a 60mm 2 handled vase decorated with red poppies for the Norfolk Broads market.   16.00

Porcelle

«PORCELLE»

W R & S

BRITISH MANUFACTURE

From c1910-1924

Trademark used by William Ritchie & Son Ltd., 24, 26, 28 Elder Street, Edinburgh.

Many, if not all, these models are from Savoy moulds and this firm was a retailer of heraldic china, obtaining supplies from Birks, Rawlins and Co. (Usual trademark Savoy). William Ritchie was an Edinburgh wholesale stationer who also issued heraldic postcards.

This mark was registered in 1910 and published in the *Pottery Gazette* in October of that year. William Ritchie and Son Ltd were described as Porcelain and Earthenware manufacturers. No information or record of this firm can be found in standard works on the pottery industry or in the *Pottery Gazette* and therefore for the moment we have little other information. The firm seems to have begun producing a large range of crested china before the Great War and would appear to have stopped doing so before the mid-twenties, as no coloured models or 'lucky' transfers have been found. Most crests recorded are from Scotland, Ireland and the North of England and obviously the firm concentrated its sales efforts in these areas.

No commemorative transfer items, view ware or any other form of decoration on miniatures or domestic ware has been recorded. A great deal of crested domestic ware has been recorded including teapot stands, plates, butter dishes and trays of various kinds. These sometimes are found with a buff instead of a white body.Porcelle china is more cream or ivory than white, and is fairly fine. The crests are rather well produced.

Numbering System. Stock numbers are sometimes found painted on the base of models and these are listed where known.

Porcelle Models
Unglazed/Parian

Bust of Robbie Burns on glazed plinth. *Burns* outpressed.	
2 sizes: 115mm.	30.00
135mm.	30.00
Bust of Sir John Jellicoe, impressed: *W.C. Lawton sculp. copyright. 23rd Sept 1914.* 170mm.	47.50

Ancient Artefacts

Altar Candlestick. 144mm.	3.00
Newbury Leather Bottle. 65mm.	3.00
Puzzle Jug. 70mm.	5.50
Whiskey Quaich. 30mm.	4.00

Buildings - White

Burns Cottage, Model of.	
3 sizes: 70mm long.	16.00
108mm long.	30.00
115mm long.	30.00
Cottage. 75mm long.	6.50
Windmill, with revolving sails. 108mm.	25.00

Historical/Flklore

Mary Queen of Scots Chair, Edinburgh Castle, Model of. 70mm.	6.50

Traditional/National Souvenirs

Irish Harp with moulded shamrocks. 105mm.	10.50
Bagpipes. 115mm long.	15.00
Thistle vase. 48mm.	3.00
Welsh Hat. 63mm.	5.50

Seaside Souvenirs

Bathing Machine, inscribed: *Morning dip.* 87mm.	10.00
Rowing Boat, no seats. 132mm long.	10.50

Lighthouse on rocky base. 104mm.	5.00
Fisherman, with Tub, inscribed: *Waiting for the smacks.* 67mm.	30.00
Shell ashtray. 81mm long.	3.00
Scallop Shell. 70mm long.	3.00
Whelk Shell. No. 451. 100mm long.	3.50

Countryside

Acorn. No. 119. 56mm.	7.50
Milk Churn with fixed top. 60mm.	4.00

Animals

Cat, sitting, long neck and tail joined to shoulders. 105mm.	20.50
Cat, sitting. 51mm.	10.50
Cat, squatting, wide grin. 105mm.	30.00
Dog, puppy begging. 68mm.	12.50
Labrador Puppy sitting, all legs forward. 80mm.	13.00
Dog, sitting with short turned down ears. 67mm.	13.00
Dog, Terrier, looking out of kennel, inscribed: *Black Watch,* dog black. 55mm.	10.50
Donkey. 90mm.	19.00
Elephant with Howdah. 70mm.	30.00
Hare, sitting, one ear raised. 110mm.	30.00
Hare, sitting up. Pepper Pot. 106mm.	40.00
Lion, walking. No. 288. *Be Briton...*	20.50
Pig, kneeling. 65mm long.	12.50
Pig, lying down. 80mm long.	12.00
Pig, standing. 70mm long.	11.00
Rabbit, crouching with flat ears. No. 548A. 30mm.	7.50
Rabbit, sitting. 80mm.	20.00
Seal. 50mm.	11.00
Grotesque animal/bird. 105mm.	10.00
Animal jug, tail is handle. 70mm.	5.50

Birds (including Eggs)

Duck, swimming. 70mm long.	8.00
Hen, sitting. 93mm long.	7.50
Cockerel Pepper Pot, egg shaped. 85mm.	10.00
Owlet, plump. No. 549. 62mm.	18.50

Penguin. 75mm.	16.00
Swan. 50mm.	6.50
Swan. 55mm long.	6.50
Cruet in form of pair of eggs in egg cups. 70mm.	15.00
Pepper Pot, Egg in wooden egg cup. 68mm.	pair 12.00

Great War

Sailor, standing with hands on hips. 130mm.	65.00
Bust of Sailor. Inscribed: *HMS Queen Elizabeth*. 90mm.	34.50
British Airship on stand. 130mm long.	30.00
Battleship, inscribed: *HMS Lion*, with 3 funnels, 168mm long.	75.00
Battleship, inscribed *HMS King George V*, with 2 funnels. 168mm long.	75.00
HMS Queen Elizabeth Battleship. 165mm long.	75.00
Torpedo Boat Destroyer, Model of. 2 sizes: 110mm long. (Arcadian mould)	25.00
140mm long. (Savoy mould)	100.00
Submarine, inscribed: *E1*. 150mm long.	40.00
Submarine, inscribed: *E4*. 95mm.	19.50
Armoured Car with 2 guns. 127mm long.	110.00
British Motor Searchlight, Model of 90mm long.	145.00
Red Cross Van. 110mm long.	30.00
Tank with 2 inset steering wheels, inscribed: *HMS Donner Blitzen* and *Model of British tank first used by British troops at the Battle of Ancre Sept. 1916.* 2 sizes: 130mm long.	30.00
160mm long.	40.00
Field Gun. 170mm long.	25.00
Howitzer. 2 sizes: 140mm.	30.00
168mm long.	30.00
Machine gun, Model of, on tripod (2 pieces). 80mm.	145.00
Trench Mortar Gun. 98mm long.	47.50
Land Mine. Similar to curling stone but with rectangular firing mechanism. No. 429. 52mm.	75.00
Mills Hand Grenade. 80mm.	17.50

Shell inscribed: *Iron rations for Fritz*. 78mm.	8.50
Glengarry. 2 sizes: 70mm.	16.00
100mm long. (Ornate). Larger model has coloured heather in band.	19.00
Anzacs Cap, Model of, with maple leaf, impressed: *CANADA*. 90mm long.	25.00
Colonial Soldiers Hat. 90mm long.	16.00
Peaked Cap. No. 516. 70mm long.	10.50
Pith Helmet or Solar Topee. 80mm.	25.00
Poilu, French Trench Helmet. 84mm long.	40.00
RFC Cap. 80mm long.	43.00
Sailors Cap. 70mm dia.	56.50
Tommy's Steel Helmet. 82mm long.	30.00
Bell Tent, open flap. 64mm.	16.50
Fireplace, inscribed: *Keep the home fires burning*. 70mm.	14.50
Nurse Cavell, standing on plinth, holding bandage. 167mm.	125.00

Home/Nostalgic

Baby's Cradle. 55mm.	10.00
Grandfather Clock. 132mm.	10.50
Holdall. 95mm long.	17.00
Iron and stand. 70mm long.	10.50
Jelly Mould. 55mm.	13.00
Lady in bonnet and muff, candlesnuffer. 80mm.	16.00
Policeman's Lamp. 67mm.	10.00
Stool, 3-legged. 36mm.	9.00
Sundial on square base. 84mm.	5.50
Thimble. 57mm.	19.50
Watering Can, miniature. 2 sizes: 50mm.	10.50
67mm.	10.50
Wheelbarrow. 114mm long.	10.50
Wooden Tub. 39mm.	4.00

Comic/Novelty

Felix the Cat on oval base.	82.50
Hindu God on circular base wearing beads. No. 35. 88mm.	9.00
Policeman, hands behind back. No. 327. 113mm.	24.50

Cartoon/Comedy Characters

Winkie the Gladeye Bird. 65mm.	19.00

Winkie the Gladeye Bird cruet set,
  salt, pepper and mustard.
  68mm.   each 14.50
  Can be found coloured.   each 35.00

Alcohol
Beer Bottle. 92mm.   6.50
Toby Jug. 60mm.   8.50

Sport/Pastimes
Curling Stone. 52mm.   14.50
Golf Club Head. 65mm.   19.00

Musical Instruments
Banjo. 137mm long.   12.50

Transport
Open Motor Car.   40.00

Modern Equipment
Square Gramophone. 55mm.   20.00

Hats
Top Hat. 45mm.   5.50

Footwear
Ankle Boot. 72mm long.   5.00
Boot. 58mm long.   5.00
Dutch Sabot. 75mm long.   5.00
Ladies 18th century Shoe.   7.50
Oriental Shoe with turned up toe.
  2 sizes: 88mm long.   5.00
            107mm long.   8.50

Miniature Domestic
Cup and Saucer. 40mm.   5.00
Mug. 47mm.   2.00
Thistle Shaped Jug. 65mm.   3.00

Premier

Trademark used by a wholesaler on china
  manufactured by Taylor & Kent (Ltd),
  Florence Works, Longton. (Usual
  trademark Florentine).
For details of this china and manufacturer
  see Florentine China.
This china was made by the great mass
  producers of crested ware, Taylor & Kent.
  H. & M. Co. were probably a London firm
  of wholesalers, as crests are found from all
  over Britain but mostly from the South of
  England. A colour transfer has been found
  on china with this mark and one military
  crest has been recorded. 'Royal Military
  College, Camberley' (This must be the
  most common military crest – presumably
  everyone bought a souvenir of their stay
  there!) Domestic ware, including Bagware
  and 'smalls' are often found.

Premier Models
Ancient Artefacts
Fountains Abbey Cup. 48mm.   3.00

Monuments (including Crosses)
Iona Cross. 108mm.   10.50

Traditional/National Souvenirs
Welsh Hat. 57mm.   5.00

Seaside Souvenirs
Lighthouse, open base. 105mm.   5.00

Animals
Cheshire Cat always smiling. 87mm.   7.50
Manx Cat. 61mm.   19.50

Elephant, kneeling.
  88mm long.   20.00
Fish. 120mm long.   3.00
Frog Jug. 50mm.   6.50
Pig, standing, inscribed: *The pig that*
  won't go. 95mm long.   10.50
Toad. 72mm long.   19.50

Birds (including Eggs)
Baby Bird Jug. 65mm.   5.50

Home/Nostalgic
Bellows. 107mm long.   10.50
Coal Bucket. 64mm.   5.00
Coal Scuttle, helmet shaped.
  65mm.   4.00
Oriental Lamp. (Aladdin's Lamp).
  100mm long.   3.00
Portmanteau. 77mm.   4.00
Shaving Mug. 60mm.   6.50
Watering Can. 68mm.   6.50

Musical Instruments
Tambourine. 70mm dia.   6.50

Footwear
Shoe, Ladies, 18th Century.
  95mm long.   7.50

Miniature Domestic
Coffee Pot with lid. 55mm.   7.50

Miscellaneous
Sack, tied with blue ribbon.
  48mm.   5.00
Vase, dark red, black trim and
  handles. 85mm.   4.00

Princess China

Trademark used for a Blackpool retailer probably by Wilhelm Kutzscher & Co., Schwarzenberg Porzellanfabrik, Schwarzenberg, Saxony. (This firm used several trademarks and produced a large number of German models just labelled; Germany, Saxony or foreign).

Princess Models
Buildings - White
Blackpool Tower, with buildings.
  155mm.   10.00

Traditional/National Souvenirs
Blackpool, Big Wheel. 89mm.   10.50

Birds (including Eggs)
Bird standing on rock. 80mm.   12.00

Seaside Souvenirs
Lighthouse with pierced windows.
  125mm.   4.50

Queen China

Queen China

Unknown German manufacturer's mark, possibly the product of a German prison where the inmates specialised in exporting souvenir ware to the English market to avoid competition with their own German potteries at home. The mark is very like those used by several German potters, especially HofMoschendorf (Bayern). Two models known:

Domestic Wares
Napkin ring with a crest of Ripon.
   50mm dia.   4.00
Small square dish, crest of Swanage.   2.00

Trademark used by an unknown manufacturer, possibly Taylor & Kent (Ltd), Longton, as the only pieces recorded are similar to Florentine.

Queen China Models
Birds
Baby Bird Cream Jug. 68mm.   6.50

Domestic
Ewer. 80mm.   3.00

Queens China or Ware

Trademark used by Birks, Rawlins & Co (Ltd), Vine Pottery, Stoke. (Usual trademark Savoy). Pieces marked Queens are usually seconds and have firing flaws, only pristine wares carrying the Savoy mark. Prices are the same as Savoy however unless flaws are particularly noticeable.

For further details of this china and manufacturer see Savoy China.

Birks, Rawlins & Co. manufactured china and earthenware and advertised Queens China as a line of tableware. This mark is found on much heavier models generally than those marked Savoy so one can only assume that this was a cheaper range. (The lack of the usual initials B.R. & Co. seems also to indicate that the firms were not very proud of this range.) The mark appears to have been used during the same period as Savoy, but no models of buildings have been recorded. Some of the models below have not been recorded in the Savoy range.

'Smalls' have been found with the same Great War commemorative inscriptions and crests as recorded on Savoy models, and the badge of the Royal Army Medical Corps. No other transfer devices or views have been found.

Stock numbers were used and do not coincide with Savoy stock numbers. (Birks & Rawlins use of stock numbers is often unreliable – see Savoy China for details.) Stock numbers are given where known in the following lists.

Queens Models
Ancient Artefacts

Chester Roman Vase. 60mm.	3.00
Glastonbury Bowl. 40mm.	3.00
Phoenician Vase. 85mm.	3.00
Puzzle Jug. 68mm.	13.00
Reading Silchester Vase, unnamed. No. 49. 55mm.	3.00
Shakespeare's Jug. 63mm.	5.00

Historical/Folklore

Burns Chair. 76mm.	7.50
Execution Block. 98mm long.	8.50
Mons Meg Cannon. 132mm long.	16.00
Rufus Stone. 100mm.	5.00

Traditional/National Souvenirs

Cornish Pasty. 104mm long.	7.50
Welsh Hat. 50mm.	7.50

Seaside Souvenirs

Bathing Machine. No. 425 and No. 428. 60mm.	7.50
Lighthouse on rocky base. 134mm.	5.50
Rowing Boat. 127mm long.	10.50
Oyster Shell dish. 80mm long.	3.50
Shell on base. 80mm long.	4.00
Sea Urchin Vase. 45mm.	3.50

Countryside

Beehive. 70mm.	7.50

Animals

Bear dancing, with muzzle. 102mm.	40.00
Camel Jug, sitting with hexagonal opening on back. 80mm.	40.00

Cat, detailed fur. 80mm.	11.50
Manx Cat. 80mm.	16.00
Dog, angry and barking.	
100mm long.	29.00
Dog, looking out of kennel. No. 259.	
55mm.	15.00
Elephant with Howdah.	
70mm.	30.00
Fish. 102mm long.	3.00
Puffer Fish vase. 90mmm.	10.00
Frog, realistic, giant-size.	
73mm.	65.00
Grotesque Animal Jug. 72mm.	7.50
Grotesque Animal. 100mm.	10.00
Hare. 74mm.	20.00
Lion, sitting on base. (This was	
originally designed by Alfred	
Stevens for the British Museum).	
104mm.	35.00
Pig, lying down. 80mm long.	10.00
Pig, sitting, large. 100mm long.	12.50
Pig, standing. 65mm long.	12.50
Seal. 55mm long.	13.00

Birds (including Eggs)

Baby Bird jug. 70mm.	5.50
Birds on tree trunk.	23.00
Duck, swimming. 40mm long.	9.00
Duck's head feeding bottle.	
130mm long.	13.00
Penguin. 76mm.	16.00

Great War

Submarine. E1. 149mm long.	40.00
Tank. 152mm long.	45.00
Ambulance, Red Cross Van.	
108mm long.	55.00
Ambulance, with Rolls Royce front.	
115mm long.	40.00
Armoured Car. 125mm long.	110.00
Motor Searchlight.	
100mm long.	145.00
Field Gun, with fish tail.	
140mm long. (scarce).	95.00
Field Gun, with screen.	24.50
Machine Gun on tripod, two-piece.	
80mm.	145.00
British Trench Mortar Gun.	
110mm long.	47.50
Howitzer. 145mm long.	30.00
Hand Grenade. 88mm.	16.00
Shell. 70mm. No. 556.	7.50
Balmoral Bonnet. 70mm long.	20.00
R.F.C. Cap. 72mm long.	45.00
Colonial Hat. 92mm long.	16.00

French Trench Helmet. 72mm long.	
(Not named £30.00).	40.00
Glengarry. 70mm long.	19.00
Officer's Peaked Cap.	
72mm long.	11.00
New Zealand Hat. 83mm long.	25.00
Sailors Cap. No. 533. 70mm.	60.00
Bandsman's Drum. 55mm dia.	10.50
Fireplace. No. 629. 95mm.	20.00

Home/Nostalgic

Dog Kennel. 55mm.	10.50
Grandfather Clock, narrow design.	
149mm.	22.00
Post Box. 60mm.	12.00
Suitcase, closed. 96mm long.	17.00
Watering Can. 80mm.	10.50

Comic/Novelty

Hindu God. No. 550. 90mm.	8.50
Humpty Dumpty salt and pepper	
pots. 80mm.	pair 60.00
Man, shirt off, leaning into barrel.	
68mm long.	30.00
Policeman holding truncheon.	
105mm.	24.50

Cartoon/Comedy Characters

Bonzo, not named. 118mm.	75.00
Toby Jug, large hat. 75mm.	9.50

Sport/Pastimes

Cricket Bat. 120mm.	75.00
Golf Caddie with bag of clubs on	
heart shaped pin tray/ashtray.	
80mm.	40.00
Golf Club Head. 80mm.	19.00
Curling Stone, not named. 53mm.	13.00

Musical Instruments

Banjo. 136mm long.	12.50
Piano, upright, open keyboard.	
94mm long.	14.50

Footwear

Clog. 75mm long.	5.00
Lancashire Clog. No. 485.	
95mm.	5.00

Domestic

Cone Candlesnuffer. 62mm.	3.00

Queens Crest China

Trademark used for S.P. & Co Ltd, of 57 King St, Manchester, by Arkinstall & Son Ltd, Arcadian Works, Stoke-on-Trent, (usual trademark Arcadian), and Wiltshaw and Robinson, Carlton Works, Stoke-on-Trent, (usual trademark Carlton).

For details of this china and manufacturer see Arcadian China.

As models with this mark have been found with crests from all over Great Britain, and also of Paris, one must assume that S.P. & Co. Ltd. of Manchester was a wholesaler. (Possibly some wares printed with this mark would also have been used by Arkinstall to supply other retailers if they had production problems.)

Arkinstall produced a range for this firm that was much finer and more carefully finished than their own Arcadian range. Most items found with this mark are 'smalls', some of which may well be un-named ancient artefacts. The models recorded indicate that the mark was used before the Great War, several pieces have been found with the crest 'La Ville-de-Paris' and the addition to the mark of 'Importe D'Angleterre'.

Numbering System. Stock numbers found on Queens Crest models do not coincide with Arcadian numbers. Queens Crest was obviously offered as a completely separate range. Stock numbers where known are given in the following lists.

Queens Crest Models
Parian/Unglazed
Bust Albert, King of the Belgians.
153mm.   65.00

Ancient Artefacts
Colchester Vase. No. 504. 50mm.   3.00
Dorchester Jug, inscribed: *Model of old jug found in North Square, Dorchester.* No. 1774. 52mm.   4.00
Fountains Abbey Cup. No. 23821. 50mm.   3.00
Glastonbury Bowl, inscribed: *Bowl from the Ancient British Lake Village near Glastonbury.* No. 1724. 40mm.   4.00
Irish Bronze Pot. No. 1834. 45mm.   3.00
Jersey Milk Can and lid. No. 3424. 60mm.   5.00
Lincoln Jack from original in museum. No. 1564. 65mm.   4.00
Loving Cup, 3-handled. 40mm.   3.00
Newbury Bottle, inscribed: *Leather bottle found at Newbury 1644 on Battlefield now in museum.* No. 2294. 65mm.   4.00

Animals
Bear and Ragged Staff. 90mm.   40.00
Manx Cat, sitting. 63mm long.   30.00
Elephant, Indian. 77mm long.   30.00
Lion, sitting (British Museum).
2 sizes: 45mm.   30.00
            105mm.   35.00
Tortoise. 72mm long.   9.00

Miniature Domestic
Bag Vase. 45mm.   4.00

Numbered Ornamental Wares
Some of these could be unnamed ancient artefacts.
Value £3.00 each.
No. 594. Fluted jug. 54mm.   3.00

No. 1724. Small pot on three feet.
This is also the number of a
Glastonbury bowl - see above.
43mm. 3.00
No. 1824. Ewer. 60mm. 3.00
No. 3164. Pot. 50mm. 3.00
No. 3594. Vase. 50mm. 3.00
No. 3884. Vase. 54mm. 3.00
No. 7061. Vase. 65mm. 3.00
No. 14715. Vase, with narrow neck.
100mm. 3.00

Queeny China

No details of mark available.

Mark used by an unknown manufacturer for
an agent in Hastings.

Buildings - White
Cottage. 70mm long. Bears the arms
of Hastings. 6.50

Raleigh China

R & M

"RALEIGH CHINA"

Trademark used for a retailer by Sampson Hancock (and Sons), Bridge Works, Stoke and later at the Garden Works, Hanley. (renamed Corona Pottery). (Usual trademark Corona).

Raleigh Models
Historical/Folklore
Ark. 92mm long.   5.00

Traditional/National Souvenirs
Welsh Hat. No. 198. 45mm.   5.00

Great War
Submarine, inscribed: E4.   19.50
Tank, with inset wheels.
    2 sizes: 103mm.   20.00
              160mm long.   24.50
Red Cross Van. 100mm long.   30.00
Field Gun. 125mm long.   15.00
Bell Tent, open flap. 80mm.   16.00

Modern Equipment
Gas Stove. 70mm.   10.00

Musical Instruments
Upright Piano. 60mm.   16.00

Footwear
Lancashire Clog. 102mm long.   6.50

Miniature Domestic
Cheese Dish. 45mm.   5.50

Domestic
Candlestick. 105mm.   3.00

Trademark used by Roper & Meredith, Garfield Pottery, Longton. The china is similar to Leadbeater Art.

Roper & Meredith was established in 1913 and manufactured earthenwares until 1924, when the firm went out of business. This firm, like most other manufacturers, would have turned to crested models during the Great War, when skilled labour needed to make tableware was in short supply. The firm did not advertise as makers of crested china and it would be correct to assume that this was a small side line. The models recorded are however very interesting and not just copies of other manufacturers wares. R & M also made a range of unglazed busts of poets, composers and other historic personalities.

R & M Models
Birds (including Eggs)
Bird, with open wings.
    75mm long.   12.50
Chicken, standing, separate feet.
    80mm.   9.50

Great War
War Memorial, March. Parian.
    174mm.   150.00
St. Ives War Memorial Cross.
    135mm.   150.00

Comic/Novelty
Truck of Coal, inscribed: *Black
Diamonds*. Black coal. 79mm long.   19.50

Sport/Pastimes
Rugby Player, holding rugby ball,
on oval ashtray. Inscribed: *Play
up*. Fully coloured. 126mm.   95.00

Domestic
Candlestick. 128mm.   3.00

Raphael China

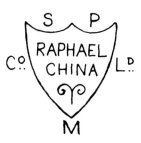

Trademark used for S.P. & Co. Ltd, of 57 King
St, Manchester, by Arkinstall & Son Ltd,
Arcadian Works, Stoke-on-Trent. (Usual
trademark Arcadian).

A range of vases were produced with
Raphael Tuck cartoons and verses. The
name RAPHAEL CHINA appearing with
Raphael Tuck cartoons seems more than a
coincidence.
The only other items known are smalls with
either printed decorations or the crests of
Russia, Canada, Sweden, Switzerland or
Austria. (Spelt that way so not for export).

Raphael Models
Ancient Artefacts
Canterbury Ewer, inscribed: *Model
of Roman Ewer found near
Canterbury and now in Canterbury
Museum*. No. 94. 62mm.   4.00
Kendal Jug. 76mm.   3.00

Alcohol
Highland Whisky Bowl, Model of.
No. 4158. 90mm dia.   5.00

Miscellaneous
Vases decorated with Raphael Tuck
cartoons.   each 15.00

Regency Ware

Mark can sometimes be found without the 'S' after the initials 'J.B.'

Trademark used for a retailer by Sampson Hancock (& Sons), Bridge Works, Stoke. (Usual trademark Corona).
For details of this china and manufacturer see The Corona China.
The Regency mark is identical to the Grosvenor mark used by Sampson Hancock with the addition of the initials. Some of the models listed below were made by Hancocks for other wholesalers including CEB.L. (see Alexandra China) so it seems probable that Hancocks used this mark for another wholesaler during the Great War.

Regency Models
Buildings - White
Model of Clifton Suspension Bridge.
   120mm long.   75.00

Seaside Souvenirs
Bathing Machine. 75mm.   8.50
Houseboat. 87mm long.   5.00
Lighthouse on Rocky Base.
   125mm.   5.50

Animals
Cat, sitting with ruff of fur round
   neck. 100mm.   17.50
Cat, standing. 60mm.   12.00
Cat, Manx standing. 60mm.   16.00
Pig, standing. 85mm long.   10.00

Great War
Zeppelin. 153mm long.   20.00
Flash Lamp. 85mm.   11.00
Ghurka Knife. 140mm long.   20.00
Bell Tent. No. 209. 84mm.   14.50
Military Drum. 50mm.   5.50

Home/Nostalgic
Cigarette Case. 70mm.   13.00
Tobacco Pouch. 72mm long.   9.50

Musical Instruments
Banjo. 140mm long.   10.00

Modern Equipment
Gas Cooker. 68mm.   10.00
Gramophone, square cabinet, no
   horn. 85mm.   15.00

Sport/Pastimes
Pawn, chess piece. 90mm.   25.00

Miniature Domestic
Jardinière on fixed stand. No. 214
   80mm.   4.00
Tea Pot with lid. 72mm.   10.50

Regis

Trademark used by Hewitt Bros, Willow Potteries, Longton. (Usual trademark Willow Art).

For details of this china and manufacturer see Willow Art China.

Models found with this mark have crests from all over Great Britain, but many pieces have crests from Jersey, Ireland and Scotland. It seems very probable that the mark was offered to retailers in these areas as an alternative to Willow Art. Many 'Weymouth' crests have also been recorded and why this seaside resort and port should have been sold 'Regis' is a mystery. (Did the Willow traveller stay in Weymouth on his way to Jersey and manage to get an order from a local retailer? It is possible the name 'Regis' derived from Weymouth and Melcombe Regis.) The mark seems to have been used for some time; from before the Great War until the early Twenties. No view ware, commemoratives or transfer devices have been recorded with this mark.

Numbering system. Where stock numbers are found they are the same as Willow Art models. Stock numbers where known are listed below.

Regis Models
Parian/Unglazed

Bust of Lord Beatty. 165mm.	55.00
Bust of *Burns*. 157mm.	30.00
Bust of *Scott*. 140mm.	30.00

Buildings - White

Weymouth Jubilee Clock Tower. 126mm.	15.00

Monuments (including Crosses)

Burns Statue. 166mm.	30.00
Highland Mary statue. 155mm.	25.50

Historical/Folklore

Mary Bull holding black cat in basket. Standing figure. (Mary Bull was a witch!) 105mm.	40.00
Mary Queen of Scots Chair, Edinburgh Castle, Model of. No. 163. 75mm.	6.50

Traditional/National Souvenirs

Bagpipes. 120mm long.	15.00
Souter Johnny sitting on chair on square base. 133mm.	30.00
Welsh Hat. 58mm.	5.00
Dutch Girl. 78mm.	10.50
Dutch Boy. 78mm.	10.50

Seaside Souvenirs

Lifeboat, coloured ropes. 118mm long.	12.50
Lighthouse, not named. 100mm.	5.00
Corbiere Lighthouse, with coloured rock base. 96mm.	26.00

Animals

Cat with bow, standing. 85mm.	12.50
Cat, chubby & standing. 70mm.	16.00
Dog, Collie, standing. 85mm.	23.00
Dog, Labrador, standing. 90mm long.	19.50
Dog, Scottie, wearing a glengarry, some colouring on hat. 85mm.	13.50
Elephant with hunter and two Indian riders on back. 90mm.	30.00
Pig, standing, fat, ears pointing forward. 80mm long.	10.00
Shetland Pony. *A Native of Shetland.* 113mm long.	25.00

Birds (including Eggs)

Swan Posy Holder. 65mm long.	5.00

Great War

Airship, *Beta*. 80mm long.	55.00
Battleship. *HMS Lion.* 140mm long.	30.00
British Tank. 92mm long.	14.00
British Tank with trailing wheels. 127mm long.	22.50

Cannon Shell salt pot. 83mm.	4.00
Kit Bag with verse: *Pack up your troubles in your old kit bag.* 74mm.	19.50
Forage Cap. 83mm long.	16.00
Officers Peaked Cap. 75mm long.	11.00
Cenotaph. 145mm.	7.50
Black Watch Memorial. 182mm.	65.00
Florence Nightingale Statue, inscribed: *Florence Nightingale 1820-1910.* 160mm.	20.00
Weymouth War Memorial. 152mm.	85.00

Home/Nostalgic

Anvil. 76mm.	7.50
Bucket, rope handle. 65mm.	4.00
Coal Scuttle. 55mm.	5.00
Grandfather Clock, inscribed: '*Make use of time let not advantage slip'.*	10.50
Pillar Box. 90mm.	17.50
Shaving Mug. 55mm.	6.50

Comic/Novelty

Billiken. 73mm.	7.50
Billiken, the God of Luck, sitting on high backed chair. 100mm.	10.50

Cartoon/Comedy Characters

Baby, standing to attention, some colouring. Inscribed: *One of the B'hoys.* 160mm.	40.00
Baby, standing with arms outstretched. Some colouring to face. 110mm.	30.00

Alcohol

Toby Jug. 83mm.	12.50

Miscellaneous

Hand holding tulip. 80mm.	5.00

Registry Ware

Trademark used by an unknown manufacturer.

This mark has been found with Scarborough crests on the curve sided lip salve pot and the small vases listed below.

Vase inscribed: *Ca' Canny but ca' awa.* 45mm.	4.00
Vase.	3.00
Lip Salve Pot, curved.	4.00

C.L. Reis and Co.

Birds (including Eggs)
Penguin. 95mm. 30.00

Miscellaneous
Basket. No. 240. 3.00
Vase inscribed: *Shamrocks from the
Dear Emerald Isle.* (Carlton
mould). 5.00

C.L. Reis is probably a retailer, trademark
being used on porcelain with Irish crests.
(It seems likely that the china was
manufactured by Alfred B. Jones & Sons
Ltd. - usual trademark Grafton). The
porcelain is much greyer than Grafton
although typical Grafton shapes.

C.L. Reis Models
Ancient Artefacts
Butter Pot, not named. 40mm. 3.00

Seaside Souvenirs
Whelk Shell. 82mm long. 5.00

Animals
Pig, standing, inscribed: *Wunt be
druv.* 70mm long. 13.00
Terrapin, 90mm long. 13.00

Rex China

RH & SL Plant

REX
CHINA

The trademark of Moschendorf, Hof, Bavaria.

Rex Models
Traditional/National Souvenirs
Tam-o'shanter. 72mm dia.   25.00

Animals
Pig, ears pointing forward.
        68mm long.   14.00

Countryside
Milk Churn and lid. 75mm.   5.00

Miniature Domestic
Cheese Dish, with gilded rope
        handle. 70mm.   6.50

For all details of this china and manufacturer, see Tuscan China.

Rialto China

Bulldog can be found coloured
black.   15.00

Great War
Battleship with inscription: *Great
War 1914-1918. The German Fleet
surrendered 74 warships Nov 21st
1918.* 153mm long.   30.00

Home/Nostalgic
Watchman's Lamp.   5.00
Ornate carved wooden Chair.
    110mm.   12.50

1920-6

Trademark used by British Art Pottery Co.
    (Fenton) Ltd, Rialto Works, High Street,
    Fenton. Resembles Carlton China.
This small firm was established in 1920 and
    manufactured china.
Although the 'Rialto' mark was registered
    and the firm appeared in the list of
    manufacturers, they did not advertise and
    one can only guess from the name of the
    firm that they produced novelty wares.
    The firm went into voluntary liquidation
    in May 1926, so could have only produced
    crested china between 1920 and 1926.
Some domestic ware has been found with the
    mark and one coloured transfer view of
    'Plas Newydd' has been recorded.

Rialto Models
Ancient Artefacts
Salisbury Kettle. 88mm.   3.00

Seaside Souvenirs
Beachy Head Lighthouse.
    105mm.   6.00
    Unnamed.   5.50
Dolphin supporting sea shell.
    85mm.   20.00

Countryside
Milk Churn. 78mm.   5.00

Animals
Bulldog in kennel, inscribed: *The
    Black Watch.* 79mm.   11.00

Ribblesdale China

Eugene Rimmel

```
"RIBBLESDALE" CHINA
ENGLISH MANUFACTURE
GIBSON & HOWORTH
13 FISHERGATE
PRESTON
```

Trademark used by an unknown English manufacturer for the Pennines market.

The only piece recorded is a one-handled mug. 39mm. 4.00

Trademark used by Wiltshaw and Robinson Ltd., Carlton Works, Stoke-on-Trent.

The only piece recorded is a small, 78mm., scent bottle known with a Brighton crest and metal screw top. Rimmel was a perfumier of great repute in the mid 19th century. 17.50

Rita China Series

Trademark used for the retailer L & L of Weston-Super-Mare by unknown manufacturers.
The models recorded are not recognisably made by any well known manufacturer. Hewitt and Leadbeater (see Willow Art), Taylor & Kent (see Florentine China) and Wileman & Co. (see Shelley China) made some similar models. It is possible that several manufacturers used the same retailer's mark.

Rita Models
Unglazed/Parian

Bunyan Statue. 125mm.	19.50
Burns, bust, on circular unglazed base. 176mm.	24.00
Rt. Hon. D. Lloyd George, on square unglazed base. 192mm.	35.00
Scott, bust, on circular unglazed base. 176mm.	23.00

Ancient Artefacts

Loving cup, 2 handled.	3.00

Buildings - White

Ann Hathaway's Cottage. 55mm long.	16.00
The Folly, Pontypool. 80mm.	125.00
Glastonbury Tor. 83mm.	40.00
Llangynwyd Church. 107mm long.	110.00

Monuments (including Crosses)

Drake Statue. 160mm.	13.00

Great Rock of Ages, Burrington Coombe, Near Cheddar, Somerset, with verses of hymn. 125mm.	16.00
King Alfred's Statue. 160mm.	47.50
Robert Blake, Statue. 170mm.	30.00

Historical/Folklore

Burns Chair, Model of. 88mm.	7.50
James V Chair, Stirling Castle.	7.50
Mary Queen of Scots Chair, Edinburgh Castle, Model of. 85mm.	6.50

Animals

Dog, sitting with bow. 75mm.	15.00
Dog, Staffordshire Bull Terrier. 115mm.	10.50
Cat, long neck, features coloured. 110mm.	7.50
Fish. 115mm long.	3.00

Birds (including Eggs)

Bird posy holder, tiny. 57mm long.	6.50
Duck posy holder, yellow beak. 74mm long.	11.00

Great War

Florence Nightingale Statue. 180mm.	20.00

Home/Nostalgic

Grandfather Clock, inscribed: *Make use of time, let not advantage slip. Shakespeare.* 145mm.	10.50

Comic/Novelty

Clown, bust.	8.50
Jester, double faced bust, inscribed: *Awake Asleep.*	8.50
Monk, jovial & plump. No glass. No. 95. 90mm.	16.00

Alcohol

Toby Jug. 95mm.	8.50

Sport/Pastimes

Castle chess piece. 48mm.	6.50

Modern Equipment

Horn Gramophone. 90mm.	25.00

Hats

Cricket Cap. 65mm long.	45.00
Straw Boater. 85mm long.	12.50

Footwear
Dutch Sabot. 85mm long.   5.00
Lancashire Clog. 87mm long.   5.50

Domestic
Egg Cup. 68mm.   4.50

Miniature Domestic
Tea Pot with lid, ball-shaped.
    78mm.   10.50

Robinson & Leadbeater

Impressed mark

Also found with a printed mark.

Trademark used by Robinson & Leadbeater, Wolfe Street, Stoke-on-Trent and subsequently a branch of J.A. Robinson Ltd.

Robinson & Leadbeater was established in 1850 and specialised in the production of Parian statuary imitation antique ivory and Ecclesiastical statuary. R & L busts are exceedingly popular with Parian collectors, the firm having made a large and well produced range, including busts of heroes (of the South African War), Royalty, Celebrities and literary figures. These busts were obviously made before the craze for crested china and cannot be considered to be 'crested china' and are therefore not listed here.

The firm became insolvent in 1904, no explanation was given, but possibly one of the partners died. Robinson & Leadbeater was taken over by Harold Taylor Robinson (see Arcadian China) in 1906, and was formed into a Limited Company, Robinson & Leadbeater Ltd in 1908. In 1910 the firm became a branch of J.A. Robinson Ltd.

It is probable that the small amount of crested china found marked R & L was produced after 1904. Some R & L moulds including busts are found overstamped 'Arcadian'. The mark was not used after 1924.

One transfer print has been found, this being a colour transfer of a battleship on a shallow bagware bowl. (No numbering system appears to have been used.)

R & L Models
Parian
Bust of John Wesley.	25.00
Bust of *Spurgeon*. 122mm.	40.00

Ancient Artefacts
Chester Roman Vase. No. 170.
2 sizes:	
63mm and 76mm.	3.00
Greek Vase 200 years old. 65mm.	4.00
Loving Cup, 2 handled. 45mm.	3.00
Loving Cup, 3 handled. 39mm.	3.00
Peterborough Tripod. 37mm.	3.00

Buildings - Coloured
Mason Croft, the house of Miss

Marie Corelli.
2 sizes: 75mm long.	85.00
90mm long.	95.00

Shakespeare's Cottage.
40mm long.	30.00

Seaside Souvenirs
Scallop Shell.
2 sizes: 73mm dia.	3.00
110mm dia.	3.00
Scallop Shell on 3 tiny feet.	
120mm long.	4.00

Birds (including Eggs)
Egg flower holder. 80mm long.	4.00
Swan with yellow beak and feet.	
70mm.	6.50

Home/Nostalgic
Bellows. 105mm long.	11.50
Thimble salt pot. 37mm.	10.50

Miniature Domestic
Cheese Dish and cover.
80mm long.	6.50
Tea pot with lid, thistle knob on lid.	
100mm.	13.00
Bagware Tea pot. No. 158. 98mm.	11.50

Domestic
Match holder, circular, unglazed.
No. 143. 76mm dia.	6.00
Trinket box and lid with floral	
decoration in relief. 115mm.	8.50

Rococo

Roman Bath China

Trademark used by a German manufacturer. The only shapes seen are very white, hard-past porcelain, decorated with ornate gold and green pattern with pink roses.

Rococo Model
Puff Box and lid, round, 68mm dia.   6.50
Variety of Vases.   About 4.00

Trademark used for a retailer by Hewitt & Leadbeater, Willow Potteries Ltd, Longton. (Usual trademark Willow Art).

One small found with this mark and Chester crest.   4.00

Rosina Queens China

Rowena China

Trademark used by George Warrilow & Sons (Ltd), Queens Pottery, Longton.

George Warrilow was established in 1887. They specialised in the production of Tea-sets, badged ware and Queens White Ware. Most firms making badged ware were capable of producing crested china, but this firm seems to have produced just a small quantity of crested domestic ware.

Domestic

Domestic items	from 2.00
Jam Pot on small dish with lid.	
Some colour. 75mm.	5.50

Trademark used by R.H. & S.L. Plant (Ltd), Tuscan Works, Longton. (Usual trademark Tuscan).

Originally Rowena models were thought to have been produced by J.A. Robinson Ltd. (see Arcadian), but are now known to have been produced by RH & SL Plant Ltd.

Rowena Models
Ancient Artefacts

Gastrica Cyprian Bottle. 71mm.	3.00

Animals

Fish posy vase. 130mm long.	5.00
Giant open-mouthed fish.	
130mm long.	8.50
Dog kennel.	5.00

Home/Nostalgic

Anvil on block. 57mm.   7.50

Comic/Novelty

Lemon, open top. 75mm long.   6.50
Loaf of Bread. 65mm.   20.00
Two seater Car ashtray, inscribed:
   Petrol consumption nil.
   135mm long.   175.00
The car ashtray is identical to the
   Tuscan example called 'Dennis
   Two Seater'
Tomato, green leaves.
   57mm dia.   16.00

Cartoon/Comedy Characters

These fine coloured models form a
   series from The Daily Sketch
   Cartoon. Some white, glazed,
   examples have been seen.
Don, little boy in short trousers and
   blue cardigan. 130mm.   85.00
Dr. Dromedary, camel, in black top
   hat and suit. 130mm.   85.00
Lord Lion, lion in pale blue jacket
   with coloured head and feet.
   139mm.   85.00
   Glazed version, inscribed:
   Souvenir of Wembley 1924.   100.00
Oo Jah, Flip Flap, Elephant, in pink
   striped pyjamas. 130mm.   85.00
Pa Piggins, Pig, in Edwardian
   Sporting clothes, some colour.
   139mm.   85.00
   Glazed version, inscribed:
   Souvenir of Wembley 1924.   160.00
Snooker, or the kitten cat, yellow with
   crown on head. 130mm.   85.00

Royal Albert Crown China

Mark used 1905-7

Trademark used by Thomas C. Wild, Crown
   China Works, High St, Longton.
This mark used by Thomas C. Wild, the well
   established china manufacturers, is found
   on domestic ware and 'smalls' made
   between 1905 and 1907. This firm
   obviously did not need to turn to model
   making during the Great War but
   survived by selling the table wares and
   fine china they specialised in.

A small range of domestic ware and
   'smalls' has been found with this
   mark. One vase bears a cartoon
   featuring children and insects.   18.00

Royal Arms China

Trademark used for a Birmingham retailer by an unknown manufacturer.

Royal Arms Models
Buildings – White

Thatched cottage. 48mm.	10.50

Animals

Frog. 70mm long.	19.50
Toad. 73mm long.	19.50

Royal China

Mark used 1912-41

Trademark used by E. Hughes and Co., Opal Works, Fenton. (Also used marks, Fenton & E. Hughes & Co.).
For details of this china and manufacturer see Fenton China and E. Hughes & Co. China.
This mark has only been found on two models with crests, which are listed below. The mark is usually found on badged hotel ware and domestic china.

Royal Models
Miniature Domestic

Cheese Dish and cover. 50mm.	6.50
Cup & Saucer. 35mm.	5.00

Royal China Works, Worcester

1889-1902

Trademark used by Grainger, Worcester, when taken over by the Worcester Porcelain Co. Ltd.

The very famous firm of George Grainger at Worcester was taken over by the Worcester Royal Porcelain Co. Ltd. in 1889. This mark was only used after the takeover and not after 1902, so china with this mark can be accurately dated. A small number of 'smalls' have been found and the models listed below. The china, as one would expect, is very fine and the crest well produced.

Royal China Works Models
Miniature Domestic

Two handled Loving Cup. 45mm.	15.00
Mug, with one handle. 40mm.	12.00
Vase, swirl pattern. 65mm.	15.00

Royal Coburg

Trademark used by an unknown manufacturer.

This mark was not registered and there are no initials or country of origin given to help with identification. Most pieces found are 'smalls' and carry crests of the South of England. It is possible that the china, which is a hard paste porcelain, was manufactured in Germany, but unlikely. The Royal Family's connection with Coburg would have made this a respectable name before the Great War and this mark was probably used before 1914.

Royal Coburg Models
Home/Nostalgic

Chair with 2 gold tassels.	10.00

Footwear

Ladies open shoe. 115mm long.	7.50

Miniature Domestic

Cheese Dish and cover. 50mm.	6.50

Royal Doulton

Mark used from 1902

Trademark used by Doulton & Co. (Ltd), Nile St, Burslem.

This well-known firm produced a very small range of crested ware. Most of it seems to have been for export, crests recorded including New Zealand, Seal of Wellington and Jamaica. Most pieces of Doulton with crests are small vases, jugs or domestic ware. The RN Training School badge has been recorded and Taunton Theological College. As one would expect the china is well produced.

Royal Doulton Models
Range of smalls with foreign and
English crests.   8.00-12.00 each

Ancient Artefacts
Loving Cup, 3 handled. 49mm.   10.00

Royal Grafton

Mark used from 1957.

Trademark used by Alfred B. Jones and Sons Ltd., Grafton China Works, Longton, Staffs. (Usual trademark Grafton). The above mark is usually found on fairly modern pieces with the crest of St. Helena.

Domestic
Ashtray. 118mm dia.   5.00

Royal Ivory Porcelain

1905-1924

Trademark used by Robinson & Leadbeater Ltd and for the London wholesalers E.B. & Co. (Usual trademark R. &L.).

For details of this china and manufacturer see R. & L.

Royal Ivory Porcelain was the printed mark used on small crested wares by Robinson & Leadbeater Ltd., Wolfe Street, Stoke-on-Trent, which subsequently became a branch of J.A. Robinson Ltd. The same mark occurs with the initials E.B. & Co., these same initials appearing with another mark used by a London wholesaler (see The Dainty Ware).

E.B. & Co. china with the Royal Ivory mark is much finer than the Dainty Ware range, and probably was more expensive. Most items which are recorded are found with boths sets of initials, indicating that E.B. & Co. sold the whole R. & L. range.

Most pieces with this mark are 'smalls' or domestic ware, including pill boxes. No view ware, commemoratives or transfer devices have been recorded. Royal Ivory was exported and some foreign crests have been found. Crests of the Allies are found on 'smalls' with the E.B. & Co. initials.

Royal Ivory Models
Ancient Artefacts
Chester Roman Vase. 63mm.	3.00
Kendal Jug. 70mm.	3.00
Loving Cup, 2 & 3 handled. 45mm.	3.00

Buildings – White
Cottage on rectangular base. 57mm.	10.50

Animals
Bill Sykes Dog, model of. Bulldog. 95mm long.	20.00

Birds (including Eggs)
Swan posy holder. Some colouring. 70mm.	5.00

Home/Nostalgic
Bellows. 115mm long.	11.00

Alcohol
Highland Whisky Bowl, Model of.	4.50

Hats
Bishop's Mitre.	13.00

Footwear
Slipper wall pocket. 100mm long.	7.50

Miniature Domestic
Cheese Dish and cover. 74mm long.	8.50
Tea Pot with lid. 55mm.	7.50

Royal Scenic China

Trademark used by a Czechoslovakian manufacturer.

There are no details of crested china models recorded so far.

Royal Stafford China

Mark used from 1912

Mark used from 1929-40

Egg Cup, goblet shaped. 45mm.   5.00
Tea Plate. 105mm. 105mm dia.   2.00

The above mark has been found on a 68mm cup and saucer with a Perth crest, and would have been used specifically for Watson's of Perth who were a local retailer.

Trademark used by Thomas Poole, Cobden Works, Longton. Products identical to Willow Art.

This firm obviously turned to crested china production for a short time during the Great War as many firms did. Why they produced crested domestic ware with the guaranteed English Bone China mark is rather a mystery, unless the wares were for export. (One item has been found with a Bulawayo Municipal Council crest but the exact mark was not recorded). Most items recorded are domestic, including the inevitable ashtrays.

Royal Stafford Models
Animals
Elephant, walking. 52mm.   17.00
Elephant cream jug. 65mm.   12.50

Great War
Submarine, inscribed: *E4*.
    115mm long.   19.50
Kitchen Range, inscribed: *Keep the
    home fires burning*. 78mm.   14.50
Bell Tent, open flap. 70mm.   16.00
Bugle. 72mm.   19.50
'Florence Nightingale 1820-1910'
    statue. 170mm.   19.50

Sport/Pastimes
Spade, playing card suit. 68mm.   4.00

Domestic
Cup and saucer. 68mm.   3.00

Royal 'Vale' China

Mark used from 1908

Mark used 1928-37

The above mark has also been recorded, apparently for a retailer, J.W. Alder of Coolancatta.

Trademark used by H.J. Colcough, Vale Works, Goddard Street, Longton for goods supplied by Taylor and Kent (Ltd), Florence Works, Longton (usual trademark Florentine).

View ware can be found on the domestic and table ware which this firm made. (In 1907 the firm advertised 'Best English China at Foreign prices. Seaside and present ware or Bazaar Goods in Views, plain or coloured or gilt'). However the range of crested china was bought in from Taylor & Kent.

Royal Vale Models
Ancient Artefacts

Hastings Kettle, not named. 55mm.	3.00

Seaside Souvenirs

Lighthouse. 105mm.	5.00
Lighthouse on circular base. 115mm.	5.50

Animals

Pig, fat, lying forward, pricked ears. 100mm long.	65.00
Pig, fat, sitting. 63mm.	12.50

Great War

Water Bottle. 70mm.	13.00
Cenotaph. 146mm.	5.50

Footwear

Ladies 18th Century Shoe. 95mm long.	7.50

Domestic

Tall Jug. 110mm.	4.00
Octagonal Vase. 74mm.	3.00
Sugar Bowl, fluted. 100mm dia, 65mm high.	2.50
Tea Plate. 163mm dia.	2.00

Royal Worcester

Trademark used by Worcester Royal Porcelain Company Ltd. (Royal Worcester).

The majority of small items carrying the famous Worcester mark were made at the turn of the century. Items of domestic ware and pierced vases and dishes can be found with well produced crests. It seems that well established firms only made crested ware when it was considered tasteful and new, in other words a 'middle class' souvenir. Some pieces have been found with a cream instead of a white body. One 39mm. mug has been recorded with a transfer print of the Manx legs and a black bird (thought to be the Manx Shearwater).

Royal Worcester Models
Ancient Artefacts

Chester Roman Vase. 60mm.	10.00
Loving Cup. 2 & 3 handled. 40mm.	10.00

Miniature Domestic

Mug, one handled. 45mm.	10.00
Jug, with high looped handles and acanthus leaves under spout. 55mm.	10.00

Ryecroft China Series

Trademark used by Robinson & Leadbeater, Wolfe Street, Stoke-on-Trent.

Ryecroft China Series
Unglazed/Parian

Bust of *Burns* on circular base. 176mm.	40.00

Buildings – White

Roche Abbey, ruins, unglazed. 85mm.	75.00
Town Hall, Stockton-on-Tees, glazed. 94mm.	65.00

Monuments (including Crosses)

Woodhouse Eaves Cross.	40.00

Seaside Souvenirs

Lifeboat. 101mm long.	12.50

Birds (including Eggs)

Duck posy bowl, yellow beak. 50mm.	7.50

Sport

Cricket Cap. 65mm long.	45.00

S

St. George China

Trademark used by P. Donath, Tiefenfurt. (Silesia).

Very little crested china of this manufacture has been found and all known pieces are domestic items of only nominal value. One of the firms main areas of specialization was pink souvenir domestic ware and white souvenir ware bearing transfer printed views. The company was nationalised after the last war, and is now in Poland.

Animals
Full size Fish Tray. 350mm long.
(Bognor crest).   12.00

AUSTRIA

Trademark used by Wilhelm Kutzscher & Co., Schwarzenberger Porzellanfabric, Schwarzenberg, Saxony. (Now in Germany). (Usual trademark Saxony)

This manufacturer made many unmarked pieces for the English market.

This mark is found on some typically German comic animal models. The elephants on the slide are often found unmarked, and it is possible that this manufacturer usually left his models unmarked. One small jug has been recorded with a black transfer view of 'The Old Curiosity Shop' on one side and 'Charles Dickens' on the other. (German manufacturers specialised in transfer view production and exported a great deal to Great Britain before the Great War.)

St. George Models
Ancient Artefacts

Loving Cup, 3-handled. 53mm.	3.00
Puzzle Jug, with verse. 60mm.	5.00
Puzzle Tankard. 50mm.	5.00

Seaside Souvenirs

Lighthouse. 121mm.	5.00

Animals

Two Puppies and a Kitten in a basket. 62mm.	22.50
Cat, with drumstick, sitting on a drum. 90mm.	22.50
Dog, coal hod with handle. 80mm.	18.50
Elephants, two on a sledge on slope. 70mm.	75.00
Grotesque Animal with winged legs, sitting. 80mm.	9.00

Birds (including Eggs)

Hen and Cock on circular base, one pecking and one standing. 80mm.	14.00

Home/Nostalgic

Basketweave Basket. 90mm.	4.00
Jardiniere on stand, fixed. 95mm.	4.00
Pail with wire handle. 45mm.	4.00

Sport/Pastimes

Tennis Racquet with ball. 140mm long.	17.50

Footwear

Ladies heeled shoe. 84mm.	7.50
Ladies heeled shoe with eyelets. 85mm long.	12.50

Domestic

Hatpin Holder. 110mm.	10.50

St. Pauls

Trademark used for export to Canada by Hewitt & Leadbeater, Willow Pottery, Longton. (Usual trademark Willow Art).

St. Pauls Models
Traditional/National Souvenirs

Welsh Hat. No. 75. 54mm.	8.50

Historical/Folklore

Skull, inscribed: *Alas Poor Yorick*. 65mm. (This has a crest of Alberta).	12.00

Sandifords Ceramic China

Trademark used by the manufacturers of Ceramic China (usual trademark Ceramic China), for the retailer Sandifords.

Only a pin tray and two 'smalls' recorded all with the Chorley crest.   each 4.00

San Juan

Mark used by an unknown manufacturer. One model has been found with this mark; it carried a Madrid Crest. It would have been made by any English firm that exported to tourist areas. The initials S.M. & Co. were not used by any manufacturer working during the 'crested china' period and so are probably the initials of the retailer.

San Juan Model
Ancient Artefacts
Portland Vase. 51mm.   4.00

Savoy China

1910-1933

Trademark used by Birks, Rawlins and Co (Ltd), Vine Pottery, Stoke. Merged in 1932 with Wiltshaw & Robinson Ltd. (Makers of Carlton).

CHINA
MADE IN ENGLAND

Mark found on a Carlton mould fisherman and on a black cat on pouffé – obviously after firms merged.

The firm Birks, Rawlins and co., China Manufacturers, was founded in 1900. It had previously been known as L.A. Birks and Co. (founded 1896). Who Mr Rawlins was will probably remain a secret but Mr L.A. Birks managed the pottery and was responsible for the designs. The firm's early products were 'breakfast and teas' in the usual number of printed patterns and other decorative domestic ware including pierced white pieces.

Birks, Rawlins and Co. began producing what were described as china miniatures for the seasonal souvenir trade around 1910 using the trade-name Savoy China. The production of this work was stepped up in 1919 to take advantage of the gap left in the market by the banning of German goods. It was reported in the *Pottery Gazette* in 1919 and 20 that the firm were producing miniature architectural models and could execute copies of any well known building to order. Aberystwyth University, St. Paul's, Westminster Abbey, Truro Cathedral, King Charles Tower, Hastings Clock Tower and Portsmouth Town Hall were all said to be in production. (Only some of these have been found so far.) Even more perplexing to the collector is a list printed in 1920 of 'Small figures which aim at filling a need that was created when German supplies to this country ceased. 'Birks Grotesques' included 'Old Bill' in camouflage or in khaki, 'Sunny Jim', 'Weary Willy', 'Artful Eliza', 'Saucy Sue', 'Peter Pan', 'Conchy', 'Blighty' and 'C3' – all well known cartoon and comic strip characters of the time. None of these have been reported with or without crests or marked Savoy and one wonders if they were ever produced in any numbers.

Many coloured novelties were made in the 1920s including figures, birds, floating bowl decorations (butterflies and other insects) and plump pixies sitting on toadstools. These were not crested so have not been listed here.

In 1925, Birks, Rawlins and Co. exhibited at the British Empire Exhibition, showing Parian China and novelties. Presumably the return of cheap continental souvenir ware and the effect on trade of the

Depression were too much for the firm, for by 1931 the company was put into the hands of the Receiver. F.W. Carder ceased to act as Receiver on 7th March 1932 and it was announced that Birks, Rawlins and Co. had merged with Wiltshaw and Robinson Ltd (makers of Carlton China). Wiltshaw and Robinson continued to use the Savoy trademark for a short time and some Carlton moulds can be found with the Savoy mark.

The Savoy range, although described as 'china' and even 'porcelain miniatures', cannot really be considered delicate or even fine, and the crests are not at all well produced. It is obvious that Birks, Rawlins and Co. lowered their standards to produce cheap items for the lower end of the souvenir market. Very few Savoy models are found with transfer prints of any kind and these are mostly domestic pieces. 'Lucky Black Cat' transfers are occasionally encountered but no 'Lucky White Heather' devices have as yet been recorded.

Birks, Rawlins and Co. produced a few military badges, these being:

Argyll & Sutherland Highlanders
Army Medical Corps
Army Service Corps
Black Watch
Cameronians, Scottish Rifles
Gordon Highlanders
Highland Light Infantry
Queen's Own Cameron Highlanders
Royal Army Medical Corps
Royal Engineers
Royal Field Artillery
Royal Military College, Camberley
Royal Scots Greys
Seaforth Highlanders
Worcestershire Regiment
H.M.S. Lion

They did however print the most interesting range of Great War commemorative inscriptions sometimes found on military models but more often on 'smalls'. These celebrate, if that word can possibly be used to describe such carnage, battles and events in the war and carry matching crests. The following are known:

Albert 'British advance commenced July 1st 1916. Battle of the Somme.'

Amiens 'Germans defeated at Moreuil and Ovise near Amiens August 27-29, 1914. Amiens taken by the Germans September 11914.'

Antwerpen 'Antwerp invaded Oct. 1st 1914. Bombarded 1914, evacuated Oct. 7th 1914. Captured Oct. 13th 1914.'

Armentiers 'Desperate Battles between British and Germans, Nov. 1914, June 1915.'

Arras 'Great Battle between French and Germans. French gain trenches June 1915.' Or '13,000 German prisoners, 160 guns captured 1917.'

Australia 'Herbertshone German Pacific Island captured by Australian Navy September 11th 1914. The German cruiser Emden attacked and burnt by H.M.S. Sydney Nov. 8th 1914.'

Advance Australia 'The Australians have made an undying name in storming the Turkish trenches April May 1915.' This inscription is in addition to the previous inscription.

La Basee No details of inscription available.

Beaumont 'British victory German fortress of Beaumont-Hamel, Beaucourt and St. Pierre Divion, captured Nov. 13-14 1916.'

Belgium 'Belgium invaded by Germany August 4th 1914. Capital occupied August 20th 1914.'

Boulogne 'Hospital base for British wounded soldiers.'

B.E. Africa 'South Togoland seized by Great Britain August 7th 1914.

British East Africa 'South Togoland seized by Britain August 7th 1914.'

Brugge/Bruges 'Bruges occupied by the Germans Oct. 16 1914.'

Brussels 'Occupied by the Germans August 20th 1914.'

Bucharest 'Rumania declares war on Austria-Hungary August 27th 1916.'

Calais 'German life and death advance.'

Combles 'Great German fortress captued by the British Sep. 26. 1916. Greatest British success of the war.'

Compiegne 'Battle of Compiegne Sept. 1st. 1914.'

Dinant 'Sacked and burnt by the Germans August 23rd 1914.'

Dornock No details of inscription available.

Doullens No details of inscription available.

Dunkerque 'Dunkerque bombarded by long range German guns.'

Egypt 'Defended by British troops with Australian and Indian contingents.'

French Republic 'French Territory invaded by German troops August 2nd 1914. Battle of the Marne Sept. 8th to Sept. 12th.'

Gand 'Ghent. Occupied by the Germans October 13th 1914.'

Greece 'Allies land at Salonika October 5 1915.'

Hartlepool 'Bombardment of Hartlepool by the German fleet December 16th 1914.'

Japan 'Declared war on Germany Aug. 23rd 1914. The fortress Kido-Chau stormed and taken by the Japanese Nov. 7th 1914.'

Liege Invested and bombarded by the Germans August 9th 1914.

Lille 'Lille captured by the Germans Sept. 1914.'

Loos No details of inscription available.

Louvain 'Louvain burned and destroyed by the Germans, August 25th 1914.'

Luxembourg 'Luxembourg invaded by Germans Aug. 1914.'

Malines 'Town and cathedral bombarded by Germans August 27th 1914.'

Messines Battle of Messines. Great British victory 7342 German prisoners. June 7 1917 also 47 guns captured.'

Mons 'Battle of Mons, Historic Retreat begun August 23rd 1914.'

Namur 'Namur Forts destroyed by the large German guns August 23rd 1914.'

Neuve Chapelle 'Brilliant British Victory over Germans at Neuve Chapelle March 10th 1915.'

Neiuport 'Bombarded January 1915.'

Ostend 'Occupied by the Germans October 16th 1914. British ships begin to take part in coast battle October 8th 1914.'

Paris 'German rush on Paris; reached 20 miles from Paris Sept 3rd 1914.'

Persia 'Persia; British defeat Turks at Kut-el-Amara Sept 28th 1915.'

Rheims 'Rheims bombarded by Germans Sept 2 1914; Cathedral destroyed Sept 19 1914.'

Russia 'Przemysl captured by the Russians 119,600 prisoners of war March 22nd 1915.'

Russia 'War declared upon Russia by Germany Aug. 1st 1914.'

Servia 'Austrians defeated by Serbians at Kolubra Dec 3-6 1914.'

Sheringham 'German air raid on Sheringham Jan. 19th 1915.'

Soissons 'Battle of Soissons.'

Union of South Africa No details of inscription available.

United States of America 'America declared war on Germany, Good Friday April 6 1917.'

Verdun 'German defeat before Fort Douardmont February 26th 1916.'

Ypres 'German push stemmed by the Valour of the British troops October 27th 1914. 2nd battle of Ypres the Canadian's gallantry saved the situation April 24th 1915.'

Some superb patriotic transfers were made including Black Watch (depicting a private), Gordon Highlanders, soldier of the King, 13th Manchester, Seaford Camp, Grenadier Guards (private), Territorial Soldier (private), and the 11th Welsh.

Commemoratives can also be found of the Scottish Exhibition, Glasgow 1911 and the Wembley British Empire Exhibition 1924/5.

Numbering System. Savoy models tend to be over endowed with printed and painted numbers on their bases. Many models have a very clear printed number which was obviously a stock number. Unfortunately for the collector the same low numbers often appear on different models. There are possibly one or two reasons for this, one theory being that as models were deleted from the range new models were given their numbers. Another theory for which there is some evidence is that the numbers were badly printed and often only the first or last one or two are in evidence. Sometimes where this has happened a larger stock number is painted in black beside the printed number. Other coloured painted numbers found near the mark seem to be paintresses' marks, these often appearing directly under the painted stock number also in black.

Where stock numbers have been found consistently (printed or painted on models) they have been recorded in the following lists.

Savoy Models
Parian/Unglazed

Bust of Edward VII as the Prince of Wales with inscription. 135mm.	65.00
Bust of *Albert King of the Belgians*, round glazed base. 155mm.	75.00
Bust of Admiral Sir David Beatty, found with inscription: *British Naval Victory, German Cruiser Blucher sunk January 24th 1915. England declared War on Germany August 4th 1914.* 150mm.	75.00

Bust of David Lloyd George with
  inscription on reverse. 186mm.   40.00
Bust of Lord Kitchener, found with
  inscription: *Lord Kitchener of*
  Khartoum Field Marshall KG KP
  Secretary for War. Born 1851. June
  15th, drowned at sea off the Orkneys
  1916.
  2 sizes: 107mm.   40.00
           120mm.   40.00
Bust of Sailor, inscribed:
  HMS Iron Duke
  HMS Lion
  HMS Ocean and
  HMS Warspite
  (rare), on round glazed base.
  No. 532. 135mm.   160.00
Bust of John Travers Cornwell,
  inscription: *John Travers Cornwell,*
  age 16. Faithful unto death. Hero
  Battle of Jutland, impressed: *HMS*
  Chester on cap band. No. 580.
  108mm.   325.00

Ancient Artefacts

Ancient Jug. No. 87. 74mm.   4.00
Ancient Jug, Model of. Dug out of the
  Foundations of Lichfield Museum.
  62mm.   4.00
Barrel Mug, Model of. No. 7.
  45mm.   4.00
British Urn. 50mm.   3.00
Carlisle Elizabethan Measure,
  inscribed: *Model of gallon Elizabethan*
  standard measure in Carlisle
  museum by permission of Com.
  Tullie House. No. 183. 58mm.   5.50
Carlisle Jug, *14th Century Jug found*
  in an old tank at Carlisle gaol, by
  permission of Com Tullie House.
  No. 179. 70mm.   4.00
Carlisle Salt Pot 14th Century
  No. 182. 65mm.   3.00
Carlisle Vase. No. 177. 70mm.   3.00
Chester Roman Vase, inscribed:
  Roman Vase, original now in
  Chester Museum. No. 134. 70mm.   3.00
China Tot, Model of. No. 33.   3.00
Chinese Vase in South Kensington
  Museum. No. 67 or 219. 70mm.   3.00
Chinese Jade Vase, inscribed: *Model of*
  Vase of Chinese Jade. No. 152. 68mm.   3.00
Colchester Vase. *Ancient Vase*
  original in Colchester Museum.
  No. 349. 50mm.   3.00

Colchester Roman Vase, inscribed:
  Roman Vase found in Cloaca, now in
  Colchester Castle. No. 196.
  30mm.   3.00
Exeter Vase from original in Museum.   4.00
Globe Vase. No. 62. 42mm.   3.00
Greek Vase. No. 77. 69mm.   3.00
Hastings Kettle. No. 140. 60mm.   3.00
Irish Bronze Pot. 50mm.   3.00
Italian Vase. No. 30.   3.00
Itford Urn. 44mm.   3.00
Launceston Bottle. No. 193.
  65mm.   3.00
Lewes Vase, inscribed: *Model of*
  Roman Vase in Lewes Castle.
  No. 197. 35mm.   3.00
Loving Cup. *Model of Loving Cup,*
  original by Henry of Navarre, King
  of France. No. 49. 42mm.   4.00
Maltese Fire Grate. No. 39 and
  No. 721. 45mm.   7.50
Newbury Leather Bottle. *Model of*
  Leather Bottle found at Newbury
  1044 on battlefield now in museum.
  No. 14. 63mm.   3.00
Pear Bottle. No. 17. 70mm.   4.00
Penrith Salt Pot. No. 182. 60mm.   3.00
Persian Bottle. No. 68. 95mm.   4.00
Pilgrims Bottle Nevers ware.
  No. 172. 75mm.   4.00
Pompeian Vase. No. 161. 124mm.   4.00
Pompeian Vessel. No. 264.   4.00
Portland Vase. No. 16. 51mm.   4.00
Puzzle Jug. No. 378. 68mm.   13.00
Salt Maller, Model of. No. 106.
  60mm.   4.00
Scarborough Jug. No. 454 or No. 10.
  48mm.   3.00
Silchester Roman Urn. No. 74.
  51mm.   3.00
Shakespeare's Jug, *the jug of William*
  Shakespeare, with his signature.
  60mm.   5.00
Shrewsbury Ewer. No. 19.
  72mm.   4.00
Southwold Jar. No. 175. 90mm.   3.00
Staffordshire salt glaze tea pot, Model
  of, with separate lid. No. 202.
  75mm.   12.50
Tear Bottle. 70mm.   4.00
Teapot, copy of early 18th century
  stoneware (shaped as as camel).
  100mm long. (Rare).   30.00
Tyg, two-handled. 62mm.   3.00

Windsor Roman Urn. *Roman urn dug up at old Windsor from original now in British Museum.* No. 138. 45mm.   4.00

York Roman Ewer. *Roman Ewer from the original in Hospitium found at York.* No. 20.   4.00

Buildings – Coloured

Exeter Cathedral, brown coloured. 150mm long.   125.00

St Paul's Cathedral, brown unglazed. 125mm long, 88mm high.   125.00

Tumbledown Cottage, not named, highly coloured and glazed. Impressed 1800. 105mm long.   95.00

Buildings – White

Aberystwyth, The University. No. 68. 146mm long.   125.00

Burns Cottage. 70mm long.   17.50

Citadel Gateway, Plymouth. No. 209. 114mm.   27.50

Birmingham Town Hall. 94mm long, 62mm high.   25.00

Clifton Suspension Bridge. 132mm long.   75.00

Clock Tower. 126mm.   14.50

Cottage, not named, inscribed: I wouldn't leave my little wooden hut for you. 63mm long.   20.00

Derry's Clock, Plymouth. No. 17. 152mm.   16.00

First and Last Refreshment House in England. No. 301. 72mm.   16.00

Hastings Clock Tower. No. 274. 156mm.   16.00

Margate Clock Tower. 160mm.   16.00

Monnow Gate, Monmouth. 112mm.   40.00

Portsmouth Town Hall. No. 7. 80mm.   47.50

Tumbledown Cottage. 105mm long.   40.00

Monuments

Model of Lewes Martyr's Memorial. Erected in 1901 to the memory of the 16 Protestants burnt to death in front of the Star Hotel 1555-1557. 140mm. No. 791.   70.00

Rufus Stone, with usual inscriptions. 100mm.   5.50

Historical/Folklore

Burns Chair, Dumfries. 85mm.   7.50

Elizabethan Girl, full figure. 155mm.   82.50

Execution Block. 100mm long.   14.00

Gargoyle or Devils Head, open mouth, inscribed: *My word if you're not off.* No. 230. 90mm long.   10.50

Mary Queen of Scots Chair, Edinburgh Castle. 77mm.   6.50

Traditional/National Souvenirs

A Cornish Pasty. 100mm long.   7.50

Ripon Horn Blower. No. 497. 100mm.   16.00

Ye Olde Devonshire Milk Can. 78mm.   9.00

Bagpipes. 115mm long.   20.00

Monmouth Cap. 50mm.   25.00

Tam o'shanter.   20.00

Thistle Vase. 47mm.   3.00

Welsh Hat with longest place name round brim. No. 6. 2 sizes: 35mm.   6.50

55mm.   7.50

Welsh Lady carrying a basket. 110mm.   30.00

Dutch Boy, standing coloured, salt pot. 128mm.   35.00

Seaside Souvenirs

Bathing Machine, inscribed: *Morning Dip.* 62mm.   10.00

Boat. No. 434. 128mm long.   10.50

Lifeboat. If inscribed: *Zetland,* add £7.00. No. 341. 125mm long.   13.50

Rowing Boat. No. 118. 130mm long.   10.50

Yacht. 115mm long.   12.50

Beachy Head Lighthouse. No. 377. 130mm.   12.50

Lighthouse, candlesnuffer. 95mm.   9.50

Eddystone Lighthouse. No. 136. Also found inscribed: *St. Catherines Lighthouse.* 92mm.   5.50
    17.00

Lizard Lighthouse.   17.50

Lighthouse salt pot, inscribed: *salt.* 105mm.   13.00

Lighthouse pepper pot, inscribed: *pepper.* 120mm. No. 768.   13.00

Crab ashtray or dish. 52mm long.   7.50

Lobster pintray with lid. No. 426. 97mm long.   16.00

Child draped in towel, standing on a rock. 133mm.   25.00

Whelk Shell. No. 451. 81mm long.   5.00

Countryside

Acorn, Model of. No. 110. 56mm.   7.50
   Can also be found as a pepper
   pot marked 'P'.   6.00

Animals

Bear, inscribed: *Model of Stoneware*
Bear, a performing bear on hind
   legs with gilded muzzle. No. 205.
   106mm.   82.50
Cat, Cheshire. No. 17. 80mm.   7.50
Cat sitting, miniature, with long
   neck. 68mm.   10.00
Cat, angry with arched back,
   inscribed: *Me backs up.* No. 195.
   100mm long.   15.50
Cat with long neck. No. 217.
   105mm.   16.00
Cat, sitting, detailed fur.
   2 sizes: 56mm.   10.50
           94mm. No. 245   75.00
Cat, standing with huge grin, erect
   bushy tail. Comic, black cartoon
   cat. 105mm long.   170.00
Cat, on oval lustre base. Inscribed:
   Good Luck. Cat coloured black.
   90mm. (Carlton mould).   26.00
Cat, Manx, standing. 80mm long.   20.00
Dog cream jug. No. 106. 60mm.   13.00
Dog (no particular breed) sitting.
   55mm.   40.00
Dog (curly tail) standing. 65mm.   13.00
Dog, Basset/Dachshund. No. 296.
   132mm long.   30.00
Dog, Spaniel, sitting. No. 561.
   65mm.   40.00
Bulldog, lying, inscribed: *Another*
   Dreadnought. 118mm long.   40.00
Bulldog, standing, with verse. *Be*
   Briton Still to Britain True. No. 364.
   130mm long.   27.50
Bulldog, standing, feet outwards.
   Inscribed: *'Another Dreadnought'.*
   135mm long.   27.50
Dog, crouched and barking.
   No. 253. 100mm long.   29.00
Dog, Scottie, wearing glengarry.
   No. 477. 86mm.   15.00
Dog, Scottie, wearing a tam-
   o'shanter.
   2 sizes: 63mm.   10.50
           80mm.   14.50

Dog, Scottie, looking out of kennel.
   Can be found with inscription:
   The Black Watch. No. 154.
   80mm long.   15.00
Dog, Spaniel, begging. 65mm.   12.50
Donkey, standing. No. 308.
   120mm long.   75.00
Elephant, sitting with trunk in the
   air. No. 218. 63mm.   17.50
Elephant, standing. No. 250. 65mm.   15.00
Elephant, standing, trunk raised.
   No. 253. 100mm long.   20.00
   Can be found coloured green.   47.50
Elephant with howdah. No. 228.
   66mm.   30.00
Fish. 104mm long.   7.50
Fish Jug. 70mm.   8.50
Fish Vase. No. 33. 88mm.   5.00
Frog, sitting, well detailed. No. 321.
   70mm.   65.00
Frog on a rock. Green.
   110mm long.   35.00
Hare, crouching, No. 235.
   80mm long.   20.00
Hare, sitting, ears raised. No. 245.
   70mm.   20.00
Hare, looking left, upright ears.
   No. 253. 80mm.   40.00
Hippo, with pointed teeth.
   113mm long.   65.00
Lion, sitting on square base. This
   was originally designed by
   Alfred Stevens for the British
   Museum. 108mm.   35.00
Lion, walking. Inscribed: *Be Briton...*
   No. 123. or *'Another Dreadnought'*
   No. 288. 134mm long.   25.00
   Without inscription.   17.50
Mouse. 65mm long.   14.50
Pig, lying down. No. 544.
   80mm long.   10.00
   Can be found inscribed: *Wunt be*
   druv.
Pig, standing and fat. No. 109.
   2 sizes: 70mm and 100mm long.   12.50
   Large size can be found
   inscribed: *Model of Irish Pig.*   20.00
Pig, standing, open mouthed.
   122mm long.   100.00
Pig, lying down. No. 859.
   80mm long.   30.00
Pig, inscribed: *Model of Sussex Pig.*
   No. 198 and No. 281. 78mm long.   10.50
Pig, standing, alert ears. No. 199.
   100mm long.   10.50

Pig, sitting, long nose. 110mm.	35.00
Piglet with long ears. No. 33.	
65mm long.	13.50
Polar Bear. No. 236. 145mm long.	75.00
Rabbit, ears flat. 66mm long.	7.50
Rabbit, crouching. No. 247.	
88mm long.	13.00
Rabbit, sitting, one ear up. No. 548.	
70mm long.	40.00
Rabbit, sitting on hind legs, upright.	
No. 242. 104mm.	30.00
Rhino, grotesque. No. 284.	
130mm long.	47.50
Seal.	
2 sizes: 63mm long.	13.00
80mm long.	15.50
Snail. No. 252. 84mm long.	30.00
Teddy Bear. 90mm.	19.50
Tiger, sabre toothed, or Wild Cat	
with inscription: *My word if you're*	
not off. 128mm long.	100.00
Toad. No. 331. 75mm.	20.00
Warthog or Wild Pig, open mouth.	
Grotesque. 122mm long.	82.50

Birds (including Eggs)

Bird, coloured yellow, orange and	
black, shaped salt pot. 90mm.	50.00
Bird mustard pot, orange, yellow,	
red and black. 86mm long.	55.00
Bird alighting on edge of bowl.	
No. 248. 97mm.	25.00
Grotesque Bird. 100mm.	11.00
Clara Cluck candlesnuffer. No. 324.	
87mm.	30.00
Duck, swimming. No. 562.	
65mm long.	13.50
Duck, standing. 150mm.	30.00
Duck, standing on green base.	22.00
Can be found coloured. 170mm.	40.00
Duckling, standing on tree trunk,	
colouring on trunk and beak.	
186mm.	40.00
Duckling, comic, with a wasp on its	
beak.	40.00
Also found partly coloured.	
165mm.	40.00
Duck, lying down, could be dead.	
No. 237. 105mm long.	35.00
Duck, comical, airing wings on	
circular base. 155mm.	75.00
Egg with Cock face, comb and tail	
on round base. 90mm.	20.00
Grotesque Bird jug. No. 127.	10.50

Goose in full length cloak.	
72mm.	30.00
Hen, sitting, red comb. No. 23.	
55mm.	9.00
Hen, sitting. 50mm.	10.50
Owl, comic. No. 33 or No. 329.	
60mm.	15.00
Penguin. No. 484. 70mm.	16.00
Penguin. No. 549. 76mm.	16.00
Penguin. No. 332. 80mm.	19.00
Penguin on heart shaped ashtray.	
85mm.	16.00
Swan, detailed plumage. No. 579.	
50mm.	7.50

Great War

Highland Infantryman, with pack,	
rifle and bayonet. Either glazed	
or parian, both on round glazed	
plinth. No. 530. 165mm.	170.00
Sailor, standing, arms folded,	
unglazed on round glazed base.	
(Very rare) No. 538. 160mm.	225.00
Nurse, with red cross on chest,	
holding bandage. Can be found	
inscribed: *Nurse Cavell.* No. 531.	
165mm.	125.00
Biplane, with movable prop.,	
2 different models exist:	
(a) One has open struts between	
the wings. (see page 60 of *Take Me*	
Back To Dear Old Blighty by Robert	
Southall.)	300.00
(b) The other model is identical	
but has the struts filled in solid	
between the wings. No. 633.	
140mm long.	
Both models have coloured	
roundels and tail.	300.00
Monoplane, pointed wings and	
fixed prop. No. 523.	
130mm long.	60.00
Monoplane, pointed wings and	
revolving prop. No. 527.	
130mm long.	75.00
Zeppelin with revolving 2-bladed	
propeller, can be found with	
inscription: *Zeppelin destroyed by*	
Lt. Robinson V.C. at Cuffley Essex	
Sept. 3rd 1916. No. 567.	
175mm long.	195.00
Battleship, *HMS Iron Duke*, 2	
funnels. No. 524. 165mm long.	75.00
Battleship, *HMS Lion*, 3 funnels. No.	
524. 168mm long.	75.00

Battleship, *HMS Queen Elizabeth*, 3
funtnels. No. 615. 170mm long. 75.00
Battleship, *HMS Queen Elizabeth*, 2
funnels. No. 524. 165mm long. 75.00
Battleship, *HMS Barham*. 2 funnels.
168mm long. 75.00
Battleship, *HMS Tiger*, 2 funnels. No.
525. 168mm long. 75.00
Battleship, *HMS Warspite*, 2 funnels.
168mm long. 75.00
British Minesweeper, Model of. No.
641. 150mm long. (very rare). 250.00
Torpedo Boat Destroyer, model of. Rare.
No. 615. 140mm long. 100.00
Submarine, inscribed: *E1*. Usually
found with inscription:
*Commander Noel Lawrence. Large
German Transport Sunk July 30th
1915. German Cruiser Moltke
torpedoed August 19th 1915.*
No. 525. 150mm long. 40.00
Ambulance with 'Rolls Royce' front
and three red crosses in grey
circles. No. 520. 115mm long. 55.00
A similar model exists with two
red crosses moulded in relief on
sides of ambulance. 60.00
Armoured Car (reputedly a 'Talbot'
but not named). 125mm long. 110.00
Can also rarely be found named
Belgian Armoured Motor Car. 175.00
British Motor Searchlight. No.123.
103mm long. (Rare). 145.00
*Model of British Tank first used by
British Troops at the Battle of Ancre,
Sept. 1916* with inset steering
wheels and inscribed *HMS
Donner Blitzen, 515*. Long or short
rear facing guns.
2 sizes: No. 597. Short guns.
138mm long. 30.00
Long guns.
138mm long. 40.00
No. 586. Short or long guns.
160mm long. 40.00
Tank with no trailing wheels,
inscribed exactly as above. Short
forward and rear facing guns
protruding from side gun turrets.
Also a short gun protruding from
front of upper turret.
2 sizes: No. 651. 135mm long. 30.00
No. 643. 155mm long. 45.00
Tank with no trailing wheels
inscribed: *HMS Donner Blitzen*

and *515* on side only. Has a
curved exhaust pipe on roof, and
one small gun protruding from
front of side turrets. It differs
from the other tanks and is rather
flat in appearance. No. 675.
108mm long. (Rare) 85.00
Field Gun, Model of, with fish tail.
No. 616. 140mm long. 95.00
Howitzer. No. 520. 140mm long. 30.00
Howitzer. No. 518. 170mm long. 30.00
Machine Gun, 2 pieces, swivels on
tripod. No. 402. 153mm long. 145.00
British Trench Mortar Gun. No. 613.
98mm long. 47.50
Shell, if inscribed: *Iron rations for Fritz*. Add
£5.00
3 sizes: No. 581 or No. 556. 75mm. 7.50
No. 558 or No. 537. 110mm. 8.50
No. 170. 117mm. 10.50
(Shell 'salt' and 'pepper' pots also
found. No. 663. 80mm). each 10.50
Model of Stokes Bomb. No. 575. 24mm
dia. at base (very rare).
105mm long. 250.00
Trench Mortar Bomb. Often found not
named. No. 574. 86mm. 95.00
Hand Grenade. No. 576. 75mm. 16.00
Can be found inscribed: *Model of
Mills Bomb*. No. 326.
Anzacs Hat, Model of. No. 554.
90mm long. 25.00
Unnamed. 20.00
Balmoral Bonnet, Model of. No. 611.
74mm long. 20.00
Colonial Hat. No. 554. 92mm long. 16.00
*French Trench Helmet, worn by the
Dauntless French Poilu*. No. 569.
82mm long. (Not named £30.00). 40.00
Glengarry. No. 508. 78mm long. 19.00
New Zealand Hat, Model of. No. 612.
80mm long. 25.00
Officer's Peaked Cap. No. 516.
72mm long. 11.00
German Steel Helmet. No. 566.
60mm long. 35.00
*Rumanian Soldier's Steel Helmet,
Model of*, found with Bucharest
Crest and Rumanian War
declaration inscription.
82mm long. 65.00
R.F.C. Cap, Model of. Cap badge
clearly moulded. No. 577.
80mm long. 43.00

Sailor's Hat, inscribed on band:
HMS Lion, HMS Queen Elizabeth
or *HMS Tiger.* Blue bow. No. 533.

71mm dia.	60.00
Inscribed: *HMS Iron Duke.*	82.50

Tommy's Steel Helmet. No. 566.

82mm long.	30.00

German Picklehaube with tall spike.

88mm long, 65mm high. Very rare.	200.00
Bandsman's Drum. 55mm dia.	10.50
Bell Tent. No. 118. 65mm.	16.00
Water Bottle. No. 219. 57mm.	13.00

Tommy in Dug Out, not named. No.

669. 85mm. Very rare.	170.00

Fireplace, inscribed: *Keep the home
fires burning till the boys come home.*

No. 629. 94mm.	20.00

Cenotaph, inscribed: *The Glorious
Dead.* 130mm.   7.50

*Folkestone War Memorial, May Their
Deeds be held in reverence.* 160mm.   65.00

Edith Cavell Memorial, Norwich,
inscribed: *Nurse Cavell.* Red Cross
on apron. No. 110. 168mm.   22.00

Home/Nostalgic

Babies Cradle on rockers.

74mm long.	14.00
Bellows. 140mm long.	12.50
Candlesnuffer.	5.50
Funnel shaped. No. 437. 62mm.	12.50
Flat Iron. 65mm.	12.50

Kennel, inscribed: *Beware of the dog.*

No. 397. 53mm.	10.50

Trivet for flat iron. No. 544.

70mm long.	5.00

Grandfather Clock, inscribed: *Nae
man can tether time nor tide.* No.

622 and No. 110. 150mm.	22.00

Jardiniere on stand. No. 86.

77mm.	5.50
Lantern. 82mm.	8.50
Pillar Box, miniature. 56mm.	12.50
Stool, 3 legged. No. 471. 33mm.	5.00

Suitcase with straps. No. 745.

58mm.	17.00
Sundial. 93mm.	8.50
Watering Can. No. 455. 76mm.	10.50
Wheelbarrow. 120mm long.	12.50

Comic/Novelty

Billiken. 75mm.	5.50

Boy bending down into beer barrel,
Waiting for the smacks inscribed on

his bottom. 90mm.	38.00

Boy in nightshirt, holding candle.
Impressed on base *NIGHT.*

Candlesnuffer. 126mm.	65.00

Candlesnuffer in form of young boy
in nightwear, yawning and

stretching. No. 542. 85mm.	20.00

Caterpillar with human face.

No. 543. 74mm.	16.00
Also found coloured	30.00
Choirboy. No. 542. 85mm.	13.00
Choirboy, coloured. 104mm.	30.00

Edwardian Girl candlesnuffer
wearing bonnet, coat and muff.

77mm. No. 541, and 86mm. No. 175.	19.50

Edwardian Lady, very large, huge

skirt, neck frill and cap. 140mm.	120.00

Hindu god sitting on rock, blue
beads. No. 28 or No. 554. 90mm.

(Blue beads add £3.00).	8.50

Huntley and Palmer's Biscuit hat pin

holder.	26.00
Policeman, short and fat. 103mm.	60.00

Policeman. Boy carrying truncheon,

salt pot. Inscribed: *SALT.* 130mm.	75.00

Tea pot in shape of man's head,
spout coming out of mouth. No.

332. 60mm.	22.00

Cartoon/Comedy Characters

Billy Bunter, fully coloured.

120mm.	47.50

Bonzo, dog (1920s cartoon
character). No. 927. 2 sizes: 80mm

& 96mm.	55.00

Felix the Cat, crouching. Black with
white face and yellow eyes.

80mm.	195.00

Tweedledum and Tweedledee, fully
coloured, pair of separate sitting

figures. 70mm.	each 30.00
Wilful Wilfred, fully coloured figure.	45.00
Winkie the Gladeye Bird. White.	14.50
Or coloured. 80mm long.	30.00

Winkie the Glad Eyed Bird, not
named, as pepper pot. Fully

coloured. 70mm.	30.00

Winkie can also be found as salt

or mustard pots, in colour.	30.00

Alcohol

Beer Barrel. No. 406. 55mm.	3.00

Beer Barrel with separate base.

57mm.	7.50

Old Beer Jug, Model of. No. 84.

80mm.	4.50

Bottle. No. 408. 90mm. 7.50
Bottle, inscribed: *Real Scotch.*
  No. 409. 88mm. 10.50
Carboy. No. 92. 80mm. 4.00
Soda Syphon. 10.00

Sport/Pastimes
Cricket Bag. No. 745. 95mm long. 12.50
Cricket Bat. 115mm long. 75.00
Golf Ball, Model of. No. 111. 40mm. 7.50
Golf Club head. No. 442. 70mm. 19.00

Musical Instruments
Banjo. 137mm long. 12.50
Double Bass. 145mm long. 75.00
Upright Piano. No. 887.
  83mm long. 14.50
Violin. 136mm long. 75.00

Transport
Charabanc, (24 seater). No. 811.
  134mm long. 40.00

Modern Equipment
Gramophone, square with large
  horn. 102mm. 22.00

Footwear
Lancashire Clog, gilded studs.
  No. 403. 83mm long. 6.50
Dutch Clog. No. 424. 70mm long. 5.00
Oriental Slipper. No. 312.
  85mm long. 11.00

Hats
Straw Hat. 92mm long. 19.00
Top Hat. 44mm. 5.50

Miniature Domestic
Barrel shaped Mug. 50mm. 3.00
Basket weave Mug. 60mm. 3.00
Cheese Dish, one piece. 40mm. 9.00
Cheese Stand, Model of, with lid. No.
  200. No. 45. 55mm long. 10.00
Jug. No. 102. 62mm. 3.00
Jug. No. 755. 60mm. 3.00
Jug, ribbed. No. 116. 60mm. 3.00
Kettle and lid. No. 494. 13.50
Teapot with lid, diamond shaped.
  No. 202. 80mm. 10.50
Teapot with lid. 62mm. 10.50
Teaset on Tray. No. 401. 30.00
Tray 106mm long. 20.00
Trinket Set on Tray. No. 436. 20.00
Vase. No. 317. 35mm. 3.00

Vase, circular on two feet. No. 163.
  88mm. 3.00
Vase. No. 107. 52mm. 3.00
Vase. No. 192. 56mm. 3.00
Vase, long-necked. No. 407.
  65mm. 3.00

Domestic
Inkwell, square, with lid and pen
  rest. No. 433. 45mm. 14.50
Pins, Tray with wavy border. No.
  231. 149mm long. 22.00
Pin Tray, inscribed: *Pins* in blue
  script in relief. 146mm long. 10.00
Tray, oval with wavy border. No.
  436. 140mm long. 20.00

Miscellaneous
Bell, Model of, porcelain clapper.
  No. 5. 85mm. 7.50
Post and railings, posy vase.
  140mm long. 8.00

Saxony

Country of origin mark used by Wilhelm Kutzscher & Co, Schwarzenberger Porzellanfabrik, Schwarzenberg, Saxony. Many pieces were not factory marked and can be found listed in the unmarked section.

Ancient Artefacts

Model of old Beer Jug. No. 84. 74mm.	4.00
Carlisle Salt Pot, not named.	3.00
Irish Bronze Pot. 45mm.	3.00
Old Roman Salt Pot, 14th Century, found near Carlisle by Permission of Tullie House Committee. 63mm.	4.00
Puzzle Jug with verse. 66mm.	5.00

Buildings – White

Hall Cross, Doncaster. 158mm.	35.00
Holy Trinity Church, Margate. 100mm. An impressive model.	55.00
Iona Cathedral. 50mm.	30.00
Llandudno Church.	40.00
Margate Clock Tower. 145mm.	20.00
Ross-on-Wye, *Town Hall.* 85mm.	40.00
St Tudno's Church. 60mm long.	40.00
Skegness Clock Tower. 123mm.	7.50
Wallingford, Town Hall. 90mm.	35.00
Weymouth Clock Tower. 124mm.	16.00
Windmill, fixed sails. 85mm.	14.00

Monuments (including Crosses)

Banbury Cross. 146mm.	20.50
Captain Scott Memorial. 148mm.	20.00
Drake Monument. 125mm.	12.50
Largs Memorial.	14.50
Fishermens' Memorial.	16.00

Traditional/National Souvenirs

John Bull standing with Bulldog. 102mm.	20.00
Gretna Priest, standing figure.	30.00
Welsh Hat, with longest place name round brim. 44mm.	6.50
Welsh Lady, seated. 102mm.	24.50

Seaside Souvenirs

Beach Chair, wicker. 70mm.	12.50
Fisherwoman with bundle. 117mm.	25.00
Lifeboat. 135mm long.	10.00
Lightboatman. 114mm.	15.00
Beachy Head Lighthouse	6.50
If with black band.	9.00
Corbiere Lighthouse. 103mm.	11.50
Lighthouse with open windows. 115mm.	7.50
Lighthouse, narrow. 135mm.	10.50
Flamborough Lighthouse.	25.00
Needles Lighthouse. 125mm.	19.50
Sea Waves.	6.50
Mermaids, two on an oval base holding up a large shell. 105mm.	20.00

Countryside

Four bar Gate and stile with milestone. 100mm long.	6.50

Animals

Cat singing, holding sheet music. 66mm.	22.50
Cat, holding book. 74mm.	22.50
Cat in Bandages. 90mm.	20.00
Cat with Mandolin. 74mm.	20.00
Cat, Manx, drinking from jug. 72mm long.	24.00
Cat in Gladstone Bag, right paw raised. Can be found inscribed: *Good Morning.* 55mm long.	20.00
Cat in Gladstone Bag, left paw raised. 55mm long. (pair).	20.00
Dogs, two King Charles Spaniels in Top Hat. 78mm.	15.00
Cow Creamer and lid. 148mm long.	16.00
Frog under Tulip, candleholder. 100mm.	14.00
Hare, sitting. 95mm long.	8.50
Pig, ears forward. 90mm long.	11.00
Pig, sitting on haunches, ears forward. 76mm.	19.00
Spaniel sitting. 60mm.	12.50
Three Puppies in a Basket. 65mm.	20.00

Two Puppies and a Kitten in a
basket. 65mm.   20.00
Polar Bear on ashtray. 85mm.   20.00
Tortoise dish with shell lid.
75mm long.   7.50

Birds (including Eggs)
Duck, airing wings, some colouring.
88mm.   13.00
Duck on round base, brown beak
and feet. 98mm.   12.00
Egg, imprisoning a rabbit (he looks
through a barred window). A
large hare in tail coat standing
beside it. 67mm.   40.00
Eagle on Perch.   17.00
Seagull on rock, black edging on
wings. 109mm.   12.50
Seagull on rock, huge spread wings.
130mm.   25.00
Seagull posy holder. 114mm.   6.00
Seagull on rock, raised tail, black
edging to wings. 86mm.   19.50
Seagull on rock, black edging to
wings. 96mm.   19.50
Swan, open wings. 80mm.   5.00
Wagtail on tree trunk, black edging
to wings. 110mm.   14.00

Great War
Monoplane, fixed prop and pilot.
100mm long.   30.00
Clacton War Memorial, with
inscription. 140mm.   14.50
Folkestone War Memorial.
160mm.   25.00
Great Yarmouth War Memorial.
130mm.   22.50
Margate War Memorial.
185mm.   45.00
Matlock Bath War Memorial.
150mm.   15.00

Home/Nostalgic
Basket, rectangular, 75mm long.   4.50
Coal Scuttle. 58mm.   4.00
Grandmother Clock. 85mm.   5.50
Mantle Clock with twisted side
pillars. 92mm.   6.50
Pillar Box, inscribed: *I cant get a
letter from you...* 72mm.   10.00
Shaving Mug. 54mm.   5.50
Watering Can. 67mm.   5.50
Wheelbarrow. 105mm long.   12.00

Comic/Novelty
Edwardian Lady chauffeur's
companion with scarf and full
length coat. 80mm.   45.00
Monk holding lantern. 113mm.   24.00

Sport/Pastimes
Football with gilded stitches. 60mm.   12.00

Musical Instruments
Harp with wide base. 90mm.   6.50

Transport
Steam Locomotive, inscribed: R.H.
and D.R. (Romney Hythe and
Dymchurch Railway).
115mm long.   75.00

Modern Equipment
Gramophone, with horn. 85mm.   19.50

Footwear
Ladies Shoe. 115mm long.   8.50

Miniature Domestic
Tea Pot and lid. 57mm.   7.50

Miscellaneous
Mans Head spill vase or pin
cushion. 85mm.   7.50

S.C.H.L.

S.C.H
L

Trademark used by Shore, Coggins and Holt of Longton, Staffordshire. This mark was used from 1905-1910. The factory then became Shore and Coggins and used the Bell China mark (now Royal Doulton Group). The only piece recorded carries the crest of Bolton Abbey.

Sport/Pastimes
Vase, or possibly hatpin holder, in the form of cricket bat and stumps. 103mm.   20.00

Scotch Porcelain

Trademark used for a Scottish retailer by an unknown manufacturer.
This china is fine and well produced, but the manufacturer is unknown.

Scotch Models
Parian/Unglazed
Bust of Scott, on circular glazed base. 108mm.   20.00

Traditional/National Souvenirs
Thistle Vase. 55mm dia.   4.00

Alcohol
Tankard. 62mm.   4.00

Shamrock China

Trademark used by Arkinstall and Sons.
(Usual trademark Arcadian).
This mark was used by Arkinstall and Sons
for the Irish market. It was thought to have
been used by the Belleek factory, but I do
not now think it was. It is similar to
Colleen China.

Shamrock Models
Ancient Artefacts

Canterbury Roman Ewer. 64mm.	4.00
Grecian Bronze Pot found at Pompeii.	
No. 138. 50mm.	4.00
Puzzle Jug. 68mm.	6.50
Shrewsbury Romano-Salopian Ewer.	
No. 613. 80mm.	4.00

Traditional/National Souvenirs

Bust of Irishwoman decorated with green shamrocks on shawl. Coloured features. Inscribed: *My simple graceful Nora Cricna.* 87mm.	75.00
Shamrock. 90mm wide.	16.00

Animals

Frog, green eyes, gilded webbed feet, croaking. 75mm.	30.00
Model of Irish Pig, standing, inscribed: *Wun't be druv.* Can be found inscribed: *The Dear Little Shamrock....* No. 148. 60mm high, 70mm long.	30.00

Birds (including Eggs)

Cockerel, with orange face and yellow beak. 100mm.	20.00

Miniature Domestic

Cheese Dish and cover. 76mm long.	12.50

Shamrock Crest China

Animals

Standing Pig.   11.50

Birds (including Eggs)

Open Egg Shell. 65mm long.   5.00

Alcohol

Carboy. 68mm.   5.00

Miscellaneous

Jug.   2.50
Vase. 95mm.   2.50
Vase.   2.50

Trademark used for a Belfast wholesaler by
   R.H. & S.L. Plant (Ltd), Tuscan Works,
   Longton. (Usual trademark Tuscan).
The initials N.P.O. were not used by any
   known manufacturer and are likely to be
   those of a Belfast wholesaler. All pieces
   with this mark were sold with Irish crests
   or transfers, including Glenariff Glen,
   Newtownards, The Honeycombe, Giants
   Causeway and The Irish Jaunting Car.

Shamrock Crest Models
Ancient Artefacts
Irish Bronze Pot. 45mm.   4.00

Traditional/National Souvenirs
Irish Harp.   10.00

Seaside Souvenirs
Shell. No. 56. 85mm long.   10.50

J. Shaw

Shell China

Trademark used by J. Shaw & Sons, Longton, subsequently John Shaw & Sons (Longton) Ltd, Willow Pottery, Longton.

This firm usually produced tableware and fine bone china. Although most firms producing small quantities of crested ware usually stuck to 'smalls', the only crested ware recorded from this firm are the three models below.

J. Shaw Models
Buildings – White
Shakespeare's Cottage.
   130mm long.   40.00

Countryside
Milk Churn and lid. 72mm.   5.00

Comic/Novelty
Biscuit impressed: *Huntley and Palmer.* Biscuit coloured on white shaped base. 68mm long. (Has been recorded with a Dolgelly crest).   30.00

Trademark used by an unknown Staffordshire Pottery but resembles Arcadian.

This mark has only been recorded on two miniature models listed below.

Shell Models
Traditional/National Souvenirs
Welsh Hat. 55mm.   5.00

Miniature Domestic
Cheese Dish and cover. 45mm.   6.50

Shelley China

1890-1910. On small, decorative and domestic items.

1910-1923/4. On small, decorative and domestic items. The words 'LATE FOLEY' were incorporated 1910-1916.

1912-1925.

THE FOLEY CHINA

1890-1910. On numbered models.

SHELLEY CHINA LATE FOLEY

1910-1925. On numbered models.

SHELLEY CHINA

1910-1925+.

Trademark used by Wileman & Co, Foley Potteries and Foley China Works, Fenton, Longton and subsequently renamed Shelleys Ltd.

The firm of Wileman and Co. was founded in or around the year 1860 by Mr J.F. Wileman and Mr J.E. Shelley. From 1883 the business was run entirely by the Shelley family; the founder and his son Percy Shelley, and later his grandsons. Wileman and Co. were well known and respected manufacturers of fine china, specialising in tea and breakfast sets for the comfortable middle class market both at home and abroad. Several other firms used the tradename 'Foley' (notably E. Brain and Co.) and this can be confusing for the collector looking for early pieces. Obviously the tradenames were causing confusion in the 1900's for in 1910 the company decided to change its tradename to 'Shelley', using the name of the owners rather than the pottery. In its advertising to the trade the company announced, perhaps rather unfairly, 'The World Wide reputation of Foley china has caused many cheap imitations, and in future to protect the public the real genuine Foley china will always be indelibly marked Shelley'.

For sometime the tradename Shelley was accompanied by the title late Foley and one suspects that this was dropped from the markings on 'Crest China' before other domestic wares. The firm changed its name legally to Shelleys Ltd in 1925, but the new mark seems to have been used before this date.

The Shelley family produced commemorative and view ware before 1900, and seem to have begun producing Crest China as they called it in 1903 as a sideline. One suspects that this was in direct competition with W.H. Goss. Foley, and later Shelley fine crest china was sold in the best china shops, rooms and halls and not in bazaars, post offices, cafes and other dubious outlets. At first crests were applied to domestic wares (the same shapes can be found decorated in the usual styles of the day) and small trays and vases. Early models include simple small shapes such as books, hats, animals and some souvenir items of the South African War. All of these being rather more in line with the cheaper crested china firms than Goss, but by 1906 the Shelleys were producing small models of ancient artefacts, very like the Goss products. Over the next few years the firm produced the most interesting range of these, always in the delicate white china for which they were well known and with carefully painted crests.

With the coming of the war years, and the loss of skilled men to the battlefields of France, the production of moulded models obviously became financially more important to the firm. (Models made during and after the Great War tend to be heavier and cruder than other products of the firm – obviously the work of unskilled labour). In 1920 at the British Industries Fair the Shelley family showed 'Crest China' and advertised it in that year for the first time. Great War souvenirs and some novelty items were added to the range, but they never quite reached the vulgarity displayed by other manufacturers. Shelley stopped producing crested china much earlier than other firms, in fact they appear to have added very few items to their range after 1923 and do not mention its production in advertising after that date. Obviously they continued to produce the domestic ware which was always the speciality of the

firm and made a feature of children's ware in the later 1920's as did many other manufacturers. Shelley Potteries Ltd. is now part of the Doulton Group.

The Shelley models are not very exciting for those who like the colourful and bizarre. A few half-hearted 'novelties' can be found, but basically 'respectable' and not to amuse on the mantelshelves of the 'working classes'. However, collectors of fine china are very drawn to Shelley/ Foley pieces, especially to the named historic shapes which are so like Goss. (New collectors should be warned that the less common of these already change hands among seasoned collectors for more money than the common Goss models).

Early Foley/Shelley view ware is very beautiful, both monochrome (red, black and brown) and polychrome transfers can be found. Later Shelley transfers are rather disappointing being very highly coloured and not so attractive. The firm also produced models with transfer prints of a regional nature instead of crests. (A few early models marked FOLEY or SHELLEY/LATE FOLEY can be found with deep tinted pictorials printed all over. These are numbered but not named.)

Foley/Shelley also produced commemorative ware and souvenirs of most Royal events from 1860 onwards can be found. Commemoratives, view ware and crested pieces were also made for the American, Australian, New Zealand and South African markets but examples of these are difficult to find in Britain.

The only military badges recorded are the R.G.A., Royal Marines, RFC, Royal Artillery and 2nd Life Guards, but a 1914 War inscription can be found on some models. Commemoratives of the Boer War, although not crests, are of great interest to the military collector as they name generals and colonial supporters. (These are naturally marked Foley.)

Some late Shelley models do carry 'Lucky Black Cat' transfers but these are rare so it seems likely that they were only made in a limited way. Some 'Lucky White Heather' pieces have been found and the firm made very few coloured crested models. 'How Ink is Made' being a noticeable exception. Other coloured models were made in the 1920's, including a striking range of birds.

These however were not crested and are not listed here.

Very keen Shelley collectors are probably already aware of the wonderful range of crested domestic ware made by the firm. Collectors of 1920's and 30's china can find vases and bowls in lustred finishes and very evocative nursery ware designed by Hilda Cowham and Mabel Lucie Atwell.

Numbering System. This was the only firm to *print* (paint in the case of low numbers) a stock number on every model and to do so throughout that model's production. They appear to have begun to do so from around 1906 onwards, and so some early pieces marked Foley are not numbered.

From registration numbers and trade names found on numbered models one can deduce the approximate date of original production. The following is offered as a rough guide to dating:

Models 1-120 designed 1903-1910.

Models 130-413 designed 1910-1923/24

Models 500-507+ designed after 1923/24.

Stock numbers 91-99, 121-129, 216-299 (with the exception of a Bulldog which is found numbered 238), 390-399 and 414-499 do not appear to have been used. It seems that in four of the above five cases when a new series of models was added to the range the numbering recommenced at the nearest hundred above the last number. The exception, the gap between stock numbers 121 and 129, seems to have been caused by the introduction of the new Shelley/late Foley mark.

Real Shelley addicts may like to make their own list of models in numerical order – if they do they will find that 60 individual numbers have not yet been found. These unrecorded numbers must have been used and hopefully these models will eventually be recorded. Almost certainly a numbered model not listed here is rare.

NB: These lists include pieces marked Shelley, Foley and Shelley late Foley.

Shelley Models
Unglazed/Parian

Bust of *Albert*, King of the Belgians. 1915. 118mm.	47.50
Bust of *Burns* on square glazed base. 140mm.	30.00

Bust of *The Right Hon. Winston Churchill First Lord of the Admiralty.* 125mm.	95.00
Bust of HM King George V. 130mm.	55.00
Bust of French, with inscription: *Field Marshall Sir John French, Commander in Chief of the Expeditionary Force.* 118mm.	40.00
Bust of Jellicoe, with inscription: *Admiral Sir John Jellicoe. In Supreme Command of the North Sea Fleet.* 118mm.	43.50
Bust of Joffre, with inscription: *General Joffre, Commander in Chief of the French Army 1915.* 130mm.	47.50
Bust of Kitchener, with inscription: *Field Marshall Earl Kitchener, Secretary of State for War.* 118mm.	40.00
Bust of *The Rt Hon David Lloyd George.* 2 sizes: 118mm & 130mm.	47.50
Sailor standing with hands on hips, square base. Inscribed: *Ready! Aye! Ready!* and impressed: *HMS Lion.* Coloured. 170mm.	·125.00

Ancient Artefacts

Early Models (marked Foley) are sometimes found with no printed number or inscription. Models can be found with coloured transfer views, etc., instead of crests. All inscriptions begin: *Model of* so this will not be repeated throughout the list.

Ancient Cyprian Water Bottle. No. 140. 45mm.	8.00
Antique Tea Caddy – Queen Anne. No. 153. 70mm.	7.50
Aqua Mivel for pouring water over the hands of the priest. No. 137. 74mm wide.	7.50
Arabian Wine Vessel. No. 203. 75mm.	6.50
Caerswys Roman Vessel. No. 204 55mm.	5.00
Celtic Jar (an ancient). No. 200. 65mm.	4.00
Celtic Water Bottle. No. 205. 63mm.	4.50
Chester Roman Urn, inscribed: *A very rare Roman urn found near Chester now in possession of J.W. Salt Esq.* No. 118. 54mm.	5.00

Chinese Jar 12th Century. No. 304.
121mm.   11.00
*Chinese Vase of great antiquity and
beauty date about 5000 BC. Belongs
to the nation.* No. 115. 62mm.   5.00
Chinese Vase, about 500 AD. No. 213.
60mm.   5.00
Cinerary Urn of rare form. from
Northants. No. 134. 40mm.   7.00
Cleopatra's Vase, inscribed: *An
Egyptian vase taken from the tomb of
Cleopatra.* No. 114. 50mm.   7.50
Colchester Famous Vase, inscribed:
*Famous Colchester Vase in the
museum.* No. 110. 48mm.   4.00
Cyprian Vase about 3000 BC. No. 206.
62mm.   4.00
Cyprian Water Bottle. No. 192.
76mm.   4.00
Derby Roman Vase, inscribed:
*Roman Vase found at Little Chester,
Derby.* No. 83. 65mm.   7.50
Dorset Cinerary Urn, inscribed:
*Cinerary Urn with handles found at
Dorset.* No. 132. 56mm.   6.50
Dover Cinerary Urn, inscribed:
Cinerary Urn found in Dover.
No. 141. 63mm.   7.50
Eastern Olive Jar. No. 208.
53mm dia.   4.00
Egyptian Vase, inscribed: *Ancient
Egyptian Vase about 250 BC.*
No. 84. 43mm.   5.50
Ely Saxon Vase, inscribed: *Ancient
Saxon Vase, found in Ely.* No. 310.
88mm.   8.50
Exeter Vase. Unnamed Foley model.
No. 117. 55mm.   4.00
Flemish Jug 14th century. No. 312.
70mm.   15.00
Gastrica Vase, inscribed: *Vase or
bottle found in Gastrica. Ancient
Cyprian pottery 900 BC.* No. 138.
51mm.   5.00
Glastonbury Bowl, inscribed: *Bowl
from the ancient British lake village
near Glastonbury.* No. 101. 50mm.   4.00
Glastonbury Vase, inscribed: *Vase
from the Ancient British Lake Village
near Glastonbury.* No. 104. 50mm.   4.00
Hanley Chinese Vase, inscribed:
*Chinese Vase, originally in Hanley
Museum.* No. 80. 63mm.   5.00
Hanley Egyptian Vase, inscribed:
Ancient Egyptian vase now in

Hanley Museum. No. 88.
63mm.   10.50
Herpes Jug, inscribed: *Jug from
cemetary at Herpes, Charente.*
No. 133. 45mm.   6.50
Indian Wine Vessel from Temple, Delhi.
No. 303. 162mm.   21.00
Irish Bronze Pot. No. 109.
35mm.   5.00
Italian Vase. 16th Century. No. 301.
100mm.   7.50
Italian Vase. 16th Century. No. 309.
100mm.   6.50
*(The) Kai Ping Vase, date about 2500
BC.* No. 119. 63mm.   5.50
Kang Hi Tea Caddy. No. 144. 63mm.   8.50
Kang Hi Vase, presented to George V.
No. 305. 120mm.   12.50
Kent Roman Urn, inscribed: *Roman
urn from warriors grave, Kent.*
No. 211. 52mm.   5.00
Lesser Pyramid Vase, inscribed:
*Vase taken from a tomb under the
Lesser Pyramid about 3500 BC.*
No. 117. 57mm.   5.50
Letchworth Celtic Urn, inscribed:
Celtic Urn found in Letchworth. No.
199. 80mm.   6.50
Lord Byron's Vase, inscribed: *Fine
model of a Greek vase presented to
this nation by Lord Byron. Now in
South Kensington Museum.* No.
116. 57mm.   7.50
Loving Cup, 3 handled. Not found
numbered. 40mm.   4.00
Malta Chatty. No. 89. 44mm.   7.00
Mayer Jug 1870, Model of. No. 326.
71mm.   14.50
Newbury Leather Bottle, inscribed:
*Leather Bottle found on battlefield of
Newbury. 1644. Now in Museum.*
No. 103. 60mm.   4.00
Notre Dame Candlestick, inscribed:
*Altar Candlestick in church of Notre
Dame.* No. 306. 115mm.   9.50
Penmaenmawr Urn, inscribed:
*Ancient Urn found on
Penmaenmawr.* No. 108. 48mm.   4.00
Persian Cafeterre (fine), 15th Century.
No. 302. 118mm.   10.50
Persian Scent Bottle 700 AD. No. 212.
55mm.   5.50
Persian Wallace Vase. No. 82.
55mm.   8.00
Persian Wine Server. 13th Century.
No. 308. 105mm.   8.00

Phoenician Vase, original in Stoke-on-Trent Museum. No. 86. 57mm.   5.50
Phoenician Water Jar 1000 BC. No. 207. 65mm.   6.00
Pompeian Vessel in Burslem Museum. No. 87. 60mm.   5.00
Pompeian Wine Bottle, inscribed: *Wine Bottle taken from ruins Pompeii.* No. 135. 54mm.   15.00
Potters Vessel, found in Temple to Bhudda. No. 150. 54mm.   5.50
Puzzle Jug, with verse. No. 180. 65mm.   8.50
Roman Money Box, found at Lincoln AD 307. No. 131. 53mm.   7.50
Roman Tear Vase, 200 BC. No. 201. 63mm.   5.00
Roman Wine Vessel, 500 BC. No. 142. 51mm.   6.00
Sacred Vessel found in Bethlehem. No. 146. 51mm.   15.50
Salamis Lampshade, inscribed: *Ancient Cyprian pottery.* No. 130. 60mm.   7.00
Salonika Vase, inscribed: *Ancient Greek vase found at Salonika by the British troops when entrenching Jan 1916.* No. 170. 70mm.   17.50
Scandinavian Water Bottle. No. 143. 83mm.   5.50
Sevres Vase, 18th Century. No. 300. 88mm.   11.00
Sherborne Vase, inscribed: *Model of Roman Vase found in Sherborne.* A rather detailed, battered shape. Reg. No. 456392. 95mm.   30.00
Silchester Urn, inscribed: *Roman Urn, from Silchester in Reading Museum.* No. 107. 50mm.   4.00
Silchester Vase, inscribed: *Vase from Silchester in Reading Museum.* No. 102. 51mm.   4.00
Silver Rose Bowl. No. 147. 63mm.   8.00
Sofia Cup, inscribed: *Very quaint cup found with silver belt, Sofia, Bulgaria.* No. 139. 42mm.   7.50
Swindon Vase, inscribed: *Vase dug up near Swindon.* No. 105. 58mm.   4.00
Tara Vase, now in the Vatican, Rome. No. 113. 50mm.   6.00
Tibet Sacred Vase, inscribed: *Sacred Vase from Temple in Tibet.* No. 209. 60mm.   4.00
Turkish Scent Jar. S.K. No. 202. 66mm.   6.00

Vatican Urn, inscribed: *Golden Urn in the Vatican.* No. 145. 78mm.   10.00
Vestal Lamp, inscribed: *Roman vestal lamp. 500 BC.* No. 149. 78mm.   12.50
Has been found with a black boy's head popping out of lamp.   55.00
Water Bottle, inscribed: *Ancient water Bottle of rare form.* No. 136. 80mm long.   5.50
Water Bottle from tomb of Rameses II. No. 210.   10.00
Weymouth Vase, inscribed: *Roman Vase found at Jordan Hill, Weymouth now in Dorset Museum.* No. 85. 56mm.   7.50
York Roman Ewer, inscribed: *Roman Ewer from original in Hospitium, found in York.* No. 81. 63mm.   4.00

Buildings – White

The Tower, Blackpool, Model of. No. 322. 2 sizes: 125mm.   14.50
135mm.   14.50
Blackpool Tower with buildings. No. 412. 160mm.   14.50
Burns Cottage, Model of. No. 189. 68mm long.   19.50
Douglas Clock Tower – see Monuments.
Forth Bridge. 130mm long.   40.00
Glastonbury Tor, not found numbered. 85mm.   40.00
Manx Cottage, Model of (as Burns cottage above. No. 198 – with different inscription). 68mm long.   25.00
Monmouth Clock Tower –see Skegness Clock Tower.
Ross-on-Wye, Town Hall, with Clock Tower (not found numbered). 123mm.   70.00
Skegness, Clock Tower, can also be found inscribed: *Monmouth clock tower.* No. 371. 155mm.   22.50 / 33.50
Windsor Round Tower. No. 372. 88mm.   20.00

Monuments (including Crosses)

Douglas Isle of Man. Queen Victoria Jubilee Clock Tower. 1887. No. 388.   55.00
King Alfred, Statue (not found numbered). 165mm.   30.00
Peel Monument. Inscribed: *Peel Monument Halcombe Hill*

Ramsbottom. *Built 1851 in Commemoration of the Repeal of the Corn Laws*. No. 385. 123mm. This is a square tower on a square building, detailed brickwork.   115.00

Southport Lifeboat Memorial. No. 318. 140mm.   20.00

Rock of Ages, with verse (not found numbered). 125mm.   16.00

Rufus Stone, with lengthy inscriptions (not found numbered). 95mm.   5.50

Historical/Folklore

Bunyan's Chair (also found inscribed: *The old armchair*). No. 347. 90mm.   19.00

Burn's Chair. No. 336. 86mm.   9.00

Burn's Clock, Model of old Grandfather clock on Burns Cottage, Ayr. No. 307. 130mm.   20.00

Ducking Stool, two-piece, Leominster. 120mm long.   85.00

Mother Shipton with black or white hat and cat. With verse: *Near to the Knaresboro Dropping Well. I first drew breath as records tell*. No. 409. 110mm.   40.00

Sir Walter Scott's chair at Abbotsford, Model of. No. 325. 68mm.   12.50

Traditional/National Souvenirs

Highland Mary Statue. No. 411.   30.00

Burns and Highland Mary on oval base (not found numbered). 118mm.   35.00

Blackpool Ferris Wheel. No. 373. 117mm.   20.00

Legs of Man, model of. No. 351. 90mm.   20.00

Lincoln Imp, model of the, on pedestal. No. 160. 122mm.   14.50

Ripon Horn Blower, model of the, with inscription: *The old time custom of sounding the horn at 9pm each day is still observed*. No. 158. 110mm.   16.00

Manx Loving Cup, 3 handles as legs of Man. 80mm. (Foley mark only).   25.00

Channel Island Milk Can, fixed lid. No. 34. Unnamed. 60mm.   4.50

Kathleen Mavourneen, standing figure of Irish lady. Some colouring. No. 405. 98mm.   80.00

Pat's Hat and Dudeen, model of. (Irish Topper with pipe moulded on top). No. 159. 53mm.   17.00

Thistle Vase, can be found inscribed: *Just a wee deoch-an Doris*. No. 181.
2 sizes: 50mm.   5.00
65mm.   6.00

Welsh Lady, seated, inscribed: *Cymru-Am-Byth*. No. 404. 95mm (rare).   57.50

Welsh Hat, model of the. Can be found with longest Welsh place name round brim. (Very occasionally the hat can be found painted black with a red hat band). No. 154. 55mm.
Plain   7.50
Welsh name   12.50
Coloured   20.00

Swiss Cattle Bell. No. 314. 95mm.   17.00

Swiss Cattle Bell, not found numbered, with 'Late Foley' mark. 63mm.   15.00

Seaside Souvenirs

Bathing Machine. No. 320. 75mm long.   20.00

Lifebelt. No. 47. 100mm dia.   16.00

Lifebelt with cord on top. 92mm dia.   20.00

Lifeboatman, standing by Capstan, inscribed: *A Life Saver*. Some colouring. No. 410. 112mm.   75.00

Lifeboat, with gold anchor. No. 323. Can be found inscribed: *Maud Pickup*, add £7.00. 115mm long.   14.50

Boat, almost canoe shaped on two supports, with hole at top possibly for candle. 160mm long. (Foley mark only).   15.00

Motor Boat with driver. No. 353. 112mm long.   19.50

Paddle Steamer, model of. No. 362. 160mm long.   95.00

Yacht in full sail. No. 401. 112mm.   20.00

Fisherman's Basket, inscribed: *A good catch*. No. 186. 88mm long.   7.50

Beachy Head Lighthouse. No. 178. 100mm.   11.00

Pharos Lighthouse. No. 73. 98mm.   9.00

Lighthouse on rock. 90mm.   7.50

Lyme Regis Ammonite. 98mm.   16.00

Scallop Shell. No. 166. 78mm wide. — 8.00
Whelk Shell, inscribed: *What are the wild waves saying.* No. 168. 78mm long. — 12.00
Can also be found inscribed. *Sheringham Whelk.* Add £6.00.
Whelk Shell. No. 169. 70mm long. — 10.50

Countryside
Milk Can and lid. No. 34. 64mm. — 6.00
Milk Churn. No. 46. 71mm. — 7.00
Can be found inscribed: *Straight from the Coo.* — 10.00
Pine Cone, closed, on its side. 90mm long. — 4.00

Animals
Bear, walking. No. 67. 80mm long. — 40.00
Camel, kneeling (1 hump). No. 64. 102mm long. — 19.50
Cat, angry, inscribed: *Me backs up.* 2 sizes: No. 195. 90mm. — 25.00
          No. 198. 76mm. — 35.00
Latter with no tail-Manx.
Cat, comical, and sitting with red bow. No. 333. 132mm. — 34.50
Cat, sitting. No. 68. 64mm long. — 27.00
Cat, sitting, head slightly to one side, tail curled around, ruffled fur. No. 268. 96mm. — 26.00
Cat, standing, with long body. No. 381. — 35.00
Cheshire Cat, model of the Real, impressed: *Tim.* Can be found black. No. 148. 82mm. — 30.00
Cow, *Staffordshire Cow cream jug.* No. 317. — 20.00
Bulldog, seated, inscribed: *Another Dreadnought.* No. 233. 63mm. — 30.00
Bulldog, black, in kennel, inscribed: *Blackwatch.* (Also found with bulldog not painted and no inscription £12.00). No. 316. 95mm. — 14.00
Bulldog, seated. No. 324. — 22.00
Pup, standing on hand mirror, inscribed: *Some pup!* No. 382. (This number 382 is also found on a large comical Pup, inscribed: *Some pup!* It has black ears and spots. 116mm). — 110.00
Dog, alert terrier. No. 377. 80mm. — 34.50
Dog, Scottie, sitting. No. 505. 76mm. — 30.00
Dog, Scottie, wearing black tam-o'shanter. No. 506. — 40.00

Dog, Scottie, wearing glengarry. No. 507. 75mm. — 55.00
Dogs, 2 Scotties sitting, one wearing tam-o'shanter and other wearing glengarry. Both hats beautifully coloured. Can be found inscribed: *Scots Guards.* No. 386. 88mm. — 65.00
Donkey. No. 376. 115mm. — 30.00
Elephant, lying down. No. 70. 80mm long. — 24.50
Elephant, standing. No. 363. 70mm. — 47.50
Fish Jug (tail forms handle). No. 350. 105mm. — 21.00
Fox, sitting. No. 62. 78mm. — 50.00
Hare, sitting, looking behind. No. 66. 90mm long. — 75.00
Lion. No. 369. — 45.00
Monkey, sitting, can be found inscribed: *Who hung the monkey?* No. 61. 64mm. — 17.00
Mouse, sitting with paws raised. No. 65. 70mm. — 65.00
Pig, standing with inscription: *You can push, you can shuv but I'm hanged if I'll be druv.* — 32.00
or *Putney on a Pig.* No. 74. 90mm long. — 45.00
Pig, sitting, with folded arms, found inscribed: *Very umble* — 45.00
or *Sussex Pig, won't be druv.* — 29.50
or *Putney on a pig.* No. 60.
Rd. No. 447312. 80mm. — 65.00
Piglet, standing. No. 90. — 15.00
Toad. No. 71. 47mm. — 22.00
Terrapin. No. 69. 85mm. — 14.50

Birds (including Eggs)
Chick hatching from egg. 55mm. — 9.00
Duck, sitting. *A real prize Aylesbury Duck.* Reg. No. 582115. 85mm. — 40.00
Goose, plump. No. 63. 93mm. — 40.00
Penguin, with black beak, and holding newspaper. No. 384. 100mm. — 85.00
No. colouring. — 65.00
Swan, open wings, with coloured beak. No. 321. 85mm long. — 19.00

Great War
Scottish Soldier, standing figure, inscribed: *Scotland for ever.* No. 402. 114mm. — 115.00
Britannia, standing figure inscribed: *Rule Britannia.* Some colouring. No. 403. 108mm (rare). — 125.00

Britannia. Very much larger standing figure. *Rule Britannia* inscribed on front and also *Peace*. Naked child at side blowing trumpet. No. 409. Very rare. 120mm. 400.00

Marianne, inscribed: *Vive la France*. Some colouring. No. 406. 108mm (rare). 90.00

Soldier, playing concertina outside tent, inscribed: *Blighty is the place for Me-e-e*. No. 341. 108mm long. 90.00

Medical Orderly *For King & Country*, two red crosses on sleeves. 170mm. 500.00

Biplane, usually found with a fixed prop, but can be found with a movable one. No. 344. 150mm long. 120.00

Bleriot Warplane, model of. monoplane with fixed prop. No. 311. 150mm long. 65.00

Zeppelin, model of. No. 332. 154mm long. 65.00

Battleship, not found named. No. 319. 125mm long. 19.50

'AQUITANIA' 4 funnelled liner. An armed merchant cruiser used later as a troop transporter and hospital ship. No. 357. 160mm long. Very rare. 450.00

Submarine, inscribed: *E9*. No. 328. 150mm long. 40.00

Armoured Car, model of. No. 329. 120mm long. 45.00

Staff Car, Vauxhall. No. 361. 135mm long. 145.00

British Tank, model of, with trailing steering wheels. No. 400. 115mm long. 23.00

Model of British Tank without trailing wheels, with sponsons. No. 400A. Rd. No. 658586. 100mm wide, 145mm long. 200.00

Tank Bank, as above but as money box. No. 413. 140mm. Also found numbered 511. 65.00

Red Cross Van, model of. No. 330. 95mm long. 35.00

Howitzer. No. 340. 148mm long. 45.00

Field Gun. No. 331. 132mm long. 23.00

Trench Mortar, model of. Inscribed: *For freedom*. No. 179 or No. 327. 63mm. 17.00

9.2mm Shell, model of. No. 175. 90mm. 11.00

Not named. 7.00

With Lydd crest. 14.00

German Zeppelin Bomb, model of. No. 177. 85mm. 19.50

Mills Hand Grenade, model of. No. 334. 78mm. 19.50

Model of German Mine washed up on the East Coast. No. 188. 55.00
Can be found wrongly inscribed: *Head of German torpedo (Model of)*. No. 187. 68mm (rare). 65.00

Head of German Torpedo, Model of. No. 187. 70mm (scarce). 110.00

Bandsman's Drum. No. 57. 32mm. 10.50

Drum. No. 49. 60mm. 10.50

Bugle. No. 354. 112mm. 40.00

Field Glasses. No. 343. 83mm. 20.00

Peaked Cap. No. 54. 53mm dia. 10.50

Glengarry. No. 176. 86mm long. 17.00

Anti Zeppelin Candlestick as used during the Great War – souvenir. No. 348. 83mm. 45.00

Fireplace, inscribed: *Keep the home fires burning*. No. 338. 70mm. 20.50

Coal Hod, inscribed: *Coal rations; Yours to a Cinder* or *Your rations to a cinder*. No. 183. 55mm. 19.50

Cenotaph, flags in relief. No. 368. 2 sizes: 130mm. 20.00
152mm. 28.00

Florence Nightingale, sitting figure. No. 408. 102mm (rare). 125.00

Matlock Bath War Memorial, not found numbered. 180mm. 32.00

Home/Nostalgic

Anvil, inscribed: *Every morning sees some task to be done*. No. 183. 83mm long. 7.50

Armchair, inscribed: *The old armchair*. 8.50
(Also found inscribed: *Bunyan's Chair*). No. 347. 90mm. 19.00

Baby's Cradle. (Often found not numbered when marked *Foley*). Found No. 50 and No. 503 (Shelley). 80mm long. 17.00

Bellows. No. 55. 95mm long. 14.50

Book. No. 56. 63mm. 10.50

Box of Matches, open to reveal contents. Some colouring. No. 190. 74mm long. 23.00

Cheese. 45mm. 8.50

Cigarette Case holding 6 gold-tipped cigarettes. No. 349. 35.00

Clock, long case, inscribed: *Model of
14th Century clock in Wallace
collection.* Usually inscribed: *Wake
up and get to business,* or more
rarely: *The moving finger writes and
having writ moves on* (add £10.00),
or *Burns Clock* (add £4.00).
No. 307. 130mm.   16.00
Desk, roll-topped. No. 380.
80mm long.   24.00
Lace Iron. No. 504. 70mm.   12.50
Garden Roller. No. 358.
104mm long.   17.00
Handbag. No. 184. 85mm.   12.50
Kennel. No. 49. 55mm.   11.50
Lantern, inscribed: *Model of ye olde
lanterne* and *Ancient lights.*
No. 346. 105mm.   14.50
Pocket Watch and Matchbox
Holder. No. 379. 100mm.   40.00
Shaving Mug. No. 164. 54mm.   7.50
Sundial, octagonal with transfer of
dial face. No. 359. 120mm.   16.00
Swing Mirror on stand. No. 376.
88mm.   17.00
Tobacco Pouch, 2 crossed pipes in
relief on front. No. 501.
98mm long.   19.00
Trunk. No. 167. 54mm.   11.00
Valise, half open. No. 53.
2 sizes: 73mm long.   7.50
          120mm long.   19.50
Victorian Pillar Box, model of.
No. 157. 90mm.   30.00
Watering Can. No. 163. 63mm.   10.50
Water Pump. No. 51. 83mm.   11.00
Wheelbarrow. No. 355. 110mm long.   14.50

Comic/Novelty
Black Boy in bath, inscribed: *How
ink is made.* Partly coloured.
No. 374. 108mm long.   85.00
Coal Hod. No. 185. 55mm.   13.00
Japanese Lady, inscribed: *Yum, Yum,*
some colouring. No. 407. 123mm.   150.00
Santa Claus, partly coloured,
carrying sack of coloured toys.
No. 378.   250.00
Truck of black coal, inscribed: *Black
diamonds from...* No. 389.
62mm long.   20.00

Alcohol
Beer Barrel. No. 48. 63mm.   7.50
Beer Barrel on stand. No. 161. 65mm.   9.00

Bottle with cork, sometimes
inscribed: *All Scotch.* No. 214.
90mm.   8.50
No inscription.   6.50
Soda Syphon. No. 502. 96mm.   16.00
Toby Jug, with verse: *No tongue can
tell* etc. No. 335. 95mm.   16.00

Sport/Pastimes
Boxer, inscribed: *England's hope.*
Brown boxing gloves. No. 375.
100mm.   170.00
Golf Bag and Clubs. No. 197.
108mm.   75.00
Golf Ball. No. 210. 50mm.   9.50
Golf Ball on Tee. No. 215. 52mm.   11.00
Tennis Racquet with 3 Balls. No. 194.
116mm long.   19.00

Musical Instruments
Banjo. No. 72. 127mm long.   12.50
Piano, upright. No. 345. 76mm.   20.00

Transport
Charabanc, inscribed: *The Monarch.*
No. 352. 125mm long.   47.50
Cycle Lamp, very rarely found
inscribed: *Model of cycle oil head
Lamp.* No. 342. 83mm.   75.00
Locomotive. No. 365. 150mm long.   160.00
Motor Coupé. No. 360. 135mm long.   240.00
Single Decker closed Motorbus 'K'
type. No. 370. 120mm long.   170.00
Double Decker Omnibus. No. 370.   255.00

Modern Equipment
Flash Lamp, model of. No. 191.
70mm.   13.00
Horn Gramophone. No. 337. 95mm.   30.00
Steamroller. No. 364. 130mm long.   390.00

Hats
Bishop's Mitre. No. 58. 70mm.   10.50
Top Hat, found numbered 11 and 35.
60mm wide.   10.50
Top Hat, large. 75mm.   30.00
Trilby Hat, with black band.
No. 500.   40.00

Footwear
Dutch Sabot. No. 36. 84mm long.   7.50
Leather Highboot. No. 47. 69mm.   16.00
Lancashire Clog. No. 162.
98mm long.   14.00

Miniature Domestic

Cheese Dish and lid. No. 196. 50mm.	14.00
Cup and Saucer. 38mm.	5.00
Tea Pot, fixed lid, inscribed: *Take a cup of tea.* No. 38. 50mm.	16.00

Domestic

Candleholder. No. 339. 107mm long.	15.00
Candleholder. 135mm long.	15.00
Coffee Pot with lid, ribbed and fluted. 140mm.	5.50
Hatpin Holder, circular base. 122mm.	12.50
Inkwell and pen rest. No. 165. 60mm long.	16.00
Pin Tray. 75mm dia.	3.00
Pin Tray, diamond. 92mm long.	3.00

Numbered Ornamental Wares

No. 1. Pin Tray.	4.50
No. 2. Vase.	3.00
No. 3. Dish with ribbed sides. 120mm dia.	8.00
and mug, 38mm. 120mm dia.	4.00
No. 4. 2 handled Loving Cup. 40mm.	4.00
No. 5. Fluted Trinket Tray. 70mm dia.	4.00
No. 6. Bell shaped vase.	4.50
No. 7. Vase, 2 handled with crinkle top. 56mm.	4.50
No. 11. 2-handled pot. 35mm.	4.50
No. 16. Jug, with high looped handle. 63mm.	11.00
No. 18. Small Jug. 44mm.	3.00
No. 20. Jug. 65mm.	5.00
No. 21. Vase. 70mm.	5.00
No. 22. Vase, shaped. 38mm.	3.50
No. 23. 2-handled Vase. 50mm.	4.50
No. 24. Pot, with lid. 50mm dia.	8.50
No. 25. Vase, 2 handles, with bulbous base. 60mm.	4.50
No. 26. Vase, 2 handles. 40mm.	4.50
No. 27. Vase, 2 handles, with crinkle top. 85mm.	5.00
No. 28. Jug, square. 35mm.	4.00
No. 29. Two-handled Vase. 64mm.	10.00
No. 30. Jug. 72mm.	5.00
No. 31. Cauldron. 2 handled. 35mm.	4.00
No. 32. Jug, small. 38mm.	5.00
No. 33. Vase, 2 handles. 54mm.	10.50
No. 34. Milk Can and lid. 62mm.	5.50
No. 40. Cream Jug. 55mm.	4.00
No. 41. Jug. 63mm.	4.00
No. 42. Jug. 65mm.	5.00
No. 43. Vase, 2 handles. 54mm.	4.00
No. 44. Jug, 2 handles. 50mm.	6.00
No. 45. Vase, crinkle top. 52mm.	3.00
No. 80. Jug. 74mm.	4.00
No. 106. Vase. 65mm.	4.00
No. 109. Irish Bronze Pot. (Unnamed). 36mm.	5.00
No. 111. Urn. 58mm.	3.00
No. 112. Taper Vase. 60mm.	6.50
No. 120. Box, heart-shaped. 32mm.	7.00
No. 121. Pin Box and lid. 40mm.	6.50
No. 123. Pin Box and lid, square. 32mm.	6.50
No. 124. Pin Box, crinkle edge. 30mm.	6.50
No. 146. Jug. 66m.	6.50
No. 147. Silver Rose Bowl. 64mm.	8.00
No. 151. Bulbous Vase with 2 handles and spout.	4.00
No. 171. Salt Pot.	10.00
No. 173. Salt Pot, circular. 100mm.	11.00
No. 174. Pepper Pot, circular. 100mm.	11.00
No. 181. Pin Box, waisted. 50mm long.	4.50
No. 417. Ewer. 75mm.	4.00

Miscellaneous

Ewer with shamrock shape top. 38mm.	4.00
Horseshoe. No. 182. 100mm.	17.50
Horse's Hoof. No. 52. (often found not numbered). 45mm.	6.50
Shield on stand, not found numbered. 52mm.	9.00
Urn with lid. 88mm.	3.50
Wall Pocket. 90mm.	5.00

Signal Series or Signal China

Skarab China

Trademark used for J. Baker & Son, Bristol, by an unknown manufacturer.

Only one small and two animals found with this mark.

Skarab Models
Animals

Pig, kneeling. 70mm long.	10.00
Squirrel eating nut. 60mm.	30.00

Miniature Domestic

Cheese Dish, one piece. 65mm long.	6.50

Trademark used by Hewitt and Leadbeater, Willow Potteries, Longton (Usual trademark Willow Art) for their Dublin agent.

'Smalls' only found with this mark, except for the following:

Signal Models
Home/Nostalgic

Anvil. 65mm long.	7.50
Fireplace, inscribed: *There's no place like home*, with black kettle and cauldron, red fire in relief. 65mm.	15.00

Miniature Domestic

Cheese Dish and cover.	7.50

Snowdon China

Souvenir Series

Trademark used for the Snowdon Mountain Tramroad and Hotels Co. Ltd, on china manufactured by Arkinstall & Sons Ltd, Arcadian Works, Stoke-on-Trent. (Usual trademark Arcadian).

For further details of this china and manufacturer see Arcadian China.

All crests found on china with this mark are either of Snowdon or Snowdon Mountain Tramroad & Hotels Co. Ltd. (This is a most striking red, white and black crest with the initials S.M.T.) The china is very fine and well produced.

Snowdon Models
Traditional/National Souvenirs
Welsh Harp. 80mm.   8.50
Welsh Hat, model of, with longest
   Welsh place name round brim.
   52mm.   8.50
Welsh Tea Party, 3 Welsh ladies
   taking tea. Coloured. 50mm.   35.00

Animals
Black Cat sitting on a pouffe
   inscribed: *Good Luck*. 95mm.   24.00

Great War
Cenotaph. 83mm.   4.00

Home/Nostalgic
Umbrella, open. 50mm dia.   14.50

Comic/Novelty
Bookmaker with greyhound and
   hare on ashtray. Some colouring.
   90mm long.   45.00

Modern Equipment
Camera folding. 60mm.   40.00

Trademark used by an unknown manufacturer for a London wholesaler or retailer.

Two 'smalls' have been found with transfer prints of four flags of the Allies with the inscription: *We are fighting for a just cause.*

Souvenir Models
Seaside Souvenirs
Whelk Shell. 90mm long.   3.00

Animals
Pig. Inscribed: *The Pig that wont go.*
   95mm long.   12.50

Home/Nostalgic
Coal Scuttle. 53mm.   5.00

Footwear
Lancashire Clog. 85mm long.   5.00

S P Co Ltd

Spencer Art China

^{SPENCER}
ART
CHINA
FENTON
STAFFS

Trademark used for a wholesaler or retailer in Manchester by an unknown manufacturer.

SP Models
Ancient Artefacts
Swindon Vase (not named).   3.00

Domestic
Pin Tray 75mm long Rectangular.   3.00
Stamp Box and lid. 63mm long.   5.50
Small Vase. 55mm.   2.00

Trademark used for a retailer by a Fenton manufacturer.

The models below all have Isle of Wight crests and one would assume that 'Spencer' was a retailer or wholesaler on that island. (No potter or pottery named Spencer was working in Fenton from 1900-1920.) The three Fenton manufacturers known to have produced a quantity of crested china were E. Hughes Ltd., A.G. Harley Jones and James Reeves. E. Hughes mostly made domestic ware so they were hardly likely to have produced the models below. The other two manufacturers could have used this mark but A.G. Harley Jones is possibly the most likely candidate as he used the term Art China in his marks (see Wilton China).

One 'small' has been found with a Leeds crest, which could have been used to fill another order.

Spencer Art Models
Buildings – White
Osborne House. 150mm long.   82.50
The Old Village, Shanklin, IoW.
     100mm long.   120.00

Monuments (including Crosses)
Arch Rock, Freshwater Bay. 82mm.   28.00

Historical/Folklore
Mons Meg, Edinburgh Castle, model of.
     130mm long.   11.00

Animals
Calf. 102mm.   22.00
Cheshire Cat, inscribed: *Still*
    Smiling. 82mm.   7.50

Alcohol
Barrel with open top. 45mm.   3.50

Sport/Pastimes
Rook chess piece. 48mm.   6.50

Sphinx

Trademark used by a foreign (French or
    German) manufacturer for the Belgian
    souvenir market.

The only model found has crest of
    Bruxelles.

Sphinx Models
Historical/Folklore
Coach and Horses with 3 figures,
    coloured, on base. 100mm long.   40.00

Sporting Series

SR

Trademark used by Arkinstall & Son Ltd., Arcadian Works, Stoke-on-Trent, usual trademark Arcadian.

Only one piece has been recorded with this mark, a spade trump with colour transfer of pheasants. It would appear that the Sporting Series was not a commercial success.   20.00

Mark used before 1913.

Trademark used by Samuel Radford (Ltd), High St, Fenton.
This china manufacturer established in 1879 did not produce a large range of crested china.

SR Models
Ancient Artefacts
Loving Cup, 3 handled. 35mm.   3.00

Countryside
Milk Churn and lid. 70mm.   5.00

Miniature Domestic
Cheese Dish and cover. 64mm long.   6.50

Standard China

Trademark used by an unknown British porcelain manufacturer.

Standard China Model
Domestic
Cup and saucer.   3.50

Stanley China

Trademark used by Charles Amison (& Co. Ltd), Stanley China Works, Wedgwood St, Longton.
The firm was established in 1889 and manufactured porcelain. (The factory closed in 1941 and was reopened in 1946, and continues to make Stanley fine bone china today.) Like most fairly successful firms, Amison made a small range of crested china wares when these were very fashionable. The models made seem to have sold well in the north of England.
No view ware or transfer devices have been recorded.

Stanley Models
Ancient Artefacts
Puzzle Jug. 66mm.   5.50

Animals
Dog, bulldog sitting. Some
    colouring. 68mm.   15.00

Birds (including Eggs)
Parakeet, some colouring.
    110mm.   20.00

Great War
Battleship. 119mm long.   18.00

Home/Nostalgic
Grandfather Clock. 105mm.   10.50
Pillar Box. 76mm.   10.00

Footwear
Boot. 70mm.   7.50

Lancashire Clog.
   2 sizes: 125mm long   6.50
          135mm long.   6.50
Sabot. 80mm long.   5.00

Miniature Domestic
Cheese Dish and cover. 50mm.   6.50

Domestic
Pepper Pot. 80mm.   4.00
Pin Box and Lid, rectangular.
   56mm long.   4.00

Star Bazaar Art China

Trademark used for the Star Bazaar, Douglas,
Isle of Man, on china thought to have been
manufactured by Hewitt & Leadbeater,
Willow Potteries, Longton. (Usual
trademark Willow Art).

For details of Hewitt & Leadbeater see
Willow Art China.

This mark is only found on china with
Douglas or Isle of Man crests. Hewitt &
Leadbeater often used Art China in marks
designed for retailers, and the models
below could have been produced by them.

Star Bazaar Models
Ancient Artefacts
Puzzle Jug. 70mm.   5.50

Traditional/National Souvenirs
Manx Man, John Bull mould with
   extra leg at back. 126mm.   95.00

Animals
Manx cat with collar, not named.
   63mm.   19.50

Home/Nostalgic
Anvil. 50mm.   7.50

Strand China

Success (Art) China

Trademark used for a London retailer by Podmore China Co, Elm Street, Hanley. (Usual trademark Podmore). This retailer obviously supplied towns all over the country as crests other than London are found.

Strand Models
Monuments (including Crosses)

Nelson's Column. 144mm.	40.00

Animals

Angry Cat, with arched back and tail. 100mm.	12.50
Dog in kennel, inscribed: *Black Watch*. 67mm.	10.50
Elephant, standing. 75mm.	20.00

Birds (including Eggs)

Penguin. 84mm.	11.50
Woodpecker.	20.00

Great War

Cenotaph, inscribed.	
3 sizes: 80mm.	4.00
130mm.	6.50
165mm.	7.50
Edith Cavell Memorial, London Inscribed: *Edith Cavell Brussels dawn October 12th 1915. Humanity sacrifice*. 142mm.	14.50

Home/Nostalgic

Thimble. 43mm.	19.50

Trademark used by an unknown retailer, supplied by Hewitt & Leadbeater (usual trademark Willow Art), and possibly another manufacturer as well.

The fact that two quite different marks are found can either indicate that the tradename was used for a long time or that the name was used by more than one manufacturer. There are so few models found with these marks (and unfortunately the two were not recorded separately) that one must accept that they could be from two manufacturers.

The Art China mark would have been used by Hewitt & Leadbeater (see Willow Art China). The Garter mark is much more difficult, for several firms used this device, including Hewitt & Leadbeater in retailers' marks. No models have stock numbers or inscriptions which give clues to the manufacturer so until such a piece is found the marks must remain unidentified.

The Salisbury Kettle listed below has a coloured transfer print of Beachy Head.

Success (Art) Models
Parian/Unglazed
Bust of *John Peel* with details of
    verse. 136mm.   75.00

Ancient Artefacts
Lincoln Jack. No. 34. 52mm.   3.00
Salisbury Leather Kettle. 61mm.   3.00

Traditional/National Souvenirs
Thistle vase with inscription: *A wee*
    Deoch-&-Doris. 50mm.   4.00

Seaside Souvenirs
Lighthouse, black band. 105mm.   5.50

Great War
Torpedo. 145mm long.   55.00

Home/Nostalgic
Anvil. 58mm.   7.50
Grandfather Clock. 121mm.   10.50

Sussex China

Trademark used for an Eastbourne retailer by Sampson Hancock (& Sons), Bridge Works, Stoke. Pieces were sold with Sussex towns coats of arms. (Usual trademark Corona).

For further details of this china and manufacturer see The Corona China.

For the most part the models are identical to those found in the Corona range, except that there were two versions of Beachy Head Lighthouse made specially for this retailer. The models were probably made during the Great War.

Sussex China Models
Buildings – White
Bridge. Rarely found inscribed
    Weymouth Bridge Add £15.00
    130mm long.   19.50

Historical/Folklore
Ark. 90mm long.   5.00
Mother Shipton. 73mm.   17.00

Traditional/National Souvenirs
Laxey Wheel. 80mm.   40.00

Seaside Souvenirs
Lighthouse. 104mm.   5.50
Beachy Head Lighthouse, black band.
    3 sizes: 102mm.   7.50
            118mm.   7.50
            150mm.   11.00

Animals
Staffordshire Bull Terrier. 79mm.	12.50
Teddy Bear, sitting. 85mm.	19.50

Great War
British Airship on base.
128mm long.	30.00
Lusitania. 163mm long.	75.00
Submarine, inscribed: *E4*.	
102mm long.	19.50
Submarine, inscribed: *E5*.	
125mm long.	20.00
Torpedo. 150mm long.	55.00

Home/Nostalgic
Cigarette Case. 70mm long.	13.00
Hip Bath. 95mm long.	10.50

Footwear
Lancashire Clog. 105mm long.	6.50

Musical Instruments
Harp. 90mm.	6.50

Sport/Pastimes
King, chess piece. 110mm.	25.00
Pawn, chess piece. 60mm.	25.00

Modern Equipment
Box Gramophone with arm on
record, no horn. 60mm square.	15.00

Domestic
Candlestick, column. 89mm.	3.00

Sussex China S.P. Co.

Trademark used for a Sussex wholesaler by Arkinstall & Son Ltd, Arcadian Works, Stoke-on-Trent. (Usual trademark Arcadian).

For further details of this china and manufacturer see Arcadian China.

S.P. Co. must have been a wholesaler in fancy goods or had a chain of shops because china models with this mark have crests from all over Sussex. Coloured transfer prints of Sussex views have been recorded but no other transfer devices, indicating that the mark was probably only used between 1914 and 1920.

One jug has been found with an Ashford crest, so Kent crests must also have been used.

Sussex S.P. Co. Models
Ancient Artefacts
Newbury Leather Bottle. 65mm.	4.00

Buildings – White
Cottage. 55mm.	8.50
Hastings Clock Tower. 157mm.	14.00

Traditional/National Souvenirs
Welsh Hat. 35mm.	5.00

Seaside Souvenirs
Houseboat. 58mm.	5.00
Lifeboat, inscribed: *Charles Arkcoll*	
115mm long.	18.50
Whelk Shell. 100mm long.	3.00

Countryside
Hay Stack, circular. 57mm.	6.50
Milk Churn and lid. 60mm.	5.00

Animals

Dog, Staffordshire bull terrier, sitting. 72mm.	12.00
Pig, sitting. 63mm long.	20.00
Rabbit, lying, ears along back. 70mm long.	8.50
Tortoise. 70mm long.	9.00

Birds (including Eggs)

Swan. 62mm long.	7.50

Great War

British Airship found wrongly named *Model of Super Zeppelin.* 128mm long.	20.00
Battleship, 3 funnels and tiny gun fore and aft. 120mm long.	17.50
Red Cross Van. 85mm long.	30.00
Howitzer. 140mm long.	20.00
Mills Hand Grenade, model of. 62mm.	19.50
Colonial Hat. 88mm long.	16.00
Bell Tent. 64mm dia.	16.00
Ghurka Knife, model of. 110mm long.	20.00
Sandbag, model of. 73mm long.	22.50
Trench Dagger, model of. 102mm long.	47.50

Home/Nostalgic

Old Armchair, not named. 90mm.	6.00
Lantern. 90mm.	6.50

Comic/Novelty

Bean Pod, curved and split to reveal peas. 133mm long.	16.00
Policeman, no inscription. 140mm.	28.00

Sport/Pastimes

King, chess piece. 110mm.	25.00
Knight, chess piece. 63mm.	14.50

Musical Instruments

Banjo. 140mm long.	10.50
Double Bass. 151mm.	30.00
Piano, upright. 70mm long.	16.00

Footwear

Lancashire Clog. 100mm long.	5.50

Domestic

Pin Box and lid -- circular. 64mm dia.	4.00

Sussex Ware

No details of mark available.

Trademark used for Cheesman & Co, Brighton by Hewitt & Leadbeater, Willow Potteries, Longton. (Usual mark Willow Art).

For further details of this china and manufacturer see Willow Art China.

The sixth edition of the Goss Record published in 1906-7 carries an advert for the Goss Agent in Brighton, Cheesman & Co, 169 North Street, Brighton. In the advert the firm announces the sale of their 'Sussex Ware; including 'Ye Olde Sussex Pig', green with ivory decoration or brown with hop decoration. In 1905 when the new firm of Hewitt & Leadbeater was given a write-up in the *Pottery Gazette*, 'Hop Ware' was one of their newly invented lines. Hewitt & Leadbeater obviously went on to make heraldic china for Cheesman & Co. until well after the Great War.

No 'Ye Olde Sussex Pigs' have been recorded but would be a delightful novelty to look out for. They would probably not carry the Sussex China Garter mark.

A model of 'Ye Olde Sussex Pig' was reputedly made but so far has not been seen.	16.00

Swan China

Trademark used by Charles Ford, Cannon St, Hanley, subsequently a branch of J.A. Robinson & Sons Ltd. (Usual trademark Arcadian).

The original firm, known as T. & C. Ford at this address, was formed in 1854. By 1871 it was known as Thomas Ford, and in 1874 it became Charles Ford. (Presumably all these Fords were members of the same family.) Production of view ware and crested china seems to have begun at the turn of the century. Very shortly after this, in 1904, Mr Harold Taylor Robinson gained control of the firm and merged it with Robinson & Beresford in 1907. In 1910, Charles Ford was made a branch of J.A. Robinson & Sons Ltd, and production of Swan China was moved to the Arcadian Works. It is very difficult to distinguish original Charles Ford moulds from Arkinstall moulds, as both were used at the Arcadian Works and models were marked Swan or Arcadian. (Pieces are often found with both marks.) Early Swan models seem to be heavier than Arcadian China, these include miniature domestic items, small vases and animals. Later Swan and Arcadian models are identical. The Swan mark does not seem to have been used after 1925.

Early Charles Ford models can be found with views, monochrome only, and crests, often accompanied by suitable long and learned historic details concerned with the place or person. These do not appear on Arcadian China. An interesting range of all the crests of English Monarchs (about forty) can be found, each crest on a different small piece, with the relevant historical information printed on the reverse.

Polychrome view ware is the same as Arcadian, as are other transfer decorations including tropical birds, cockerels and Raphael Tuck cartoons. (These are always found with 'By special permission of Raphael Tuck & Sons Ltd.' printed on the base when marked Swan.)

Great War commemoratives and inscriptions are the same as Arcadian including crests of the Allies, but as yet the only military crests recorded are:

Black Watch
5th Dragoon Guards
Gordon Highlanders
2nd Life Guards
Royal Berkshire
Royal Irish Dragoon Guards

A Lucky Black Cat transfer has been found, but these are not common. No Lucky White Heather devices have been recorded.

Numbering System. Original Charles Ford models carry painted stock numbers, but few of these have been recorded. Models made at the Arcadian Works have printed stock numbers which do not correspond to the numbers found on similar Arcadian pieces. Stock numbers are given where known in the following lists.

Swan Models
Unglazed/Parian

These busts can be found with crests on their glazed bases, add £10.00 if the bust carries the correct Royal coat of arms.

Bust of King Edward VII on circular glazed base. 140mm.	40.00
Bust of Queen Alexandra, on circular glazed base. 140mm.	47.50
Bust of King George V, on circular glazed base. 135mm.	47.50
Bust of Queen Mary, can be found inscribed: *Queen Mary, born May 26th 1867.* 135mm.	47.50
Bust of *HRH Prince of Wales Born June 23rd 1894*, dressed as midshipman. 125mm.	47.50
Bust of Sir John Jellicoe on square glazed base. 175mm.	75.00

Bust of General Joffre, on square
glazed base. 155mm.   65.00
Bust of Lloyd George, on circular
glazed base. 135mm.   55.00
Bust of Burns. 80mm.   17.50
Bust of Wordsworth on glazed base.
118mm.   17.50

Ancient Artefacts

British Bronze Pot. No. 160. 70mm.   4.00
Butter Pot, old, of 17th Century.
45mm.   4.00
Canterbury Roman Ewer, inscribed:
Roman Ewer found near Canterbury
original in Canterbury Museum.
No. 294. 64mm.   4.00
Canterbury Roman Vase. 65mm.
No. 282.   4.00
Chinese Vase original in Hanley
Museum. 58mm.   4.00
Club Vase. No. 582. 68mm.   3.00
Devon Oak Pitcher. 60mm.
No. 192.   3.00
Dogger Bank Bottle. 70mm.   3.00
Eddystone Jug, inscribed: *old*
Spanish jug dredged up near
Eddystone now in Atheneum,
Plymouth. No. 585. 58mm.   4.00
Egyptian Vase, inscribed: *Ancient*
Egyptian Vase 230BC. No. 155. 42mm.   4.00
Egyptian Water Bottle. No. 156.
58mm long.   4.00
Fountains Abbey Cup. No. 709.   3.00
Glastonbury Vase. No. 642. 50mm.   4.00
Highland Whisky Bowl inscribed:
Model of Highland Whiskey Bowl.
No. 158. 90mm wide.   5.50
Highland Whisky Bowl.
134mm wide.   7.50
Irish Bronze Pot. No. 110. 35mm.   4.00
Kendal Jug. 75mm. No. 210.   3.00
Lincoln Jack from Original in
Museum. 62mm. No. 50.   4.00
Loving Cup originated by Henry of
Navarre, King of France. 3
handled.
2 sizes: 40mm.   4.00
52mm.   4.00
Newbury Leather Bottle. 67mm.   4.00
Phoenician Vase, originally in Stoke-
on-Trent Museum. No. 217. 60mm.   4.00
Puzzle Jug, original in South
Kensington Museum, with verse:
Try how to drink and not to spill.
No. 147 and No. 303. 70mm.   5.50

Puzzle Teapot. 86mm long.   10.50
Salopian Roman Ewer inscribed:
Roman Salopian Ewer found at
Uriconium now in Shrewsbury
Museum. 70mm.   3.00
Shakespeare's Jug. 54mm.   3.00
Southwold Jar.   3.00
Toby Jug.
2 sizes: 61mm.   7.50
75mm.   8.50
Upstones Jug, inscribed: *Ancient jug*
found near Upstones, Staffs.
No. 221. 62mm.   4.00
(Also found inscribed Ipstones).
It seems Upstones was a spelling
mistake.
Winchelsea Vase. 82mm.   3.00
Winchester Vase.   4.00
York Roman Ewer. No. 57. 55mm.   3.00
York Roman Urn.   3.00

Buildings – Coloured

Shakespeare's House. 84mm long.   20.00

Buildings – White

The Tower Blackpool. 104mm.   ·10.50
Hamsfell Hospice. 70mm.   30.00
Ann Hathaway's Cottage, Shottery,
near Stratford-on-Avon.
83mm long.   11.00
First and Last Refreshment House
in England. 73mm long.   12.50
Highland Cottage, model of. 80mm.   20.00
Irish Round Tower. 106mm.   13.00
Marble Arch. 65mm.   28.00
Southampton Bargate. 66mm.   24.50
Tower Bridge. 92mm.   35.00
Welsh Cottage, Model of. Same model
as Highland Cottage).
79mm long.   20.00

Monuments (including Crosses)

Barrow's Monument, Ulverston.
145mm.   52.50
Celtic Cross, not named. Usually
Irish crest. 125mm.   14.00
Iona Cross, not named. 120mm.   6.00
Lifeboat Memorial. 117mm.   16.00
Margate Surf Boat Statue.
120mm.   20.00
Plymouth Armada Memorial.
180mm.   30.00

Historical/Folklore

Ancient Coaching Hat, model of.
65mm long. ... 7.50
Davey Safety Lamp '1836'. 85mm. ... 16.50
Font, inscribed: *Model of ancient font in Tideswell church dates back to the 14th century.* 90mm. ... 28.00
Jenny Geddes Stool. 45mm. ... 10.50
Judge, bust, with inscription: *Defend the children of the poor and punish the wrong doer. Copy of inscription of New Bailey Court, London.* With inscription add £10.00
3 sizes: 55mm. ... 14.00
60mm. ... 17.50
70mm. ... 20.50
Robinson Crusoe, holding Rifle.
120mm. ... 110.00
Mother Shipton, with verse: *Near to Knaresboro dropping well.*
2 sizes: 76mm. ... 8.00
115mm. ... 15.00
Man in Stocks. 88mm. ... 20.00

Traditional/National Souvenirs

John Bull, bust.
2 sizes: 66mm. ... 14.50
86mm. ... 14.50
Luton Boater. 78mm dia. ... 8.50
Monmouth Hat with verse. 54mm. ... 20.00
Melton Mowbray Pie, The. Pie with moulded pastry adornments and verse. 50mm. ... 19.50
Ripon Horn blower with inscription. 130mm. ... 10.50
Irish Colleen. Bust. 85mm. ... 30.00
Irish Harp with Shamrocks. 112mm. ... 10.50
Thistle Vase, with verse: *Just a wee deoch-&-doris* No. 14. 65mm. ... 3.00
Welsh Hat. 50mm. ... 8.50
Welsh Hat with longest place name on brim. 50mm, 78mm dia. ... 8.50
Welsh Lady, bust. 65mm. ... 14.00
Welsh Leek, can be found with inscription: *King Henry V. The Welshmen did gcot servace (at Crecy) in a garden where leeks did grow. Shakespeare.* 98mm. ... 5.00
Japanese Lady, sitting with fan.
No. 61. 62mm. ... 34.00

Seaside Souvenirs

Bathing Machine with '32' above the door.
2 sizes: 60mm. ... 10.00
85mm. ... 20.00
Bell Rock lighthouse. 141mm. ... 25.00
Lifeboat with blue band and yellow rigging. 113mm long. ... 12.50
Sometimes found named *James Stevenson, Albert Edward, Elizabeth Simpson, John Birch* or *Nancy Lucy.* ... 18.50
Novel Collecting Box for the Royal National Lifeboat Institution Robin Hoods Bay, model of fish standing on square base inscribed: *My diet is £.s.d.*
128mm. ... 40.00
Lifeboatman bust. 85mm. ... 19.50
Lifebelt. 80mm dia. ... 10.50
Fishing Basket, found inscribed: *A good catch.* 50mm. ... 5.50
Beachy Head Lighthouse,
2 sizes: 102mm. ... 7.50
140mm. ... 12.50
Eddystone Lighthouse.
2 sizes: 105mm. ... 7.50
140mm. ... 17.00
Pharos Lighthouse, Fleetwood, model of.
2 sizes: 88mm. ... 14.50
130mm. ... 14.50
Lighthouse on circular base.
100mm. ... 4.00
Crab. 85mm long. ... 13.00
Scallop Shell. 70mm dia. ... 3.50
Scallop Shell Menu Holder.
62mm. ... 10.50
Shell candlesnuffer. 28mm. ... 10.50
Shell ink well, one open shell inverted on another inscribed: *We are always glad to hear from you.*
105mm. ... 10.50
Whelk Shell, inscribed: *Listen to the sea.* 85mm long. ... 5.00
Mussel Shells, pair, top one upturned. 80mm long. ... pair 10.00
Punch, bust, not named, some colouring. 83mm. ... 30.00

Countryside

Beehive on table. 78mm. ... 11.00
Hay Stack, circular. 58mm. ... 6.50
Hay Stack, rectangular. 50mm. ... 8.50
Milk Churn with lid. 63mm. ... 5.00
Pinecone. 90mm long. ... 4.00

Animals

Cat, angry, standing with arched
back and green eyes. 63mm long. 16.00

Cat, Cheshire. 100mm. 7.50

Cat, climbing in boot, chasing
mouse (peeping out of toe).
105mm long. 40.00

Cat, long necked and sitting. 9.00
Inscribed: *My word if you're not
off.* 108mm. 16.00

Cat, sitting, and smiling (grotesque,
rather similar to Cheshire Cat).
75mm. 7.50

Cat, sitting, with bow round neck.
56mm. 11.00

Black Cat, sitting in octagonal dish.
100mm wide. 24.50

Black Cat, sitting, operating radio.
63mm. 100.00

Three Black cats on Sledge.
118mm long. 135.00

Bulldog, ferocious. 129mm long. 12.50

Bill Sykes Bulldog, inscribed: *My
word if you're not off.*
100mm long. 17.00

Dog, standing. 95mm long. 12.50

Dog, Collie, lying down, 12.50
inscribed: *Shetland Collie.*
78mm long. 19.50

Dog, lying, with crossed paws.
108mm long. 16.00

Great Dane, sitting, wearing top hat,
1 ear raised, gold band around
hat. 112mm. 45.00

Dog, King Charles Spaniel, begging
on cushion.
2 sizes: 68mm. 10.50
95mm. 12.50

Spaniel wearing black top hat,
coloured with glass on green
ashtray base. Reg. No. 67858.
70mm. 52.50

Dog, pup, with one ear raised.
68mm. 9.00

Dog, Pug, standing. 78mm. 14.00

Dog, Pug, sitting. 78mm. 10.50

Dog, puppy, sitting, inscribed:
Daddy wouldn't buy me a bow-wow.
75mm. 17.50

Dog, *Scottish Terrier.*
66mm long. 13.00

Dog, sitting wearing top hat.
118mm. 14.00

Dog, standing looking left, curly
tail, wearing disc on chain.
85mm long. 19.50

Donkey, inscribed: *Hee Haw.*
120mm. 43.00

Elephant, African (big ears).
58mm. 15.00

Elephant, Indian, trunk modelled
free from body, small ears,
inscribed: *Baby Jumbo.* 50mm. 30.00
If inscribed add £5.00.

Fish, open-mouthed.
108mm long. 5.50

Fish shaped dish. Inscribed: *A
"Plaice" for everything.* 7.50

Fish, curly, 98mm long. 10.50

Frog, open-mouthed and usually
green eyes.
2 sizes: 62mm. 16.00
80mm. 20.00

Hare. 73mm long. 15.00

Lion, walking. Found inscribed:
King of the Forest. 110mm. Add
£4.00. 16.00

Monkey, sitting, hand to mouth.
73mm. 13.00

Monkey, sitting, wearing coat.
75mm. 13.00

Otter with fish in mouth.
125mm long. 47.50

Pig, lying, decorated with pink
roses and shamrock collar.
118mm long. Rare. 75.00

Pig, lying down, alert ears.
78mm long. 8.50

Pig, lying down, inscribed: *I wunt be
druv.* 90mm long. 10.00

Pig, sitting and fat. No. 587, can be
found inscribed: *My word if you're
not off.* 90mm long. 14.50

Pig, fat with floppy ears, inscribed:
Wunt be Druv. 105mm long. 40.00

Pig, standing, with drooping ears.
No. 300.
2 sizes: 90mm long. 16.00
105mm long. 8.50

Irish Pig, model of. Alert ears.
Inscribed: *You can push...* 90mm long.
35.00

Sussex Pig, model of, standing thin
pig, inscribed: *You can push or you
can shuv but I'm hanged if I'll be
druv.* No. 148. 78mm long. 12.50

Piglet, standing, with erect ears,
inscribed: *WUNT BE DRUV.* Add
£2.00. No. 277. 73mm long. 10.00

Polar Bear.

2 sizes: 100mm.		55.00
136mm long.		65.00
Rabbit, crouching. 70mm long.		7.50
Shetland Pony. 105mm long.		25.00

Teddy Bear.

2 sizes: 68mm.		19.50
87mm.		30.00

Large size can be inscribed with verse: *Come and be my Teddy Bear.*

	Add £6.00	
Tortoise. 72mm long.		9.00

Welsh Goat, model of, inscribed: *Yr Afr Cymreig.* 100mm long.   45.00

Birds (including Eggs)

Chick breaking out of egg.

2 sizes: 63mm.		9.00
73mm long.		9.00

Egg, with flattened base.
44mm.   4.00

Cock, standing, legs modelled separately, inscribed: *Cock o'th' North.* Some colouring to head.

100mm.		20.00
No inscription.		19.50

Can be found fully coloured, in black with red face, white beak, and feathers outlined in gold with no crest. Rd. No. 35594. 95mm. Add £10.00

Hen, roosting. 54mm.		7.50

Norwich Canary.

2 sizes: 90mm.		7.50
125mm. With whistle.		25.00
Owl, baby. 40mm.		12.50
Owl, long eared. 95mm.		16.00

Parrot inscribed: *Pretty Polly.*

2 sizes: 65mm.		11.00
75mm.		12.50

Swan. No. 12.

2 sizes: 70mm long.		7.50
83mm long.		9.00
Swan. No. 295. 55mm long.		7.50

Great War

British Soldier, model of, on oval domed base. 135mm.   95.00

Scottish Soldier on oval domed base, gun down. 140mm.   170.00

Despatch Rider, model of, on motorbike. 120mm long.   75.00

Nurse and Wounded Tommy, model of. 108mm long.   125.00

Nurse, inscribed: *Soldier's friend.* Red Cross on chest. 132mm.   75.00

Russian Cossack, model of, on horseback. 122mm.   180.00

Sailor, bust, found with hatband impressed: *HMS Dreadnought* or *HMS Queen Elizabeth.* Inscribed: *The handyman.* 92mm.   35.00

Sailor, bust, inscribed: *Sailor beware* and with verse: *Hearts of Oak.* (Add £5.00). 95mm.   30.00

Sailor, standing with hands on hips. 132mm.   75.00

Sailor, Winding Capstan, model of. 105mm.   110.00

Soldier, bust, inscribed: *Tommy Atkins* with verse: *Soldiers of the King* or *Territorial.* Some colouring. 90mm.   45.00

With verse		47.50

Soldier with Respirator, bust inscribed: *Model of new gas mask* (rare). 95mm.   220.00

Tommy Driving a Steam Roller over the Kaiser, inscribed: *To Berlin.* 120mm long. (Very Rare).   475.00

Tommy in Bayonet Attack, model of. 130mm.   135.00

Tommy and his Machine Gun. 100mm long.   40.00

Tommy on Sentry Duty, model of. 110mm.   82.50

Tommy Throwing Grenade, model of. 130mm.   150.00

New Aeroplane, model of. Biplane with fixed prop, and roundels in relief. 120mm long.   120.00

New Aeroplane, model of, with revolving prop. 135mm long.   65.00

Monoplane, V-winged, fixed 2 blade prop. 117mm long.   85.00

British Airship on stand. 128mm long.   35.00

Observer or Sausage Balloon, model of. 84mm.   75.00

Super Zeppelin, model of. 127mm long.   30.00

Battleship, inscribed: *HMS Queen Elizabeth.* 115mm long.   30.00

Battleship, 3 funnels. 120mm long.   17.50

Torpedo Boat Destroyer, model of. 126mm long.   25.00

Submarine, inscribed: *E4.* 95mm long.   19.50

Submarine, inscribed: *E5.* 126mm long.   23.00

Armoured Car, model of.
95mm long. 40.00
Red Cross Van, red cross on each
side and rear. 'EH 139' printed on
radiator. 115mm long. 30.00
Tank, model of. 115mm long. 17.00
Tank, model of, with inset steering
wheels. 115mm long. Can be
found inscribed: *Original Made in
Lincoln* – add £10.00. 19.50
Tank, model of. 160mm long.   25.00
Tank, model of, with one wheel.
145mm long. 350.00
Tank, model of, with trailing steering
wheels. Can be found inscribed:
Original made in Lincoln with
Lincoln crest and £15.00 should
be added for this. 144mm long. 30.00
Field Gun.
2 sizes: 112mm long. 20.00
140mm long. 23.00
Field Gun with screen.
100mm long. 23.00
German Howitzer. 140mm long. 20.00
Trench Mortar, model of.
70mm long. 17.50
Revolver, model of. 83mm long. 47.50
Anti Aircraft Shell, model of.
98mm. 17.50
Cannon Shell.
3 sizes: 70mm. 4.50
90mm. 3.50
132mm. 12.50
The 90mm and 132mm sizes are
often inscribed: *Jack Johnson* – add
£8, or *Hartlepools Bombardment
Dec 16th 1914* – add £13.
Clip of Bullets, model of.
57mm. 17.50
Bomb dropped on Bury St Edmunds.
75mm. 17.00
*Bomb which killed a chicken at
Southend, Model of.* (Rare)
75mm. 45.00
Bomb dropped from Zeppelin,
model of. 75mm. 17.00
British Aerial Bomb. 75mm. 40.00
Canister Bomb, model of. 60mm. 17.50
Plum Pudding Bomb, Model of.
72mm long. (rare) 80.00
German Aerial Torpedo.
88mm long. 30.00
Hair Brush Grenade.
105mm long. 130.00

Mills Hand Grenade, Model of.
2 sizes: 62mm. 19.50
90mm. 45.00
Bandsman's Drum. 53mm. 10.50
Bell Tent, open base and flap. 70mm.
Inscribed: *Camping Out.* 19.50
Capstan. 56mm. 11.50
Gurkha Knife, model of.
110mm long. 20.00
Pair of Field Glasses, model of.
78mm long. 16.00
Sandbag. 70mm long. 23.00
Tommy's Hut, model of.
105mm long. 47.50
Trench Dagger. 102mm long. 47.50
Trench Lamp. 70mm. 13.00
Water Bottle, model of. 65mm. 17.50
Colonial Hat, model of.
88mm wide. 16.00
Named. 20.00
Glengarry. 90mm long. 19.50
Officer's Peaked Cap, with coloured
badge and hatband. 70mm dia. 15.50
If inscribed: *Territorials Cap* in
blue and red. 25.00
Pith Helmet. 85mm long. 16.00
Tommy's Tin Hat. 68mm dia. 40.00
Anti-Zeppelin Candle Holder.
62mm. 17.50
Fireplace, inscribed: *We've kept the
home fires burning.* 90mm. 14.50
Kitchen Range with pot. Inscribed:
Keep the home fires burning.
78mm long. 9.00

Home/Nostalgic
Anvil. 66mm. 6.50
Baby in Bonnet Handbell. 100mm. 47.50
Can be found without bonnet. 47.50
Bellows. 95mm long. 12.00
Chair, highbacked. 90mm. 6.50
Cradle. 70mm long. 10.00
Firebucket. 55mm. 4.00
Flat Iron. 81mm long. 14.50
Frying pan. 110mm long. 17.00
Grandfather Clock, narrow.
103mm. 10.50
Grandfather Clock, model of a
usually found inscribed: *Make use
of time let not advantage slip.
Shakespeare.* 12.00
Can be found inscribed: *The time
of day* or *Time and tide wait for no
man.* 110mm. 17.00
Kennel inscribed *Beware of the Dog*
54mm. 6.50

Lantern, horn. 85mm.   6.50
Pillar Box, inscribed: *GRV* and *If you
  haven't time to post a line here's the
  pillar box.* 63mm.   16.00
Saucepan and lid. No. 178.
  80mm long.   9.00
Stool, 3 legged. 40mm.   7.50
Sundial, inscribed: *Life's but a
  walking shadow.* Square base. 83mm.   12.00
Table, square. 39mm.   5.50
Warming Pan, inscribed: *Model of old
  Warming Pan* and *Polly warm the
  Bed* 125mm long.   17.00
Water Pump. 90mm.   10.00
Watering Can. 78mm.   12.00
Wicker Basket, twisted handle,   3.50
  inscribed: *Fruit Basket.* 63mm.   6.50
Young Girl Handbell, wearing
  bonnet, with clapper. 96mm.   47.50

Comic/Novelty
Arry, Bust of a Pearly King.
  83mm.   40.00
Arriet, Bust of a Pearly Queen. 82mm.   80.00
Billiken. 65mm.   6.50
Clown, bust, inscribed: *Put me
  amongst the girls,* some colouring.
  80mm.   25.00
Golliwog, fully coloured, verse to
  rear.   85.00
Jester, double faced, happy and sad,
  and eyes open and closed. Can be
  found inscribed: *Ye jester awake, ye
  jester asleep.* Add £2.50.
  2 sizes: 65mm.   11.50
            90mm.   12.50
Policeman on duty, with verse.
  Controlling The Traffic. 148mm.   34.50
Potato, gilded eyes. 77mm long.   30.00
Suffragette handbell, double-faced.
  Front, sour old lady, inscribed:
  Votes for women. Back pretty
  young girl, inscribed: *This one
  shall have the vote.* Some
  colouring.
  2 sizes: 70mm.   47.50
            98mm.   47.50
Suffragette double faced bust. Same
  face and inscriptions as the
  handbell above.98mm.   55.00

Cartoon/Comedy Characters
Ally Sloper, Bust with verse. Some
  colouring. 100mm.   40.00

Harry Lauder, bust, not named.
  Inscribed: *Stop ye're tickling Jock*
  and *Tja can sit on the thistle noo.*
  2 sizes: 83mm.   17.00
            95mm.   32.00
Mrs Gummidge, standing figure,
  with inscription: *A lone lorn
  creetur and everything goes
  contrairy with her.* 112mm.   47.50

Alcohol
Beer Barrel, on stand. 40mm.   4.00
Monk, jovial and holding glass,
  with verse: *A jovial Monk am I.*
  2 sizes: 70mm.   12.50
            112mm.   19.50
Soda Syphon. 100mm.   11.50
Beaker, inscribed: *Tak a thimblefull.*
  40mm.   4.00
Toby Jug. 62mm.   8.50
Toby Jug with verse. 74mm.   12.50

Sport/Pastimes
Cricket Bag. 80mm long.   12.50
Football. 50mm dia.   6.50
Golf Ball, inscribed: *The game of golf
  was first played in the year 1448.*
  42mm.   12.50
Golf Club head. 100mm long.   17.00
Golfer standing on golf ball.
  76mm.   40.00
Tennis Racquet. 90mm long.   10.50
Trophy, 2 handled. 49mm.   10.00
Knight chess piece. 62mm.   14.50
Rook chess piece. 55mm.   6.50

Musical Instruments
Banjo. 154mm long.   10.50
Guitar. 153mm long.   13.00
Harp. 105mm.   5.50
Piano, upright. 70mm long.   16.00
Tambourine. 70mm dia.   10.00

Transport
Car, Saloon, inscribed: *EH 139.*
  76mm long.   40.00
Open Sports Car, inscribed: *EH 139.*
  110mm long.   40.00
Can of Petrol, impressed: *Motor
  Spirit.* 55mm.   16.00

Modern Equipment
Gramophone with horn. 112mm.   25.00

Hats

Bishop's Mitre. 55mm. — 6.50
Fireman's Helmet. 82mm long. — 25.00
Mortar Board. 66mm long. — 40.00
Straw Boater. 73mm long. — 12.00

Footwear

Oriental Shoe. No. 302.
102mm long. — 6.50
Ankle Boot. 83mm long. — 5.00
Lancashire Clog. 92mm long. — 5.00
Leather Highboot. 75mm. — 17.50

Miniature Domestic

Cheese Dish, one piece. 50mm. — 7.50
Cheese Dish and cover. 50mm. — 7.50
Cup and saucer. 37mm. — 6.00
Cup and saucer, fancy. 49mm. — 4.50
Tea Pot with lid. No. 145. 40mm. — 7.50

Domestic

Hair Tidy and lid. 110mm wide. — 6.50
Horses Hoof Inkwell, with
inscription: *We're aye prood to hear
fra ye.* — 11.00
Trinket box and lid, heart shaped.
No. 321. 60mm. — 5.50

Miscellaneous

Handbell, no clapper. 53mm. — 4.00
Horses Hoof Vase. 60mm long. — 4.00

Sylvan China

1919-1921.

Trademark used by Dura Porcelain Co. Ltd, Empress Pottery, Hanley.

This very short lived firm, established in 1919 and closed in 1921, seems to have been created to make crested souvenirs and dolls' heads to fill the market for cheap German wares that could no longer be imported. An advert for the firm in the *Pottery Gazette* of September 1920 illustrates some of their products including dolls' heads, and crested china boot, monoplane, red cross van, Florence Nightingale statue, hen and Shetland Pony. Some models appear to have been bought in from the Carlton Works. Presumably when German goods returned to Britain after the war they were still cheaper to import than the Dura Company could manage to produce them for – a constant problem for British manufacturers except during the war.

The china is actually quite reasonable and the crests are very well produced.

Sylvan Models
Ancient Artefacts

Puzzle Jug. 70mm. — 5.50

Historical/Folklore

Burns Chair, model of. — 7.50
*Mary Queen of Scots Chair, Edinburgh
Castle, Model of.* 76mm. — 6.50

Traditional/National Souvenirs
Welsh Hat. 55mm.   5.00

Animals
Cat sitting on circular pouffe,
   inscribed: *Luck* in orange. 80mm.   10.50
Scottie Dog, black, looking out of
   Kennel. Inscribed: *Black Watch*.
   Green bow. 68mm.   15.50
Scottie Dog, sitting wearing tam-o'-
   shanter. 76mm.   10.50
Scottie Dog, standing. 90mm long.   11.50
Pony, standing. 123mm long.   20.00

Birds (including Eggs)
Cockerel. 65mm.   16.00

Great War
Lady of the Lamp, Florence
   Nightingale. 1820-1910.   14.50

Home/Nostalgic
Fireplace, inscribed: *East or West
home is best, Home Sweet Home.*
Some colouring, vases and clock
on mantlepiece. 95mm long.   20.00

Comic/Novelty
Billiken sitting on throne, inscribed:
the God of things as they ought to be.
100mm.   7.50

Cartoon/Comedy Characters
*Mr Pussyfoot, all water!! We don't
think.* 97mm.   40.00

Alcohol
Toby Jug with verse. 90mm.   12.00

Sport/Pastimes
Golf Ball, inscribed: *The ancient game
of golf was first played in 1448.* 48mm.   12.50

Modern Equipment
Box Gramophone with Horn.
100mm.   20.00

Footwear
Clog. 76mm long.   5.50

Miniature Domestic
Cheese Dish and cover. 45mm.   6.50

Miscellaneous
Hand holding tulip. 90mm.   4.00

Syren China

Trademark used by Wiltshaw & Robinson
Ltd, Carlton Works, Stoke-on-Trent.
(Usual trademark Carlton).
For details of this china and manufacturer
see Carlton China.
This mark has only been found on the few
models listed below and one small vase.
As the duck is normally painted and
rather more delicate when marked
Carlton, one suspects that this mark was
used for a cheap range for a small retailer
or a mark used by the company on wares
which were not good enough to be
marked Carlton.

Syren Models
Animals
Cat seated on upright piano.
95mm.   40.00

Birds (including Eggs)
Comic Duck on green base.
108mm.   40.00

Comic/Novelty
Oval Dish with two bananas in
relief. 120mm long.   13.00

Cartoon/Comedy Characters
Felix, walking on armchair. All white.
75mm.   55.00

Sport/Pastimes
Sports Trophy. 132mm.   17.50

Talbot China

Trademark used for a retailer by Sampson
  Hancock (and Sons), Bridge Works, Stoke.
  (Usual trademark Corona).
For further details of this china and
  manufacturer see The Corona China.
The models listed below are obviously from
  the Corona range. H.B. and Co. must have
  been a retailer, the only crest recorded
  being Castle Coombe, so it is probable that
  he had a shop in that area.

Talbot Models
Seaside Souvenirs
Bathing Machine. 68mm.	8.50
Lighthouse. 105mm.	5.50
Whelk Shell. 102mm long.	4.50

Historical/Folklore
Noah's Ark. 95mm long.	5.00

Animals
Fish vase. 60mm.	5.00
Pig, standing. 45mm.	10.00

Home/Nostalgic
Desk Top. 55mm long.	9.00
Pillar Box. 70mm.	14.50
Sofa. 95mm long.	14.50

Musical Instruments
Harp. 95mm.	6.50

Modern Equipment
Gas Cooker. 70mm.	10.00

Sport/Pastimes
King chess piece. 115mm.	25.00
Queen chess piece. 112mm.	24.50

Taylor and Kent

1912+

Mark found on model exported to Australia.

Trademark used by Taylor and Kent (Ltd), Florence Works, Longton. (Usual trademark Florentine).

For details of this china and manufacturer see Florentine China.

Taylor and Kent only used the crown mark on coloured buildings without crests. I suspect these were finished to a higher standard than the Florentine range and so the company were happy to have their name on them. The mark was registered in 1912 so it is probable that these models were made before the Great War. Taylor and Kent made some models of buildings after 1930 but these have a slightly different mark, with the addition of a new trade name for the china.

Temple Porcelain

Trademark used by an unknown manufacturer. It closely resembles products of the Nautilus Porcelain Co of Glasgow.

Crests from all over the south of England and Wales are found on crested china with this mark. Most items found are 'smalls' and the models listed below appear to be produced by the Nautilus Porcelain Company.

The china is for the most part quite fine and the crests are reasonably well produced. No view ware or any other transfer devices have been recorded.

Taylor and Kent Models
Buildings – Coloured
Ann Hathaway's Cottage.

4 sizes: 50mm long.	17.50
70mm long.	20.00
115mm long.	30.00
135mm long.	40.00

Shakespeare's House.

2 sizes: 70mm long.	17.50
115mm long.	30.00

Birds (including Eggs)

Swan, posy holder. 81mm.	5.00

Home/Nostalgic

Baby in hip bath. 100mm long.	12.50

Miniature Domestic

Cheese Dish and cover. 70mm long.	6.50

Temple Models
Ancient Artefacts

Beer Bowl, 3-handled 74mm dia.	3.00
Loving Cup. Three handled. 39mm.	3.00
Puzzle Jug. 70mm.	5.50
Staffordshire Tyg, one handled, not named. 63mm.	2.00

Traditional/National Souvenirs

Indian Canoe, high sides. 135mm long.	17.00

Home/Nostalgic

Bellows.	6.50
Bucket with upright handle. 70mm.	4.00
Coal Scuttle, shell shaped, on two ball feet.	5.50
Cradle. 62mm long.	7.50
Lantern. 67mm.	5.50
Milk Churn and lid. 75mm.	5.00
Half-open Suitcase. 62mm long.	5.00

Alcohol
Carboy.   4.00

Sport
Curling Stone.   14.50

Footwear
Oriental Slipper. 98mm long.   5.50

Miniature Domestic
Cheese Dish and cover. 50mm.   6.50

Domestic
Oval Trinket Box. 80mm long.   4.00

Thistle China
T.C. & P.G.

Trademark used for L.M. Mack, Ayr, by
   Hewitt & Leadbeater, Willow Potteries,
   Longton. (Usual trademark Willow Art).
For details of this china and manufacturer
   see Willow Art China.
China with this mark has always been
   recorded with Scottish crests, often the
   crest of Ayr. The models listed below and
   'smalls' are from the Willow Art range.

Thistle Models
Parian/Unglazed
Bust of *Burns*. 150mm (with Ayr
   crest).   30.00

Buildings – Coloured
Model of Burns cottage, inscribed:
   Robert Burns The Ayrshire Bard was
   born at Alloway, near Ayr on Jan

*25th 1759. He died on 21st July 1796
at Dumfries where he was buried.*
107mm long.   35.00

Monuments (including Crosses)
Burns, statue.
   2 sizes: 108mm.   20.00
         177mm.   30.00

Animals
Rat, with curled tail.
   80mm long.   35.00

Great War
Monoplane with fixed prop.
   146mm long.   55.00
New field gun with screen and sight
   groove. 109mm long.   19.00

Home/Nostalgic
Bucket. 76mm.   9.00

Alcohol
Carboy in Basket. 70mm.   4.00

T.M.W. and Co Ltd/ and S Ltd.

This mark can also be found with the initials
TMW & S Ltd.

Trademark used for a wholesaler by an
unknown manufacturer, possibly Willow
Art.

The models listed below have been found
with a number of different crests,
indicating that this was a wholesaler's
mark. (The mark seems to be a print of a
Bargate which may provide a clue.) No
known potters used the initials T.M.W.
and the models below could have been
made by any British manufacturer.

T.M.W. Models
Historical/Folklore
Mother Shipton. 105mm.   8.00

Traditional/National Souvenirs
Welsh Leek. 55mm.   4.00

Seaside Souvenirs
Bathing Machine, inscribed: *A
   Morning Dip*. 78mm.   12.50
Yacht in full sail. 117mm.   12.50

Animals
Bull, *King of the Herd*. 120mm long.
   (Willow).   47.50
Cat, sitting. 65mm.   10.00
Bulldog with black collar, sitting.
   55mm.   19.00

Scottie Dog, wearing blue, red and
   black glengarry. 60mm.   12.50
Tortoise. 85mm long.   9.00

Birds (including Eggs)
Fluffy Chick. 65mm.   17.00

Great War
Bugle. 72mm.   19.50

Alcohol
Barrel. 33mm.   3.00

Tourist Art China

Trademark used for Frank Duncan Ltd,
Auckland, New Zealand, by Hewitt &
Leadbeater Ltd, Willow Potteries,
Longton. (Usual trademark Willow Art).
For details of this china and manufacturer
see Willow Art China.
Models with this mark are invariably Kiwi
miniatures. The crests found include New
Zealand and Wellington. The New
Zealand crest is often accompanied by the
inscription: 'A Souvenir from Auckland'
or 'Wellington'. A vase and the lighthouse
below have been found with transfer
prints of a view of the 'New Bath Building,
Rotorua, N.Z.' Fortunately this view is
recognisably a product of Willow
Potteries. Hewitt and Leadbeater were the
only firm to outline their views with a
black scroll border, so the mark can be
identified. Frank Duncan Ltd was no
doubt a New Zealand fancy goods
wholesaler.

Tourist Art Models
Buildings – Coloured
Model of Maori Whare from Rotorua
   N.Z. Brown coloured. 85mm.   150.00

Buildings – White
Model of Maori Whare. 50mm.   95.00

Seaside Souvenirs
Lighthouse. 110mm.   10.00

Birds (including Eggs)
Kiwi. 66mm.   40.00

Home/Nostalgic
Wheelbarrow. 110mm long.   12.00

Alcohol
Barrel on stand. No. 35. 58mm.   5.50

Towy China

$$\text{TOWY CHINA}$$
$$\text{BRITISH}$$
$$\text{MAKE}$$

Trademark used for a Welsh retailer by
Hewitt and Leadbeater Ltd, Willow
Potteries, Longton. (Usual trademark
Willow Art).

This mark has only been found on a Welsh
Hat with an unrecognisable crest which
has not been named on the model but is
obviously Welsh. The hat fortunately is
not only identical to the Willow Art model
but carries the same stock numbers, so one
can confidently assume that this mark was
used for a Welsh retailer by Hewitt and
Leadbeater.

Towy Models
Traditional/National Souvenirs
Welsh Hat. No. 75. 57mm.   5.00

Tre-Pol-Pen Series

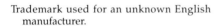

Trademark used for an unknown English manufacturer.

Only one model recorded.

Traditional/National Souvenirs
Cornish Pasty, inscribed: *Will ye ave a piece of my pasty*. 95mm long.   10.50

Triood

From 1919.

Trademark used by Hoods Ltd, International Works, Fenton. Products are identical to the Corona factory.

Hoods Ltd was established in 1919 and manufactured earthenwares. Obviously the firm made crested china souvenirs of the Great War very early in their history and probably only made a range of such wares until the early twenties, when Germany competition returned. The models produced are very ordinary and do not carry inscriptions. The range includes domestic items and 'smalls', which, like the models tend to be rather heavy.

Crests recorded are from all over the Midlands and south of England. One military crest, The Worcestershire Regiment, has been found.

Triood Models
Ancient Artefacts
Salisbury Kettle. 105mm.   3.00
Welsh Milk Can. 70mm.   5.00

Buildings – White
Bottle Oven, (Inside of). 81mm.   19.50
Clifton Suspension Bridge.
        120mm long.   75.00
Micklegate Bar, York. 110mm.   19.50

Traditional/National Souvenirs
Welsh Hat. 49mm.   5.00

Seaside Souvenirs
Lighthouse. 108mm.   5.50

Animals

Collie Dog, sitting.	20.00
Elephant, standing trunk down.	
75mm long.	17.00
Pig, standing, ears forward.	
85mm long.	10.00
Rabbit, ears raised. 62mm long.	7.50

Birds (including Eggs)

Swan posy holder. 58mm.	5.00

Great War

Airship on base. 130mm long.	30.00
Monoplane with movable prop.	
150mm long.	65.00
Battleship. 120mm long.	17.50
Submarine, impressed: *E4*.	
104mm long.	19.50
Red Cross Van. 100mm long.	30.00
Tank, with inset steering wheels.	
102mm long.	19.50
Field Gun. 130mm.	17.00
Bell Tent, with open flaps.	16.00
Pickelhaube. No. 58. 52mm.	30.00

Home/Nostalgic

Cigarette Case. 70mm.	13.00
Grandfather Clock. 125mm.	10.50
Iron Trivet. 74mm long.	4.00
Jardiniere on stand, fixed.	
80mm.	5.00
Tobacco Pouch. 75mm long.	10.50
Writing Slope. 50mm long.	7.50
Water Bottle, rectangular. 66mm.	8.00

Musical Instruments

Upright Piano. 62mm.	16.00

Modern Equipment

Gas Cooker. 70mm.	10.00

Footwear

Hob Nail Boot. 70mm long.	5.50
Ladies Shoe. 90mm long.	7.50
Lancashire Clog. 95mm long.	5.00

Miniature Domestic

Cheese Dish, one piece. 58mm.	6.50
Cheese Dish and cover. 82mm long.	6.50
Club speciman vase. 72mm.	2.00
Coffee Pot with lid. No. 205. 70mm.	7.50

Domestic

Candlestick, round base. 85mm.	3.00

Tudor Arms China

Trademark used by a wholesaler for ware by Hewitt & Leadbeater Ltd, Willow Potteries, Longton. (Usual trademark Willow Art), and by Sampson Hancock of Hanley. (Usual trademark Corona Pottery).

Most models with this mark have Welsh Crests and it is possible that C.J. and Co. were Cardiff wholesalers. The only military badge recorded is that of the R.F.C. All models listed below are from either the Willow Art or Corona range and stock numbers where they occur are the same.

Tudor Arms Models
Buildings – White

Bottle Oven. 85mm.	19.50
Lloyd George's Home.	
102mm long.	47.50

Historical/Folklore

Model of Burns Chair. 88mm.	7.50
Corner seat version.	15.00
Gladiators Helmet. 80mm.	20.00
The Man in the Sun. 100mm.	47.50

Traditional/National Souvenirs

Welsh Hat, with blue ribbon and	
longest place name around brim.	
No. 75. 57mm.	6.50

Seaside Souvenirs

Bathing Machine. 65mm.	10.00

Animals

Black Cat in Boot. 88mm long.	45.00
Bulldog, standing.	
125mm long.	15.00
Dog, Alsatian, standing. 82mm.	20.00
Elephant, walking. 52mm.	17.00

Great War

Tank with trailing wheels.	
125mm long.	17.50
Lusitania (as Corona model).	
165mm long.	82.50
Submarine, *E4*. 97mm long.	19.50
Bell Tent with open flaps. 80mm.	16.00
Kit Bag with verse: *Pack up your troubles in your old kit bag.*	
74mm.	19.50

Home/Nostalgic

Church Bell, inscribed: *Curfew must not ring tonight.* 70mm.	7.50
Coal Scuttle, helmet shaped. 53mm.	5.00

Footwear

Boot. 112mm long.	11.00
Button-up Boot. 74mm long.	7.00

Miniature Domestic

Bagware Tea Pot with lid. 68mm.	8.50

Tuscan China

R.H. & S.L. PLANT
ENGLAND

R.H. & S.L. PLANT
ENGLAND

Trademark used by R.H. and S.L. Plant (Ltd), Tuscan Works, Longton.

Mr Richard Hammersley Plant was born in Longton in 1847 and began work at the Daisy Bank Pottery at the age of seven. He was employed there for twenty five years, eventually becoming the Manager. In 1880 he started his own business with his brother which was known as R.H. and S.L. Plant. Mr R.H. Plant died in 1904, and his two sons and his brother carried on the business which is still in existence today.

Messrs Plant were known for their tea and breakfast wares produced for the home, colonial and foreign markets. They were represented in London by Messrs Mogridge and Underhay, 10, Barletts Buildings, Holborn Circus, EC. In 1906 R.H. and S.L. Plant added Arms Ware in 'superb ivory porcelain', with the arms of all Nations, the Colonies and the United Kingdom', to their range using the Tuscan trademark. In 1908 they were advertising 'Heraldic Ware' in Tuscan China, adding that arms of towns could be applied to small fancy pieces and teaware.

During the Great War the company obviously made china miniatures a speciality and by 1916 were also producing 'Present from . . . Ware' and 'Nursery Rhyme Ware'. In 1919 the firm could offer 'Heraldic Ivory China, Heraldic Bone China, View Ware, Nursery Rhyme Ware and Present from . . . Ware'. Like so many high and medium class china manufacturers they had to turn to cheaper wares during the war years. By the 1920 British Industries Fair the company was showing 'High Class Services' as well as 'Seaside Ware'. The firm continued to produce Heraldic Wares until at least 1925 but no mention is made of them however in adverts after that date.

Tuscan China is quite fine and well produced, the range of models is however rather unimaginative and the majority of crested china made by the firm appears to have been domestic ware, little of which survives as it would have been in constant use. A large number of small pots and vases have survived and unless numbered, these have not been listed as they are of interest only to collectors specialsing in crests of specific areas or towns. Miniatures and 'smalls' can be found with views and other 'twenties' transfer decorations, but no 'Lucky Black Cats' or 'Lucky White Heather' transfers have been recorded.

Foreign and colonial crests were obviously made but the only recorded one is 'British Honduras'. Great War Commemoratives can be found on 'smalls' and models, these being 'Flags of the Allies' transfers with the inscription: *Freedom and Honour*. ('Tuscan' advertised ashtrays decorated with planes and flags in 1938 but it is not known if these were ever made.)

In the thirties the firm made a range of coloured animals and 'Crinoline Ladies' and these appeal to collectors of the Goss and Arcadian Ladies, but obviously they have nothing whatsoever to do with crested china.

Numbering System. Stock numbers do appear on the base of some models and can be painted in any colour. These are recorded in the following lists where known. Paintresses' marks are painted initials or dots and dashes.

Tuscan Models
Ancient Artefacts

Loving Cup, 3 handled. No. 82. 39mm.	3.00
Nose of Brasenose. 95mm long.	11.00
Roman Lamp. 84mm long.	3.00

Buildings – White

Newquay Look-Out-House with three portholes, some colouring. 100mm.	55.00
Tower of Refuge, Isle of Man. 93mm.	30.00

Historical/Folklore

Diakonon, mythical grotesque figure of squat man with flat head which bears the crest. Found with Southsea crest. No. 156. 60mm.	13.00
Coronation Chair, ornate. 80mm.	7.50
The Chertsey Abbey or *Curfew Bell*, cast circa 1370. With clapper. Sometimes on wooden base. 88mm.	20.00
No base.	14.50
Peter Pan statue, not named. 140mm.	65.00
Miners Dish, inscribed: *Model of the Ancient Miners Dish cast in the 3rd year of the reign of K. Henry VII.* 142mm long.	75.00

Traditional/National Souvenirs

Welsh Hat. 50mm.	5.00
Can be found with longest place name around brim.	7.50
Welsh Lady jug. Can be found named: *CYMERWCH DOGON O LEFRITH*. 82mm.	20.00
With inscription.	27.50

Seaside Souvenirs

Lifeboat. 125mm long.	12.50
Lighthouse, not named. 90mm.	5.00
Withernsea Lighthouse, with details. 110mm.	19.50
Crab. 88mm long.	13.00
Seashell. 118mm long.	5.00
Seashell. No. 36. 84mm long.	5.00

Countryside

Milk Churn and Lid.	5.00
Pine Cone. 75mm.	4.00

Animals

Camel with two humps, kneeling.
No. 118. 125mm long. — 40.00
Cat, fat and angry with tail in air.
80mm. — 16.00
Cat, Cheshire with one bead eye.
91mm. — 11.00
Cow, said to be Indian, lying down.
155mm long. — 19.00
Dog, Bulldog. 72mm long. — 16.00
Dog, Hound, running. 200mm long. — 35.00
Dog, Spaniel, sitting. 53mm. — 12.50
Donkey, lying down, yellow bead
eyes. 125mm long. — 40.00
Elephant, sitting and comical, with
yellow bead eyes. 80mm. — 32.00
Fish, large, open mouth, looking
upwards, wavy tail. 120mm long. — 6.50
Fish, curled. 105mm long. — 7.50
Fish, open mouthed with green
glass eyes. 120mm. — 8.50
Fox, running. Yellow bead eyes.
145mm long. — 110.00
Frog, red bead yes. 55mm. — 18.00
Hippopotamus, inscribed: *My word
if I catch you bending.* 58mm. — 65.00
Lion, (Daily Sketch), white. 130mm. — 65.00
Monkey, hanging by tail from
branch of tree. 155mm. — 95.00
Mule. 130mm long. — 30.00
Pig, ears point forward.
80mm long. — 11.50
Pig, running, red bead eyes. 87mm. — 25.00
Sloth on tree trunk, bead eyes.
110mm long. — 70.00
Rabbit. — 7.50
Snail. 85mm long. — 14.50
Terrapin. 95mm long. — 14.00
Tortoise/Turtle, standing with bead
eyes. 108mm long. — 30.00

Birds (including Eggs)

Bird Bowl, grotesque. 98mm long. — 16.00
Egg, cracked open and lying on
side. 65mm long. — 5.00
Chick hatching from egg. 77mm long. — 12.50
Chicken, plump. 55mm. — 9.00
Finch, coloured, on flower holder
rock. 140mm. — 40.00
Penguin. 88mm. — 18.50
Swan. 60mm. — 6.50

Great War

E4, Submarine. 118mm long. — 19.50
Kit Bag, with no inscription. 63mm. — 20.00

Bandsman Drum. 33mm. — 10.50

Home/Nostalgic

Anvil. 60mm. — 7.50
Baby, naked, lying on tummy.
105mm long. — 65.00
Bellows. 106mm long. — 12.50
Feeding Bottle. 80mm long. — 8.50
Grandfather Clock, inscribed: *Time
for tea 5 o'clock.* 128mm. — 10.50
Inkwell Vase. 55mm. — 4.00
Loaf of Bread. 62mm. — 20.00
Shaving Mug. No. 180. 57mm. — 6.50
Watering Can. 72mm. — 7.00

Comic/Novelty

Boy Scout, saluting. 140mm. — 100.00
Girl dressed as clown, hands outstretched, on square base. 130mm. — 35.00
Boy dressed as clown on square
base, hands in pockets. 130mm. — 35.00
Lemon, open top. No. 35.
75mm long. — 6.50
Marrow with green stalk. 75mm. — 16.00
Boy in nightshirt and nightcap,
candlesnuffer. Could be Wee
Willie Winkie.
2 sizes: 60mm. — 19.00
90mm. — 24.00
Tomato with green leaves.
60mm dia. — 16.00

Cartoon/Comedy Characters

Snooker or the Kitten Cat, cat sitting
on square base putting on crown.
Can be found coloured and
unglazed. (Daily Sketch Cartoon
Character). 130mm. — 85.00

Alcohol

Bottle. No. 104. 87mm. — 6.00
Carboy. No. 11. 70mm. — 4.00

Transport

Racing Car. 135mm long. Inscribed
*Dennis Two Seater, Petrol
Consumption Nil.* — 175.00
or *Gamage two seater Petrol
consumption nil, no tax on this car.* — 200.00

Footwear

Ladies buttoned decorative heeled
shoe. 103mm long. — 20.00

Hats

Top Hat matchstriker. 45mm.   5.50

Miniature Domestic

Cheese Dish and cover. 2 pieces.
    50mm.   7.50

Numbered 'smalls'

No. 5. Cone Vase. 65mm.	2.50
No. 6. Vase. 60mm.	2.50
No. 10. Ewer. 70mm.	2.50
No. 21. Vase.	2.50
No. 22. Vase. 30mm.	2.50
No. 24. Jug. 45mm.	2.50
No. 42. Crinkle top vase. 42mm.	2.50
No. 57. Ewer. 58mm.	2.50
No. 58. Ewer.	2.50
No. 59. Vase. 43mm.	2.50
No. 71. Vase. 63mm.	2.50
No. 72. Jug. 63mm.	2.50
No. 89. Vase. 55mm.	2.50
No. 97. Vase. 50mm.	2.50
No. 100. Urn. 65mm.	2.50
No. 101. Ewer.	2.50
No. 110. Jug. 51mm.	2.50

Miscellaneous

Bamboo hat pin holder. 100mm.	7.50
Bamboo Vase. 100mm.	3.00
Hammer head match striker. 88mm long.	5.00

Tuskar Rock China

Trademark used for a Wexford retailer by an unknown manufacturer.

Only one 'small' and the model below have been found with a Wexford crest.

Traditional/National Souvenirs

Pearly Queen with ostrich feathers
    on her hat, inscribed: *Harriet*.
    Reg No. 448566. 70mm.   80.00

Miscellaneous

Urn. 41mm. (Rosslane crest).   3.00

Union Crest China

Trademark by an unknown manufacturer although it does resemble Carlton China.

Historical/Folklore
Model of Ancient Coaching Hat.
No. 217. No details of size.   7.50

Alcohol
Highland Whisky Bowl. 120mm dia.   7.50

Union K

Trademark used by the German firm Klosterle (near Carlsbad), the former Graflich Thun'sche Porzellanfabric.
The use of the term Czechoslovakia indicates that this mark, used on domestic ware, was produced after the Great War. One interesting item recorded is a card box with the four suits on the sides.

Domestic ware.   £2.00 upwards.

Sport/Pastimes
Card Box, with four suits on the sides.   20.00

Unity China

UNITY

CHINA

Trademark used by the German firm of Max
Emanuel and Co, Mitterteich. (Bavaria).
(Usual trademark Mosanic).
See Maxim China for further details of this
manufacturer.
This mark is identical to one used by Max
Emanuel and Co., on pink view ware
china, with the addition of the words
Unity China. If, as I suspect, this mark was
used after the Great War the use of the
word Unity is very apt, if not, a little
tactless, as no mention of the country of
origin is made.
Even more surprisingly, one model carries a
commemorative to Field Marshall Sir John
French.

Unity Models
Birds (including Eggs)
Swan posy holder. Flags of Allies
    and bunting around rim. Central
    transfer print of *General Joffre*
    encircled by Flags of Allies and
    inscribed: *Unity.* 90mm.   22.00

Miniature Domestic
Cheese Dish. 50mm.   7.50

Universal Series

UNIVERSAL

SERIES

Trademark used by an unknown
    manufacturer but bears a remarkable
    resemblance to Porcelle China, which was
    made for William Ritchie and Son Ltd,
    24/26/28 Elder Street, Edinburgh. The
    porcelain is more cream than white, and
    reasonbly fine. All pieces found bear
    Scottish crests.

Universal Models
Great War
Bandsman's Drum. 57mm dia.   10.50

Footwear
Oriental Slipper. 95mm long.   6.50

Vale China

Mark used from 1928-37.

Trademark used by H.J. Coldough, Vale
Works, Longton. For all further details of
this china, see Royal Vale entry.

Vectis/Victis Models

VECTIS
MODELS
NIGH
VENTNOR
I.O.W.

VICTIS
MODELS
NIGH
VENTNOR
I.O.W.

Trademark used for Nigh, a fancy goods
    dealer in the Isle of Wight by J.A. Robinson
    and Sons, subsequently Cauldon Ltd.
    (Usual trademark Arcadian).
For details of this china and manufacturer,
    see Arcadian China.
There seems to have been some indecision in
    the Arcadian Works as to how to spell
    Vectis, which is of course the Roman name
    for the Isle of Wight. The models with this
    mark could have been made by any of the
    branches of J.A. Robinson, which included
    Arkinstall ('Arcadian'), Robinson and
    Leadbeater (R. and L.) and Wardle's Art

Pottery Ltd. The parian models listed below would almost certainly have been made by R. and L.

All the models are souvenirs of the Isle of Wight, and carry Isle of Wight crests. A number of 'smalls' have been recorded with the coloured transfers of tropical birds on Arcadian and Cauldon wares.

Vectis Models
Parian/Unglazed

Osborne House, Isle of Wight. 140mm long.	85.00
Sleep of Innocence. Osborne House, Cowes. I.O.W. Two babies lying on a couch, glazed or unglazed.	
2 sizes: 96mm long.	145.00
114mm long.	165.00

Ancient Artefacts

Cadogan Teapot, not named. 50mm.	11.00

Buildings – Coloured

The Old Village, Shanklin, I.o.W. 100mm long.	175.00

Buildings – White

Carisbrooke Castle Gateway, Isle of Wight. 96mm long.	110.00
Cottage on rectangular base, no inscription. 50mm.	7.50
Old Church, Bonchurch. 105mm long.	130.00
The Old Village, Shanklin, I.o.W. 100mm long.	120.00
Osborne House, Cowes, I.O.W. 48mm.	85.00

Monuments (including Crosses)

Arch Rock, Freshwater Bay, I.O.W. 80mm.	28.00
Maiwand Memorial Forbury Gardens, Reading. 98mm.	14.50

Traditional/National Souvenirs

Donkey in Wheel, donkey coloured, Carisbrooke Castle. 90mm.	85.00
Map of Isle of Wight. A coloured map standing upright on an oval ashtray. 106mm long.	45.00
Sleep of Innocence, Osborne House, Cowes, I.O.W. See Parian/ unglazed section.	

Seaside Souvenirs

Needles Rock and Lighthouse. 125mm long.	40.00

Animals

Calf, often found with *Isle of Wight Calves* transfer and verse.	
100mm long.	30.00
No verse.	24.50
Lion, walking. 145mm long.	19.50

Birds (including Eggs)

Brooding Hen. 50mm.	7.50

Home/Nostalgic

Coal Bucket.	4.00

Venetia China

Trademark used by Charles Waine (and Co), Derby Works, Longton.

Charles Waine and Co. worked in Longton, manufacturing china from 1891 to 1920, but only used the initials C.W. until 1913. The firm made a range of 'smalls' and small models probably at the turn of the century when many other established firms added crests to their shapes. One commemorative has been found on a small jug, this being a coloured transfer view of the 'Imperial International Exhibition'. Venetia is rather heavy and more like earthenware than china, the view and crests are adequate but by no means exceptional.

Venetia Models
Ancient Artefacts

Loving Cup, 3 handles. 40mm.	3.00

Seaside Souvenirs

Lighthouse on rocky base. 114mm.	5.50

Birds (including Eggs)

Swan posy bowl. 80mm.	5.00

Home/Nostalgic

Coal Scuttle. No. 35. 80mm.	5.00

Miniature Domestic

Cheese Dish and cover. 55mm.	6.50
Circular Cheese Dish and cover. 71mm dia.	7.50
Tea Pot with lid. 58mm.	7.50

Victoria Arms China

Trademark used on china produced by Hewitt & Leadbeater Ltd. (Usual trademark Willow Art).

Victoria Arms Models
Historic/Folklore

HRH Prince of Wales in his investiture costume, standing on base. 88mm long.	150.00

Great War

Tank with trailing wheels, inscribed: *Model of British Tank.* 130mm long.	20.00
Kit Bag, drawn string. 70mm.	20.00
Kitchen range, with pot on fire, inscribed: *Keep the home fires burning.* Some colouring. 78mm long.	14.50

Victoria China

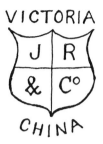

Mark used approx 1910-1924.

Marks used approx 1910-1924.

Trademark was thought to have been used on crested wares by James Reeves, Victoria Works, Fenton. However, it is probable that J.R. & Co was a china wholesaler who purchased ranges from J.A. Robinson (Usual mark Arcadian). Taylor & Kent (Usual mark Florentine) and Sampson Hancock (Usual mark Corona).

James Reeve was established in 1870 and produced tableware and ornamental earthenware. It seems likely that the firm began making some miniatures just before the Great War and continued to do so as the craze for war souvenirs grew and the supply of skilled operatives diminished. The firm continued in business until 1948, but seems not to have made crested ware and other miniatures after the mid-Twenties. They obviously saw such production as a sideline, as they never advertised it or bothered to register the mark used on their range.

Victoria china is rather heavy as one would expect from an earthenware manufacturer but it is quite well finished. Some models showed a marked similarity to Botolph China. Other models shows a great similarity to Florentine China (Taylor and Kent) but there is no known connection between the two firms. No view ware, 'Lucky White Heather' or 'Lucky Black Cats' have been recorded with this mark but two different coloured transfers entitled 'Welsh Costume' have been found on Welsh Hats. (J. Reeves seemed to have found a good market in Wales, many Welsh crests and models have been recorded. Some military badges have also been recorded.

Army Service Corps
Australian Commonwealth
5th Battalion Bedfordshire Regiment
Brecknockshire Regiment
Cambridgeshire Regiment
6th Battalion Duke of Wellington's West
    Riding Regiment
1st Battalion Hertfordshire Regiment
18th London Irish Rifles
5th Battalion Norfolk Regiment
4th Battalion Northamptonshire Regiment
Northumberland Fusiliers
4th Queen's Surrey Regiment
Royal Fusiliers, 1st City of London Brigade.
5th Suffolk Regiment
5th Battalion, the Welsh Regiment
2nd West Riding Brigade R.F.A.
5th West Riding Regiment
West Yorkshire Regiment
No other commemoratives have been found
    with this mark.
Numbering System. No stock numbers are
    found on crested models. The painted
    numerals, dots and dashes found on the
    base are paintresses' marks. A few items
    of crested domestic ware have been
    recorded and some of these carry stock
    numbers, e.g. Salt Pot 148 and Candlestick
    144. It is possible that the firm offered a
    range of these items, but very few have
    survived.

Victoria Models
Ancient Artefacts
Carlisle Salt Pot. 70mm.	3.00
Chester Roman Vase, named. 58mm.	4.00
Fountains Abbey Cup. 50mm.	3.00
Puzzle Jug. 67mm.	5.50
Tyg. 1 handle. 70mm.	3.00

Buildings – White
Blackpool Tower, with buildings. 142mm.	10.50
Bottle Oven. 82mm.	16.00
Old Pete's Cottage, I.o.M. 75mm long.	30.00

Monuments (including Crosses)
Iona Cross. 108mm.	7.50
Wallace Tower, Stirling. 120mm.	40.00

Historical/Folklore
Man in Pillory. 105mm.	17.00
Miner's Lamp. 84mm.	14.00
Mother Shipton. Sometimes found named. 70mm.	8.00

Suffragette handbell. 72mm.	20.00

Traditional/National Souvenirs
Blackpool Ferris Wheel. 108mm.	10.50
Laxey Wheel. Isle of Man. 95mm.	40.00
Legs of Man, inside life belt. 90mm.	16.00
Ripon Horn. 90mm.	17.50
Ripon Hornblower. 90mm.	16.00
Bust of Scotsman wearing tam-o'shanter and plaid. 63mm.	16.00
Welsh Bardic Chair. 86mm. (identical to Old Arm Chair.)	19.50
Welsh Harp. 90mm.	10.00
Welsh Hat with thin blue ribbon band. 48mm and 58mm.	5.00
Welsh Hat, two different moulds one with twisted cord band, and the other with blue band with gold tassels. Can be found with Llanfair...etc. around brim. 62mm.	5.00
Inscribed	7.50

Seaside Souvenirs
Baby seated on rock. 109mm.	16.00
Bathing Machine. 65mm long.	10.00
Yacht in full sail. 126mm.	12.50
Canoe. 102mm long.	10.50
Houseboat, rectangular. 90mm long.	7.50
Fisherman, bust. 87mm.	19.50
Fisherwoman, bust. 87mm.	19.50
Lighthouse. 97mm.	5.50
Lighthouse, unnamed Flamborough. 110mm.	30.00
Whelk Shell, inscribed: *Listen to the sea.* 95mm long.	5.00

Countryside
Acorn on plinth, pepper pot. 75mm.	7.00
Milk Churn and lid. 70mm.	5.00

Animals
Cat, with long neck. 115mm.	10.00
Cat, The Cheshire. Inscribed: *Always smiling.* 80mm.	6.50
Cat, Manx. 80mm long.	23.00
Bulldog in kennel. 70mm long.	12.00
Dog, King Charles Spaniel in cradle. 90mm long.	14.00
Dog, King Charles Spaniel, begging on cushion. 70mm.	10.50
Dogs, two King Charles Spaniels in Top Hat. 70mm.	15.00
Puppy sitting. 88mm.	10.50

Donkey, walking. 92mm long.	20.00
Elephant, kneeling. 80mm long.	20.00
Fish, inscribed: *Caught at...*	
102mm long.	5.50
Frog cream jug. 75mm.	6.50
Frog, singing, hands on chest, open	
mouth. 95mm.	75.00
Hare, ears down. 77mm long.	9.50
Monkey, crouching, hands to	
mouth. 88mm.	13.00
Mouse playing Mandolin. 90mm.	25.00
Pig, kneeling. 70mm long.	10.00
Pig, standing. Sometimes inscribed:	
The pig that won't go. 88mm long.	10.50
Rabbit with upright ears.	
75mm long.	7.50
Rabbit, 98mm long.	12.50
Seal with ball. 73mm.	19.50
Teddy Bear, sitting. 98mm.	30.00
Toad. 39mm.	16.00

Birds (including Eggs)

Canary on rock. 100mm.	10.50
Chick hatching from egg.	
65mm long.	9.00
Hen, roosting. 92mm long.	7.50
Kingfisher cream jug. 58mm.	5.50
Kingfisher, with long beak. 80mm.	20.00
Owl.	
2 sizes: 70mm.	10.50
95mm.	12.50
Parrot. 76mm.	10.50
Pelican jug. 63mm.	5.50
Swan.	
2 sizes: 70mm.	6.50
90mm long.	6.50
Swan posy bowl. 80mm long.	5.00

Great War

Tommy and his Machine Gun.	
97mm long.	40.00
Bust of Sailor. 90mm.	35.00
Airship on base. 128mm long.	30.00
Zeppelin. 132mm long.	30.00
Monoplane with roundels and	
4-bladed movable prop.	
170mm long.	110.00
Battleship, two guns fore, one aft.	
120mm long.	17.50
Lusitania, 165mm long.	75.00
Torpedo Boat Destroyer.	
110mm long.	23.00
Submarine, inscribed *E4.*	19.50
Submarine, inscribed *E9.*	
147mm long.	20.00

Armoured Car (Arcadian).	
94mm long.	40.00
Red Cross Van. 102mm long.	30.00
Red Cross Van, with painted not	
moulded crosses. 90mm long.	30.00
Renault Tank. 82mm long.	65.00
Tank, with inset steering wheels.	
100mm long.	19.50
Tank, with large side turrets.	
120mm long.	21.00
Field Gun. 127mm long.	17.00
Trench Mortar. 65mm.	16.00
Torpedo, fixed prop. 155mm long.	47.50
Mills Hand Grenade, not named.	
Rd. No. 657211. 60mm.	17.50
Capstan. 55mm.	11.50
Colonial Soldier's Hat.	
73mm long.	19.50
Officer's Peaked Cap. 65mm long.	10.50
Drum. 38mm.	10.50
Field Glasses. 80mm long.	17.50
Ghurka Knife. 143mm long.	20.00
Grandfather Clock, usual model but	
with clock transfer at 3.25. With	
inscription: *World War 1914-1919.*	
Peace signed 3.25pm June 28 1919.	
110mm.	56.50
Bell Tent, hexagonal, open flat.	
89mm.	16.00
Kit Bag, open. 70mm.	20.00
Sandbag. 74mm long.	17.50
Water Bottle. 64mm.	13.00
Cenotaph. 135mm.	5.50
Florence Nightingale statue.	
148mm.	16.00
Matlock Bath War Memorial.	
178mm.	75.00
Ripon War Memorial. 118mm.	82.50

Home/Nostalgic

Baby in bath. 100mm long.	12.50
Broom Head. 105mm long.	20.50
Coal Bucket. 62mm.	4.00
Cradle. 80mm long.	14.00
Dolly tub with clothes. 80mm.	26.00
Garden Roller. 85mm long.	12.50
Girl in Bonnet, salt pot. 93mm.	12.50
Gladstone Bag. 45mm.	4.00
Grandfather Clock. 120mm.	12.00
Grandmother Clock. 87mm.	6.50
Lamp. 100mm long.	5.00
Lantern. 86mm.	5.50
Oil Lamp. 100mm long.	3.00
The Old Armchair, with inscription.	
83mm.	7.50

Pillar Box, inscribed: *I cant get a
letter from you, so send you the box.*
70mm.   12.50
Portmanteau. 55mm.   4.00
Sundial on large square base,
inscribed: *Tempus fugit.* 109mm.   10.50
Shaving Mug. 30mm.   6.50
Tobacco Pouch. 72mm long.   11.50
Watering Can. 70mm.   6.50
Writing Desk. 55mm.   9.00

Comic/Novelty
Boy's face, smiling on cream jug.
73mm.   9.50
Boy's head, smiling on match
holder shoulders. 75mm.   7.50
Boy on Scooter. 106mm.   17.50
Jack in the Box. 95mm.   17.50
Pierrot playing banjo, some
colouring. 120mm.   25.00
Screw, inscribed: *You could do with a
big fat screw (wage rise).* 76mm.   40.00
Suffragette Handbell, two sided.
One side ugly old lady, inscribed:
Votes for women. Reverse, a pretty
young girl, inscribed: *This one
shall have a vote.*
2 sizes: 72mm.   30.00
108mm.   47.50

Cartoon/Comedy Characters
Ally Sloper bust, not named. 83mm.   32.50
Harry Lauder, bust. 63mm.   17.00

Alcohol
Carboy. 72mm.   7.50
Champagne Bottle in ice bucket
inscribed: *Something good – a bottle
of the boy.* 83mm.   13.00
Whisky Bottle.   7.50

Sport/Pastimes
Cricket Bag. 115mm long.   12.50
Pawn chess piece. 60mm.   25.00

Musical Instruments
Banjo. 137mm long.   10.00
Grand Piano, with closed lid.
80mm long.   15.00
Upright Piano. 63mm.   13.00
Tambourine. 68mm dia.   8.50

Transport
Charabanc, with driver.
115mm long.   33.00

Motor Horn, inscribed: *Pip Pip.*
90mm long.   22.50
Saloon Car. 80mm long.   40.00

Modern Equipment
Cash Register. 47mm.   16.00
Gas Cooker. 70mm.   10.00
Gramophone, square without horn.
58mm.   15.50
Radio Horn. 95mm.   18.00

Footwear
Ladies 18th Century Shoe.
92mm long.   7.50
Lancashire Clog.
2 sizes: 85mm long.   5.00
100mm long.   5.50
Oriental Shoe with pointed turned-
up toe. 95mm long.   4.00

Miniature Domestic
Candleholder, circular. 45mm.   3.00
Cheese Dish and cover. 50mm.   6.50
Coffee Pot with lid.
2 sizes: 69mm.   7.50
125mm.   7.50
Cup and Saucer, diamond shaped.
50mm.   4.50
Tea Pot with lid. 60mm.   7.50
Tea Pot with lid, ball shaped.
75mm.   7.50

Miscellaneous
Candlestick with snake entwined.
106mm.   8.50
Hair Brush Trinket Box and lid.
140mm long.   14.00
Mustard Pot and lid, on 3 small
feet, with spoon. 70mm.   8.50

Miscellaneous
Lily Vase. 115mm.   5.50

Victorian China

Trademark used by Robinson and Leadbeater, Wolfe St, Stoke-on-Trent. (Usual trademark Robinson & Leadbeater).

For further details of this china and manufacturer see R. and L.

This mark was definitely used before Robinson and Leadbeater were taken over by Harold Taylor Robinson in 1906 and subsequently a branch of J.A. Robinson. The china found with this mark is very fine and translucent, and was probably made at the turn of the century. Robinson and Leadbeater would have offered a small range of crested wares while they were still a respectable souvenir.

Most of the items recorded with this mark are 'smalls' or small domestic pieces such as beakers. One loving cup has been found with a colour transfer print of a ship in full sail.

Victorian Porcelain Models.
Ancient Artefacts

Loving Cup, 2 and 3 handled. 39mm.	3.00
Oxford Jug. 83mm.	3.00
Scarboro Jug, inscribed: *Jug about 600 years old found in ancient moat Scarboro (sic)*. No. 180. 42mm.	3.00

Birds (including Eggs)

Swan posy holder, yellow beak & feet. 75mm long.	5.50

Home/Nostalgic

Bellows. 110mm long.	10.50

Victoria (China)

Trademark used by two German manufacturers, Schmidt and Co, Carlsbad (Bohemia), and Moschendorf, Hof, Bavaria.

For further details of manufacturer see Gemma.

This mark is usually found on domestic wares but the models listed below have been recorded. The ware is very fine and one would assume that Schmidt and Co made this china in another works or offered it as an alternative range to Gemma. This china is often found in pearl lustre. It can also be found coloured in maroon and green with gilded flowers on a variety of domestic shapes.

Victoria Models.

Seaside Souvenirs

Bathing Hut. 80mm.	7.50
Yacht, yellow/brown lustre.	
No. 2276. 105mm long.	6.50
Conch Shell on 4 stubby feet.	
100mm.	3.50

Birds (including Eggs)

Hen, pepper pot, red comb & beak.	
70mm.	5.00
Swan posy bowl. 58mm.	3.50

Home/Nostalgic

Grandmother Clock, lustre. 88mm.	5.00
Watering Can. 78mm.	5.50
Wheelbarrow. 100mm long.	5.00

Musical Instruments

Grand Piano, removable lid. 103mm.	10.00

Footwear

Sabot. 84mm long.	4.00

Miniature Domestic

Cauldron. 58mm.	2.00
Cheese Dish and cover. 30mm.	5.00
Cup and Saucer with lithophane of	
Blarney Castle. 60mm.	35.00
German Beer Mug. 50mm.	3.00
Jug and Bowl set. 69mm.	7.50

Domestic

Inkwell and lid. 40mm.	7.50
Pin Box and lid, heart-shaped.	
84mm long.	5.00
Salt Pot. 80mm.	3.00

Vignaud

FRANCE
VIGNAUD
LIMOGES

Trademark used by a French china manufacturer, Vignaud, Limoges, France for the French souvenir market.

Only 60mm vase with a Paris crest recorded.	4.00

Viking China

W

Pieces were bought in for resale in the Isle of Man by D.W. Kee from Hewitt and Leadbeater, Willow Potteries, Longton (see Willow Art), and Taylor & Kent (Ltd.), Florence Works, Longton. (Usual trademark Florentine).

Animals
Manx Cat. 90mm long.   25.00

Miscellaneous
Jug. 55mm.   3.00

Trademark used by H.M. Williams and Sons, Bridge Pottery, Longton.

This firm, established in 1858, according to an advert in the *Pottery Gazette,* were well known for their china tea and dinner sets. They used the mark above on cheaper wares from 1900 and probably for only a short time. (The mark is shown in an advert in the *Pottery Gazette* in 1903.) Their range of crested china is quite well produced, but by no means exceptionally so, and most of the items found could be described as 'smalls'. Many models are recorded with the commemorative transfer 'The Triple Entente' which consists of shields of the flags of France, Great Britain and Russia.

W Models
Ancient Artefacts
Loving Cup, 3 handles. 55mm.   3.00
Salisbury Kettle. 102mm.   3.00

Animals
Cat, long necked. 112mm.   10.00
Cat, Manx. 60mm.   19.50
Frog cream jug. 60mm.   10.50
Pig, standing. 100mm long.   11.00
Rabbit, sitting. 86mm.   7.00
Seal.   16.00

Birds (including Eggs)
Kingfisher cream jug. 58mm.   7.50

Swan posy bowl. 80mm long.   5.00

Home/Nostalgic
Oil Lamp. 58mm.   4.00
Policeman's Lamp. 71mm.   10.00
Portmanteau. 80mm long.   4.00
Shaving Mug. 55mm.   6.50
Watering Can. 55mm.   5.50

Sport/Pastimes
Cricket Bag. 110mm long.   12.50

Footwear
Ladies Shoe with high heel.
90mm long.   7.50

Miniature Domestic
Cheese Dish. 45mm.   6.50
Tea Pot with lid. 70mm.   7.50

Miscellaneous
5-mouthed Vase.   2.00

W & Sons

W & Sons
"MIKADO"
WARE
Rᴰ No 438118

The only piece known is a ewer with pale green trim and handle displaying colour transfers of Japanese scenes. This is remarkably similar to a series of vases (unmarked) with a sprig of holly and crest of carpe: Diem. The manufacturer is unknown, but a similar quality porcelain was produced by Albion China (Taylor and Kent Ltd), Florence Works, Longton, usual trademark Florentine. Albion also produced ware with green trim instead of gilding.

Mikado Ware Models
Ewer, pale green with Japanese
scenes.   20.00

Wade

Warwick China

No details of mark available except that mark incorporates 'Wades'.

Trademark used by Wade & Co, Union Pottery, Burslem, subsequently Wade, Heath & Co. (Ltd).

This company which went on to make coloured cartoon models in the thirties and later Wade miniature animals and Disney characters, (Hat Box series), did not surprisingly make a large range of crested china. The odd items found with their name are domestic pieces, the crest almost appearing to have been added as an afterthought. The firm before 1927, when it became Wade, Heath and Co., manufactured earthenwares so the crested wares tend to be heavy and useful rather than ornamental.

A small range of earthenware
domestic wares was produced.
$$\text{£2.00 upwards}$$

Trademark used for W.H. Smith and Sons by Arkinstall and Son Ltd, Arcadian Works, Stoke-on-Trent. (Usual trademark Arcadian).

For further details of the china and manufacturer see Arcadian China.

This range of china made for W.H. Smith is of a higher quality than one normally associates with Arcadian China and the crests are boldly and beautifully produced. The models are, however, made from Arcadian moulds and if one can judge from the models recorded, seem to have been made before and during the Great War, but not afterwards.

Numbering System. Numbers can either be printed or written and are usually in the style of a fraction. the lower numbers occur on many different models and could possibly be an order number. The following lower numbers have been recorded: 010, 01½, 06½, 09, 012, 014, 015 and 030. The upper numbers appear to be stock numbers and where recorded they coincide with Arcadian stock numbers. Stock numbers where known are given in the lists below.

Warwick Models
Ancient Artefacts

Ancient Tyg, model of. 70mm.	4.00
Cambridge Roman Jug. 58mm.	4.00
Canterbury Roman Urn, inscribed: *Roman Urn found near Canterbury, original in Canterbury Museum.* 70mm.	4.00

Chester Roman Vase. 60mm. — 4.00
Egyptian Vase, about 230BC. 41mm. — 4.00
Highland Whisky Bowl. 90mm dia. — 4.00
Lincoln Jack, from original in Museum.
  62mm. — 4.00
Newbury Leather Bottle. 65mm. — 3.00
Norwich Urn, inscribed: *Model of*
  cinerary urn found at Norwich. No.
  135. 50mm. — 4.00
Roman Lamp. 90mm long. — 4.00
Reading Vase, inscribed: *Model of*
  vase from Silchester in Reading
  Museum. 53mm. — 4.00
Winchelsea Roman Cup, inscribed:
  Roman cup found near Winchelsea.
  51mm. — 4.00

Buildings – White
Rowton Tower, with inscription: *King*
  Charles I stood on this tower Sept
  24th 1645 and saw his army defeated
  on Rowton Moor. 105mm. — 40.00

Historical/Folklore
The Brading Stocks, man sitting in
  stocks. 82mm. — 25.00
Yorick's Skull, inscribed: *Alas poor*
  Yorick. 57mm. — 13.00

Traditional/National Souvenirs
Prime Cheddar Cheese, with slice out.
  60mm. — 12.50

Seaside Souvenirs
Fishing Basket, inscribed: *A good*
  catch. 70mm long. — 8.50
Lighthouse. 148mm. — 8.50

Animals
Dog, Collie. 95mm. — 12.50
Otter, holding fish in mouth.
  120mm long. — 47.50
Polar Bear. 96mm. — 40.00
Pony, Shetland. 105mm long. — 25.00
Teddy Bear, sitting. 90mm. — 19.50

Birds (including Eggs)
Chick breaking out of egg.
  63mm long. — 9.00
Hen, roosting. 54mm. — 7.50
Egg shaped salt pot, inscribed: *s*
  56mm. — 4.00
Egg shaped pepper pot, inscribed:
  p. 56mm. — 4.00

Great War
British Airship on stand.
  128mm long. — 20.00
E4 Submarine. 95mm long. — 20.00
Red Cross Van, red cross on each
  side and rear. *'EH 139'* inscribed
  on radiator. 85mm long. — 30.00
Pith Helmet. 80mm long. — 25.00
Field Glasses. 78mm long. — 13.00
Bell Tent with open flap inscribed:
  Camping Out 65mm. — 14.50
Anti-Zeppelin Candleholder.
  62mm. — 17.50

Home/Nostalgic
Grandfather Clock. 113mm. — 10.50
Lantern, inscribed: *Watchman What*
  of the Night. 82mm. — 10.00
Sundial on square base. — 5.50
Thimble, inscribed: *Tak A Thimble*
  Full. 40mm. — 20.00
Three-legged stool. 42mm. — 5.50

Alcohol
Highland Whisky Bowl. 90mm dia. — 4.00

Sport/Pastimes
Cricket Bag. 80mm long. — 12.50
Ashtray with central raised heart/
  club/diamond/spade indicator.
  The more we are together the merrier
  we will be. — 20.00
Rook chess piece. 55mm. — 7.50

Musical Instruments
Banjo. 155mm long. — 9.50

Miniature Domestic
Cheese Dish and cover. 50mm. — 6.50

Domestic Wares
Candlesnuffer, cone. 65mm. — 3.50
Pair – salt and pepper pots,
  octagonal. Inscribed: *Salt* and
  Pepper. 88mm. — 5.00

Waterfall Heraldic China

F C   CH
COPYRIGHT

Trademark used for a Northern wholesaler by Hewitt and Leadbeater, Willow Potteries, Longton. (Usual trademark Willow Art).

For further details of this china and manufacturer see Willow Art China.

All crests and model souvenirs of monuments and buildings found with this mark are northern. The most commonly found crests are Withernsea, Grimsby, Hull and Filey, indicating that the models were sold in northern towns, resorts and ports. Most models are identical to those found in the Willow Art range but some models were obviously made especially to be sold in Hull, Grimsby and Hedon.

Stock numbers where they occur, coincide with Willow Art numbers.

Waterfall Models

Ancient Artefacts

Lincoln Jack, not named. No. 44.
60mm.   3.00
Portland Vase, not named. 53mm.   3.00

Buildings – White

Grimsby Hydraulic Tower.
165mm.   28.00
Grimsby Hydraulic Tower designed by Sir W. Armstrong. Erected first stone laid 1849. Finished 1854. Height 320ft. Width 28ft. Tank capacity 30,000 gallons. On square base. 150mm.   82.50

Monuments (including Crosses)

Hull Fishermans Memorial, with inscription.
2 sizes: 135mm.   20.00
160mm.   20.00
Hull South African War Memorial, with inscription. 165mm.   24.00
Kilnsea Cross, Hedon with inscription: *Erected at Ravenspurne 1339 by King Henry IV. Re-erected at Hedon.* 134mm.   55.00
Rufus Stone with inscription.
110mm.   7.50
The Monument, Laceby, with inscriptions. 154mm.   27.50
Sir William de la Pole, Statue of, with long inscription. 160mm.   25.00
Charles Henry Wilson, First Baron Nunburnholme, statue, inscribed on front: *The largest private shipowner in the world. Born 1833. Died 1907. 32 years a member of parliament for Hull and a great benefactor to the city. Erected by public subscription, in the year AD 1912.* 154mm.   55.00

Historical/Folklore

James V Chair, Stirling Castle, Model of. No. 200. 100mm.   7.50
Mary Queen of Scots Chair.
82mm.   6.50
Skull. 60mm long.   12.00

Traditional/National Souvenirs

Bagpipes, with turquoise ribbon.
118mm long.   15.00
Welsh Hat. 53mm.   5.00
Dutch Boy. 80mm.   10.50

Seaside Souvenirs

Grimsby fisherman, bust. 83mm.	19.50
~~Lifeboatman, bust,~~ inscribed: *Hull Fisherman.* 83mm.	19.50
Lighthouse, not named. 115mm.	5.00
Spurn Lighthouse, with inscription. 130mm.	19.50
Withernsea Lighthouse, with inscription. 3 sizes: 105mm, 113mm & 130mm.	16.00

Countryside

Milk Can and lid. 60mm.	5.00

Animals

Cat, Cheshire, inscribed: *Still smiling.* 95mm.	7.50
Cat, sitting, with shield. No. 62. 75mm.	10.50
Cat with arched back. 65mm.	11.00
Cat, sitting, medallion on chest. 72mm.	12.00
Black Cat on Boot. 90mm long.	19.50
Dog, Bull Terrier, standing. 60mm.	12.50
Dog, King Charles Spaniel, begging on cushion. 95mm.	13.00
Elephant, walking. 52mm.	17.00
Fish with open mouth. 103mm long.	4.00
Lion, walking. 120mm long.	14.50
Pig, sitting on haunches, upright ears, inscribed: *You may push me. You may shuv. But I'm hanged if I'll be druv.* 75mm.	16.00
Pig, large, sitting laughing. Inscribed: *You may push...* No. 137. 105mm long.	16.00
Teddy Bear, sitting. 76mm.	19.50

Great War

Standing Sailor, *Our Brave Defender.* 128mm.	55.00
Despatch Rider. 115mm long.	75.00
Observer Sausage Balloon. 85mm.	55.00
Monoplane, with revolving prop. 150mm long.	65.00
Battleship, impressed: *HMS Lion.* 140mm long.	30.00
Submarine impressed: *E4.* 116mm long.	19.50
Submarine *E5.* 124mm long.	20.00
Red Cross Van. Red cross on side. 84mm long.	30.00
British Tank, Model of. 92mm long.	14.50
British Tank, Model of with trailing wheels. 130mm long.	17.50
Armoured Car. 95mm long.	40.00
Field Gun. 120mm long.	17.00
Field Gun, with screen. 115mm long.	19.00
Howitzer. 115mm long.	16.00
British Aerial Torpedo. 102mm long.	30.00
Glengarry, some colouring. 83mm long.	16.00
Trench Lamp. 70mm.	13.00
Kitchen Range, with cooking pot, inscribed: *Keep the Home Fires...* No. 199. 80mm long.	13.00

Home/Nostalgic

Coal Scuttle. 65mm long.	4.00
Flower Basket. 70mm.	3.50
Grandfather Clock. 125mm.	10.50
Watering Can. 75mm.	8.50

Comic/Novelty

Billiken, not named. 73mm.	7.50

Alcohol

Beer Barrel on stand. 58mm.	5.50
Beer Tankard, silver on circular ashtray base, inscribed: *The more we are together the merrier we will be.* 100mm dia.	17.50

Sport/Pastimes

Cricket Bat. 115mm long.	30.00
Golf Ball. 45mm.	7.50
Knight chess piece. 62mm.	14.50

Hats

Mortar Board. 65mm long.	20.00

Footwear

Ladies Shoe with blue bow. 114mm long.	13.00
Slipper Wall Pocket. 152mm long.	11.50

Miniature Domestic

Cheese Dish and cover, circular. 45mm.	7.50
Coffee Pot with lid. 70mm.	7.50

Domestic

Trefoil Cruet with lids. 60mm.	3.50

Miscellaneous

Horse's Hoof. 60mm long.	3.50

Waterloo Ware

Trademark probably used by a retailer for items thought to be produced by Sampson, Hancock & Sons, Stoke. (Usual trademark Corona).

Waterloo Models
Buildings – White
Bottle Oven, inside of. 84mm.   16.00

Great War
Ghurka Knife. 135mm long.   20.00

Waverley China

Trademark used for Wyman & Sons Ltd, by Arkinstall & Son, Ltd, Arcadian Works, Stoke-on-Trent. (Usual trademark Arcadian).

Alternative factory mark used for an agent in Glasgow.

For further details of china and manufacturer see Arcadian China.
This mark has only been found on 'smalls' and ancient artefacts, and was probably only used before the Great War.

Waverley Models
Ancient Artefacts
Arundel, model of vase found near.
  64mm.   4.00
Dorothy Vase, Model of. bagware
  vase. No. 100. 48mm.   7.50
Glastonbury Bronze Bowl. 2
  models. No. 74. 40mm. No. 100.
  41mm.   3.00

Hastings Kettle. No. 237. 62mm.   3.00
St. Davids Vase, inscribed: *Vase found*
   at St. Davids. 69mm.   4.00

WCG

Trademark used by an unknown
  manufacturer.

Domestic ware only.   from 2.00

Wedgwood

Wellington China

***
WEDGWOOD
*
ENGLAND

Used after 1900.

WEDGWOOD
ETRURIA ENGLAND

c1900.

Trademark used by Josiah Wedgwood (and
Sons Ltd), Etruria.

The famous firm of Wedgwood
made a few small vases with
crests at the turn of the century.
The china is very fine and the
crests are beautifully enamelled.
These heraldic wares were
obviously also exported, as crests
of Le Havre and Monaco have
been recorded.   10.00

There is also a series of small vases
with gold ramshead handles with
coloured transfers of soldiers.
The regiments are named on the
back of the vases. 60mm.   from 20.00

A 43mm three-handled loving cup
with a gilded handle has also
been recorded.   10.00

Trademark of J.H. Cope & Co., Wellington
Works, Longton, Staffs. from 1924-1947.
The firm produced high quality porcelain.

Domestic
Cup, saucer and plate, Lucky White
Heather from Brecon.   Set 8.00

Wembley China

WEMBLEY CHINA

Trademark used on china for sale at the British Empire Exhibition of 1924 and 1925 by the Cauldon Group of Companies. (Usual trademark Arcadian). All pieces therefore carry B.E.E. crests and are priced accordingly.

Wembley Models
Parian/Unglazed

George V statue on glazed plinth inscribed: *A souvenir from Wembley*, with inscription: *King George V – Born June 3rd 1865 – Ascended the throne May 6th 1910.* 2 sizes: 125mm & 140mm.	55.00
Prince of Wales, (Edward VIII) bust on glazed plinth, with inscription: *HRH The Prince of Wales, Born June 23rd 1894.* 135mm.	75.00

Buildings – White

Cottage on base. 92mm long.	15.00
Wembley Stadium, fully inscribed. 130mm long.	95.00

Historical/Folklore

Miner's Lamp. 70mm.	19.00
Mother Shipton. 115mm.	15.00
Man in Stocks. 88mm.	24.00

Traditional/National Souvenirs

Thistle Vase. 70mm.	5.50
Welsh Hat. 52mm.	8.50
Welsh Tea Party. 98mm.	43.50

Seaside Souvenirs

Bathing Machine. 65mm.	11.50
Yacht. 125mm.	16.00
Trawler with sails set on both masts. 125mm long.	20.00
Lighthouse, not named. 2 sizes: 110mm.	8.50
140mm.	8.50

Countryside

Beehive on table. 78mm.	13.00
Haystack, circular. 55m.	9.00

Animals

Cat with long neck, sitting. 108mm.	10.50
Black Cat, sitting on armchair. 55mm.	29.00
Fawn. 50mm.	34.50
Frog, with open mouth. 62mm.	18.00
Kangaroo. 75mm.	75.00
Monkey sitting. 69mm.	17.00
Pig, sitting and smiling. 63mm long.	23.00

Birds (including Eggs)

Cock, red comb and yellow beak. 90mm.	23.00

Great War

Nurse and Wounded Tommy. 108mm long.	130.00
Sailor winding capstan, Model of. 105mm.	110.00
Tommy, driving a steamroller over the Kaiser. 120mm.	480.00
Soldier Bust, unnamed Tommy Atkins. Some colouring. 90mm.	43.00
Biplane, in lustre. 120mm long.	82.50
Observer or Sausage Balloon. 82mm.	75.00
Armoured Car, model of. 95mm long.	40.00
Red Cross Van. 2 sizes: 90mm long.	32.00
100mm long.	32.00
Tank, Model of. 115mm long.	20.00
Field gun with screen and sight hole. 107mm long.	31.00
Howitzer. 135mm.	24.00
Trench dagger. 105mm long.	50.00
Capstan. 56mm.	14.00
Pair of Field Glasses, Model of. 78mm long.	19.00
Colonial Hat. 86mm long.	19.50
Officer's Peaked Cap. 65mm dia.	11.50
Cavell Memorial, inscribed: *Nurse Cavell.* 160mm.	25.00

Home/Nostalgic

Fireplace, no inscription but much colouring. 90mm.	13.00
Grandfather Clock. 108mm.	14.50
Kennel. 50mm.	8.50
Lantern, horn. 85mm.	7.00

Comic/Novelty

Billiken. 60mm.	8.50
Hand holding Pig's trotter. 110mm long.	10.50
Policeman on duty. 145mm.	37.50

Sport/Pastimes

Curling Stone. 49mm.	18.00
Bishop chess piece. 72mm.	19.50

Transport

Car, open tourer, (2 seater). 110mm long.	42.00

Hats

Boy Scout's Hat. 73mm dia.	19.50

Miniature Domestic

Tea Pot, one piece. 48mm.	7.50

White Horse China

Trademark used for the Royal Mail Steam Packet Company by an unknown manufacturer, but resembling Carlton China and Arcadian.

Some pieces display transfer prints of ships.

White Horse Models
Historical/Folklore

Carlisle Ancient Stone Roman Altar, Model of. 122mm. (Bears the arms of Reading.)	35.00
Coaching Hat, not named. No. 124. 39mm.	12.50

Animals

Squirrel eating nut. 68mm.	30.00

The White House

Trademark used for a Lancashire retailer by an unknown manufacturer (possibly Arcadian).

Only one 'small' and two animals have been found with this mark. A.H. and S.M. Manchester was not a manufacturer so one can assume that the White House, Manchester, was a retail outlet.

White House Models
One small recorded.   4.00

Animals
Upright Cat playing flute.
  70mm.   35.00
Squirrel eating nut. 68mm.   30.00

W.H.H. and S.

Trademark used by a German manufacturer, Wilhelm Kutzscher & Co. Schwarzenberger Porzellanfabrik, Schwarzenberg, Saxony, for an outlet in south-west England.

The initials W.H.H. and S.P. are retailer's initials. The inclusion of the four Plymouth models indicates that the P under the mark may stand for Plymouth.

W.H.H. and S. Models
Buildings – White
Clock Tower, not named. 125mm.   7.50

Monuments (including Crosses)
Sir Frances Drake, statue. Plymouth.
  163mm.   16.00
Plymouth Armada Memorial.
  175mm.   35.00

Seaside Souvenirs
Eddystone Lighthouse. Pepper Pot.
  107mm.   10.50

Animals
Dog, Spaniel, sitting. 60mm.   7.50
Elephants, two on a sledge on slope.
  76mm.   75.00

Birds (including Eggs)
Duck posy bowl, yellow beak.
  83mm long.   7.50

Great War
Monoplane with revolving
   propellor. 145mm long.   20.00
Plymouth War Memorial. 175mm.   30.00

Sport
Cricket Cap. 70mm long.   20.00

Miniature Domestic
Cheese Dish and cover. 76mm long.   5.50

Wilco Series

Trademark used by Wilkinson & Co., a
Derbyshire retailer, by Hewitt and
Leadbeater. Willow Potteries. Longton.
(Usual trademark Willow Art).

Wilco Models
Animals
Rabbit, crouching with alert ears.
   No. 97. 60mm long.   7.50

Miniature Domestic
Cheese Dish and cover. 50mm.   6.50

Williamsons

Trademark used by H.M. Williamson and
  Sons, Bridge Pottery, Longton.
For more details see W.
This mark was used by Williamson and Sons
  on domestic china with the usual patterns,
  and has also been found on domestic ware
  with crests. It also appears on the two
  models listed below.

A range of crested domestic ware.

Williamson Models
Ancient Artefacts
Guernsey Milk Can, with lid.
  105mm. (Found with a Guernsey
  crest).   7.50

Alcohol
Tankard. 75mm.   4.00

Willow Art and Willow China

WILLOW
ART CHINA
LONGTON

Early mark 1905-c1910.

Can have STAFFORDSHIRE added.

Marks used between 1907 and 1925. (Models
  with these marks can also be found
  impressed H & L 1907-1920 and Hewitt
  Bros. 1920-1925).

Mark found on domestic ware, 1925-1930.

Can be found with "ware" rather than "china". Used between 1925-1930.

H & L

Impressed mark 1905-1919.

H. BROS
WILLOW
ENGLAND

Impressed Mark 1919-25.

Trademark used by Hewitt and Leadbeater, Willow Potteries, Longton, subsequently, Hewitt Bros, and eventually Willow Potteries Ltd, a branch of Cauldon Ltd.

Hewitt and Leadbeater joined in partnership in 1905 as manufacturers of 'artistic and useful specialities in great variety'. Mr Edwin Leadbeater was the son of the senior partner of Robinson and Leadbeater (R. and L. makers of Parian busts), and brought his experience to the new business. Arthur Hewitt was his brother-in-law. Edwin Leadbeater, as already mentioned (see: Leadbeater Art China), always received a good press from the *Pottery Gazette* and so we have more information about the products of the Willow Pottery than any other 'arms ware' firm.

As well as flower holders and vases in many shapes and colours, the new firm produced ecclesiastical and art statuary in

Early mark 1907-1925.

WILLOW CHINA

Mark found on late coloured models from 1925.

plain white, antique ivory and art colours. (These were marked H. and L.) The firms early ornamental wares are very beautiful, vases were made in the form of open flowers, the most striking being an arum lily with green leaves. 'Hop Ware' and 'Vine Ware' were also made, these vases and jugs having moulded bunches of green hops on dark green grounds or purple grapes and green vine leaves on cream grounds. They are delightful and delicate. (These early items are very rare and carry the earliest Willow mark.)

But 'Heraldic Ware' was one of the firm's leading lines from the beginning and its production helped Hewitt and Leadbeater to establish themselves. The company supplied miniatures with crests, views and other decorations including poppies. The range at this time was called 'Daisy Arms China' but this title does not appear on the models. By 1914, the firm was heavily involved in the production of heraldic novelties, and were said to specialise in models of churches, crosses and buildings of historic interest, also introducing models of a car, battleship, aeroplane, soldier, sailor and nurse to their range. A quote from the *Pottery Gazette* of December 1914, will give some idea of the firm's production.

'For a town such as Stratford, for instance, they have a model of Shakespeare's house in five sizes, Ann Hathaway's Cottage in five sizes, three distinct bust models of Shakespeare embracing in all ten different sizes, Shakespeare's font and desk, and a bust of Ann Hathaway in three sizes'.

(The Parian models would have been marked H. and L. Not all the Ann Hathaway's cottages have been found.)

The war years were very kind to this firm as they could easily manufacture the cheap souvenirs usually supplied by the German china industry. Hewitt and Leadbeater produced a range of topical interest, but cannot be said to have made many original Great War souvenirs. They did begin to produce dolls' heads but this seems to have been short-lived. They had become well known in the trade as specialists in the production of miniatures and parian, but their real speciality in terms of originality was coloured buildings. These sold cheaply at the time but are becoming particularly sought by collectors today. Although Goss cottages change hands for hundreds of pounds, the Willow Art coloured buildings are much more interesting and typical of the period, showing the same good eye for design and colour that was used on the early decorative vases. By 1920 the firm offered a range of 200 different miniatures from stock and offered to make copies of any building of which a photograph or postcard was supplied.

In November 1919 Edwin Leadbeater left the firm to start a pottery business on his own account. (See: Leadbeater Art China for details.) The remaining Mr Hewitt took his brother into partnership and the firm at Willow Pottery became known as Hewitt Bros. Hewitt Bros. continued to use the same tradename on heraldic china and described themselves as 'Novelty Potters'. They produced the usual post-war memorials, figures and comic items. In 1922 they introduced their 'Teddy Tail' and 'Black Cat China'. Teddy Tail transfers, from the original drawings by M. Charles Folkard, creator of the cartoon for the *Daily Mail*, were applied to nursery ware. (Very few, if any, of these mugs and plates have survived.) Black Cat transfers, from the original drawings by Mr H.H. Hosband were applied to domestic ware such as plates, hair tidies, trinket boxes and small vases.

Hewitt bros. did not survive the Depression but it is difficult to understand why the firm came to grief so early, except that they produced only novelties which were the last things people could afford. By 1925 Mr Harold Taylor Robinson had bought the firm and had formed a new company. Willow Potteries Ltd., using the tradename 'Willow Crest'. Willow Potteries Ltd. became part of the Cauldon group almost immediately. By 1927 Willow China was produced along with Arcadian at the Arcadian Works. It is difficult to tell if the late models were originally Hewitt Bros. or Arkinstall moulds. The Willow mark was not used after 1930 but many recognisably Willow buildings are found marked Goss England, so the Willow moulds obviously were being used after that date.

The *Pottery Gazette* of December 1914 tells us that 'Willow Art Arms Ware, is of a warm, ivory caste, of an excellent body and well treated both as regards the potting and the painting'. Praise indeed! Very few exceptionally fine pieces of Willow Art arms ware are found, for the most part the ware is heavy and the painting of crests is just about adequate. This heraldic china sold well because it was cheaply produced and novel. The early wares, especially the parian and coloured buildings made by the firm however, would have sold on their technical merit, and early view ware is found on very fine china.

Very little view ware has been recorded. Early coloured views are found on small dishes and vases, they are pleasant but unremarkable. More exciting are monochrome (brown) pictorials found on small Willow Art pieces, occasionally finished in yellow lustre, and coloured transfers of a regional nature which include Peeping Tom (Willow Art) and Kiaora from Maoriland, Tiki, New Zealand, (Willow).

Willow Art was exported too, so foreign crests are found: Australia, New Zealand and Gibraltar have been recorded. A Jerusalem crest is often found but this is an indication that the model was purchased from the 'Jerusalem and Oriental Bazaar, Great Yarmouth' and not from the Middle East.

The following military crests were also produced by Hewitt and Leadbeater:

Army Cyclists Corp
Army Ordnance
Army Service Corps
Canadian General Service Corps (Maple Leaf)
Coldstream Guards
Grenadier Guards
Hendon Flying School
King's Own Yorkshire Light Infantry
Leicestershire Regiment
1st Life Guards
2nd Life Guards
Lincolnshire Regiment
Loyal North Lancs Regiment
Machine Gun Corps
North Staffordshire Regiment
Northumberland Fusiliers
Notts & Derby Regiment
Royal Air Force
Royal Army Medical Corps
Royal Army Ordnance Corps

Royal Artillery
Royal Engineers
Royal Field Artillery
RE Longmore Camp (2 versions – Edward VII cipher and George V cipher)
Royal Military College, Camberley
Royal Flying Corps
Royal Naval Air Service
Royal Sussex Regiment
Royal West Surrey Regiment
Royal West Surreys, the Queen's
Scots Guards
Somerset Light Infantry
York & Lancaster Regiment

'Flags of the Allies' Great War commemoratives are found inscribed: 'United We Stand'. Other Willow Art commemoratives found are 'Franco British Exhibition 1908' and 'BEE'.

Willow Art and Willow China can be found decorated with red poppies and 'Lucky Black Cat' transfers. Willow Art 'smalls' can be found with a coloured transfer of a Kingfisher and edged in blue, these have the inscription 'Happy Days at . . . ' .

Numbering System. Willow Art models in general production, not made for a specific retailer, do sometimes have painted stock numbers, and these have been listed where they are known. Paintresses' marks are usually initials found under these numbers.

Some late models usually marked Willow have impressed stock numbers, for example the Willow black cat on a pouffe is impressed 539. These numbers are very difficult to spot and equally difficult to read clearly as they are usually covered in thick glaze and more often than not have the trademark printed over them. They have not yet been recorded, it is hoped that as clear examples are found they will be noted.

Models can be found marked Willow or Willow Art.

Willow Art and Willow Models
Parian/Unglazed

All the busts can be found impressed H. and L. (Hewitt and Leadbeater).

Bust of Albert King of the Belgians, not named, on square glazed base. 170mm.   75.00

Bust of French, not named, on
square glazed base. 170mm.   75.00
Bust of Sir John French, square base,
unglazed. 168mm.   95.00
Bust of General Roberts in uniform,
square base, unglazed. 168mm.   95.00
Bust of Jellicoe, wearing peaked cap,
named, on circular glazed base.
165mm. (Rare).   85.00
Bust of Kitchener. 170mm.   95.00
Bust of Burns impressed: *Burns* and
impressed on the reverse *H. Bros*
on square unglazed base with a
crest. 150mm.   30.00
Bust of Burns impressed: *Burns H &*
L, circular plinth. 175mm.   30.00
Bust of Burns, on circular glazed
base. 140mm.   30.00
Bust of Sir Walter Scott, not named,
on circular glazed base.
2 sizes: 130mm.   30.00
          163mm.   40.00
Bust of Gladstone, not named, on
circular glazed base. Can be
found with crest of W.E.
Gladstone on glazed base when
£5 should be added. 160mm.   30.00
Bust of *Ann Hathaway* on square
base. 135mm.   45.00
Bust of *Tom Morris.*   350.00
Crest possibly St. Andrews.
Bust of John Peel with full
inscription, circular base.
140mm.   75.00
Bust of Shakespeare, on circular
base. 120mm.   17.50
Bust of *Smuts* in military uniform,
unglazed. 150mm.   130.00
Bust of *Grace Darling.* 152mm.   55.00
Bust of *Peeping Tom,* unglazed.
134mm.   30.00
Mr Pickwick, Pickwick Papers. Parian
figure. 119mm.   65.00
Scold's Bridle, on circular base, with
verse, from Walton on Thames.
112mm.   65.00
Bill Sykes and his dog, standing
figure on base. Coloured beige,
no crest. 128mm.   47.50
Girl Doll, head marked *Willow*
England, fixed glass eyes, head/
shoulder height. 285mm. Whole
doll.   130.00

Girl Doll, in pink robe, fully
coloured, with real hair. 185mm.   145.00

Ancient Artefacts
Beccles Ringers Jug, with full
inscription. 67mm.   17.50
Chester Roman vase, not named.
55mm.   3.00
Lincoln Jack, not named. No. 74.
53mm.   3.00
Loving Cup. 2 and 3 handled.   3.00
Persian Wine Server, not named.
105mm.   3.00
Phoenician Water Jug, not named.
66mm.   3.00
Plymouth Jug, not named. No. 24.
47mm.   3.00
Pompeii Lamp. 95mm long.   4.00
Puzzle Jug with verse: *Try how to*
drink. 70mm.   5.50

Buildings – Coloured
Coloured buildings can be found
glazed or unglazed. Some of
these models can also be found
white.
Ann Hathaway's Cottage.
5 sizes: 50mm long.   16.00
          60mm long.   16.00
          65mm long.   25.00
         105mm long.   30.00
         130mm long.   40.00
Battle Abbey Gateway. 139mm
long.   82.50
Bell Hotel, Abel Fletcher's House in
John Halifax Gentlemen.
3 sizes: 57mm long.   40.00
          84mm.   75.00
         124mm.   75.00
John Bunyan's Cottage. 75mm long.   82.50
Burns Cottage, Model of. 108mm long.   40.00
Burns House, inscribed: *The poet*
occupied this house from 1793 until
his death 21st July 1796. 90mm.   145.00
Cat and Fiddle. 92mm.   145.00
Feathers Hotel, Ludlow.
112mm long.   125.00
Godalming Old Town Hall.
100mm.   195.00
Harlech Castle. 200mm long.   195.00
Knox's House, inscribed: *Model of*
the house in Edinburgh where John

Knox the Scottish reformer died 24th Nov 1572. 102mm.	145.00
Leycester Hospital. 157mm long.	170.00
Mason Croft, The House of Miss Marie Carelli. 90mm long.	125.00
Old Blacksmiths shop and marriage room, Gretna Green. 85mm long.	40.00
Old Chapel, Lantern Hill, Ilfracombe. 76mm long.	60.00
Old Curiosity Shop. No. 14, Portsmouth Street. 80mm long.	150.00
Old Maids Cottage, Lee near Ilfracombe. 59mm long.	47.50
Old Ostrich Inn, Colnbrook. 80mm.	125.00
Historical, Old Mint House, Pevensey 1342 AD. 120mm long.	160.00
The Olde Trip to Jerusalem Inn, 1199 AD, inscribed: *Home Brewed Ales.* 106mm long.	250.00
St. Bennet's Abbey, Norfolk Broads on pintray base. 70mm.	100.00
St. Bernards Monastery, Coalville. 102mm long.	125.00
St. Ann's Well, Gt. Malvern. 167mm long.	125.00
St. Nicholas Church, Great Yarmouth. 140mm long. Also found unglazed.	115.00
Shakespeare's House.	
6 sizes: 52mm long.	16.00
65mm long.	17.50
110mm long.	30.00
125mm long.	30.00
130mm long.	40.00
157mm long.	40.00
210mm long.	40.00
Stokesay Castle Gate House. 100mm.	150.00
Tan House, Little Stretton. 120mm long.	125.00
Upleatham Church. 90mm.	100.00
Waltham Abbey Tower, grey unglazed, black windows. 100mm.	75.00
Whittington Inn, with inscription. 100mm long.	110.00
Wilberforce Museum with inscription. Coloured grey. 115mm long.	115.00

Buildings – White

Bath Abbey, West Front. 110mm.	25.00
Battle Abbey Gateway, front. 95mm.	38.50
Bell Hotel, Abel Fletchers House in	

John Halifax Gentleman.	
2 sizes: 84mm long.	25.00
124mm long.	30.00
Bell Hotel, Abel Fletchers House in John Halifax Gentleman, on ashtray base. Some colouring.	
75mm long.	40.00
Big Ben. 146mm.	20.00
Blackpool Tower. 125mm.	13.00
Blackpool Tower, with buildings. 150mm.	14.00
Blackpool Tower, with buildings, impressed: *Variety, Dancing, Concert.* 165mm.	20.50
Bourne Abbey, West Front. 108mm.	65.00
John Bunyan's Cottage, Model of. 75mm long.	22.00
Burns Cottage, Model of, with inscription.	
2 sizes: 66mm long.	16.00
105mm long.	17.50
Burns Mausoleum, Dumfries. 95mm.	95.00
Bury St. Edmunds, Abbey Gate. 80mm.	75.00
Canterbury Cathedral, West Front. 125mm.	40.00
Canterbury, West Gate. 90mm.	30.00
Carillon Tower. 159mm.	65.00
Carnegie's Birthplace, inscribed: *The birthplace of Andrew Carnegie.* 85mm long.	75.00
Castle Hill Tower, Huddersfield. 115mm.	47.50
Chantry Front, Model of. 95mm long.	55.00
Chatham, Town Hall, Model of. 146mm.	65.00
Chesterfield Parish Church, Model of, found with inscription. 125mm.	40.00
Citadel Gateway, Plymouth. 110mm.	28.00
Clifton Suspension Bridge, Model of, with long inscription. 120mm long.	75.00
Conisborough Castle, The Keep. 95mm.	75.00
Cottage, inscribed: *Built in a day 4th June 1819.* 43mm long.	26.00
Crofter's Cottage. 55mm long.	30.00
Fair Maids House, Perth. 78mm long.	50.00
First and Last House in England. 83mm long. With green door.	20.00
First and Last House in England, with annexe. 95mm long.	35.00

Gretna Green Marriage Room.
60mm long.   20.00
Grimsby Hydraulic Tower.
165mm.   28.00
Hampton Court Palace, flat frontage
on ashtray base. 108mm long.   30.00
Hamsfell Hospice, Grange over Sands.
(Often found not named). 72mm.
An odd square building with
outside stairs and flat roof, and
with impressed Greek inscription
over door.   65.00
Hastings Castle Ruins. 100mm.   25.00
Hastings Clock Tower. 165mm.   17.50
Hay Castle, Brecon. 94mm.   55.00
Hop Pole Hotel, flat frontage on
ashtray base, with long quotation
referring to the inn from Chapter
50 'The Pickwick Papers' by
Charles Dickens, on ashtray.
60mm long.   40.00
King Charles Tower, Chester, with
outer steps. 100mm.   47.50
John Knox's House, with inscription
110mm.   40.00
Lancaster, Castle Gateway. 90mm.   34.50
Leicester Clock Tower. 175mm.   40.00
Lincoln Cathedral, West Front.
100mm and 118mm.   30.00
Lincoln, Stonebow. 104mm long.   30.00
Lloyd George's Home, inscribed.
102mm long.   47.50
Loch Leven Castle, Kinross. 75mm.   75.00
Old London Bridge on ashtray base,
small. 105mm long.   40.00
The Marble Arch. Unglazed.
98mm long.   25.00
Margate *Jubilee Clock Tower.*
120mm.   16.00
Mickelgate Bar, York. 116mm.   24.00
Monnow Bridge, Monmouth. 92mm.   40.00
Monument, The. 160mm.   110.00
Morpeth Castle, Model of. 78mm.   75.00
Nottingham Castle, Model of.
92mm long.   40.00
Old Bridge House, Ambleside.
88mm.   65.00
Old Nottingham Inn. Ye Olde Trip to
Jerusalem, 1199 AD, Model of.
95mm.   75.00
Old Ostrich Inn, Colnbrook.
80mm.   55.00
Park Tower, Barnsley. 137mm.   65.00
Peterborough Cathedral, West Front.
80mm long.   30.00

Peveril Castle. 115mm long.   55.00
Pump Room, Harrogate. 75mm.   47.50
St. Albans Clock Tower. 120mm.   45.00
St. Ann's Well, Buxton. 120mm.   55.00
St. Ann's Well, Great Malvern.
102mm long.   65.00
St. Benet's Abbey, Norfolk Broads,
castle ruins on pintray base.
70mm.   40.00
St. Botolph's Church, Boston.
112mm.   47.50
St. Denny's Church, Sleaford.
2 sizes: 95mm & 140mm.   65.00
St. Nicholas' Church, Great Yarmouth.
Unglazed. 143mm long.   65.00
St. Paul's Cathedral. 140mm.   22.50
Saville Fountain, Saville Gardens,
Windsor. No. 730. 140mm.   65.00
Saxon Church, Bradford on Avon.
74mm.   65.00
Shakespeare's House.
2 sizes: 120mm long.   14.00
160mm long.   16.00
Skegness, Clock Tower.
2 sizes: 125mm.   14.00
165mm.   17.50
Skegness, Pier Entrance.
85mm long.   75.00
Solomon's Temple, Grinlow Tower,
inscribed: *Erected on site of a*
prehistoric barrow, Buxton.
88mm.   40.00
Temple Bar, Waltham Cross.
100mm long.   56.50
Tennysons House, Mablethorpe.
85mm long.   75.00
Tudor Gabled House, Taunton AD 1800
also *AD 1578.* 100mm.   55.00
Upleatham Church, Redcar. 88mm.   40.00
Uttoxeter Market Place, Conduit, Scene
of *Dr. Johnson's Penance.* 123mm.   40.00
Wainhouse Tower, Halifax. 130mm.   65.00
Wallingford, Town Hall. 84mm.   55.00
West Malling, Abbey Tower. 94mm.   125.00
Westminster Abbey, West Front.
2 sizes: 114mm.   24.00
130mm.   28.00
Whittington Inn, with inscription.
100mm long.   47.50
Wilberforce House, Hull. 86mm.   50.00
Windmill, with sails. 85mm.   35.00
Windsor Castle. 125mm long.   40.00
Windsor Castle, Round Tower.
2 sizes: 68mm.   28.00
83mm.   28.00

Worcester Cathedral. 144mm long.	40.00
Worksop, Priory Gate House.	
88mm.	65.00

Monuments (including Crosses)

Ancient Runic Cross, Bakewell.	
110mm.	47.50
Arwenack Monument, erected by	
Martin Killigrew. AD 1787,	
Falmouth. 120mm.	30.00
Ashington Boer War Memorial.	
135mm.	75.00
Banbury Cross. 140mm.	30.00
Bovey Tracey, Old Cross. 140mm.	40.00
Bruce Statue, Stirling. 160mm.	60.00
Burns Statue, standing, right hand	
on chest. 176mm.	30.00
Burns Statue, seated on rock, with	
dog, pipe and tam-o'-shanter, all	
on plinth. 167mm.	47.00
Burns and Highland Mary.	
2 sizes: 117mm.	30.00
130mm.	30.00
Bunyan Statue. 165mm.	20.00
Bunyan Statue on heavy base.	
170mm.	20.00
Burmah Cross, Taunton. inscribed:	
Burmah 1885-6-7 and *Somerset*	
Light Infantry. 118mm.	75.00
Burton Statue, inscribed: *Michael*	
Arthur, first Baron Burton.	
128mm.	25.00
Caister-on-Sea Lifeboat Memorial.	
Moulded in relief: *1903* and	
Caister Lifeboat on lifebelt.	
162mm.	28.00
Andrew Carnegie, statue.	
150mm.	30.00
Cleethorpes Fisherman's Memorial,	
with inscription: *Erected by Public*	
Subscription to the memory of	
George Henry Smith (skipper) and	
William Richard Leggatt (Third	
Hand) etc. unveiled August 30th	
1908. 155mm.	30.00
Cleopatra's Needle, with lions.	
128mm.	135.00
Old Cornish Cross, Model of,	
100mm.	19.50
Drake, Statue, Plymouth.	
160mm.	13.00
Druids Well, Sutton Park, Sutton	
Coldfield. 45mm.	30.00
Flodden Cross, inscribed: *Flodden*	
1513, to the brave of both nations.	
136mm.	20.00

Sir John Franklin, discoverer of the	
north-west passage, born at Spilsby,	
April 1786. Died in the Arctic	
Regions June 1847. Statue.	
163mm.	82.50
General Sir Redvers Buller's Cross at	
Crediton, model of. 115mm.	58.00
Gibbet Cross, Hindhead, inscribed:	
Post Tenebras Lux In Luce Spes In	
Obrtu Pax Post Obitum Salus.	
136mm.	12.00
Gladstone Statue, Blackburn.	
130mm.	40.00
Hall Cross, Doncaster. 133mm.	110.00
Hector Macdonald Memorial,	
Dingwall. 112mm.	75.00
Highland Mary Statue, Dunoon, on	
plinth. 150mm.	25.00
Huddersfield, Market Cross.	
150mm.	35.00
Tom Hughes Monument, Rugby	
School. 140mm.	40.00
Hull Fisherman's Memorial.	
2 sizes: 135mm.	20.00
160mm.	20.00
Hull South African War Memorial,	
with inscription: *Erected to the*	
memory of the men of Hull who fell	
in the late South African War.	
165mm.	24.00
Keppels Column 1778. 140mm.	43.50
King George Stone, Kingstown.	
135mm.	65.00
Laceby, The Monument.	
2 sizes: 120mm.	25.00
150mm.	27.00
Laceby Memorial. 160mm.	27.00
Lord Myton of Holderness.	
155mm.	75.00
Lowestoft Fisherman's Memorial.	
130mm.	26.00
Maiwand Memorial, Forbury Gardens,	
Reading. Lion sometimes coloured	
black or brown, add £5.00.	
98mm.	20.00
Margate Lifeboat Memorial.	
135mm.	20.00
Margate Surf Boat Monument,	
inscribed: *IN MEMORY OF NINE*	
HEROIC MEN WHO LOST	
THEIR LIVES BY THE	
CAPSIZING OF THE MARGATE	
SURFBOAT "FRIEND TO ALL	
NATIONS" IN ATTEMPTING TO	
ASSIST A VESSEL IN DISTRESS	
AT SEA 2ND DEC 1887. 110mm.	75.00

Martyrs' Memorial, Coventry, 2 piece cross. 134mm.	125.00
Nelson's Column. 160mm.	75.00
Isaac Newton, statue. 165mm.	23.00
Peter Pan, statue. 140mm.	80.00
Queen Victoria's Statue, Blackburn.	40.00
Queen Victoria's Statue, Wakefield. 115mm.	40.00
Queen Victoria's Statue, Windsor. 2 sizes: 65mm.	30.00
160mm.	55.00
Richmond Market Cross. 137mm.	20.00
Rock of Ages, usual verse & inscription. 80mm.	8.50
C.S. *Rolls* Memorial, inscribed: *Memorial to the late Honourable C.S. Rolls*. 128mm.	40.00
Rufus Stone. 110mm.	7.50
Ruskin Memorial, Friars Crag. 2 sizes: 150mm.	20.00
180mm.	20.00
Sailor's Stone, Hindhead. 95mm.	12.00
St. Alban, Statue of. 146mm.	40.00
St. Anne's Lifeboat Memorial. 120mm.	16.00
Saville Fountain, Saville Gardens, Englefield Green. 140mm.	75.00
Saxon Soldier, statue on square base. 125mm.	40.00
Scone, The Cross. 142mm.	40.00
Toad Rock, Tunbridge Wells. 83mm.	20.00
Todmarden Memorial (obelisk on 4-sided base). Also known as the Stoodley Pike. 130mm.	60.00
Model of Wallace Statue. 141mm.	85.00
Wallace Statue, model of. Figure with arm outstretched, sword in other hand on stone plinth. 155mm.	125.00
Waltham Abbey Tower, *Model of Tower Waltham Abbey*. Grey unglazed. 100mm.	125.00
Sir William de la Pole, Statue of, with long inscription of its presentation and the history of Sir William. 160mm.	25.00

Historical/Folklore

Archbishops Chair, Canterbury Cathedral. 100mm.	10.00
Inscribed.	12.50
Bangor Abbey Bell, inscribed: *Model of the old bell, Bangor Abbey, Co. Down*. Rare. 85mm.	40.00

Bishop's Jester, Wells Cathedral. Fully coloured. No crest. 2 sizes: 110mm.	60.00
125mm.	60.00
Bunyan's Chair, Model of. 90mm.	19.00
Bunyan's Cushion, Model of. 105mm long.	30.00
Burns Chair, Dumfries. 85mm.	7.50
Can be found as corner seat.	15.00
Daniel Lambert, sitting on chair. With long inscription. 118mm.	50.00
Devil looking over Lincoln. 115mm.	19.50
The Ducking Stool, with inscription as Arcadian. Can be found coloured brown with no crest. 2-piece. 120mm.	85.00
Father Christmas carrying sack of toys. 110mm.	145.00
Font, not named. 2 sizes: 55mm & 87mm.	10.50
Gladiators Helmet. 80mm.	20.00
James V Chair, Stirling Castle. No. 200. 100mm.	7.50
Joan of Arc. 150mm.	90.00
John Knox Chair, Edinburgh. brown no crest. 122mm.	47.50
Lady Godiva on horseback, on base. 80mm.	30.00
Man in the Moon. Can be found with yellow face. No. 311. 55mm.	20.00
Man in the Sun. 94mm.	47.50
Mary Queen of Scots Chair, Edinburgh Castle, Model of. 75mm.	6.50
Mons Meg, Edinburgh Castle. 130mm long.	12.00
Mother Shipton. 2 sizes: 80mm.	8.00
105mm.	13.00
Peeping Tom, bust. 130mm.	25.00
Ripon Hornblower. 120mm.	16.00
A Rubbing Stone for Asses, a 17th century puzzle printed on a brick wall. 100mm long.	40.00
Shakespeare's Font, no plinth. Inscribed: *Model of Font in which Shakespeare was Baptised.* 85mm dia. 40mm.	17.50
Shakespeare's Font, on hexagonal plinth. Inscribed: *Model of Font in which Shakespeare was Baptised.* 128mm.	20.00
Sir Walter Scott's Chair, Abbotsford, Model of. 80mm.	7.50

Skull, can be inscribed: *Alas poor*
  Yorick. 60mm long.   12.00
Skull, brown. 60mm long.   22.00
Skull. 45mm.   13.00
Sword, ornate in scabbard.
  135mm long.   72.50
Sundial, Tideswell Church, Model of.
  110mm.   16.00
Trusty Servant, with verse on both
  sides, fully coloured. 132mm.   110.00

Traditional/National Souvenirs
ARRIET, Bust of Pearly Queen.
  92mm.   80.00
ARRY, Bust of Pearly King.   40.00
John Bull, standing. 120mm.   40.00
Banbury Cake. 105mm wide.   35.00
Bolton Trotter. 135mm long.   12.00
Blackpool Big Wheel.
  2 sizes: 88mm.   12.00
          100mm.   16.00
Blackpool Big Wheel, rectangular
  base. 120mm.   17.50
Cheddar Cheese, slice out,
  inscribed: *Prime Cheddar Cheese.*
  34mm high, 67mm dia.   12.50
Cornish Pasty. 100mm long.   7.50
Chester Imp, The. 80mm.   30.00
Englishman, bust, wearing black
  hat. No. 114. 76mm.   25.00
<u>*Leaking Boot.*</u> Grimsby. Standing
  figure of young boy holding boot
  aloft (attached to his hand by
  string).   65.00
Lincoln Imp. 63mm.   6.50
Lincoln Imp, on pedestal. 102mm.   8.50
Manx Man, John Bull as above but
  with an extra leg added at rear.
  Same colouring. 120mm.   95.00
Map of Isle of Wight,
  coloured map. 60mm.   25.00
Melton Mowbray Pie with verse.
  55mm.   19.00
Reading Biscuit, can be found with
  verse: *Than Reading biscuits there*
  are no finer, Here's a good one
  reproduced in china. (Add £8).
  Coloured biscuit. 85mm long.   35.00
  Coloured biscuit on ashtray base.   40.00
  Can also be found on stand.   30.00
  Can also be found as hatpin
  holder, on stand with verse.   35.00
River Thames Pleasure Punt,
  175mm long.   55.00
  With coloured cushions add £20

Yarmouth Bloater. 121mm.   6.50
Irish Harp. 105mm.   10.00
Irishman, bust. No. 115. Wearing
  Black hat. 78mm.   25.00
Bagpipes. 118mm long.   20.00
Blacksmiths Anvil, Gretna Green,
  often found not named, with
  inscription.
  2 sizes: 70mm.   7.50
          76mm.   7.50
Gretna Green Priest, standing on
  square base. 136mm.   55.00
The Old Priest's Chair, Gretna
  Green. 82mm.   35.00
Jimmy Strength, with inscription: *A*
  well known Border character whose
  name was James Stuart a descendant
  of the Royal Family of that name. He
  was famous for his age and great
  strength and died in his 123rd year.
  Figure on square plinth. 114mm.   110.00
Scotsman, bust. No. 116. Wearing
  coloured tam-o'shanter. 80mm.   25.00
Scotsman matches holder. Comic
  fully coloured figure. Inscribed:
  Matches. 90mm.   65.00
Souter Johnny, sitting figure, with
  verse. 130mm.   30.00
  Coloured.   47.50
Tam-o'shanter, sitting figure, with
  verse. 135mm.   30.00
  Coloured.   47.50
Thistle vase.
  2 sizes: 50mm.   3.00
          68mm.   3.50
Leek Vase. 98mm.   4.00
Welsh Hat, Model of, with longest
  place name. 52mm. (Arcadian
  mould).   6.50
Welsh Hat, can have blue hat band.
  Can be found with longest Welsh
  place name printed round brim.
  57mm.   5.00
  Inscribed: 6.50
Welsh Harp, very delicate.
  90mm.   8.50
Welsh Lady, bust, with black hat.
  No. 117. 110mm.   19.00
Welsh Leek. 55mm.   4.00
Welsh Tea Party, a figure group,
  some colouring. 50mm.   35.00
Dutch Boy. 80mm. Can be found
  fully coloured, when £10.00
  should be added.   10.50

Dutch Girl. 80mm. Can be found
fully coloured, when £10.00
should be added.   10.50
(A pair to the Dutch Boy).

Seaside Souvenirs
Bathing Machine, inscribed: *A*
morning dip.
2 sizes: 65mm.   10.00
        80mm.   12.50
Lifeboat, coloured ropes, if found
inscribed: *A.E. Davies* or *Mark*
Lane add £10.00. 118mm long.   12.50
Motorboat, with driver, at sea.
115mm long.   19.50
Paddlesteamer. 154mm long (rare).   82.50
Rowing Boat on rocks.
109mm long.   14.00
Yacht in full sail. 122mm.   12.50
Fisherman's Basket with handle
77mm long.   6.50
Fish Basket without handles. 80mm
long.   5.50
A Yarmouth Fish Swill, basket.
40mm.   10.00
Lighthouse, not named. 105mm.   5.00
Lighthouse, octagonal. No. 145.
110mm.   6.50
Lighthouse on rocks with brown
rowing boat. 133mm.   20.00
Beachy Head lighthouse, with black
band. 2 sizes: 100mm & 136mm.   11.00
Flamborough Lighthouse. 110mm.   30.00
North Foreland Lighthouse. 135mm.   30.00
Spurn Lighthouse, with details of size
and power. 125mm.   19.50
Withernsea Lighthouse, with details
of size and power. 110mm and
127mm.   16.00
Crab. 83mm long.   13.00
Oyster Shell posy holder. 89mm.   4.50
Shell menu holder on coral base.
No. 360. 90mm.   9.00
Scallop Shell hatpin holder on rocky
base. 92mm.   7.50
Whelk shell, inscribed: *Listen to the*
sea. 110mm.   5.00
Stick of Rock, pink stick with resort
printed (very realistic), so far
Great Yarmouth, Southsea and now
Clacton have been recorded. Has
been found as a salt and pepper
pot. 75mm.
White   55.00
Pink   125.00

Truck of Sand, same model as truck
of coal but with coal painted
yellow, can be inscribed: *Sand for*
the kiddies from... or *A truck of sand*
from... 90mm long.   65.00
Mermaid, seated on rock, combing
hair. 105mm.   30.00

Countryside
Milk Can with lid. 60mm.   5.00
Pinecone. 90mm.   4.00
Treetrunk hat pin holder. 80mm.   10.50
Treetrunk Vase. 80mm.   6.50

Animals
Bear, inscribed: *The Bear of*
Bromsgrove, with Bromsgrove
arms. 95mm long.   55.00
Boar, standing on rocky base.
102mm long. Two varieties of
base may be found.   47.50
Cat, angry, with tail in the air. Blue
bow. 80mm long.   17.00
Cat, in boot, white or blue bow.
88mm long.
White bow.   12.50
Blue bow.   14.50
Cat, Cheshire, with coloured face.
Inscribed: *Always smiling* or more
rarely: *Cheshire Cat, 'still smiling'.*
95mm.   7.50
Cat, Manx, walking.
100mm long.   30.00
Cat's head on base. 60mm.   25.00
Cat, sitting, bow round neck.
80mm.   10.00
Cat, sitting, blue or red bow.
60mm.   10.00
Cat, sitting, large red bow, and red
and green eyes. 70mm.   13.00
Cat, sitting, looling left, crest on
shield. 74mm.   12.50
Cat, sitting, detailed thick coat, and
tail around paws. Candlesnuffer.
57mm.   13.00
Cat, standing, chubby, blue bow.
70mm.   16.00
Cat, standing (long back), green
eyes and red tongue. 117mm long.   35.00

Black Cats
Black Cat on Cushion. 100mm.   25.00
Black Cat on diamond ashtray,
inscribed: *Ashtray and Good Luck.*
120mm long.   20.00

Black Cat on Pouffe, inscribed: *Good luck*. Can be found with red or blue bow. 85mm. Impressed. No. 539. 80mm, 90mm and 95mm.   26.00

Black Cat on pepper pot. 90mm.   25.00

Smaller Arcadian type Black Cats.

Black Cat, playing bagpipes. 60mm.   82.50

Black Cat with bottle. 70mm. (Arcadian mould).   65.00

Black Cat in boot, blue bow. 95mm long.   25.00

Black Cat, wearing kilt and sitting on a curling stone.   75.00

Black Cat, playing bagpipes, and wearing kilt, standing on thistle ashtray. 88mm long.   75.00

Black Cat, playing a harp. 60mm.   85.00

Black Cat, wearing kilt and glengarry, standing on golf ball. 70mm.   82.50

Black Cat, standing beside thistle vase. 57mm.   65.00

Black Cat, wearing a Welsh hat, standing beside a leek. 67mm.   82.50

Black Cat, sitting in cup, inscribed: *May your cup of Good Luck brim over*. 90mm.   75.00

Cow, kneeling. 105mm long.   47.50

Cow, standing. 100mm long.   30.00

Deer, sitting. 2 sizes: 64mm.   30.00

     115mm long.   40.00

Dog, Bulldog, sitting, feet moulded separately. Black collar and red mouth. 55mm.   19.50

Dog, Bulldog, sitting, feet integrally moulded. 54mm.   17.00

Dog, Bulldog, black, emerging from kennel, inscribed: *The Black Watch*. 70mm long.   19.50

Dog, Bull Terrier, standing. 60mm.   12.50

Dog, Collie, sitting. 78mm.   12.50

Dog, Collie, standing. 85mm.   23.00

Dog, Dachshund, sitting, long ears and rather comic. 75mm long.   40.00

Dog, Foxhound. 69mm.   20.00

Dog, Labrador, walking. 90mm long.   19.50

Dog, The Manx three legged, often found not named. Inscribed: *Prince Toby Orry*. 70mm.   40.00 / 65.00

Dog, rather like St. Bernard. No. 511, 95mm long, 50mm high.   24.00

Dog, Scottie, wearing a glengarry. 3 sizes: 60mm.   12.50

     85mm.   13.50

     100mm.   13.50

Dog, Scottie, wearing a dark blue tam-o'shanter. 2 sizes: 60mm.   10.50

     80mm.   16.00

Dog, Scottish Terrier, standing. 90mm long.   14.50

Donkey in harness. No. 294. 110mm long.   40.00

Elephant, large. 104mm long.   40.00

Elephant, with trunk in the air, curled back against the head. No. 336. 90mm long.   40.00

Elephant, walking. Can be inscribed: *Baby Jumbo*. No. 113. 52mm. (Coloured add £10).   17.00

Elephant Jug. 70mm.   12.50

Fish Ashtray, in shape of plaice. 78mm long.   6.50

Fish, curved. 75mm long.   5.00

Fish, straight. 130mm long.   5.00

Fish, straight, with open mouth. 115mm long.   4.00

Fox. 100mm.   40.00

Hare. 77mm long.   12.50

Highland Bull, inscribed: *King of the Herd*. 115mm long.   75.00

Kangaroo. 115mm.   75.00

Lion, crouching. Red open mouth. 82mm long.   23.00

Lion, crouching. Red open mouth, on base, roaring at a tiny mouse on a green apple, inscribed: *Much ado about nothing*. 110mm.   82.50

Lion, walking. (Different moulds). 5 sizes: 105mm long.   12.50

     110mm long.   12.50

     115mm long.   14.50

     125mm long.   14.50

     160mm long.   14.50

Lion with mane and 'furry' legs. 164mm long. (Pair with Arcadian Lioness).   65.00

Monkey, holding coconut. 85mm.   17.00

Three Wise Monkeys, with inscription. 124mm.   14.00

Three Monkeys on diamond shaped ashtray. Monkeys inscribed: *See not evil, speak not evil, hear not evil*. 130mm long.   15.00

Mouse. 62mm long.	20.00
Pig, standing, thin ears pointing forwards. 97mm long.	15.00
Pig, sitting on haunches can be found inscribed: *You may push* etc.	
2 sizes: 60mm.	11.00
72mm.	16.00
Pig, standing. Very fat, with double chin. 96mm long.	19.50
Pig, standing fat, ears pointing forward. 82mm long.	10.00
Polar Bear, on hind legs.	
2 sizes: 82mm.	40.00
96mm.	47.50
Polar Bear, sitting. 83mm.	40.00
Pony, inscribed: *A Native of Shetland.* 108mm long.	25.00
Rabbit, lying down. 54mm long.	7.50
Rabbit, sitting, alert or laid back ears. 60mm long.	7.50
Ram, with curly horns. 90mm long.	43.00
Rhinoceros, standing. 87mm long.	56.50
Stag, lying down. 115mm long.	40.00
Teddy Bear, sitting. No. 112. 65mm and 75mm.	19.50
Toad, grotesque. 80mm long.	20.00
Tortoise. 88mm long.	9.00
Tortoise, realistic. 95mm long.	40.00
Tortoise, standing wearing a blue hat/helmet. Rd. No. 70961. 62mm.	55.00
Isn't this Rabbit a Duck: On its base a rabbit, turned on its side, a duck. 75mm.	25.00

Birds (including Eggs)

Bird (reputedly a tit). 77mm long.	12.00
Bird on plinth. 103mm.	10.50
Bird posy holder. 104mm long.	6.50
Canary on rock, can be found coloured yellow on green base, 98mm.	
White	13.00
Coloured	26.00
Chicken, very fluffy. No. 325. 65mm.	17.00
Chicken pepper pot. 70mm.	11.00
Chicken, yellow, emerging from egg, inscribed: *Every little helps mother will be pleased.* 50mm.	24.00
Cock. 46mm and 100mm.	14.00
Goose, comical, with long neck, some colouring. 155mm.	47.50

Pelican, with inscription: *A wonderful bird is the pelican, his beak will hold more than his belican.* 75mm.	30.00
Swan, can be found with yellow beak, add £1.00. 60mm.	
White beak.	6.50
Swan, with head on breast. 58mm.	6.50
Swan posy holder.	
2 sizes: 65mm.	5.00
93mm long.	5.00
Turkey. 57mm.	13.00
Wise Owl with verse: *An aged owl sat in an oak* etc.	
2 sizes: 98mm & 115mm.	14.50

Great War

Airman, standing to attention. 140mm.	175.00
Air Force Officer, a hero holding medal. 140mm. Scarce.	220.00
Can rarely be found coloured.	300.00
Nurse, inscribed: *A friend in need.* 130mm.	40.00
Sailor, at attention, inscribed: *Our brave defender.* 130mm.	55.00
Solder, with rifle, inscribed: *Our brave defender.* Always found with gun broken off at top. It is still classed as perfect. 132mm.	47.50
Monoplane, with fixed prop. 164mm long.	55.00
Monoplane with revolving prop. no colourings. No. 67. 150mm long.	65.00
Monoplane with revolving prop., coloured roundels on wings, and stripes on tail. 150mm long.	110.00
Aeroplane Propeller. No. 216 and No. 214. 150mm long.	25.00
Can be found with RAF or RFC crest. If RAF or RFC crest.	40.00
Airship (Observation Balloon), inscribed: *Beta.* 80mm long.	55.00
Battleship. 4 funnels. 127mm long.	19.00
Battleship, impressed: *HMS Lion.* 140mm long.	30.00
A rare variety with black mast and red striped funnels has been seen.	70.00
Troop Carrier, Liner converted. No. 213. 140mm long.	95.00
Can rarely be found inscribed: *HMS Lion.*	115.00
Can also be found with 2 forward facing guns mounted on forward deck (rare).	125.00

Submarine, impressed: *E5.*
116mm long. 20.00
Submarine, inscribed: *E4.*
2 sizes: 95mm long. 19.50
118mm long. 22.50
Red Cross Van, red cross on side.
No. 812. 84mm long. 30.00
British Tank, Model of.
92mm long. 14.50
Can be found either with side
guns moulded flat against tank,
or with side guns standing proud
protruding from side turrets.
British Tank, Model of. With trailing
wheels. 130mm long. 20.00
Can be found with a Lincoln crest
inscribed: *Model of 'British Tank'*
original of which was made in
Lincoln. 30.00
Field Gun. 120mm long. 17.00
Field Gun, with screen.
115mm long. 19.00
Howitzer. 115mm long. 16.00
British Hand Grenade. 86mm. 20.00
Cannon Shell. 70mm. 5.00
Bandsman's Drum, with cording.
60mm. 10.50
Bell Tent, with open flaps.
70mm. 20.00
Bugle.
2 sizes: No. 370. 70mm. 19.50
No. 379. 115mm. 38.50
Field Glasses. 83mm. 20.00
Kit Bag with verse: *Pack up your*
troubles in your old kit bag. No. 220.
74mm. 19.50
Airman's Cap. 82mm long. 75.00
Forage Cap. 83mm long. 16.00
Glengarry. Some colouring.
83mm long. 16.00
If with Scottish crest. 17.00
Officer's Peaked Cap. No. 100.
70mm dia. 10.00
Officer's Peaked Cap, inscribed
Souvenir of Canadian Forces 1915 40.00
Pickelhaube (German spiked
helmet). No. 58. 50mm. 30.00
Tommy's Steel Helmet. No. 221.
76mm long. 21.00
Trench Lamp. 70mm. 13.00
Fireplace, inscribed: *Keep the home*
fires burning. Some colouring.
100mm long. 17.00
Kitchen range, with pot on fire,
inscribed: *Keep the home fires*

burning. Some colouring. No. 199.
78mm long. 13.00
Edith Cavell. Statue, London,
inscribed: *Brussels dawn Oct 12th*
1915. Sacrifice, Humanity. No. 281.
4 sizes: 110mm. 16.00
130mm. 16.00
150mm. 16.00
160mm. 16.00
Edith Cavell, Nurse. Patriot and
martyr, memorial Statue. Norwich.
2 sizes: 155mm. 23.00
170mm. 25.00
The Black Watch Memorial,
Edinburgh. Scottish soldier on
square base, often not named.
127mm. 65.00
Cenotaph, inscribed: *The Glorious*
Dead MCMXIV-MCMXIX with
green wreaths.
3 sizes: 70mm. 4.00
145mm. 7.50
184mm. 12.50
Chatham *Naval War Memorial.*
160mm. 82.50
Coalville War Memorial.
135mm. 105.00
Dumfries War Memorial, inscribed:
Black Watch. 130mm. 65.00
Florence Nightingale Statue, Model of.
Can be found inscribed: *Florence*
Nightingale 1820-1910.
2 sizes: 120mm. 19.50
160mm. 20.00
Folkestone Road of Remembrance
Memorial. 77mm. 47.50
Folkestone *War Memorial May Their*
Deeds be held in reverence.
160mm. 75.00
Great Yarmouth War Memorial. With
inscription. 174mm. 21.00
Ilkeston War Memorial, with
inscription. 160.00
Langholm War Memorial. 180mm. 130.00
Loughborough War Memorial, Carillon
Tower. 155mm. 60.00
Matlock Bath *War Memorial,*
inscribed.
2 sizes: 182mm. 40.00
155mm. 75.00
Scarborough Lighthouse, with
inscription: *This lighthouse was*
damaged in the bombardment by
German warships on Wednesday
December 16th 1914. 132mm. 75.00

Scarborough Lighthouse, with
  rectangular buildings, depicting
  shell damage. 110mm.   75.00
Southsea. *Royal Naval War Memorial.*
  160mm. (Chatham, Plymouth and
  Southsea War Memorials are
  identical in design).   40.00
War Memorial with one soldier
  leaning over another, found with
  a York crest. 165mm.   35.00
Worthing War Memorial, inscribed:
  Duty Nobly done 1914-1918.
  175mm.   56.50

Home/Nostalgic
Ali Baba Basket, very detailed.
  75mm.   4.00
Anvil on base, can be found
  inscribed: *A Sussex Legend,* with
  verse, but more usually
  Blacksmith's Anvil.
  4 sizes: 35mm.   7.50
          45mm.   7.50
          55mm.   7.50
          75mm.   7.50
Baby's Bottle. No. 42. 90mm long.   10.50
Bag, open with four feet.   7.00
Basket, oval with handle.
  70mm long.   3.50
Basket of Milk, six bottles with
  brown tops. 64mm.   19.50
Bell. 58mm.   5.00
Bell, inscribed: *Curfew must not ring
  tonight.* No. 107. 65mm.   7.50
Book, Model of. No. 71. 57mm.   6.50
Chest and lid. 90mm long.   7.50
Child smiling, bust. 60mm.   17.50
Chinese Lantern. 80mm.   10.50
Coal Scuttle, helmet shaped.
  53mm.   5.00
Desk, rolltop. 80mm long.   20.00
Dressing table mirror, with one
  drawer. 87mm.   12.50
Fireplace, inscribed: *There's no place
  like home.* 70mm.   15.00
Fireplace/Range with saucepan.
  Sometimes inscribed: *May yer
  fireside aye be cheers and yer kail-pat
  aye be fou. Copyright Allan Junior.*
  75mm long.   16.00
  With verse.   25.00
Flat Iron. 64mm.   12.50
Flat Iron on stand. (2 pieces).
  66mm.   15.00

Garden Roller. 51mm.   12.50
Garden Trug. 75mm long.   7.50
Ginger Jar with fixed lid.   3.00
Grandfather Clock, found inscribed:
  *Make us of time let not advantage
  slip. Shakespeare,* or more rarely:
  *Nae man can tetha time or tide.
  Burns* (add £3.00).
  2 sizes: 112mm and 128mm.   10.50
Hand mirror with reflective
  silvering. 150mm long.   20.00
Jardinière, 2-piece. 130mm.   6.50
Oil Lamp. 95mm long.   5.50
Old Armchair with verse. 88mm.   7.50
Pail, with moulded rope handle.
  63mm.   3.50
Pillar box, G.R., in red and blue,
  with open slot. Inscribed: *If you
  haven't got time to post a line here's
  the pillar box.* 78mm.   17.50
Pillar Box, outpressed G.R. open
  slit. 90mm.   24.50
Pipe. 2 sizes: 76mm & 93mm long.   16.00
Shaving Mug. No. 125.
  2 sizes: 55mm.   6.50
          70mm.   6.50
Sundial, circular with round base,
  with inscription: *I mark not the
  hours.* 118mm.   10.50
Sundial, circular on square base,
  No. 205, with inscription: *I mark
  not the hours.* 98mm.   7.50
Sundial on octagonal base.
  125mm.   13.00
Tobacco Jar with crossed coloured
  pipes on lid. Inscribed: *tobacco.*
  115mm.   17.00
Umbrella. 50mm.   14.50
Valise, half-open. 77mm long.   7.50
Watering Can. 75mm.   8.50
Wedding ring, gold, in open box.
  60mm.   30.00
Wheelbarrow. 105mm long.   10.50

Comic/Novelty
Alarm Clock. Inscribed: *Many are
  called but few get up.* 65mm.   20.00
Billiken, The god of luck, often found
  unnamed. 73mm.   4.00
Billiken, The god of luck, sitting on
  high backed chair. 100mm.   7.50
Biscuit Lid trinket box on tray base.
  Impressed: *Oval High Tea.* Biscuit
  coloured. 75mm long.   30.00

Box of Matches, half-open. 75mm.	20.00
Boy's smiling head. 64mm.	20.50
Boy Scout. *Be Prepared.* 110mm.	110.00
Boy on Pig's back, boy fully	
coloured. 94mm long.	95.00
Broadbean pod splitting open,	
occasionally inscribed: *Good old*	
bean. 130mm long.	16.00
Fan, open, hat pin holder. 90mm.	19.00
Fat Lady on weighing scales, scale	
registers 20 stone, inscribed:	
Adding weight. Blue Bonnet. 90mm.	43.50
Policeman, very jolly. 80mm. *Willow*	
version found fully coloured.	40.00
Regimental Sergeant-Major Pepper	
Pot. 84mm.	47.50
Sack of Meal with Mouse, inscribed:	
May the mouse ne'er leave yer meal-	
poke wi' a tear- drop'n its e'e.	
63mm.	14.50
With brown or grey mouse.	16.00
Sailor, comical,some colouring.	
95mm.	55.00
A truck of coal from... Wagon of black	
coal. 90mm long.	30.00
Also found with coal painted	
grey or brown and inscribed: *A*	
truck of iron ore from...	47.50

Black Boys

All of these boys are fully coloured	
but sit on white boxes etc. All	
uncommon.	
Black Boy, standing with hands in	
pockets. 94mm.	120.00
Black Boy, playing drum. 70mm.	120.00
Black Boy, in bath of ink, inscribed:	
How ink is made. 110mm long.	105.00
Black Boy, in bed with spider,	
inscribed: *A little study in black*	
and fright. Boy can have red or	
blue pyjamas. 70mm long.	115.00
Black Boy in bed, face coloured,	
inscribed: *Just a little Study in*	
black and white. 62mm long.	60.00
Black Boy, eating slice of melon,	
sitting on soap box. 80mm.	120.00
Black Boy with pumpkin. 80mm.	120.00
Black Boy, at table eating a boiled	
egg which has a chicken popping	
out. 70mm.	95.00
Two Black Boys, heads popping out	
of box, inscribed: *Box of chocolates.*	
Can be found with boys painted	
as white children, yellow hair	

and blue eyes and is often found	
not coloured at all. 60mm.	
Coloured	75.00
No colouring	30.00
Black Boy, holding container for	
Cigarettes. 102mm.	110.00
Black Boy, holding container for	
matches. 100mm.	110.00
Black Boy and Girl sitting on tree	
trunk. Some Colouring. 68mm.	82.50

Children

Girl and Boy sitting in armchair,	
both fully coloured. 60mm.	95.00

Little Birds

From Arcadian moulds. Head fully	
coloured, eggs white.	
Flapper's head hatching from egg,	
inscribed: *A little bird from ...*	
50mm long.	20.00
Black Boy's head hatching from egg,	
inscribed: *A blackbird from ...*	
50mm long.	30.00

Comic Ashtrays

Scotsman, really grotesque, sitting	
on white bench on white ashtray.	
95mm.	30.00
Scotsman can be found coloured.	47.50
Bookie with coloured hare and	
greyhound on octagonal ashtray	
base. 70mm.	34.50

Cartoon/Comedy Characters

Baby, with arms outstretched,	
inscribed: *Cheerio.* Some	
colouring on face. 125mm.	30.00
Baby, saluting, inscribed: *One of the*	
b'hoys. Can be found with	
A.W.W.H. on chest. Some	
colouring on face. 3 sizes: 125mm,	
150mm & 160mm.	40.00
Harry Lauder, bust. Brown hat with	
thistle. 80mm.	17.00
Can be found named.	25.50
Dr. Beetle (impressed). 142mm.	125.00
Teddytail, impressed. 142mm.	82.50
Two Cartoon Characters sitting in	
Armchair. 90mm. (Thought to be	
Dr. Beetle and Sunny Jim!)	70.00
"Sunny Jim", glazed bust (name	
impressed).	95.00
Winkie, not named, inscribed: *Glad*	
Eyes on beak. 60mm.	19.00

Alcohol

Barrel. 50mm.	3.00
Barrel on stand. No. 35. 58mm.	5.50
Barrel with opening on one side. 54mm long.	3.50
Barrel Jug with grapevine in relief. 90mm.	15.00
Beer Bottle with red hand. 98mm.	12.50
Beer Bottle and Tankard on horseshoe ashtray, with inscription: *The more we are together the merrier we'll be.* Silver Tankard. 85mm.	12.50
Bottle, syphon and glass on horseshoe tray, inscribed: *Scotch and Soda.* Menu holder on back. 65mm high, 110mm long.	14.50
Beer Bottle and Tankard on square ashtray. 78mm wide. Verse as above.	12.50
Bottle. No. 104. 90mm.	6.50
Can be inscribed: *One Special Scotch.*	7.50
Drunk in Top Hat and Tails draped drunkenly around a white female statue (bust on column). Inscribed: *How cold you are tonight.* On blue ashtray base. 96mm.	125.00
Drunks, two on ashtray, inscribed: *Another little drink wouldn't do us any harm.* 92mm.	47.50
Hand, holding beaker, inscribed: *Good health.* 50mm.	6.50
Man, Mr Pickwick character (As in Arcadian range) on rim of beaker. 75mm.	47.50
Monk holding tankard. 155mm.	16.00
Stud, lapel with miniature bottle attached, inscribed: *The More We are together, the Merrier we will be.*31mm. Rare.	30.00
Tankard candlesnuffer, foaming inscribed *The more we are together...* or *Here's Health.* 58mm.	6.50
Thimble, inscribed: *Just a thimbleful.* 50mm.	20.00
Thistle vase, with verse: *A wee Deoch an Doris.* 56mm.	4.00
Toby Jug. 78mm.	12.50
Whisky Bottle, inscribed: *One special scotch.* 63mm.	7.50
Whisky Bottle, with cork, usually inscribed: *One special scotch.* No. 64. 88mm.	7.50
Whisky Bottle inscribed: *Here's a bottle and an honest friend, what wad ye wish for mai man?*	15.00
Whisky Bottle and Soda Syphon on Tray, inscribed: *Scotch and soda.* 88mm dia.	12.50
Whisky Bottle, Soda Syphon and Tumbler on horseshoe ashtray. With inscription: *The more we are together, the merrier we will be* or *Scotch and Soda.* Some colouring. 2 sizes: 87mm long.	16.00
115mm long.	16.00

Sport/Pastimes

Golfer's Caddie holding golf bag, figure coloured. 110mm.	125.00
Golf Clubs in Bag. 108mm.	75.00
Football. 50mm dia.	6.50
Jockey on Racehorse on oval base found in different coloured silks. Can be found coloured but unglazed. 2 sizes: 104mm & 112mm.	55.00
Racehorse, impressed. 102mm.	75.00
Racehorse on circular base. 115mm.	65.00
Bridge Trump indicator. Coloured suit symbols on circular base, spinning cover allowing only one suit to be seen. Very ornate. Rd. No. 693774. No. 1015. 104mm dia.	30.00
Diamond Trump indicator 65mm.	4.00
Sometimes inscribed: *Trumps* – add £2.00.	
Playing Cards, box and lid. 154mm long.	13.00

Musical Instruments

Banjo. 160mm long.	9.50
Guitar. 163mm long.	10.50
Lute. 159mm long.	35.00
Piano. open keyboard. 80mm.	22.50
Piano, upright. 65mm.	18.00

Transport

Car, open 4 seater. 2 sizes: 114mm & 140mm long.	40.00
Car, open 2 seater. 116mm long.	40.00
Car, open 2 seater, very detailed model with spare wheel on side running board. This is a Morris. 108mm long.	110.00
Charabanc. 125mm long.	35.00
Tram, double decker, open top. Inscribed: *Life on the ocean wave.* No. 333. 108mm long.	170.00
Can of Petrol, impressed: *Motor spirit.* 55mm.	17.50

Modern Equipment

Camera, folding. 60mm.	40.00
Horn Gramophone, square. 95mm.	25.00
Horn Gramophone on round base. 2 sizes: 60mm.	30.00
85mm.	35.00
Radio Horn, can be found inscribed: *Hello...* (name of town) *calling.* 70mm.	25.00
With inscription.	40.00

Hats

Crown. 60mm.	25.00
Luton Boater. 90mm long.	12.50

Footwear

Boot. 112mm long.	11.00
Edwardian Shoe, blue bow. 110mm long.	10.50
With white bow.	8.50
Ladies' Riding Shoe, square toe and blue tie. 115mm long.	13.00
Lancashire Clog, yellow buckle. 88mm long.	5.50
Sabot. No. 334. 75mm long.	4.00
Slipper wall pocket, blue bow. 2 sizes: 152 & 178mm long.	12.50

Miniature Domestic

Complete Tea Set on rectangular tray. 102mm long.	25.00
Cheese Dish, one piece. 45mm.	6.50
Cheese Dish and cover. 45mm.	7.50
Coffee Pot with lid. 70mm.	7.50
Tea Pot with lid. 60mm.	7.50

Interesting Domestic Items with Crests

Bagware Vase. No. 232. 73mm.	3.00
Basket Dish. 45mm.	6.00
Column Candlestick with snake around column. 120mm.	7.50
Hairpins, box and lid. 115mm long.	6.00
Hat Pins, curved fluted holder. 125mm.	12.50
Horseshoe ashtray. 80mm.	5.50
Horseshoe ashtray with menu holder and rectangular slot possible for matches. Rd. No. 708047. 110mm long.	15.00
Horseshoe Base menu holder. 113mm.	8.50
Muffin Dish and lid. No. 82. 70mm dia.	8.50

Pin Box and lid, horseshoe shaped. 62mm.	4.00
Pin Box, oval, with safety pin in relief on lid. 90mm long.	7.50
Pin Box, heart-shaped, ornate moulding. No. 394. 90mm long.	7.50
Preserves Jar and lid. 75mm.	10.50
Trefoil Cruet with lids. 65mm.	5.50
Trinket Box, oval on eight collar stud feet with moulded cufflinks placed between each stud. Border of moulded cufflinks and tie pin in relief on lid. 90mm long.	12.00
Hexagonal Salt Pot. 100mm.	4.00
Pepper Pot. 75mm.	4.00
Bagware Teapot and lid. 108mm.	8.50
Bagware Milk Jug. No. 179. 80mm.	6.50

Miscellaneous

Cauldron, 2 handles. 36mm.	3.00
Cauldron, on three feet. 60mm.	3.00
Bell. 60mm.	5.50
Hammer Head, Matchholder, can be found inscribed: *My speciality is striking* or *Matches.* Add £2.00. 80mm long.	13.00
Hand holding a tulip. No. 74. 80mm. (With rin on finger).	5.00
Vase with moulded key pattern. No. 277. 118mm.	8.50

Willper Heraldic China

Trademark used by Sampson Hancock & Sons, The Garden Works, Hanley. (Usual trademark Corona).

Only a few pieces have been seen to date.

Ewer with Chester crest. 53mm.	3.50
Squat Jug. 60mm.	3.50
Vase. 60mm.	3.50

Wilton China

c1923-1934

WILTON
ART
CHINA

in gilt 1932-1934

Found on models with Felix transfer or inscription.

Trademark used by A.G. Harley Jones at Wilton Pottery, Fenton. This firm specialised in lustre ware.

Mr A.G. Harley Jones started his business in Fenton in 1905, and until 1920 seems to have concentrated on producing ornamental wares. After 1920 he diversified production, adding general earthenwares and crested china to his range. In 1923 he advertised 'Wilton heraldic china' and registered the mark in 1927. Mr Harley Jones was quite successful before 1920, expanding his business and extending his premises. After this date he seems to have had great difficulty in surviving, snatching at any craze or passing whim in the china trade to make money. This makes his wares very appealing to collectors as he produced a small but very original and innovative range of crested china models, tending towards the vulgar but reeking with nostalgia. Unfortunately he turned to crested china at the end of its popularity and even this new venture could not stem the tide of his insolvency. His turnover dropped from £22,062 in 1927 to £8,915 in 1932. By 1933 he had turned his hand to making glazed tile fireplaces but to no avail: he was declared bankrupt in June 1934. The account of his bankruptcy proceedings is a sad record of business losses from 1927 onwards, enlivened only by the Official Receiver's questions regarding a marriage deed made on the eve of his bankruptcy settling his household effects on a lady he married three days later. The Official Receiver doubted whether the settlement held good in law.

Wilton China is for the most part rather heavy and is better described as 'pot'. This does not however mean that models are not attractive: they are particularly 'modern', amusing and often unique to this pottery. There are obviously very few ancient artefacts or Great War souvenirs in the range as there was little call for these after 1923, but the novelty and comic items produced are particularly exciting. Mr Harley Jones shows the same awareness of public taste as the manufacturers of Carlton China and he also made many models in lustre ware. Unlike Carlton he does not seem to have made models of Felix the Cat but he used a transfer print of him with the inscription: 'Felix the film cat' on many different models and small vases. He did make models of that other popular twenties animal 'Bonzo Dog'. 'Lucky Black Cat' transfers, transfer prints of a regional nature such as Welsh Tea Party

groups and the Devil at Devil's Bridge and view ware (both monochrome, red, black or blue and polychrome) can all be found. A few lucky white heather devices but not commemorative pieces have been recorded.

Numbering System. No stock numbers were printed or painted on Wilton models. Painted numbers, such as 018 or 012 are found on a large number of different models and must be the paintresses' marks.

Wilton Models
Ancient Artefacts

Ancient Tyg, 1 handle. 70mm.	2.00
Bronze Pot, not named. 35mm.	3.00
Loving Cup, 3 handles. 39mm.	3.00

Buildings – Coloured
These can be found with crests
Ann Hathaway's Cottage.

55mm long.	20.00
Ann Hathaway's Cottage, on ashtray base. 73mm long.	19.00
Feathers Hotel. 1600. Ludlow. 100mm long.	65.00
Shakespeare's House. 53mm long.	20.00

Buildings – White

Ann Hathaway's Cottage, in pearl lustre on oval base. 57mm long.	15.00
Ann Hathaway's Cottage, on ashtray base in lustre. 73mm long.	15.00
Ann Hathaway's night light in pearl lustre. 106mm long.	19.00
Blackpool Tower, found in lustre. 92mm.	13.00
Blackpool Tower. 175mm.	14.50
Blackpool Tower and buildings. 175mm.	17.00
Christchurch Priory. 108mm long.	55.00
Cottage, Thatched. (Probably unnamed Ann Hathaway's Cottage.) 56mm long.	15.00
Feathers Hotel, Ludlow. 100mm. (Lustre).	40.00
Lichfield Cathedral, can be lustre. 85mm.	30.00
Peterborough Cathedral, West Front of. 90mm long.	25.00
Shakespeare's House. 53mm long.	10.50
Tamworth Castle. 130mm long.	40.00

Monuments (including Crosses)

Liberty Statue. 175mm.	30.00
Toad Rock near Hathersage. 95mm long.	26.00

Historical/Folklore

Dick Whittington and cat on ashtray base, inscribed: *IV miles to London* on milestone and *Turn again Whittington* on ashtray. 110mm.	125.00

Traditional/National Souvenirs

Blackpool Big Wheel. 105mm.	12.50
Found with the Felix transfer and Pathe trademark, inscribed: *Felix the cat comes to Blackpool.*	40.00
Blackpool Tower and Wheel on ashtray base. 90mm.	21.00
Irish Harp, with green shamrocks. 105mm.	8.50
Thistle Vase. 60mm.	3.00
Welsh Hat.	
2 sizes: 35mm. (miniature)	8.50
70mm.	10.50

Seaside Souvenirs

Bathing Machine with girl in doorway. Can be found with some colouring, lustre or inscribed: *Morning Dip' 7a.m.!* 100mm.	30.00
Fisherman's Creel, fish on lid, inscribed: *A good catch.* 88mm long.	6.50
Sailing Yacht, inscribed: *Saucy Sue.* 125mm.	23.50
Can be found in lustre.	
Lighthouse, inscribed: *Sailor beware.* Found in lustre. 155mm.	9.00

Animals

Cat, angry. Raised tail, coloured bow and face. Inscribed: *My word if you're not off.* 115mm.	34.50
Cat on pouffe, outpressed *Luck* in orange. 62mm.	16.00
Cat, sitting, red bow. Can be found in lustre. 60mm.	9.00
Cat, sitting, inscribed: *Luck.* Red tongue. 102mm.	15.00
Black cat on lid of fishing creel, inscribed: *I'm here just for luck.* 80mm.	30.00
Cat, comical, sitting looking forward, looped tail as handle, painted face. 107mm.	19.00

Black cat on cheese, mouse at base. 80mm.	27.50
Bulldog, standing, inscribed: *What we have we hold.* 130mm long.	20.00
Terrier Dog, sitting, can be found in lustre. 85mm.	20.00
Dog, begging. 72mm.	12.00
Dog, Pug, 57mm.	13.50
Pig, inscribed: *You may push.*	12.50

Birds (including Eggs)

Cock. (Lustre). 70mm long.	16.00
Cockerel Pepper Pot. 70mm.	11.00
Duck, sitting. Found in lustre. 50mm.	10.50
Turkey. 55mm.	11.00

Great War

Sailor, seated and holding submarine. Blue cap band. 75mm coloured.	110.00
Battleship, tall top mast and no forward guns. 115mm long.	56.00
Fieldglasses. 83mm.	20.00
Folkestone War Memorial, inscribed: *Road of Remembrance.* 78mm.	47.50
Hay War Memorial. 150mm.	135.00
St. Anne's *War Memorial.* 152mm.	110.00
Thetford *War Memorial.* 150mm.	100.00
Walsall War Memorial. 115mm.	110.00

Home/Nostalgic

Book with clasp. 65mm.	6.50
Fireplace with clock and dogs on mantlepiece, kettle & teapot on hob. Inscribed: *Loves Old Sweet Song.* 90mm.	23.00
Grandfather Clock, inscribed: *Make us of time let not advantage slip.* 128mm.	10.50
Sundial, inscribed: *What o'clock* and *Serene I stand among the flowers and only count life's sunny hours.* 146mm.	13.00
Garden Roller. 98mm long.	12.50

Comic/Novelty

Bookmaker, standing figure, inscribed: *6 to 4 the field.* 80mm.	75.00
Broke to the wide, man standing with head and shoulders bowed. 82mm.	75.00

Open Razor ashtray, inscribed: *Got me through many a scrape,* found in lustre. 106mm long. 40.00

Tramp holding glass of beer, sitting by milestone, inscribed: *Its better to be alive with eighteen pence than dead with a thousand pounds.* 76mm. 65.00

Truck of Coal, inscribed: *Black Diamonds.* Black coal, sometimes found unpainted. Found in lustre. 98mm long. 19.00

Cartoon/Comedy Characters

Bonzo Dog. (Lustre). Pink and black face. 48mm. 35.00

Can also be found sitting on a lustre ashtray base. 110mm long. 35.00

Comedian, standing figure wearing brown Oxford bags, black jacket, blue tie, brown trilby hat and black shoes. 96mm (rare). 65.00

Mutt and Jeff, on rectangular base. 105mm long. 75.00

Sport/Pastimes

Bishop chess piece. 70mm. 16.00
Pawn chess piece. 55mm. 24.00

Alcohol

Barrel. 52mm. 3.00
Barrel of Beer, on stand. 55mm. 5.50
Whiskey Bottle. 98mm. 7.50

Modern Equipment

Horn Gramophone, inscribed: *His Master's Voice.* 104mm. 30.00

Radio operator, inscribed: *Listening in.* Some colouring. Found lustre. 80mm. 110.00

Telephone, upright. 105mm. 19.00

Footwear

Lancashire Clog, with verse: *There's many a factory lass wi clogs on her feet.* 120mm long. 6.50

Domestic

Ashtray, semi circular or circular with colour transfer of a cigarette. 95mm long. 15.00

Sometimes inscribed: *Who burnt the cloth?* 20.00

Cigarettes, octagonal holder. 64mm. 4.50

Matches, octagonal holder. 64mm. 4.00

Pastry cutter, clover shaped. 90mm long. 10.50

Miniature Domestic

Cheese Dish, 1 piece. 50mm. 6.50

Cheese Dish and cover, horseshoe shaped. 45mm. 12.50

Miscellaneous

Thimble. 43mm. 17.50

Wil-Wat China

Wordsworth Art China

WIL-WAT
W.W
G
CHINA

WORDSWORTH
ART CHINA
J. W. WILLIAMS
KESWICK

Trademark used for a retailer by Alfred B. Jones and Sons Ltd, Grafton China Works, Longton. (Usual trademark Grafton).

For further details of this china and manufacturer see Grafton China.

Fortunately for the researcher, models with this mark are found with the Grafton mark printed alongside. WWG must have been a retailer, but it is difficult to draw any conclusion about when the models were made.

The two models made specially for this retailer do not carry stock numbers but the fish does, presumably being taken from the Grafton range.

Wil-Wat Models
Monuments (including Crosses)
The Monument, Laceby. 150mm.   20.00

Traditional/National Souvenirs
Leaking Boot, Cleethorpes (Statue of
  boy, boot joined to hand by
  string). 156mm.   64.00

Animals
Fish, straight, with open mouth.
  100mm long.   4.00

Trademark used for the retailer J.W. Williams, Keswick. The inclusion of the word 'Art' in the trademark suggests that it may have been produced by Hewitt and Leadbeater, Willow Potteries, Longton. (Usual trademark Willow Art).

Two items have so far been recorded, these being a 70mm ewer and a 38mm jug, both with Keswick crests, valued at £3.00 each.

W and R

Trademark used for a London wholesaler by Hewitt and Leadbeater, Willow Potteries, Longton. (Usual trademark Willow Art).

For details of this china and manufacturer see Willow Art China.

Models and 'smalls' with this mark usually carry crests of the south of England. All models are found in the Willow Art range and seem to have been made during the Great War.

W and R Models
Ancient Artefacts
Lincoln Jack. No. 34. 52mm.	3.00

Historical/Folklore
Model of Mary Queen of Scots Chair, Edinburgh Castle. 80mm.	6.50

Seaside Souvenirs
Lighthouse, not named. 110mm.	5.00

Animals
Cat, sitting, badge on chest. 72mm.	12.50
Cat, standing, chubby. 70mm.	16.00
Elephant, walking. No. 113. 52mm.	17.00
Hare, sitting, ears laid back. 74mm long.	12.50
Pig, standing. 85mm long.	10.00

Birds (including Eggs)
Swan posy holder. 65mm long.	5.00

Great War
Soldier with rifle, inscribed: *Our brave defender.* 132mm.	47.50

Monoplane with moveable propelier. 150mm long.	65.00
Battleship, impressed: *HMS Lion.* 140mm long.	30.00
Tommy's Steel Helmet. 75mm dia.	22.50

Home/Nostalgic
Anvil. 60mm.	7.50
Coal Scuttle, helmet shaped. 50mm.	5.00
Grandfather Clock. Inscribed: *Make use of time...* 125mm.	10.50
Watering Can. 75mm.	8.50

Comic/Novelty
Billiken, not named. 73mm.	7.50

Alcohol
Beer Bottle. 42mm.	7.50

Transport
Car, open 4 seater. 114mm long.	40.00

Footwear
Ladies Riding Shoe with square toe. 115mm.	13.00

Miniature Domestic
Coffee Pot with lid. 69mm.	7.50

Miscellaneous
Hand holding tulip. 80mm.	5.00
Hand holding flower. No. 74. 80mm.	5.00

W.R. & S.

Trademark used by William Ritchie and Co. Ltd, 24,26 and 28 Elder Street, Edinburgh. (Usual trademark Porcelle).

For details of this china and manufacturer see Porcelle.

This mark is identical to the Porcelle mark but the word Porcelle and the visor have been omitted.

W.R. & S. Models
Seaside Souvenirs
Whelk Shell. 100mm.	5.00

Animals
Elephant with howdah. 68mm.	30.00

Birds (including Eggs)
Swan, opening wings. 58mm.	7.50
Swan posy bowl. 58mm.	7.50

Great War
Nurse. *A Friend in Need.*	40.00
Officer's Peaked Cap.	14.50
Bell Tent. 74mm.	16.00

Hats
Top Hat. 45mm.	5.50

Wy Not? Crest China

Mark can also be found as Wy Knot.

Trademark used for a wholesaler by Hewitt and Leadbeater, Willow Potteries, Longton. (Usual trademark Willow Art).

For details of this china and manufacturer see Willow Art China.

This mark is often badly printed and can be read as IVY NOT. Crests on models with the mark are from all over England and Wales, and all the models are from Willow Art moulds, so it is impossible to suggest what the last D in the initials underneath the mark stands for.

Stock numbers were found coincide with Willow Art numbers.

Wy Not Models
Ancient Artefacts
Loving Cup, 3 handles. 39mm.	3.00
Puzzle Jug, with inscription. 68mm.	5.50
Winchester Leather Jack, not named. 50mm.	3.00

Buildings – White
Knaresborough Castle. 95mm.	70.00

Monuments (including Crosses)
Bunyan's Statue. 163mm.	20.00
Lord Byron's Monument. 165mm.	40.00

Historical/Folklore
Bunyan's Chair. 90mm.	19.00
Bunyan's Cushion. 100mm long.	30.00
Burn's Chair, Dumfries. 83mm.	7.50

*James V Chair at Stirling Castle, Model
of.* 102mm.   7.50
*Mary Queen of Scots Chair, Edinburgh
Castle, Model of.* 75mm.   6.50
Medieval Man's head candlesnuffer,
with handle. 74mm.   40.00
*Sir Walter Scotts Chair, Abbotsford,
Model of.* 85mm.   7.50
Skull, inscribed: *A Prehistoric Skull.*
No. 171. 60mm.   7.50

Traditional/National Souvenirs
Welsh Hat. 57mm.   5.00

Animals
Cat, sitting, blue bow. No. 62.
2 sizes: 60mm.   10.00
75mm.   12.50
Cheshire Cat, inscribed: *Still Smiling.*
88mm.   7.50
Dog, sitting, badge on chest.
80mm.   12.50
Dog, Collie, standing. 85mm.   23.00
Elephant, walking. 52mm.   17.00
Mouse (very fat, often described as
a guinea pig). 62mm.   20.00
Pig, 80mm long.   10.00
Teddy Bear. 75mm.   19.50

Great War
Nurse, inscribed: *A friend in need.*
130mm.   40.00
Sailor, inscribed: *Our brave defender,*
and carrying a flag on his chest
instead of a crest. The flag
transfer is inscribed: *Good Luck.
The boys in blue.* 130mm.   75.00
Soldier, inscribed: *Our brave defender.*
Only example known has Union
Jack on chest and inscribed:
Bravo!. Kitchener's Army. (A
Willow Art decoration).   75.00
Battleship, 4 funnels.
127mm long.   19.00
Red Cross Van, red crosses on side.
84mm long.   30.00
Field Gun. 120mm long.   17.00
Field Gun with screen. 115mm.   19.00
Pickelhaube. 50mm.   30.00
Kit Bag, 74mm.   19.50
Tommy's Steel Helmet. 76mm long.   20.00
Kitchen Range. Inscribed: *Keep the
Home Fires Burning.* 78mm long.   13.00

Home/Nostalgic
Book. 58mm.   6.50
Grandfather Clock, inscribed: *Make
use of time...* 124mm.   10.50
Iron and Trivet. 70mm long.   15.00
Shaving Mug. 55mm.   6.50

Comic/Novelty
Billiken. 70mm.   7.50

Footwear
Lancashire Clog, with yellow
buckle. 88mm long.   5.50

Miniature Domestic
Cheese Dish and cover. 50mm.   7.50
Tea Pot with lid. 68mm.   7.50

Miscellaneous
Hand holding a tulip. 81mm.   5.00

Zuyder Zee China

No details of mark available.

Fluted Vase 75mm, colour transfer
of children hand in hand 'called
Flying Dutchman' and 'Industry
is the parent of success'.   15.00

Unmarked Models

Many models found unmarked are
recognisably pieces from the major firms
which for some reason escaped from the
pottery without the trademark. Some
factories, such as Grafton, did not mark
pieces with firing flaws, but most firms
did not mark all their perfect ware.
However, Grafton pieces usually bear
their painted stock numbers. Models with
no crest could well be travellers samples.
Unmarked models of known origin are
not listed below. Many models in the
original listings in earlier Price Guides
have turned out to be Savoy. Certain
shapes did not have enough room on the
base to carry a factory mark. Possible
factories have been put in parentheses
where known. A trained eye can tell
which pottery made an unmarked piece in
most cases.

There are however quantities of unmarked
crested china which cannot be attributed
to any one manufacturer. This china could
have been made by several firms known
to have made crested wares but do not
appear to have used a trademark. These
firms include:

George Proctor and Co., High Street,
Longton. Advertised arms ware in 1907
but their initials G.P. and Co. L. have not
been found on recorded marks.

Barkers and Kent Ltd., The Foley Pottery,
Fenton. Were said in 1921 to be doing much
to fill the gap left by the German
manufacturers. An illustrated article in
the *Pottery Gazette* shows a range of Great
War souvenirs and animals. The initials B.
and K.L. used by the firm are not found in
known marks.

Biltons (1912) Ltd., London Road Works,
Stoke-on-Trent. Biltons had at one time
made little else except teapots, but when
they lost male operatives during the Great
War they changed to making 'small
fancies' (why women could not be taught
to make teapots has perhaps more to do
with male vanity than their own

capability). 'Small fancies' included models of soldiers, sailors, nurses, pierrots, pierrettes and animals. They were offered coloured, but look very suitable for the applying of crests. Biltons did register marks but none have been found on crested china.

C.J. Bisson and Co., 82 Liverpool Road, Stoke-on-Trent. During the Great War the firm specialised in heraldic china and the company also owned The British Doll Manufacturing Co. Both of these lines were tackled to take advantage of the lack of German competition. C.J. Bisson do not seem to have registered a mark but a photograph of their range of heraldic novelties shows Great War souvenirs, a piano, and animals.

As these firms were earthenware manufacturers the models would tend to be reasonably heavy.

Many German firms also manufactured crested china for the English souvenir market and chose not to use a trademark, especially after the Great War. German wares tend to be somewhat whiter and of poorer quality than British made wares. These include:

Max Emanuel, The Mosanic Pottery, Mitterteich, (usual trademark Mosanic).

Moschendorf, Hof, Bayern (usual trademark PM and Rex).

Hutschenreuther, Probstzella, Thuringia (Trademark P).

Klösterle, Carlsbad (usual trademark Union K).

However, many of the models listed below are known to have been produced by Wilhelm Kutzscher and Co., Schwarzenberger Porzellanfabrik, Schwarzenberg, Saxony, (usual trademark, St George China, Impero, Saxony and Princess).

Generally, pieces which have neither factory mark nor inscription are less desirable than those which do and are sometimes worth slightly less. This is not as important with rare items or with medium range wares.

Values for pieces with firing defects and therefore not finished off, i.e. mis-shapen, having no crest, colouring, or gilding are about half to three-quarters of the full value.

Busts

Bust of General Booth, can be found inscribed: *Salvation Army*.	
2 sizes: 75mm.	35.00
86mm.	40.00
Bust of Charles Dickens. 110mm.	50.00
Bust of *Gen Michael Collins* in uniform. Square base, unglazed. (R&L). 154mm.	82.50
Bust of Admiral Beatty, unglazed. 165mm.	82.50
Bust of *Jellicoe* on column base, unglazed. 164mm.	75.00

Parian/Unglazed

Brandenburg Gate, Berlin. 62mm.	100.00
Cartmel Priory Church. 100mm long.	40.00
Mow Cop Castle, Staffordshire. (Tunstall Pottery).	
2 sizes: 130mm long.	80.00
238mm long.	150.00
St Pauls, stone coloured. 87mm long. (probably Savoy)	100.00
Solomons Temple (Grinlow Tower). Inscribed: *Erected on the site of a Historic Barrow*. 85mm.	37.50
York Minster, West Front. 128mm.	25.00

Ancient Artefacts

Brading Roman Vase. No. 141. 52mm.	3.00
Lewes Vase. Unnamed. No. 305. 40mm.	3.00
Loving Cup. 3 handles. 36mm.	3.00
Loving Cup. 3 handles. Silver and black. 69mm.	10.50
Puzzle Tankard. 47mm.	5.00
Puzzle Jug. 70mm.	5.00
Salisbury Kettle. 110mm.	3.00
Winchester Bushel. 102mm dia.	8.50

Buildings – Coloured

Abbot Reginalds Gateway and old Vicarage Evesham. 130mm long.	75.00
Abel Fletchers, Bell Hotel. 120mm long.	65.00
Birthplace of Dr Andrew Carnegie. 75mm high, 83mm long.	75.00
Boston Stump. 65mm long.	20.00
Craigwell House, Bognor. 115mm long.	75.00
Canterbury Weavers, The. No. 141.	82.50
Dan Winter's Cottage, where the first orange Lodge was formed in Co.	

Armagh, Ireland. A Money Box.
128mm long.   40.00
Dunbar House, three storey house
with towers at front, 2 chimneys.
129mm.   45.00
Dundee, Royal Arch. (Willow).
95mm.   95.00
Fair Maids House, Perth. 80mm
long. (Willow).   145.00
The Feathers Hotel, Ludlow.
112mm.   125.00
Folkestone Parish Church AD1138.
103mm long.   75.00
Gabled House, not named.
Nightlight. 135mm long.   75.00
The Keep, Hawarden. Unglazed.
140mm long.   82.50
Hampton Court Palace. 80mm.   55.00
Hardys Cottage. 40mm,
55mm long.   85.00
Harvard House, with long
inscription: *Restored by Marie
Carelli...* 145mm.   170.00
Irish Cottage, Money Box.
110mm long.   30.00
Ledbury, Old Market House.
97mm long.   75.00
*Market Harborough Old Grammar
School.*
2 sizes: 126mm.   80.00
150mm.   85.00
Monnow Gate, Monmouth. 48mm.   40.00
Knaresborough Castle.   48.00
Old Falcon Tavern, Bideford on Avon.
115mm.   75.00
Old Lantern Chapel, Ilfracombe.
74mm long.   35.00
Old Town House, Dunbar. 130mm.   75.00
Pete's Cottage, Isle of Man.
57mm long.   65.00
Plas Newyd House, impressed: *The
House of the Ladies of Llangollen.*
115mm long.   82.50
Priory Church, Christchurch.
Unglazed. 223mm long.   125.00
Pump Room and Baths. Trefriw Wells,
plus long inscription.
95mm long.   100.00
St Pauls Cathedral, unglazed.
145mm long.   100.00
Shakespeare's House.
2 sizes: 65mm long.   16.00
157mm long.   25.00
Shanklin, IoW, The Old Village.
98mm long.   110.00

Stokesay Castle, Gate House.
116mm long.   150.00

Buildings – White
Archway, wooden door, large iron
hinges, steps up to door. 105mm.   20.00
Battle Abbey Gateway. 96mm.   25.00
Beverley, North Bar. 90mm.   25.00
Big Ben. 135mm.   15.00
Birmingham Town Hall.
2 sizes: 95mm long.   20.00
128mm long.   30.00
Blackpool Tower with buildings,
impressed: *The Tower of Blackpool.*
120mm.   15.00
*British Government Pavilion B.E.E.
Wembley 1924-5.* 60mm.   82.50
Castle, (unknown). 76mm.   45.00
Conduit, Uttoxeter Market Place.
120mm.   40.00
Cottage, single storey. 66mm.   10.50
Folkestone, Parish Church. AD1138.
106mm long.   40.00
Garden of Sleep, inscribed:
*On the grass of the cliff, at the edge
of the steep
God planted a garden, a garden of
sleep!
'Neath the blue of the sky in the
green of the corn.
It is there that the regal red poppies
are born!
Brief days of desire, and long dreams
of delight,
They are mine when my poppy-land
cometh in sight
O heart of my heart!
Where the poppies are born
I am waiting for thee – in the hush of
the corn.*
110mm long.   50.00
Great Yarmouth Clock Tower, not
named. 125mm.   8.50
Guildford, The Castle. 100mm.   40.00
Lincoln Stonebow. 85mm.   24.00
*Old throne of the Right Hon. D. Lloyd
George Esq. MP Llanystymdwy near
Criccieth.* 76mm long.   47.50
Mickelgate Bar, York. 98mm.   40.00
Ripon Cathedral, West Front.
80mm long.   40.00
Rowton Tower, Chester.
88mm long.   30.00
Royal Arch, Dundee front. (Willow
Art). 94mm.   120.00

St Albans, Clock Tower (very small)
74mm. 15.00
St Tudno's Church, Llandudno with
open pillars. 52mm. 65.00
Scarborough Castle Ruins.
75mm long. 30.00
Weymouth Jubilee Clock Tower.
125mm. 18.00
Whitby Abbey Ruins. 75mm. 110.00
Windmill, fixed sails. 80mm. 14.00
Windmill on stilts on square base,
fixed sails in form of scent bottle.
78mm. 16.00
York Micklegate Bar. 92mm. 40.00
York Minster, West Front. 114mm. 25.00
York Minster, West Front. 128mm. 45.00

Monuments (including Crosses)
Ashington Boer War Memorial.
138mm. 75.00
Bradlaugh's Monument, Northampton.
2 sizes: 110mm. 40.00
140mm. 47.50
Brixham Clock Tower. 120mm. 17.50
Celtic Cross. 110mm. 12.00
Cleethorpes Clock Tower. 136mm. 24.00
Captain Cook's Monument. 135mm. 30.00
Cross on square base. 107mm. 12.00
Hall Cross, Doncaster.
2 sizes: 156mm. 22.50
185mm. 27.50
King Edward VII statue (actually
Drake!). 125mm. 15.00
Larg's Tower, inscribed: *Battle of
Largs Memorial.* 166mm. 16.00
Margate Surf Memorial with
inscriptions.
4 sizes: 35mm. 17.00
80mm. 21.00
144mm. 25.00
330mm. 55.00
The Metal Man, Tramore. 150mm.
(Saxony). 45.00
Parnells Memorial. 165mm. 65.00
Ruskins Memorial, Friars Crag.
Fully inscribed, grey, unglazed.
180mm. 35.00
St David's Old Market Cross. No. 742.
95mm. 20.00
St Winifreds Statue, Holywell.
135mm. 25.00
*Sir John Franklin discoverer of the
North West Passage. Born at Spilsby
April 1786. Died Arctic Regions
June 1847.* 165mm. 65.00

Skegness Clock Tower. 120mm. 10.00
Swanage Globe.
2 sizes: 54mm white. 9.00
65mm coloured. 16.00

Historical/Folklore
Bass Rock, in relief on square plaque.
125mm long. 33.00
Baby in wraps, perhaps Moses in
bullrushes. 66mm long. 12.50
Banbury Lady on Horse. 130mm. 24.50
Auld Brig O'Doon, Ayr. Picture in
relief on wall plaque.
125mm long. 24.50
Burns Cottage, interior of, in relief on
rectangular plaque. 125mm long. 25.00
Exterior of Burn's Cottage, in relief on
plaque. 128mm long. 25.00
Devil looking over Lincoln. 114mm. 14.50
Edwardian Lady carrying black cat
and basket. 106mm. 33.50
If named *Mary Bull* 30.00
Execution Block. 100mm long. 7.50
Giant's Causeway. *Wishing Chair.*
105mm. 75.00
Idol or grotesque imp or lucky
charm. 90mm long. 11.00
*Jacobean Font at Newport, IoW. Model
of.* 70mm. 14.50
Knaresborough Dropping Well.
77mm. 20.00
Knight's Armour, torso decorated in
relief. 70mm. 85.00
Knight's Helmet and Visor, with
reclining animal on top. 80mm. 45.00
Man in the Sun. 100mm. 47.50
Monmouth Cap with verse. 45mm. 30.00
Mother Shipton, fully coloured.
110m. 20.00
Sanctuary Chair, Beverley Minster.
68mm. 19.00
Scold's Bridle, bust of old woman
wearing bridle, with story of
gossiping women. Can be found
coloured. 64mm.
White. 40.00
Coloured. 65.00
Skull. 44mm. 13.00
Sword in scabbard, ornate. 135mm. 40.00
Trusty Servant. Coloured figure on
white base. 130mm. 110.00
*Ulphus Horn, Original in York
Minster, Model of.* 110mm long. 30.00
Viking or Saxon King standing on 3
stepped base, axe in hand and
scrolls in the other. 150mm. 40.00

Dick Whittington and cat, figure
with very large sitting cat
holding shield. 100mm.   43.00

Traditional/National Souvenirs
John Bull, bust. 75mm.   8.00
John Bull, standing, with dog.
106mm.   20.00
John Bull, standing, no dog. 120mm.   17.00
Bolton Trotter. 132mm long.   5.00
Bolton Trotters, two joined as a pair.
107mm long.   9.50
A Plate o' Bolton Trotters, Three pigs
trotters on a plate.   11.00
Cheddar Cheese, Model of, with
inscription: *This famous cheese has
been made in and around Cheddar
for centuries, and to this day no
country in the world has been able to
equal it.* 60mm dia. (Grafton).   11.00
Cheddar Cheese, inscribed: *Elind
Burritt Esq USA says 'far surpasses
anything I saw in the Mammoth
Cave of Kentucky.* 40mm.   12.00
Jersey Milkmaid. 80mm.   30.00
Lincoln Imp, on pedestal. 110mm.   6.50
Lincoln Imp, wall hanging, crest on
back. 125mm.   17.00
Manx Man, 3-legged. 126mm.   47.50
Melton Mowbray Pie, with pastry
roses and leaves. 55mm.   17.50
Bust of Burns, glazed. No. 589.   17.50
Gretna Priest, inscribed: *The famous
Gretna Priest from the celebrated
Blacksmiths shop, Gretna Green.*
118mm. (Saxony).   30.00
Highland Mary, statue. 150mm.   25.00
Scotsman playing bagpipes on
pedestal. 138mm.   40.00
Scotsman standing in kilt, flower
vase. 109mm. (Arcadian). No
crest.   35.00
Tam-o'shanter, sitting in chair.
2 sizes: 94mm.   24.50
           130mm.   25.00
Jug with thistle pattern in relief.
51mm.   3.00
Miniature Toby Jug Welsh Lady,
coloured. 42mm.   20.00
Welsh Lady in chair. 100mm.   23.00
Welsh Hat. 55mm.   5.00
Welsh Hat, very tall. 70mm.   10.50
Dutch Girl, bust, flowers in relief on
base.   14.00

Seaside Souvenirs
Binnacle (looks like a lighthouse with
4pierced windows). 95mm.   6.50
Canoe. 110mm long. (Florentine).   10.50
Lifeboat. 98mm long.   12.00
Lifeboat. 125mm long.   12.00
Lighthouse. 100mm.   5.50
Eddystone Lighthouse. Three-piece
salt, pepper and mustard cruet.
Can be found with two spoons
with flags.   16.00
Lighthouse on rocks with steps,
130mm.   6.00
Lighthouse with 3 open windows.
115mm.   5.00
Lighthouse, tiny. Candlesnuffer.
70mm. (Grafton).   9.00
Lighthouse, candlesnuffer.
2 sizes: 65mm.   7.50
          106mm.   13.00
Beachy Head Lighthouse. 124mm.   11.00
Un-named Rock, no crest, original
could be off the Devon coast.
40mm.   13.00
Lifeboatman on rock base. 120mm.
(Carlton).   30.00
Fisherman holding rope. 113mm.   16.00
Fisherman/Lifeboatman Bust on
round plinth. 105mm.   12.50
Mermaid with fish. 84mm.   30.00
Waves, group of. 95mm long.   5.50
Nautilus Shell, held up by two
mermaids. 106mm.   17.00
Shell. 110mm long.   5.50
Whelk Shell.
2 sizes: 84mm long.   5.00
         95mm long.   5.00
Whelk Shell, inscribed: *Found at
Ryde.* 75mm long.   5.00
Yacht. 128mm.   11.00
Bathing Belle, poking head out of
change tent. 80mm. (Carlton).   40.00
Bathing Belle on rubber duck. 80mm.   19.00

Figures
The figures listed below are those
which do not belong under any
other heading.
Baby, on rug, naked. 130mm long.   75.00
Baby in wraps – see Historical/
Folklore
Baby, with arms outstretched and
coloured hair. 95mm.   25.00

Boy, feeding birds, standing next to
a large basket on a base. 80mm.   30.00

Child candlesnuffer, standing,
impressed *MORNING*, holding
cup. 125mm.   65.00

Girl in nightdress, standing on
square base. Inscribed: *Morning*.
125mm.   27.50

Girl on stool, with dog on floor.
(Beige/lustre). 108mm.   25.00

Girl sitting on horse beside tree
trunk. 110mm.   25.00

Edwardian Child pepper pot.
84mm.   12.00

Edwardian Lady holding cat and
basket, possibly Mary Bull.   33.50

Cook holding wooden spoon.
115mm.   40.00

Housekeeper or cook wearing mob
cap and apron, carrying keys and
a ladle. 120mm. (Saxony).   40.00

Man, Down and Out, inscribed:
Broke to the wide. 80mm. (Wilton).   75.00

Nurse candlesnuffer, fat, holding
baby. 110mm.   75.00

Two Lady Grape Treaders, with
skirts rolled up, standing in
barrel of grapes. 105mm.
(Saxony).   35.00

Washer Woman, holding basket of
washing. 118mm. (Saxony).   40.00

Woman carrying case and bottle.   25.00

Monk carrying lantern and basket.
2 sizes: 114mm.   22.50
         135mm. (Saxony).   22.50

Countryside

Acorn. 55mm.   7.50

Axe in Tree Stump. 75mm.   11.50

Butterfly with open wings and wire
legs. 90mm long. (German).   16.00

Four bar gate with stile and
milestone. 96mm long.   8.50

Pine Cone. 85mm.   4.00

Tree Trunk spill holder, with 2 sheep
in front. 75mm.   13.00

Tree Trunk spill holder, with 2 sheep
and lady with sickle. 75mm.   13.00

Animals

Bear, playing a Mandolin.
(German)   25.00

Bull's head cream jug. 78mm.   9.00

Camel kneeling on rectangular base.
122mm long.   22.00

Camel, kneeling. 80mm long.   22.00

Kitten, standing.   17.50

Black Cat, sitting up, no crest,
yellow eye and orange mouth,
comical face. *Good Luck* in orange.
133mm.   16.00

Cat, angry with arched back,
coloured face. 70mm.   14.00

Cat on Drum. 90mm. (Saxony).   22.50

Cat, in holdall, can be inscribed:
Good Morning or *Good Night*.
55mm long. (Saxony).   22.50

Cat, sitting on pouffe, inscribed:
LUCK. 70mm.   26.00

Cat on pouffe, outpressed: *LUCK*.
73mm. (Willow Art).   26.00

Cat, with toothache, bandage round
jaw tied with three bows. 95mm.   30.00

Cat, dressed, with toothache, ruff
around neck, bandage around
head, left paw raised. 105mm.   30.00

Cat, singing from long sheet of
music. 65mm. (Saxony).   22.50

Cat, singing, red mouth, green bow.
75mm. (Grafton).   33.00

Cat, reading from book. 74mm.
(Saxony).   22.50

Cat, sitting, looking up, gilded face.
67mm.   8.50

Cat, sitting, coloured face. 100mm.   10.50

Cat, sitting, comical, right ear down,
left ear up.
2 sizes: 110mm.   12.00
         120mm.   12.00

Cat, Egyptian, with long ears.
90mm long.   30.00

Cat, thin and foreign looking,
sitting. 70mm.   8.50

Cat, long necked. 115mm.   10.00

Cat, posy bowl.   13.00

Cat, comic, sitting in trinket dish.
Bow at neck, tail upright. 45mm.   45.00

Cat, standing, plump, black
features. 89mm.   16.00

Cat and Rabbit, in high Boot,
inscribed: *A jolly place for a jolly
couple*. 83mm. (Saxony).   20.00

Cat, from Alice in Wonderland, long
legs, tail wrapped around legs.
100mm. (Florentine).   24.00

Cat, angry with grotesque face,
standing on tall legs with tail
wrapped round them. 96mm.   24.00

Cat, furry kitten with open mouth.
90mm.   10.00

Cat and kitten either side of posy bowl. 105mm long.	11.00
Cat and Kitten, sitting by open square box on ashtray base. 72mm.	23.00
Cat, sitting, left paw raised. 75mm.	14.50
Cat, Cheshire, sitting, ear up. 128mm.	15.00
Cat, Manx. 90mm long.	16.00
Cat, Manx, standing drinking from jug, sometimes inscribed: *Mothers favourite*. 70mm long. (Saxony).	24.50
Cat with mouse. 77mm.	24.50
Cat, standing, hands on hips, tail forming third leg. 86mm.	20.00
Cat scent bottle and lid. 90mm. (Grafton).	40.00
Cats, three, in linen basket. 68mm.	25.00
Cheshire Cat, 90mm.	6.50
Cheshire Cat, long neck, looking left, 1 green eye, 1 winking red eye. 115mm.	10.50
Cat, frightened. 100mm. (Florentine).	45.00
Cow lying down, with gold horns, inscribed: *The Jersey Cow*. 108mm long.	20.00
Cow standing, gold horns, inscribed: *The Jersey Cow*. 2 sizes: 93mm long.	20.00
108mm long.	20.00
(Pair with above).	
Cow cream jug. 2 sizes: 110mm long.	14.00
125mm long.	16.00
Dinosaur jug. 85mm long.	5.50
Dog, Bulldog, extremely thin, sitting. 95mm long.	16.00
Dog, Collie, sitting. 80mm.	16.00
Dog wearing dress and overcoat, green colouring on hat. 92mm.	43.00
Standing Chauffeur Dog, goggles on cap, smoking pipe, wearing long overcoat. 84mm.	47.50
Dog, or possibly fox, standing, dressed in long travelling coat and flat cap, tied with scarf under chin. (Pair to the chauffeur above). 82mm.	55.00
Dog, Bulldog. 110mm long.	13.00
Dog, black bulldog in kennel. 67mm.	15.00
Dogs, two bulldogs, one seated and the other standing. 57mm. (Saxony).	23.00
Dog, Bull Terrier, sitting next to a bucket. 80mm.	23.00
Dog, Dachsund. 73mm long. (Willow).	40.00
Dogs, two Pharos Hounds, on oblong base. 76mm long.	75.00
Dog, Collie, lying down. 110mm long.	22.50
Dog, sitting, one ear raised. 69mm.	5.00
Dog, standing, tail as support. 80mm.	20.00
Dog, Terrier. 61mm.	6.50
Dog, Scottie, wearing Tam-o'shanter.	6.50
Dog, King Charles Spaniel. 67mm.	7.00
Dog, comical pup, sitting, brown patches. 61mm.	24.00
Dog, Pointer, walking. 125mm long.	20.00
Dog, walking, tail out. 120mm long.	20.00
Dog, Pointer, with spring tail (often missing). 90mm long.	30.00
Without tail.	20.00
Dog, Staffordshire Bull Terrier, long neck. 110mm.	20.00
Dog, in bandages, sitting. 90mm.	30.00
Dog, Labrador, sitting half out of kennel. (Saxony). 98mm.	40.00
Dogs, two, and cat in basket. 2 sizes: 63mm.	20.00
70mm.	25.00
Dog, Pug, lying down. 96mm long.	20.00
Dog, Spaniel with droopy ears. 60mm.	13.00
Dog, King Charles Spaniel, wearing ribbon, lying on cushion. 82mm long.	20.00
Pair of Spaniels in top hat. 82mm.	15.00
Dog, probably a Retriever, lying on oblong base. 120mm long.	22.00
Dog, sitting Labrador puppy. 70mm.	13.00
Dog Coal Scuttle. 80mm. (Saxony).	18.50
Donkey, inscribed: *Carisbrooke Donkey*. 100mm long. (Saxony).	30.00
Donkey. 90mm long.	15.00
Donkey, inscribed: *A Malvern Donkey*. 95mm long.	25.00
Elephant, gigantic, with gold tusks. Trunk raised. 130mm.	35.00
Elephant, trunk looped upwards. 85mm long. (Florentine).	19.50

Elephant, Indian, standing.	
2 sizes: 63mm long.	20.00
100mm long.	21.00
Elephant, standing, trunk looped up.	
80mm long. (Carlton).	24.00
Elephant, circus, with front feet on stool. 102mm.	82.50
Elephant, circus, doing handstand on stool. 74mm.	82.50
Elephant heads, 2 on vase as handles. 76mm.	7.50
Elephant No. 346. 50mm.	24.00
Elephant, walking. 70mm high, 110mm long.	40.00
Two Elephants on Toboggan going down hill. 70mm.	75.00
Elephant with Hunters and two Indian Bearers. 95mm.	35.00
Frog on hind legs, arms on chest, open mouth. 85mm.	19.50
Giant Frog, with huge open mouth. 80mm.	30.00
Frog with bead eyes. 72mm.	20.00
Frog cream jug. 100mm long.	6.50
Fish, inscribed: *Yarmouth Bloater*. 120mm long.	6.00
Fish salt pot, with black markings to face. 108mm long.	7.50
Fish, open mouth, raised head. 110mm long.	12.50
Fish with open back for pin cushion. 118mm long.	3.00
Fish, gilded tail. 112mm long.	3.00
Guinea Pig. 60mm long. 20.00	
Horses and Bulldogs heads in rectangular frame. 103mm.	17.00
Kangaroo. 95mm.	75.00
Lambs (two) by hollow tree trunk spill holder. See countryside.	
Lion, walking. 135mm.	13.00
Lion, on rectangular base. 116mm.	8.50
Lion, male, open mouth, looking left. 110mm long.	25.00
Lion, wearing coat and trousers holding telescope. 132mm.	75.00
Monkey, wearing coat and holding feel. 80mm. (Grafton).	15.00
Monkey with bead eyes. No. 245. 70mm. (Grafton).	15.00
Mouse. 60mm.	20.00
Mouse playing Banjo. 90mm.	28.00
Pig, standing, ears forward. 80mm long.	14.50
Pig, hairy, standing with holes in nostrils. Inscribed: *The pig that won't go*. 85mm long.	12.50

Pig sitting on haunches, Pepper Pot. 70mm.	16.00
Pig, sitting, ears flat out. 70mm.	22.00
Pink Pig posy holder.	16.00
Pig, standing, with hands on hips and pink ears. (Gemma). 83mm.	30.00
Polar Bear on ashtray base. 82mm.	25.00
Shetland Pony inscribed: *A Native of Shetland*. 80mm.	21.50
Rabbit, crouching. 65mm.	7.50
Rabbit, miniature, crouching, ears erect. 30mm.	87.50
Large Rabbit, crouching. 90mm long.	12.50
Rabbit on sledge. (Saxony).	30.00
Rabbits, 2 arm in arm on wide base. 72mm wide.	25.00
Rabbits, 2 cuddling on ashtray. 54mm.	21.00
Rhino, very grotesque. 155mm long.	30.00
Seal with ball on nose. 73mm.	19.50
Squirrel, large, in shape of milk jug. 90mm.	13.50
Teddy Bear. 79mm.	19.50
Tortoise pin box and lid.	
2 sizes: 80mm long.	7.50
128mm long.	10.50
Vole. No. 163. 60mm long.	40.00

Birds (including Eggs)

Blackbird on perch. 118mm long.	10.50
Canary on a perch. 110mm long.	10.50
Chick, yellow, hatching from egg, pepper pot. 55mm.	11.00
Chick, yellow, hatching from egg, salt cellar. 60mm.	11.00
Chicken, very plump, on circular base. 67mm.	7.00
Chick, hatching from egg. 72mm.	5.50
Cockerel, pepper pot. 71mm.	6.50
Crested Tit posy holder. 80mm long.	5.50
Duck ashtray, some colouring. 95mm long.	20.00
Duck, plump, pecking on circular base. 59mm.	15.00
Duck, ewer with handle. 130mm long.	7.50
Duck pepper pot. 77mm.	6.50
Ducks, 2 with coloured beaks and feet on oval stand. 185mm. (an enormous model).	40.00
Duckling, airing wings, comical. 69mm.	16.50
Duck, on circular base. 60mm.	14.50

Duck, circular base, some colouring.	
2 sizes: 95mm.	14.00
106mm.	16.00
Duckling with brown beak and feet,	
wings raised, beak upwards and	
open, on circular base. 85mm.	16.00
Duck posy bowl. 120mm long.	10.50
Eagle on rock, colour on beak and	
feet. 130mm.	17.00
Egg. 65mm upright.	3.00
Fledgling birds, 2 sitting on base	
sharing one open beak. Can be	
found coloured.(Grotesque).	
White.	8.50
Coloured.	33.50
Goldfinch on Rock. No. 859.	
105mm long.	16.00
Hen, brooding. 65mm long.	7.50
Hen and Cockerel on circular base.	
82mm.	14.00
Hens, two on circular base. 80mm.	14.00
Kingfisher. 60mm.	30.00
Owl, on plinth with verse. 115mm.	16.50
Owl on three books. 121mm.	25.00
Owl, long-eared, perched on rock.	
110mm.	18.50
Parakeet, fully coloured on plinth.	
215mm.	25.00
Parrot on vase. 78mm.	12.00
Pelican. 100mm.	17.50
Penguin, holding book, beak open.	
122mm. (Shelley).	125.00
Pigeon with puffed up chest,	
standing on ashtray base. 75mm.	15.00
Royston Crow. 67mm.	25.00
Stork, nesting beside chimney pot	
with baby in nest. 100mm.	23.00
Swan, head back. 72mm.	6.50
Swan trinket box and lid. 69mm.	7.00
Warbler on branch. 112mm.	24.00
Warbler on tree stump. 130mm.	26.00

Great War

Cossack, standing figure on	
rectangular base. 126mm.	82.50
Jack Ashore, boy sailor on round	
base, coloured face. 153mm.	75.00
Lion Battleship. 143mm long	70.00
Submarine, *E4*. 102mm long.	18.50
Renault Tank. 105mm long.	45.00
Bury St Edmunds Bomb. 80mm	14.00
Bugle. 70mm. (Willow Art).	19.50
Boot with puttee. 73mm. (Grafton).	22.00
Mess Pot. 40mm.	65.00
Military Cap ashtray, crest inside	
hat. 126mm long.	8.50

Peaked Cap. 60mm.	10.50
German spiked helmet, gilded	
strap. 55mm.	45.00
Pith Helmet. 55mm long.	35.00
Cenotaph, 147mm.	6.50
Dingwall War Memorial, not	
named. 125mm high,	
160mm long.	45.00
Folkestone *War Memorial*.	
138mm.	40.00
Hawick '1514' Memorial unveilled (sic)	
June 4th 1914. Rectangular upright	
plaque with Hawick War	
Memorial in relief. 145mm. Rare.	75.00
Llandudno War Memorial, not	
named. 183mm.	55.00
Margate War Memorial. 190mm.	55.00
Matlock War Memorial. 155mm.	100.00
Matlock-Bath War Memorial.	
150mm.	20.00
Matlock-Bath War Memorial.	
188mm. (Florentine).	75.00
Otley Churchyard, War Memorial	
Cross. 123mm.	75.00

Home/Nostalgic

Anvil on base. 58mm.	7.50
Armchair padded and three-legged.	
66mm.	12.50
Armchair, basket weave. 67mm.	6.50
Armchair, padded with blue forget-	
me-nots around back rest. 62mm.	14.50
Ornate French Chair. 84mm.	12.50
Armchair, upholstered. 85mm.	10.00
Basket with coloured fruit. 85mm.	
(Carlton).	20.00
Bell. 65mm.	3.00
Bucket with moulded rope handle.	
67mm.	3.00
Butter churn. 65mm.	4.00
Coal Scuttle. 70mm.	3.00
Cradle on rockers. 45mm.	8.00
Flat Iron, box style, possibly a	
money box. 65mm.	6.00
Fob Watch on horseshoe shaped	
trinket tray. 150mm.	18.50
Grandfather clock. 129mm.	9.00
Grandmother clock. 86mm.	5.00
Handbag. 84mm.	12.00
Hip Bath. 90mm long.	7.50
Jardiniere, 2-piece. 160mm.	6.00
Kettle on primus stone. 78mm.	10.50
Kitchen Funnel, silver rim. 64mm.	14.50
Mantle Clock. 94mm.	16.00
Photograph Frame, cardboard	
backing. 94mm. (Gemma).	10.00

Pillar Box, fat. 85mm.	14.00
Pillar Box, miniature. 58mm.	12.50
Pillar Box. 70mm.	10.00
Ring. 64mm dia.	20.00
Shaving Mug. 37mm.	6.50
Shaving Mug, ornate, pearl lustre. 55mm.	5.50
The above model has been found with a colour transfer of 'Mr Peggotty' with inscription.	
Shaving Mug, angular handle. 44mm.	6.50
Suitcase, closed 80mm long.	4.00
Suitcase, gilded straps. 57mm.	4.00
Trunk. 60mm long.	4.50
Umbrella. 38mm. (Arcadian).	14.50
Watering Can, oval shaped with no rose on spout. 87mm.	6.50
Watering Can. 77mm.	6.50
Water Bottle, rectangular. 66mm.	4.00

Comic/Novelty

Arriet (impressed on back). Bust of Pearly Queen. 93mm.	80.00
Apple Salt Pot. 50mm.	19.00
Baby in Bootee. 80mm long.	10.50
Baby in Coracle. 50mm.	14.50
Bean Pod, open. 125mm long.	20.00
Biscuit. Impressed *Huntley & Palmer* coloured biscuit. 53mm dia.	30.00
Biscuit. Impressed: *Huntley & Palmer* white, on base. 88mm high.	30.00
Clown playing Banjo, some colour. 120mm.	30.00
Jack in the Box with open lid. 92mm. (Florentine).	20.00
Suffragette Handbell, double faced, old/young woman. Coloured and inscribed: *Nature has endowed women with so much power that the law gives them very little. Dr. Johnson.* 107mm.	47.50
Man and woman, sitting, cuddling, in ornate alcove with balustrade. 54mm.	20.00
Man, with earphones and beer mug. 60mm.	17.50
Map of Isle of Thanet on ashtray base. 60mm.	110.00
Sailor, comic. *HMS Lion*. 85mm.	40.00
Tomato pepper pot on leaf base. 42mm.	13.00
Vaulting Horse, square looking bulldog with legs joined by 3 poles. 80mm long. Some colouring. (Saxony).	16.00

Womans Head on Turtle trinket box. 80mm long.	19.50
Womans Head tea pot, some colouring. 66mm.	14.50

Cartoon/Comedy Characters

Crested faced man white or fully coloured. 80mm.	30.00
Coloured.	40.00
Felix, standing Cat on oval base, no colouring. 87mm. (This is a really nice Felix.)	82.50
Mrs Gamp. 114mm.	44.50
Harry Lauder bust. 58mm.	22.00
Sunny Jim bust. 85mm.	40.00
Bust of Man with walrus moustache, button nose and large ears. Comical character – identity unknown! 80mm.	45.00

Alcohol

Barrel, upright. 65mm.	3.00
Thistle Ashtray with soda syphon, silvered top, beaker and 4-sidedbottle with red top. 76mm long.	18.50
Man in Bowler Hat, sitting, holding beer glass.	50.00
Bottle, inscribed: *Lacon's Fine Ales*. 90mm.	30.00
Champagne Bottle in Ice Bucket. 80mm.	11.00
Whiskey and Soda on horseshoe ashtray. 115mm long.	12.50

Sport/Pastimes

Boxer, fists up. (Florentine). 118mm.	170.00
Cricket Stumps & bat, spillholder. 105mm.	35.00
Footballer, with ball, no colouring. 130mm.	70.00
(Savoy range advertised a coloured version of this model)	
Football, leather. 55mm.	6.50
Golf Ball, pepper pot on circular base. 50mm dia.	10.00
Golf Caddie, holding golf bag. Hand in front of mouth as if laughing at players. 65mm.	75.00
Rugby Ball. 74mm long.	7.50
The Sprinter. Comic figure with cork-screw legs – wound up for action. 100mm.	47.50
Tennis Court Liner in form of a wheelbarrow. 90mm long.	20.00

Tennis Racquet with single ball attached. 135mm long.	17.50
Tennis Racquet, detailed strings. 118mm long.	16.00
Trophy. 100mm.	9.50
Artist's Easel on stand. 60mm.	1.50
Bridge Trumps. 60mm.	
Club.	4.00
Diamond.	4.00
Heart.	5.00
Spade.	4.00

Musical Instruments

Drum set with cymbals and drumsticks. 65mm. (Saxony).	10.50
Harp. 93mm.	10.00
Piano, grand. 63mm.	14.00
Piano, upright. 63mm.	12.00

Transport

Aeroplane with pilot, size varies, usually 100mm long. (Almost certainly German).	30.00
Bust of Bleriot, inscribed: *Messieur Bleriot. 1st man to cross the Channel in an Aeroplane. June 25th 1909.* 90mm.	85.00
Car with chauffeur. 85mm long.	30.00
Hot Air Balloon, square basket. 65mm.	40.00
Petrol can impressed: *Motor Spirit.* 67mm.	17.50
Sleigh, ornate. 105mm long.	19.00
Tram (Trolley Bus) 100mm long.	170.00
Charabanc 18 seater with driver. 125mm long.	33.00

Modern Equipment

Cash Register. 44mm. (Saxony).	16.00
Typewriter inscribed: *My little typewriter.* 44mm. (Saxony). Identical model to the above.	16.00
Gramophone, square. No horn. 55mm.	15.00
Gramophone with horn. 60mm.	20.00
Gramophone in cabinet. 91mm.	60.00

Hats

Boater, Straw. Unglazed. 107mm long.	8.50
Also found coloured inside, with white band.	12.00
Chauffeur's Large Peak Cap. 125mm long.	12.00
Fireman's Helmet. 63mm.	30.00

Fireman's Helmet vase. 48mm.	21.00
Knight's Helmet forming pin box and lid. 80mm.	16.00
Opera Hat. 36mm.	20.00
Top Hat, very wide brim. 60mm.	5.50
Top Hat, with antlers across brim. 65mm.	15.00
Top Hat, with umbrella across brim. 65mm.	16.00
Top Hat match striker, not glazed underneath. 42mm.	5.50
Top Hat match striker, inscribed: *The Rapid Patent Silk Hat Ironing Machine.* 45mm. (Obviously an advertising item)	19.50
Trilby. 96mm long.	22.00

Footwear

Dutch Sabot. 70mm long.	5.00
Boot with Spat. 80mm long.	7.50
Boot, ten open lace holes. 105mm long.	6.50
Boot, open, with pierced eyelets. 78mm long.	4.00
Oriental heeled shoe, curled up toe. 176mm long.	25.00
Riding Boot with Spur. 90mm.	13.00
Ladies heeled Shoe, frilled tongue. 107mm long.	7.50
Ladies Shoe, frilled edge. 113mm long.	9.50
Ladies Shoe, gilded heel and toe. 150mm long.	11.00
Ladies Shoe, frilled tongue and edge. 145mm long.	12.50
Ladies Boot, pressed eyelet holes. 2 sizes: 83mm long.	9.00
105mm long.	11.00
Lancashire Clog. 112mm long.	5.50
Sabot with turned up toe. 93mm long.	4.00
Shoe with side fastening. 80mm long.	9.00
Slipper wall pocket. 65mm wide.	4.50

Miniature Domestic

Bagware Vase. 41mm.	2.00
Candle Snuffer cone. 45mm.	3.50
Cheese Dish and cover. 64mm long.	6.50
Cheese Dish and cover in shape of horseshoe. 45mm.	17.50
Cheese Dish and cover, inscribed: *Cheshire Cheese.* 78mm long.	14.00
Cheese Dish and fixed cover. 64mm long.	6.50

Cheese Dish and cover.
85mm long.   6.50
Cheese Dish and cover, shield-
shaped base. 60mm.   7.50
Dressing table set comprising: two
scent bottles and stoppers, three
rouge pots and lids, ring tree, all
on rectangular tray.
155mm long.   Set 30.00
Horseshoe Ashtray. 68mm long.   3.00
Hot Water Jug with lid. 98mm.   8.50
Kettle and lid. 80mm.   7.50
Sheaf of Corn Jug. 79mm.   12.50
Teapot and lid. 75mm.   6.50
Miniature coffee set comprising:
coffee pot and lid, sugar basin,
milk jug, two cups and saucers on
rectangular tray. 155mm long.   25.00
Miniature tea set comprising: teapot
and lid, sugar basin, milk jug,
two cups and saucers on
rectangular or circular tray.   30.00
Bellows Box and lid. 120mm long.   9.50
Cake Slice pin box and lid.
138mm long.   14.00

Domestic
Funnel Candlesnuffer. (Savoy).   12.50
Funnel, silver rimmed. 64mm.   14.00

Miscellaneous
Gourd. 70mm.   8.50
Horseshoe. 66mm.   3.00
Loving Cup, 3 handled, with
lithophanes of King Edward,
Queen Alexandra, King George
or Queen Mary. 39mm.   40.00
Lithophane match holder/striker
with lithophane of King Edward
VII. 43mm.   30.00

ILLUSTRATED SECTION

In the following pages will be found illustrations from virtually every theme and all major factories.

Any similar item from another factory will be worth approximately the same as one shown here.

By using this easy-to-use section, one should be able to determine an idea of correct retail price.

All prices exclude VAT and are for pieces in perfect condition.

Index to Illustrations

rcelle Burns
0.00

Arcadian Queen
Mary £45.00

Swan Queen
Alexandra
£40.00

Swan
Edward VII
£47.50

Grafton Kitchener
£40.00

Shelley
Burns £30.00

Grafton Lloyd
George £55.00

lton Wordsworth
3.00

Willow Burns
£30.00

Shelley Kitchener
£40.00

Carlton Wordsworth
£17.50

H & L 112mm
Shakespeare £17.50

Podmore
Bunyan
£20.00

Willow Peeping
Tom £30.00

Arcadian Edward VII
in Trilby £57.50

H & L
Shakespeare
£17.50

Shelley Notre Dame
Candlestick £9.50

Shelley 12th
Century Chinese
Jar £11.00

Shelley Salamis
Lampshade £7.00

Shelley
Chester Roman
Urn £5.00

Arcadian
Lichfield Jug
£3.00

Arcadian
Chinese Vase
£4.00

Shelley Italian 15th
Century Vase £7.50

Carlton Etruscan Vase £4.00

Florentine Puzzle
Jug £5.50

Shelley Roman
Money Box £7.50

Shelley
Phoenician
Water Jar
£6.00

Foley
Exeter Vase
£4.00

Foley Vase
No. 25 £4.50

Shelley Greek
Salonika
Vase £17.50

Arcadian Pompeii
Lamp £5.00

Shelley Persian
Cafeterre £10.50

Shelley Arabian
Wine Vessel
£6.50

Arcadian
Ewer £2.50

Shelley
Kent Roman
Urn £5.00

Shelley Ewer
No. 41 £4.00

Gemma Puzzle
Tankard £10.50

Wilton Feathers Hotel
Ludlow £40.00

Unmarked Irish Cottage
Money Box £30.00

Willow Old Curiosity
Shop £150.00

Mosanic Pump Room
Harrogate £35.00

Mosanic Building £40.00

Carlton Lustre
Hastings Clock Tower
127mm £22.00

Unmarked Mow Cop Castle
Staffs £80.00

Savoy Exeter Cathedral £110.00

H & L Mason Croft
£110.00

Willow Ann Hathaway's Cottage
various sizes £16.00-£40.00

Carlton Rochester
Castle £47.50

Carlton Lustre Hastings
Castle Ruins £22.00

Willow Old Maids
Lee £47.50

Willow The Tan House
Stretton £125.00

Willow Burns Cottage £40.00

Willow Shakespeare's House
various sizes £16.00-£40.00

Willow Gretna Blacksmith's
Shop £40.00

Willow Pump Room
Harrogate £47.50

Grafton Tonbridge Castle £30.00

Willow Art
St. Benet's Abbey,
Norfolk Broads
£40.00

Willow Peterborough
Cathedral £30.00

Foreign Margate
Clock Tower £7.50

Podmore Lincoln
Cathedral west front
£30.00

Devonia Citadel Gateway
Plymouth £30.00

Carlton York Cathedral £28.00

Willow Solomon's Temple £40.00

Willow St Albans
Clock Tower
£45.00

Foreign Windmill
£14.50

Unmarked
The Globe
Swanage £16

Willow Canterbury
Cathedral west front £40.00

Carlton Wembley Stadium £95.00

Arcadian Martello
Tower £39.00

Arcadian Tom Tow
Oxford £25.00

arlton Hop
ln £30.00

Arcadian Marble Arch
various sizes £25.00-£30.50

Arcadian Launceston
Castle £80.00

Willow Burns'
Mausoleum
Dumfries £95.00

Willow Chesterfield Parish
Church £40.00

Cauldon Queen Victoria's
Dolls House various
sizes £30.00-£57.50

Arcadian
Westminster
Abbey west front
118mm £28.00

cadian Old London Bridge
mm £18.00

Arcadian Stowmarket
Memorial Gates £115.00

tish Manufacture
ck Cottage £9.00

Willow Nottingham Castle £40.00

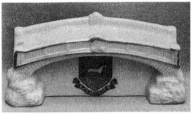

Corona Bridge with grassy banks £20.00

cadian St Nicholas Chapel
racombe £30.00

Willow Carillon
Tower £65.00

Willow Abbey Gate Bury
St Edmunds £75.00

ctis Needles & Lighthouse I of W £40.00

Grafton Smallest
House in Great
Britain £24.50

Arcadian First & Last House
with Annexe £40.00

Carlton Douglas Tower
of Refuge 73mm £37.50

Foreign Birmingham Town Hall £25.00

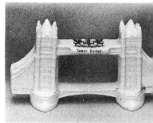

Alexandra Tower Bridge £30.50

Unmarked Mickelgate
Bar York £40.00

Willow John Bunyan's
Cottage £22.00

Willow Windsor Round
Tower £28.00

Savoy Cottage
£20.00

Arcadian Blackpool Wheel 78mm £16.00

Arcadian Temple Bar 95mm £34.50

Arcadian Windsor Cas
80mm £28.00

Grafton St Paul's Cathedral
145mm £25.00

Arcadian God's
Providence House £40.00

Arcadian Tower Bridge £34.50
Big Ben £34.50

Willow Christchurch Priory £55.

...dian Portsmouth
...hall £40.00

Arcadian First & Last House £12.00

Willow Hop Pole
Hotel £40.00

Carlton Rochester
Castle £47.50

...adian Aberystwyth
...versity £110.00

Arcadian Worcester Cathedral
127mm long £35.00

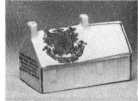

Savoy Burns Cottage £17.50

...lley
...stonbury
...£40.00

Willow Hampton Court Palace £30.00

Saxony Clock
Tower £14.50

Arcadian Highland Cottage £21.00

...w John Knox's
...se £40.00

Willow Town Hall
Wallingford £55.00

...w Bell Hotel
...m long £25.00

Carlton Wallace
Tower £82.50

Willow Saxon Church
Bradford-on-Avon £65.00

Willow Lincoln Cathedral
west front £30.00

Willow Laceby
Memorial £27.00

Willow Ruskin Memorial
Friars Crag £20.00

Arcadian King Alfred
Monument £30.00

Arcadian Margate Surf
Boat Memorial £20.00

Willow Arwenae
Monument £30

Arcadian Gibbet Cross
Hindhead £10.50

Arcadian Nelson's
Column £45.00

Carlton Celtic
Cross £12.00

Willow Flodden
Cross £20.00

Arcadian Caister Lifeb
Memorial £25.50

Grafton Sandbach Crosses £75.00

Devonia Drake
Statue £14.50

Willow Margate
Lifeboat Memorial
£20.00

Willow Bunyan
Memorial
£20.00

Willow St Alban £40.00

llow Burns'
air Dumfries
5.00

Arcadian Man in
Stocks £20.00

Willow Tam-
o'Shanter £47.50

Willow Mary Queen of Scots
Chair £6.50

rlton Biddenden
ids £40.00

Willow Daniel
Lambert £50.00

Willow Lincoln
Imp £8.50

Willow Devil
Looking over
Lincoln £19.50

Arcadian Bust of Judge
55mm £14.00

cadian Burns with Plough £75.00

Willow Souter
Johnny £47.50

Tuscan Wee
Willie Winkie
£29.50

Carlton Bust of
Harry Lauder
£26.00

llow Bunyan's Cushion
0.00

rlton John Waterson's
og £15.00

Willow Burns &
Highland Mary £30.00

Wilton Dick
Whittington £125.00

Foreign Devil
Looking over
Lincoln £14.50

Arcadian Lady Godiva
85mm £26.00

Gemma Frog
Prince £35.00

Arcadian
Trusty Servant
£110.00

Arcadian Henry V Cradle £40.00

Arcadian English Folklore
Bride beside Chest £55.00

Willow Sir Walter
Scott's Chair £7.50

Shelley Mother
Shipton £40.00

Arcadian Bust of
Suffragette £55.00

Carlton Davy
Lamp £35.00

Carlton Ulphus Horn £27.00

Grafton Box and Lid £4.00

Carlton Mary Queen of
Scot's Bed £82.50

Willow Archbishop's
Chair Canterbury
Cathedral £12.50

Shelley Ducking Stool £85.00

Tuscan Chertsey Bell & Base £20.00

Arcadian Wishing Well
Giants Causeway £56.

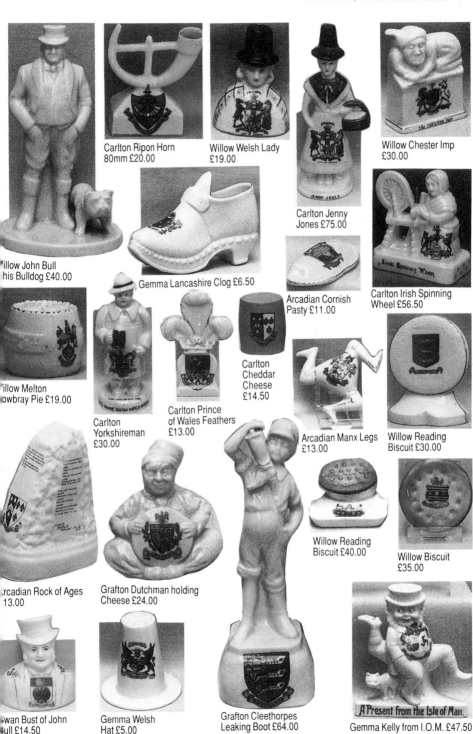

Carlton Ripon Horn
80mm £20.00

Willow Welsh Lady
£19.00

Willow Chester Imp
£30.00

Carlton Jenny
Jones £75.00

illow John Bull
his Bulldog £40.00

Gemma Lancashire Clog £6.50

Arcadian Cornish
Pasty £11.00

Carlton Irish Spinning
Wheel £56.50

illow Melton
owbray Pie £19.00

Carlton
Yorkshireman
£30.00

Carlton Prince
of Wales Feathers
£13.00

Carlton
Cheddar
Cheese
£14.50

Arcadian Manx Legs
£13.00

Willow Reading
Biscuit £30.00

rcadian Rock of Ages
13.00

Grafton Dutchman holding
Cheese £24.00

Willow Reading
Biscuit £40.00

Willow Biscuit
£35.00

wan Bust of John
ull £14.50

Gemma Welsh
Hat £5.00

Grafton Cleethorpes
Leaking Boot £64.00

A Present from the Isle of Man.

Gemma Kelly from I.O.M. £47.50

Foreign Lustre Girl
on Donkey £17.00

Unmarked
Fisherman
holding Rope
£16.00

Grafton Rowing Boat £9.50

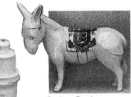

Carlton Donkey
'Gee up Neddy' £40.00

Willow Spurn
Lighthouse £19.50

Shelley Fishing
Basket £7.50

Sáxony Flamborough
Lighthouse £25.00

Foreign Bathing
Belle Pin Tray
£23.00

Foreign Mermaid on
Whelk Shell £22.00

Foreign Bathing Belle
on Shell £23.00

Arcadian Curved
Fish £6.50

Florentine Glad
Sea Waves £19.00

Foreign Yacht on
Rough Sea £10.50

Shelley Motor Boat on Waves £19.50

Victoria tall Yacht
£12.50

Arcadian Scallop Shell
Ink Well £10.50

Arcadian
Lighthouse £7.50

British Manufacture Ark £5.00

Foreign Girl in Canoe £19.50

Shelley Whelk
Shell £12.00

Foreign Bathing Belle
on Shell £23.00

Willow Bathing Machine £10.00

Foreign Bathing Belle
on Globe £14.00

Willow Lifeboat £12.50

Impero Skegness
Clock Tower £7.50

Swan (RNLI)
Fish Collection
Box £40.00

Arcadian Curved Fish £6.50

Unmarked Fish open mouth £12.50

Arcadian Whelk Shell £5.00

Grafton Whelk Shell £5.00

Grafton Girl on
Sand with Bucket
£82.50

Shelley Scallop Shell £8.00

Foreign Bathing Belle
on Turtle £25.50

Foreign Donkey £12.50

Arcadian
Kinnaird Head
Lighthouse £30.00

Foreign Coracle
(tied to stump) £5.50

British Manufacture
Lighthouse
5.50

Fish Basket
£4.00

Gemma Salt & Pepper Fish £5.00 each

Carlton Yacht in full sail £15.50

British Manufacture
Fish Vase £3.00

Foreign Bathing Belle
on Whelk Shell £23.00

Arcadian Blackpool
Tower £10.50

Savoy Crab Pin Tray £7.50

Saxony Corbiere
Lighthouse £11.50

Shelley
Lifeboatman
£75.00

Willow Crab £13.00

Arcadian Beachy
Head Lighthouse
£9.00

Florentine Houseboat £5.00

Foreign Bandstand £8.00

Arcadian Bust of
Lifeboatman 3 sizes
£15.50-£30.00

Robinson & Leadbeater
Scallop Shell Trinket
Dish £3.00

British Manufacture
Canoe £10.50

Arcadian Lifebelt
£10.50

Arcadian Plaice Ashtray £7.50

Carlton Motor Boat on Waves £22.50

low Straight Fish £5.00

Unmarked Fish open
mouth £3.00

Florentine
Bathing Chair
80mm £16.00

Willow
Lighthouse £5.00

marked Scallop
ell £5.50

Grafton Boat with Bird's
Head Figurehead £6.50

Victoria Whelk Shell £5.00

Arcadian
The Tower
Blackpool
£10.50

Arcadian
Bather in Tent £25.00

Foreign Bathing Belle
Trinket Dish £20.00

ledonia Longships
ghthouse £28.50

Foreign Crab Pin Tray
& Lid £10.50

Gemma Manx Legs
in Lifebelt £10.50

Podmore North
Foreland
Lighthouse £25.00

Unmarked Beachy
Head Lighthouse
£11.00

ton Lifebelt Ashtray £12.50

Foreign Wicker Fish Basket £4.00

Grafton Lifeboat £9.50

Saxony Sea Waves
£6.50

adian Lifeboat £12.50

British Manufacture
Curved Fish Vase £3.00

Gemma Fish Pin Cushion £5.00

Grafton Swain Studdy Series of Dogs
£25.00   £30.00   £30.00   £25.00

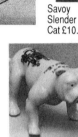

Savoy Slender Cat £10.

Arcadian Rabbit £8.00

British Manufacture Cat with Bow £14.00

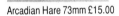

Arcadian Hare 73mm £15.00

Savoy Bonzo Dog £55.00

Florentine Two Spaniels in Top Hat £15.00

Arcadian Bulldog £17.50

Carlton Monkey holding Coconut £25.00

Grafton Monkey wearing Jacket £13.00

(Saxony) Pair of Bulldogs £23.00

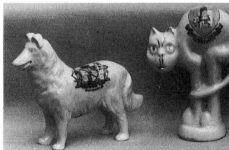

Willow Collie Dog £23.00

Unmarked Alice in Wonderland Cat £24

Carlton Black Cat on Horseshoe £27.50

Willow Fluffy Cat £13.00

Arcadian Elephant £30.00

Gemma Dog lying £24.50

Unmarked Camel lying down £22.00

Arcadian Upright Tortoise £55.00

reign Rabbit
Cat in
ots £20.00

Rita Sitting Dog £15.00

Arcadian Black Cat Radio
Operator £100.00

Arcadian Kangaroo £75.00

mma Shetland Pony £22.00

Grafton Terrapin £13.00

Arcadian
Long-neck
Cat £8.50

marked
g
auffeur
7.50

Grafton Sitting
Monkey £13.00

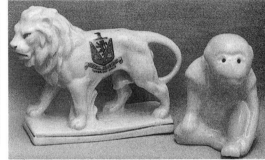

German Lion £8.00

Grafton Monkey £13.00

cadian Dog one
ar raised £9.00

Unmarked Cow £45.00

Grafton
Mouse
Candlesnuffer
£20.00

Foreign Lustre
Lion £8.00

Foreign Cow Head
Cream Jug £9.50

cadian Black
at on Armchair
mm £25.50

Black Cat on
Pouffe 80mm
£24.00

Carlton Black
Cat on Hatbox
£26.00

Black Cat on
Armchair £26.00

Grafton Squirrel £30.00

Unmarked Pointer Dog £20.00

Carlton Puppy on Mirror £33.50

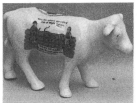

Grafton Calf £20.00

Arcadian Fox £40.00

Willow Hare £12.50

Unmarked Kneeling Camel £22.00

Foreign Pig in Cup £11.50

Arcadian Black Cat on Pillar Box £65.00

Savoy Lion £17.50

Carlton Rabbit £8.50

Arcadian Scottie Dog £13.00

Unmarked Dog lying £22.50

Grafton Seal £17.50

Carlton Scottie Dog £19.50

(Saxony) Cat on Drum £22.50

Arcadian Cheshire Cat £12.50

Foreign Elephant with White Hunter & Bearers £35.00

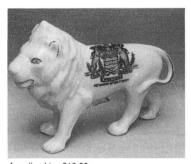

Arcadian Lion £16.00

Queens Stylised Lion £35.00

Willow Crouching Lion £23.00

Carlton Cat wearing To Hat £16.00

:adian Staffs
lldog £12.00

Carlton French
Bulldog £12.50

Saxony
Singing
Cat £22.50

Arcadian Sitting
Labrador Puppy
'Daddy won't buy me
a bow-wow' £17.50

Swan Pug Dog £18.50

emma Dog
Fly £20.00

Savoy Fluffy Rabbit £13.00

Willow Fluffy
Cat £16.00

Arcadian Sitting Pig £17.00

Devonia Cat
with Shield
£12.50

illow Mouse £20.00

Pearl Arms Elephant
Cream Jug £12.50

Grafton Labrador
Puppy £20.00

Arcadian Kneeling Piglet £11.00

Arcadian Sitting
Cat £11.00

Gemma Crouching
Cat £25.00

Willow Dachshund
£40.00

Willow Scottie
Dog wearing
Glengarry
£13.50

rcadian
abbit/Duck £25.50

Unmarked Plump
Kitten £16.00

Arcadian
Fawn £34.50

Carlton Pup
with raised
ear £14.00

arlton French
lldog £12.50
rafton Standing Bulldog £13.00

Willow Sitting
Bulldog £19.50

Arcadian Jockey on Racehorse
Pin Tray £75.00

Carlton Dog with Banjo £31.50

Willow upright Polar Bear
2 sizes £40.00, £47.50

Willow Jockey on Racehose £55.00

Gemma Standing
Cat £20.00

Carlton Pup
with raised
ear £9.00

Victoria
Begging
Spaniel £10.5

Grafton Snail £15.00

Foreign Donkey £17.00

Arcadian Black Dog
emerging from Kennel
56mm £15.00

Carlton Scottie Dogs wearing Tam o'Shante
£17.50   £11.00

Grafton Fluffy Rabbit £13.00

Leadbeater Art
Sitting Dog £16.50

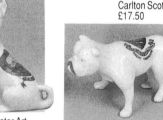

Corona Bulldog £15.00

Arcadian Bill Sykes
Dog 102mm £17.5

Grafton Frog £30.00   Willow Ram £43.00

Arcadian Crocodile £75.00

Arcadian Goat £40.00

Arcadian Tortoise £9.00   Carlton Terrapin £15.00

Gemma Pug £20.00

Unmarked Elephant
£17.00

Willow Art Elephant
£40.00

Willow Art Elephant
£17.00

Florentine Kneeling
Elephant £23.00

Florentine Seal balancing
Ball £17.50

adian Bactrian Camel £25.50

Arcadian Chimpanzee £22.00

Wilton Bonzo Dog £35.00 | Carlton Woodpecker £20.00

riffin Kneeling Camel
13.00

Gemma Egyptian Cat £24.00

Carlton Kitten
£12.00

Gemma Courtroom Pig £75.00

Florentine Toad £19.50

Unmarked Dog Coal Scuttle £18.50

Arcadian Teddy Bear £19.50

Willow Crouching Lion £23.00

Unmarked
lack Comical
at £16.00

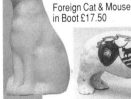

Foreign Cat & Mouse in Boot £17.50

Shelley Sitting Cat £27.00

Carlton Russian Bear £55.00

Unmarked Manx Cat £16.00

Florentine Pig £10.50

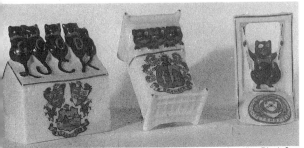

rcadian Black Cats
n House £150.00

Arcadian Black Cats in Bed £82.50

Arcadian Black Cats on a Swing £75.00

Grafton Cat
£30.00

Podmore Cat in Black Cap £40.00

Rita Duck Posy Holder £6.50

Unmarked Hatching Chick £5.50

Foreign Duckling Pepper Pot £15.50

Arcadian Parakeet £12.50

Arcadian swan £7.50

Grafton Plump Fledgling £25.00

Unmarked Crested Bird Posy Holder £5.50

Savoy Clara Cluck Candlesnuffer £30.00

Savoy Comical Duck £40.00

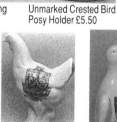

Grafton Swan Head under Wing £19.50

Saxony Seagull on Rock £19.50

Grafton Cockerel £19.50

Grafton Penguin £30.00

Arcadian Peacock on Ashtray Base £20.00

Carlton Comical Duck £40.00

Unmarked Duck £14.50

Unmarked Hatching Chick Cruet Set £11 each

Victoria Pelican Cream Jug £5.50

Arcadian Wise Owl £20.50

Arcadian Horned Owl £14.50

Arcadian Baby Owl £12.50

Carlton Turkey £40.00

Unmarked Comical Duckling £16.50

Arcadian Cock o'th' North £20.00

Grafton Duck Posy Bowl £40.00

Unmarked Duck outstretched wings £16.00

Carlton Duck £40.00

...gn Swan Posy Holder £4.00

Carlton Stork £30.00

Florentine Fledgling Bird Jug £5.50

Arcadian Swan £9.00

...y Duckling with ...tretched Wings Wasp on Beak ...00

Saxony Seagull £12.50

Arcadian Pelican £40.00

Milton Fluffy Chick £17.00

...on Gladeye £16.00

(Unmarked) Seagull on Rock £20.00

Unmarked Canary on Perch £10.50

Shelley Plump Goose £40.00

Savoy Comical Coloured Duckling £40.00

Podmore Hen £12.50

...dmore ...nguin £11.50

Arcadian Norwich Warbler with Whistle & Bubble Pipe £25.50

Willow Long-neck Goose £47.50

Unmarked Hen & Cockerel £14.00

Tourist Art Kiwi Bird £40.00

Savoy Bust of
Kitchener £40.00

Arcadian Bust of a
Sailor £34.50

Arcadian Tommy & his
Machine Gun £39.00

Arcadian Tommy wearing
Gas Mask £215.00

Willow Cheerio
Baby £30.00

Willow Monoplane £110.00

Willow
Airman
holding
Medal
£220.00

Carlton Vickers Tank £260.00

Corona Renault Tank £75.00

Arcadian Sailor
Hands on Hips
£65.00

Arcadian
Tommy in
Bayonet Attack
£135.00

Shelley Armoured Car £45.00

Willow Monoplane with
Roundels £110.00

Podmore Prince
of Wales £80.00

Arcadian Sailor
Vase £47.50

Grafton Bust of
Kitchener
£40.00

Grafton German Officer in Lifebelt
Matchholder & Striker £30.00

Shelley
Officer's Peak
Cap £10.50

Grafton 'German gun
captured by British' £40.00

Aynsley French
Soldier's Cap £45.00

th Cavell Memorials
xandra £16.00 / Arcadian £25.50

Carlton Soldier
in Flat Cap &
Puttees £75.00

Waterfall Hull
South African War
Memorial £24.00

Carlton Tunbridge
Wells War
Memorial £120.00

Willow
Florence
Nightingale
Statue £19.50

Arcadian Plum
Pudding Bomb
£80.00

Savoy
Cannon
Shell
£7.50

Arcadian
Anti-Zeppelin
Candlestick
£17.50

ens British Trench
ar Gun £47.50

Willow
Pickelhaube
£30.00

Wilton Folkestone
War Memorial 'Road
to Remembrance'
£47.50

ton British
nch
tar
.50

Unmarked
Llandudno War
Memorial £55.00

rentine Great Yarmouth
r Memorial £22.00

Willow Ilkeston War
Memorial £160.00

Carlton Edith Cavell
Memorial £23.00

Foreign
Matlock
Bath War
Memorial
various sizes
£11.00-£16.50

Carlton Field Gun with
Screen £20.00

Arcadian British
Soldier £95.00

Willow 'Brave
Defender' £47.50

Carlton Old Bill
£75.00

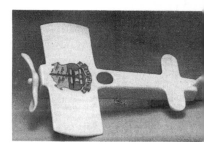

Grafton Monoplane £55.00

Carlton Bust of Sailor £35.00

Carlton Standing
Sailor £75.00

Arcadian British Aerial
Torpedo £30.00

Arcadian Despatch Rider £75.00

Unmarked
Mess Pot
£65.00

Arcadian
Standing
Sailor £55.00

Grafton Kitchener
£40.00

Shelley Bust of
Sir John French
£40.00

Arcadian Sailor
Winding Capstan
£110.00

Carlton Anti-Aircraft Motor £160.00

Savoy two-piece Machine Gun
on Tripod £145.00

Savoy Nurs
Cavell £22.

Shelley Marianne
£105.00

Shelley Bust of
John Jellicoe
£43.50

Carlton RNAS Armoured
Car £160.00

Willow Propeller £25.00

Arcadian Bury
St Edmunds
Bomb £11.00

Carlton
'British
16mm
Shell'
£17.00

Arcadian British Aerial
Bomb £40.00

Grafton Field Gun on Sledge
'French 75' £47.50

adian
mmer
£170.00

Carlton Standing
Nurse £82.50

Grafton Motor Ambulance
£55.00

ton Rolls Royce Armoured
£160.00

Arcadian
Standing
Nurse £75.00

Shelley Florence
Nightingale £125.00

Carlton E9 Submarine half
submerged £55.00

Savoy Ambulance £55.00

adian Bust of Territorial £43.00

Alexandra Tank with Inset Wheels £20.00 Arcadian
Cannon
Shell
£4.50

Carlton
Closed
Kitbag
£19.50

Arcadian
Stick Grenade
£85.00

Arcadian Super Zeppelin £30.00

Arcadian
Water Bottle
£17.50

ton
nitions
ker £125.00   Arcadian Monoplane £75.00   Grafton E9 Submarine £40.00

Grafton Tommy
'Over the Top' £145.00

Arcadian E5 Submarine £23.00

Grafton Desert Gun £75.00

Corona E4 Submarine £19.50

Willow Black Watch War Memorial £65.

Florentine Telescope £13.00

Arcadian Field Gun 140mm long £19.50
Carlton Forage Cap £17.50

Carlton HMS Humber £56.50

Carlton British Minesweeper £47.50

Arcadian Torpedo Boat Destroyer £25.00

Willow Ope Kitbag £19

Savoy E1 Submarine £40.00

Arcadian Observer Balloon £75.00

Carlton Floating Mine £55.00

Arcadian HMS Queen Elizabeth £30.0

Shelley Warship £19.50

Willow Field Gun with Screen £19.00

Carlton Zeppelin £55.00
Pearl Arms Officer's Peak Cap £11.00

Savoy Donner Blitzen Tank £30.00

Arcadian Field Glasses £16.00

Arcadian Field Gun 150mm long £23.00

Carlton Officer's Peaked Cap £22.50

Arcadian Tommy's Hut £47.5

...adian Nurse & Wounded
...my £125.00

Arcadian Russian Cossack
on Horseback £185.00

Willow
Standing
Sailor £55.00

Carlton Radio Operator
£95.00

Grafton Motor Tractor
£170.00

Willow Standing
Nurse £40.00

...fton The Bomb Thrower £145.00

Grafton
Boot with
Puttee
£22.00

Arcadian
Sentry in Box
£82.50

Carlton Map of Blighty £65.00

Arcadian
Sheringham
Bomb £82.50

...ton Bi-plane £145.00

Willow
Sailorboy £55.00

Carlton Scottish
Soldier £135.00

Savoy Monoplane £60.00

Carlton Old Bill
coloured
£125.00

...adian Armoured Car £40.00

Carlton
Capstan
£11.50

Aynsley Hand
Grenade with
Flames £40.00

Grafton 'British
Territorial Bulldog'
£160.00

Grafton Squatting
Sailor with
Submarine £110.00

Grafton Mills Hand
Grenade with
Pin £25.00

Arcadian
Anti-Aircraft
Shell £20.00

Corona Warship £20.00

Arcadian British Airship £82.50

Arcadian
Canister
Bomb £17.50

Arcadian Revolver £47.

Savoy
Cannon
Shell 'Iron
Rations for
Fritz'
110mm £14.00

Corona
Cannon
Shell £5.00

Grafton HMS Dreadnought £75.00

Savoy Bell Tent £16.00

Carlton HMHS Anglia £75.00

Arcadian
Trench
Dagger
£47.50

Savoy HMS Lion £75.00

Willow Liner Converted to
Troop Ship £95.00

Alexandra RAF
War Memorial
£85.00

Arcadian
Pith Helmet
£25.50

Carlton Capstar
£11.50

Carlton E9 Submarine £40.00

Arcadian
Mills Hand
Grenade
£19.50

Carlton Shrapnel Villa £43.00

Savoy HMS Queen Elizabeth £75.00

Arcadian Clip of
Bullets £17.50

Alexandra Torpedo £50.00

Corona British Airship on oval base £35.00

...dian Howitzer
...us sizes £19.50-£23.00

Shelley Anti-Zeppelin
Candlestick £45.00

Carlton Machine Gun £30.00 / Arcadian Sandbag £22.50

...dian Tank with Trailing Wheels £30.00

Arcadian
Anti-Zeppelin
Candleholder
£17.50

Aynsley Bell Tent
£25.00

Carlton Red Cross Van £35.00

...dian
...rush
...ade
...00

Willow British
Tank £20.00

Arcadian Gurkha
Knife £20.00

Carlton Kitchen Range
£16.00

Savoy Howitzer £30.00

Pearl Arms
Officer's
Peaked
Cap £11.00

Gemma Despatch
Rider's Cap &
Goggles £25.00

Willow Florence
Nightingale
Memorial £20.00

Arcadian Dover
War Memorial
£75.00

Carlton Scarborough Lighthouse
Damaged by Bomb £65.00

...dian
...otaph
...0

Devonia Plymouth
War Memorial £125.00

Willow Bugle
£12.50

Military Drum
£10.50

Florentine Dog in
Bandages £23.00

...by French
...antryman's
...£30.00

Arcadian Trench
Mortar £17.50

Carlton German Incendiary Bomb £25.00

Carlton HMS Tiger £75.00

Grafton HMS Iron Duke £85.00

Shelley 'German mine washed up on the east coast' £55.00

Shelley Fireplace inscribed 'Keep the home fires burning' £20.50

Aynsley Horse's Hoof Vase £20.00

Corona Bell Tent £16.50

Shelley Soldier Playing Concertina outside Tent £82.50

Corona Peace Clock £56.50

Grafton Boot with Puttee £22.00

Arcadian Anzacs Hat £16.00

Shelley Field Glasses £20.00

Clifton Red Cross Van £30.00

Savoy French Trench Helm £40.00

Carlton HMS Australia £75.00

Willow Bandsman's Drum £10.50

Arcadian Glengarry £19.5

Arcadian Red Cross Van £30.00

Grafton Colonial Hat £19.00

Carlton Tank Bank HMLS £55.00

Carlton Glengarry £16.00

Unmarked Pith Helmet £35.00

Savoy Colonial Hat £16.00

Willow Pine Cone £4.00

Queens Beehive
on Table £7.50

Willow Treetrunk
Hat Pin Holder £10.50

Bamboo
Hat Pin
Holder
£10.50

Carlton Thistle
Hatpin Holder £9.00

Arcadian Pine
Cone curved
£4.00

Arcadian Beehive
on Table £11.00

Arcadian
Acorn £7.50

Savoy
Acorn £7.50

Arcadian
Circular
Haystack £6.50

Foreign Stile & Milestone £6.50

Home/Nostalgic

Arcadian Anvil on
Treetrunk base £6.50

Carlton Sofa £19.50

Arcadian Fireplace £15.00

Shelley Garden Roller £17.00

Arcadian
Watchman's
Lantern £6.50

Gemma Coal
Scuttle £4.50

Botolph Police
Lamp £5.50

Arcadian Alarm
Clock £19.50

Unmarked Fob Watch on
Horseshoe Trinket Dish £18.50

Coronet Sofa £10.50

Carlton Closed
Book £6.50

Savoy Funnel
Candlesnuffer
£12.50

Gemma Home
Bank £5.50

Pillar Boxes
Arcadian
£12.00

Willow
£17.50

Florentine
£12.50

Foreign Mantle Clock £10.00

Carlton Coal
Hod £4.00

Keltic Coal
Bucket £5.00

Carlton
Grandfather
Clock 105mm
£10.50

Arcadian Pair
of Bellows
£11.50

Foreign Pair of
Bellows £6.50

Carlton Spinning
Wheel £20.00

Nautilus Dustpan £14.0

Savoy
Yawning
Child
Candlesnuffer
£20.00

Willow Oil Lamp £5.50

Foreign Coal Scuttle
£4.50

Corona
Cigarette
Case £13.00

Grafton Handbell
£7.00

Gemma Jardiniere
& base £7.50

Corona Tobacco Pouch £9.50

Shelley Pair of
Bellows £14.50

Foley Village Pump
£11.00

Nautilus
Rope Handled
Bucket £8.50

Arcadian Dog
Kennel £6.50

Arcadian
Three-Legged
Stool £7.50

Carlton Square
Sundial £7.50

Tuscan Loaf of
Bread £20.00

Willow Garden
Watering Can £8.50

Arcadian Fireplace £12.50

Brit. Man.
Grandfather
Clock £11.00

Warwick
Sundial
£5.50

Brit. Man.
Grandfather
Clock £11.00

Foreign
Grandmot
Clock £5.5

t. Man. Closed
itcase £4.00

Cyclone
Suitcase £4.00

Foreign Open Carpet Bag
£5.00

Carlton Valise
£4.00

Shelley Open
Valise £7.50

elley Fob Watch
lder £40.00

Florentine Sofa £10.50

Grafton Baby's
Cradle £12.00

Corona Sloping
Desk Top £8.50

Cyclone Baby in the
Bath £11.50

Willow Bean Pod £16.00

Florentine Miniature
Shaving Mug £6.50

Carlton Bed
Warming Pan
£13.00

Corona Hip Bath £10.50

cadian Baby's Wicker
adle £10.00

Botolph Bunch of
Keys £22.00

Carlton Ashtray £23.00

Arcadian Ball
Match-holder
& Striker
with Army
Camp transfer
£13.00

Shelley
Grandfather
Clock £16.00

Willow Circular
Sundial £10.50

afton Village Pump & Trough £10.50

Willow Cauldron
£3.00

Gemma Coal
Scuttle £4.50

Foreign Fireplace £10.00

Shelley Box of Matches £23.00　Florentine Old Armchair £7.50

Carlton Rocking Chair £19.50

Gemma Wheelbarrow £6.50

Arcadian Dressing Table Mirror £14.50

Carlton Shaped Clock £16.00

Arcadian Coal Scuttle £4.00

Corona Alarm Clock £30.00

Carlton Circular Sundial £13.00

Shelley Lantern £14.50

Carlton Saucepan £7.50　Arcadian Saucepan & Lid £9.00

Gemma Coal Scuttle £4.50

Foreign Clock £10.50

Coronet Milk Churn & Lid £5.00

Grafton Ornate Basket £3.00

Podmore Kitchen Range £16.00

Victoria Baby's Wicker Cradle £14.0

Willow Wicker Basket £3.50　Wicker Armchair £6.50

Foreign Grandmother Clock £5.50　Crown Sundial £5.50　Carlton Time Glass £10.00

Unmarked Primus Stove £10.50

Florentine Flat Iron £12.50

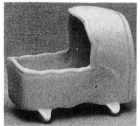

Grafton Baby's Rocking Cradle £12.00 .

Shelley Wheelbarrow £14.50　Savoy Watering Can £10.50

Shelley Handbag £12.50

Savoy Fat
Policeman £60.00

Grafton Boy swimming £75.00

Grafton Baby £95.00

Coronet Man
Standing in
Pillory £17.00

Arcadian Comic Scotsman on
Thistle Ashtray £30.00

Carlton Black Girl
in Bath £56.50

Arcadian Couple
in Armchair
£95.00

Wilton Down
& Out Man £75.00

Unmarked Baby in
Coracle £14.50

Arcadian Black Boy &
Girl on Log £82.50

Arcadian Harry Lauder
£30.00

Carmen Bust of a
Clown £25.00

Arcadian
Petrol Pump
Attendant
£47.50

Arcadian Flapper
Hatching from
Egg £30.00

Brit. Man. Pierrot
playing Banjo £30.00

Arcadian Jolly
Policeman
directing traffic
£34.50

Arcadian Negro
Minstrel £30.00

Carlton Jester Asleep/Jester Awake £25.00

Florentine
Pierrot £35.00

Arcadian Double-faced
Jester £11.50

Arcadian Bust of
Negro £30.00

Willow Art 'Sunny Jim' Comical Bust £95.00

Florentine Boy on Scooter £20.00

Willow Black Boys in 'Box of chocolates' £75.00

Florentine Head with Twin Vases £7.50

Unmarked Nurse holding Baby Candlesnuffer £75.00

Savoy Gargoyle £10.50

Arcadian Baby Girl by Hip Bath £85.00

Arcadian Girl & Boy on Log £82.50

Grafton Knave Candlesnuffer £55.00

Carlton Scotch Fishergirl £43.50

Grafton Ladies in a Punt £55.00

Swan Plump Baby Handbe £47.50

Arcadian Double-faced Suffragette £55.00

Arcadian Black Boy Eating Egg £95.00

Unmarked Housekeeper £40.00

Cyclone Jack-in-the-Box £20.00

Grafton General Kruger Teapot £82.50

Arcadian Three Wise Monkeys on a Wall £13.00

Carlton Boy Blowing Bubble £75.00

Arcadian Black Boy in Bath £105.00

Carlton Bust of Punch £35.00

cadian Man in the
un £47.50

Arcadian
Couple in
Bed £75.00

Carlton Thumbs Up
Billiken £11.00

Arcadian Billiken
£6.50

English Make
Billiken
£6.50

Grafton
Billiken
£5.50

rcadian Policeman
recting traffic £34.50

Foreign Souter
Johnny £30.00

Arcadian Fat
Lady on
Scales £40.00

Willow Cheerio
Baby £30.00

Arcadian Black
Boy Hatching
from Egg
£40.00

Carlton Bust of
Judge £30.00

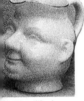

rit. Man. Man's
ead Jug £12.00

Foreign Black Momma
Candlestick £24.50

Carlton Felix Walking
on Sofa £82.50

Willow
Dr. Beetle
£125.00

Arcadian Clown
£47.50

Coronet Man in
Stocks £25.00

& L Dr. Beetle &
unny Jim £65.00

Carlton Jackie Coogan
Inkwell £47.50

Florentine Ally
Sloper £25.00

Unmarked Felix
the Cat £82.50

Arcadian Ally Sloper
£40.00

Podmore Mr. Pussy Foot £30.00

Arcadian Beaker inscribed 'Whoever ken the worth o' water' £7.50

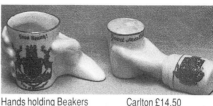

Hands holding Beakers Willow £6.50

Carlton £14.50

Podmore Toby Jug £12.50

Arcadian Scotch and Soda Pin Tray £12.50

Willow Beer Bottle & Tankard, horseshoe base £12.50

Arcadian Beaker inscribed 'They speak o' my drinkin' £7.50

Shelley Barrel on Stand £9.00

Arcadian Toby Jug various sizes £8.50-£12.50

Shelley Scotch Bottle £8.50

Grafton Champagne Bottle £10.00

Willow Scotch Bottle £7.50

Carlton Drinker with Barrel £55.00

Arcadian Man hanging on Beaker £47.50

Arcadian Drunk leaning on Statue £125.00

Arcadian Monk with Beer Glass various sizes £12.50-£19.50

Man Clinging to Scotch Bottle £40.00

Willow Closed Barrel £3.00

Shelley Open Barrel £7.50

Queens Man with head in Barrel £30.00

Unmarked Champagne in Bucket £11.00

Arcadian Soda Syphon £11.50

Arcadian Tennis Racquet £10.50

Florentine Boxing Glove £30.00

Carlton Dice Pin Box & Lid £26.00

Clifton Football £6.50

Unmarked Heart Trump Marker £5.00

Brit. Man. Canoe £10.50

Unmarked Rugby Ball £7.50

Panorama Footballer £110.00

Arcadian Caddie with Golf Clubs £55.00

Shelley Bag of Golf Clubs £75.00

Swan Cricket Bag £12.50

Willow Club Trump Marker £4.00

Grafton Golfer 'The Colonel' £38.50

Arcadian Golfer on Golf Ball £40.00

Arcadian Golf Club Head £17.00

Norfolk Cricket Cap £45.00

Unmarked Spade Trump Marker £4.00

Grafton Tennis Player Suzanne Lenglen £85.00

Wilton Pawn Chess Piece £24.00

Corona Bishop Chess Piece £20.00

Arcadian Castle Chess Piece £6.50

Carlton Jockey on Horse coloured silk £110.00

Arcadian Cricket Bat £75.00

Carlton Jockey coloured £110.00

Unmarked Diamond Trump Marker £4.00

Shelley Golf Ball £11.00

Willow Caddie with Golf Bag £125.00

Florentine Tall Yacht £12.50

Porcelle Curling Stone £14.50

Arcadian Golf Ball £7.50

Carlton Jockey on Horse £110.00

Victoria Upright Piano open lid £13.00

Willow Bagpipes £20.00

Dainty Ware
Tambourine £6.50

Shelley Upright Piano £20.0

Unmarked
Drum &
Cymbal £10.50

Florentine Grand
Piano £15.00

Arcadian Harp
£10.50

Queens Banjo
£12.50

Foreign Guitar
£14.50

Corona Harp
£6.50

Savoy
Banjo
£12.50

Arcadian
Double Bass
£75.00

Foreign Grand Piano £12.50

Pearl Arms
Bugle £19.50

Carlton Upright Piano
£20.00

Willow Lute
£35.00

Aynsley Drum
£30.00

Arcadian
Guitar £14.50

Arcadian Upright Piano
closed lid £16.00

Arcadian Motor Spirit Can £16.00

cadian 18-seater Charabanc £40.00

Carlton Open Sports Car £40.00

arlton Motor Cycle & decar £75.00

Caledonia Open 4-seater Tourer £40.00

Foreign Open Top Car £13.00

illow Truck of 'Sand the kiddies' £65.00

Florentine Charabanc with Driver £33.00

Caledonia Open 4-Seater Tourer £40.00

Carlton Locomotive £115.00

reign Open Tourer th Driver £16.00

Limoges Open Car £15.00

Florentine Boy on Scooter £20.00

Grafton Rowing Boat £9.50

Carlton Motor Scooter £47.50

Carlton Luggage Trolley 75mm £40.00

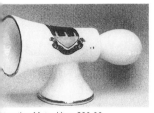

orentine Motor Horn £20.00

Florentine Saloon Car £40.00

helley Paddle Steamer £95.00

Carlton Saloon Car £65.00

Foreign Coronation Coach Inkwell £27.50

Willow Box
Gramophone with Horn
£25.00

Carlton Radio
Operator £95.00

Podmore Box Gramophones with Horns £20.00

Willow Radio
Horn £25.00

Carlton Box Gramophone
with Dog 'HMV' £70.00

Florentine Hexagonal
Gramophone with
Horn £40.00

Corona Box
Gramophone £15.00

Carlton Stick
Telephone
£23.00

Carlton Treadle
Sewing Machine
£24.00

Carlton
Gramophone
Cabinet £75.00

Arcadian Folding
Camera £40.00

Corona Gas
Stove £10.00

Willow Radio
Horn £25.00

Gemma Cash
Register £16.00

Victoria Radio
Horn £18.00

Carlton Cash Register
£20.00

Foreign Treadle Sewing
Machine £17.50

Arcadian Boy Scouts Hat £16.00

Arcadian Top Hat
£5.50

Carlton Crown
£25.00

Arcadian Welsh Hat with
inscription 52mm £8.50

Carlton Forage Cap £17.50

Gemma Bowler
Hat £20.00

Wilton Welsh Hat £10.50

Savoy Balmoral Bonnet
£22.00

Foreign Top Hat with
Umbrella £12.50

Florentine Welsh Hat £5.00

Shelley Trilby Hat £40.00

Gemma Fireman's
Helmet £40.00

Unmarked Straw Boater £8.50

Savoy Colonial Hat
£16.00

Willow Crown
£25.00

Shelley Pat's Hat
& Dudeen £17.00

Gemma Welsh Hat
£5.00

Arcadian Luton
Boater £17.50

Arcadian Top Hat £5.50 / Grafton Pork Pie Hat £30.00

Arcadian Riding Boot
73mm £16.00

Unmarked Lady's
High Boot £9.00

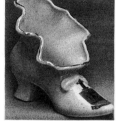

Unmarked Ladies
Frilled Shoe £12.50

Foreign Boot £6.50

Florentine Ladies 18th
Century Shoe £7.50

Grafton Oriental
Shoe £6.50

Grafton
Boot
with
Puttee
£22.00

Willow Lady's Shoe £10.50 / Foreign Open Shoe £6.50

Unmarked Ladies Frilled Shoe £9.50

Corona Lancashire
Clog £6.50

Gemma Dutch
Sabot £4.00

Florentine Baby's
Boottee £20.00

Unmarked Open Boot £6.50

Shelley
Leather
Highboot
£16.00

Arcadian Hob-nail Boot
£5.00

Arcadian Slipper Wall Pocket £7.50

Foreign Dutch Sabot with
Lobster in relief £7.50

Foreign Open Shoe £6.50

Arcadian Lancashire
Clog £5.50

Carlton Lustre Lancash
Clog £7.50

Foreign Ornate Ladies
High-heeled Shoe £10.50

Crown John Waterman's Clog £18.50

Willow Lady's Shoe blue bow £13.

yclone Teapot £7.50

Victoria Teapot £7.50

Corona Coffee
Pot & Lid £7.50

Florentine Ball
Teapot & Lid £7.50

oreign Miniature
having Mug £5.50

Gemma
Candlestick
£3.00

Arcadian
shaped £4.00

Foreign
Beaker
£2.50

Carlton Teapot & Lid £16.00

emma Toast Rack
7.50

Carlton
Pepper Pot £3.00

Carlton
Measuring Jug
£6.50

Arcadian Puzzle
Teapot £10.50

Gemma Ring Tree
Candleholder £8.00

illow Cream Jug
.50

Carlton 'Hair Pins'
Box & Lid £7.50

Nautilus Teapot
£11.00

Gemma Column Candlesticks
£3.00 each

helley Shaped
wer £5.00

Gemma Miniature
Shaving Mug £5.50

Savoy Square Coffee
Pot & Lid £10.50

Foreign Hot Water
Jug £8.50

Cups & Saucers each £3.50

Foreign Circular
Candlestick £3.00

Grafton Hereford
Kettle £10.50

Gemma Inkwell
& Lid £12.50

Carlton Kettle & Lid
£18.00

Jugs Arcadian £2.50 each

Corona Kettle £10.00

Carlton Swedish
Kettle £4.00

Arcadian Teapot & Lid £7.50

Trinket Boxes
Arcadian
Horseshoe-shaped
£4.00

Carlton
Heart-shaped
£5.00

Brit. Man. Clover
Dish £4.50

Gemma Coffee
Pot £5.50

Arcadian
Hand Bell
£7.50

Arcadian
Tankard
overflowing
£8.50

Cyclone Coffee Pot £7.5

Brit. Man.
Column
Candlestick
£3.00

Foley Ornate Teapot
& Lid £16.00

Gemma Stilton Cheese Dish
& Lid £7.50

Willow
Horseshoe
Trinket Box &
Lid £7.50

Willow Miniature
Cheese Dish & L
£7.50

Carlton Cup & Saucer £3.50

Arcadian Match-holder & Striker £5.50

Foreign Ashtray £6.50

Arcadian Ring Tree £8.00

Carlton 'Hair Tidy' & Lid £7.50

Grafton Cup & Saucer £3.50

Willow Horseshoe Match-holder & Ashtray £8.50

Arcadian Fluted Beaker £5.50

Foreign Souvenir ware Egg Cups £5.00

Victoria Lucky White Heather Mustard Pot & Lid £8.50

Carlton Lustre Vase £8.50

Willow Horseshoe Pin Tray £5.50

Willow Club-shaped Dish £6.50

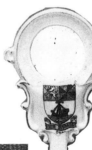

Willow Mirror £20.00

Foreign Butterfly Vase £6.00

Arcadian Heart-shaped Dish £4.00

Willow 'Cards' Box & Lid £13.00

Arcadian 'Hair Pins' Box & Lid £5.50

The Concise Encyclopaedia and Price Guide to Goss China

Nicholas Pine

Now in its sixth edition, this latest guide has much fresh information including numerous new pieces, many announced for the first time. A well illustrated domestic section clarifies this area of the factory's wares and improved layout and explanations make this chapter easier to understand and pieces easier to locate.

The dimensions and inscription for every piece are given and the Historic Models and Special Shapes section contains the correct matching arms for each model - all separately priced. The very latest revised prices are given right through the book which is also a complete descriptive listing of every piece of Goss ever produced.

The guide is the standard work on Goss china and is used by collectors, dealers and auctioneers worldwide.

The prices given form the base prices of pieces to which the values for particular arms or decorations should be added.

The work is well illustrated and is superbly bound in hardcover with colour jacket. It is a pair with **The Price Guide to Crested China** and the sequel to **The Price Guide to Arms and Decorations on Goss China** by the same author.

The major features of the Concise Encyclopaedia and Price Guide to Goss China include:

- Every chapter revised and updated incorporating thousands of detail amendments to previous editions.
- 1300 illustrations - including both common and rare items.
- Every model illustrated - even the rare Haamoga Amaui from Tonga and the newly discovered Letchworth Roman Cinerary Urn.
- All pieces designated into First, Second and Third periods.
- The original inscription on every piece given.
- Every correct matching arms recorded and priced.

- Dimensions given for each piece and variation.
- Over 2500 pieces listed.
- A complete chapter on factory marks with 40 illustrations encompassing every known mark - with dates.
- An informative history of WH Goss and Goss China and many notes for collectors.
- Additional chapters on Goss Postcards, Goss Cabinets, The Goss Records and The League of Goss Collectors.

215mm x 155mm. 1300+ illustrations. 408 pages. Casebound. £19.95

The Price Guide to Arms and Decorations on Goss China

Nicholas Pine

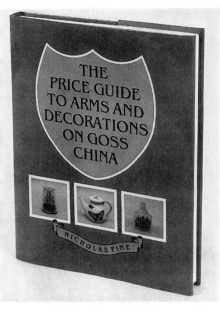

After ten years of research, Nicholas Pine and Editor Norman Pratten have produced a complete listing of all known Goss arms and decorations in a magnificent 320 page, large format Hardback book with full colour jacket.

The book provides a unique and comprehensive listing, with values, of the 10,000 plus coats of arms and decorations which adorned Goss China during its period of production spanning 80 years.

Also included are chapters on the Manufacture and Decoration of Goss China and a History of W H Goss and his factory.

The largest section, geographical place names, now contains 2,200 entries, only *one-third* of the number contained in the first (green cover) book of Arms and Decorations. The majority of those listed in this volume are now known *not* to be Goss First, Second or Third Period, but instead were introduced by Arkinstall & Son (Arcadian) when they took over the works in 1929. All these Arcadian place names, 4,400 in all, are listed in a special section of the new book so that collectors for the first time can ascertain the arms used only by the Goss factory.

The book comprises themes used by the factory including: Chapters on all Civic arms in the British Isles and overseas; Royal, Nobility and Personal; Educational, Medical and Ecclesiastical; Commemoratives and Exhibitions; Transfer Printed Pictorial Views and Enamelled Illustrations; Regimental Badges and Naval Crests; Flora and Fauna; Armour, Flags and Masonic, and late decorations known as Third Period.

The Guide contains over 2,000 illustrations, and every piece listed is priced or valued, sub-divided into over 100 easy-to-use sections.

The book has been designed for use in conjunction with **The Concise Encyclopaedia and Price Guide to Goss China** by the same author. Collectors and dealers who possess a copy of the price guide are strongly advised to acquire this new book so that accurate up-to-date values may be obtained for each piece, for, as often as not, the decoration on a particular piece is worth much more than the piece itself.

260mm x 215mm. 320 pages. 2000 illustrations. £19.95

William Henry Goss

*The story of the Staffordshire family of Potters
who invented Heraldic Porcelain.*
Lynda & Nicholas Pine

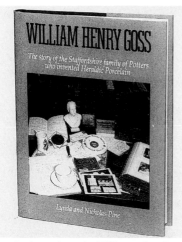

In this first ever biography of the man who is credited with inventing heraldic porcelain and his family who worked with him and at times against him, the authors tell the story of Goss china in fascinating detail.

From a promising start as a literary student, William Henry Goss used the important contacts he made in London to carve himself a career in the pottery industry in Stoke-on-Trent. At first he produced a limited, expensive range of Parian busts and figurines, but with the entry of his sons, Adolphus and later Victor and Huntley into the business, production switched to the small white models bearing colourful coats of arms for which the firm became famous.

The authors recount the stories of Godfrey, who ran away to New Jersey with a factory paintress, began a pottery there and founded the American branch of the family; the surprising Falkland Islands connection, still continuing today; why William refused to speak to his wife for the last twenty years of his life and how he came to have four homes all at the same time.

The history of the three periods of production is complemented by fascinating chapters on how the porcelain was both manufactured and sold through virtually every town in the country.

The book is illustrated with over 350 photographs and maps, includes much material not previously published and comprehensive family trees.

As the story unfolds you can discover:

- About the three periods of Goss manufacture and how the trade developed leading eventually to mass popularity nationwide.
- The amazing Falkland Islands connection, how Port Stanley and the Upland Goose Hotel came to be so-named and the exciting story of how the Goss family came to emigrate to those barren islands - and the dreadful fate that befell them.
- Why youngest daughter Florence married a bewiskered Bostonian millionaire older than her father.
- The truth about the rumour that second son Godfrey got a factory girl 'into trouble' and was banished to America. Why did Godfrey emigrate to America? and did he start a US Goss factory?

- The beginnings of William's potting career. Why did he decide to become a potter?
- How the romantic young William became an obstinate and pedantic father and eventually a near recluse.
- Why William did not speak to his wife for the last 20 years of his life - and how he came to have four homes all at the same time.
- His amazing generosity towards his friends and workforce and his unbelievable meanness and cruelty towards his wife and children.
- How William viewed his two sons Adolphus and Victor as rivals.
- Who *really* invented heraldic porcelain and how it was manufactured and marketed.

260mm x 217mm 350 Illustrations 5 Family Trees 256 pages. Bibliography and Glossary.
Casebound. £19.95

Crested China

Sandy Andrews

This title, first published in 1980, is the first and only serious and comprehensive work attempted on this subject - although written in a readable lighthearted style.

A large, lavish production with hard cover and coloured dust jacket, it contains 304 pages. Over 750 illustrations - 90 in full colour - are included, depicting over 1000 pieces from all factories and showing items from every possible theme with special emphasis on animals, buildings and Great War crested china.

The book is not a price guide, although indications of rare items are given, but a lasting, profusely illustrated reference work which is recommended to all crested china enthusiasts.

303mm x 220mm. 304 pages. Cased. 753 illustrations. £19.95

Available from bookshops everywhere or by post direct from Milestone Publications. Descriptive leaflets on this and all other titles connected with Goss and crested china are sent on request.

Goss & Crested China Ltd. are the leading dealers in Heraldic China.

We have been buying and selling for over 20 years and our experienced staff led by Lynda and Nicholas Pine will be able to answer your questions and assist you whether you are a novice or an experienced collector.

A constantly changing attractively priced stock of some 5,000 pieces may be viewed at the Goss & Crested China Centre in Horndean, including Goss cottages, fonts, crosses, shoes, lighthouses, models etc. and the full range of crested ware including military, animals, buildings etc. covering all the other manufacturers.

Visitors are welcome to call during business hours of 9.00 - 5.30 any day except Sunday. Those travelling long distances are advised to telephone in advance so that they may be sure of receiving personal attention upon arrival, but this is not essential.

Most of our business is by mail order and we publish *Goss & Crested China,* a monthly 32 page illustrated catalogue containing hundreds of pieces for sale from every theme and in every price range. The catalogue is available by annual subscription; please refer to the following page for details of this and the Goss and Crested China Club.

In addition, if you specialise, we will be pleased to offer your particular pieces or crests from time to time as suitable items become available. Please let us know your wants as with our ever-changing stock we will probably have something to suit.

Our service is personal and friendly and all orders and correspondence are dealt with by return. You will find us fair and straightforward to deal with, as we really care about crested china and this is reflected in our service.

Finally, we are just as keen to buy as to sell and offers of individual items or whole collections are always welcome. These will be dealt with by return and the very highest offers will be made.

Goss & Crested China Ltd,
62 Murray Road,
Horndean,
Waterlooville
Hampshire
PO8 9JL

Telephone: Horndean (0705) 597440
Facsimile: Horndean (0705) 591975

Would you like to join

The Goss & Crested China Club

Exclusively for collectors and customers of Goss & Crested China Ltd. Membership will provide answers to question such as:

How do I find the pieces I am looking for?

What is a fair price?

Where can I obtain information on Goss China and Goss collecting?

Where can I exchange or sell pieces I no longer require?

Join the Goss & Crested China Club without delay and receive the following benefits:

FREE   Specially designed enamel membership badge.

FREE   Membership card and number.

FREE   Telephone and postal advice service.

FREE   Information on books about heraldic china collecting.

FREE   Especially favourable Club members part-exchange rates for pieces surplus to requirements.

FREE   Without obligation search-and-offer service for any items and decorations that you seek.

FREE   Invitations to Club open days.

EXCLUSIVE   Valuation service for your collection

EXCLUSIVE   Club Members only special offers announced regularly in Club members monthly catalogue *Goss & Crested China.*

Membership is free and is available to subscribers to Goss & Crested China the club's monthly catalogue of pieces for sale.

To join, just send £12.00 annual subscription* to The Goss & Crested China Club, 62 Murray Road, Horndean, Waterlooville, Hampshire PO8 9JL, and you will receive a membership application form with your first copy of the catalogue. Upon receipt of the completed form, you will be sent your enamel badge, membership card and full details of the club's special offers and services.

*For Airmail outside Europe add £8.00

Other titles available from

Milestone Publications

Please send for a full catalogue of these and other books about antique porcelain.

William Henry Goss. The Story of the Staffordshire Family of Potters who invented Heraldic Porcelain
Lynda and Nicholas Pine

The Price Guide to Arms and Decorations on Goss China
Nicholas Pine

The Concise Encyclopaedia and Price Guide to Goss China
Nicholas Pine

The Price Guide to Crested China
Nicholas Pine

Crested China. The History of Heraldic Souvenir Ware
Sandy Andrews

The Goss Record 8th and War Editions
J.J. Jarvis A facsimile reprint.

Goss and Other Crested China
Nicholas Pine

In Search of the Better 'Ole The Life, The Works and The Collectables of Bruce Bairnsfather
Tonie and Valmai Holt

Goss & Crested China. Illustrated monthly catalogues listing items for sale. Available by Annual Subscription. Details upon request from 62 Murray Road, Horndean, Waterlooville, Hants PO8 9JL.